STATISTICAL ECOLOGY
IN PRACTICE

*A guide to analysing environmental
and ecological field data*

STATISTICAL ECOLOGY IN PRACTICE

A guide to analysing environmental and ecological field data

STEPHEN WAITE

Pearson Education Limited
Edinburgh Gate
Harlow
Essex CM20 2JE
England
and Associated Companies throughout the world

Visit us on the world wide web at
http://www.pearsoneduc.com

First published 2000
© Pearson Education Limited 2000

ISBN 0 582 23634 7

British Library Cataloguing-in-Publication Data
A catalogue record for this book is available from the British Library

Library of Congress Cataloging-in-Publication Data
Waite, Stephen.
    Statistical ecology in practice : a guide to analysing environmental
    and ecological field data / Stephen Waite.
        p. cm.
    ISBN 0-582-23634-7
    1. Ecology—Statistical methods. I. Title.

    QH541.15.S72 W35 2000
    577'.07'27–dc21   00-022115

Typeset by 60
Printed and bound in Malaysia, VVP

An imprint of **Pearson Education**
Harlow, England · London · New York · Reading, Massachusetts · San Francisco · Toronto · Don Mills, Ontario · Sydney
Tokyo · Singapore · Hong Kong · Seoul · Taipei · Cape Town · Madrid · Mexico City · Amsterdam · Munich · Paris · Milan

To my wife, Alison, and my daughters, Jessica and Catherine,
for their patience, understanding and support.

Contents

List of boxes

Preface

Ecology and environmental sciences are quantitative subjects. To be an effective research worker in these disciplines you need to be able to collect, summarise and analyse data sets that are often large and complex. Many students embark on this with a degree of trepidation, feeling poorly equipped for the task in hand. Instead of being a source of enjoyment and intellectual stimulation, fieldwork and the subsequent write-up can become a worrying and unfulfilling experience. I hope this book will prove helpful to all such students.

Many years ago, when I started postgraduate research, I rapidly became aware that my smattering of statistics, gleaned from various undergraduate introductory courses, was insufficient to meet my new needs. I also discovered that while there were many excellent introductory and advanced texts, there were few that bridged the gap between the two levels. When I began to teach, the need for such a bridging text was confirmed. Students needed a text which assumed a limited knowledge of statistics but took the reader within sight of more advanced topics and techniques. Often when I referred students to what I considered to be comprehensive, authoritative and excellent texts, such a Greig-Smith (1983), Ludwig and Reynolds (1988) and Krebs (1999), they would frequently struggle, finding them too demanding. But the equally excellent and valuable introductory texts, such as Fowler *et al.* (1998), often failed to meet the needs of more advanced students attempting final-year project work or students embarking on their postgraduate careers and those environmental professionals, who while not primarily engaged in research, often needed to analyse and summarise environmental data. This book attempts to provide a bridge from introductory to more advanced levels. No significant mathematical knowledge or skills are assumed. If you have an understanding of basic arithmetic and algebra and, perhaps most importantly, a willingness to persevere and occasionally take things on trust, you should be able to follow and hopefully apply all of the procedures presented in this book.

The range of statistical procedures is bewilderingly large and still it continues to grow. The more I researched the subject, the more methods I encountered. I have had to be selective. Although the final choice of procedures and topics covered may be idiosyncratic, I have been guided by two principles:

- The book should cover most of the situations likely to be encountered by project students and those embarking on postgraduate research or those new to ecological and environmental field research.

● The procedure should be usable without specialist computer programs. Almost all the techniques in the book can be performed by hand, with a spreadsheet program or with a common statistical package such as MINITAB.

The book does not cover generalised linear models or the GLIM software package. Few readers will have encountered GLIM as part of their introduction to statistics, and although GLIM-based methods are becoming more widely supported by many computer packages, their informed and successful application requires a level of specialist knowledge beyond the scope of this book. When deciding whether to explain a technique in detail or whether to give just an outline, I was often guided by the views of my own students. And I thank them for their forbearance and willingness to tackle tasks with enthusiasm that must have occasionally seemed needlessly trivial or excessively complex.

Although this book was not conceived as a traditional introductory statistics text, in order to make it as self-contained as possible, many of the more commonly used basic statistical procedures are presented and explained. I hope readers will find all that they need to analyse their data rigorously and identify situations where more advanced techniques might be applicable. I have provided many annotated examples and I hope they will aid the reader's understanding and encourage them to experiment on their own data sets.

References

Greig-Smith, P. (1983) *Quantitative Plant Ecology*, 3rd edn. Blackwell Scientific, Oxford.

Fowler, J., Cohen, L. and Jarvis, P. (1998) *Practical Statistics for Field Biology*, 2nd edn. John Wiley, Chichester.

Krebs, C.J. (1999) *Ecological Methodology*, 2nd edn. Addison Wesley Longman, Menlo Park, CA.

Ludwig, J.A. and Reynolds, J.F. (1988) *Statistical Ecology: A Primer on Methods and Computing*. John Wiley, Chichester.

Acknowledgements

I would like to thank all those colleagues and students who commented on drafts of parts of this book, offered advice and gave freely of their time and expertise. I would also like to thank all those at Pearson Education who have helped and been involved with the production of this book.

How to use this book

Organisation of the book

The material in this book is divided into three parts. Part 1 covers methods that may be used to analyse single-sample data sets. It also includes Chapter 3 on estimating population parameters and density, and Chapter 4 on the analysis of pattern. Part 2 covers a range of procedures that allow samples to be compared with one another. Chapters 6 and 7 outline approaches that may be applied to small data sets by hand or with the aid of a spreadsheet program. More complex multivariate methods are presented in Chapters 8 and 9. The two chapters in the Part 3 cover methods that can be used to explore the relationship between sets of variables within complex multivariate data.

Required level of mathematics

No significant mathematical knowledge or skills are assumed. If you have an understanding of basic arithmetic and algebra, and perhaps most importantly a willingness to persevere and occasionally take things on trust, you should be able to follow and apply all the procedures in this book. Since this is not primarily a book on mathematics or the theory of statistics, I have tried to keep theoretical explanations and formula derivations to a minimum. I hope to give sufficient detail so that you can apply the appropriate techniques with confidence.

For every type of analysis, I have presented several possible methods and approaches. These vary in complexity and difficulty, but regardless of mathematical background, readers should be able to find an appropriate method and apply it with reasonable ease.

Chapter structure

Each chapter begins with a brief summary. The introduction provides an outline and reviews key concepts. From the introduction it should be possible to identify which sections are most relevant to your particular problem. Where appropriate, recommendations are given at the end of the chapter, or sometimes at the end of a section.

As far as possible, the chapters have been written to stand alone. Although it should not be necessary to read an earlier chapter in order to follow methods in a later chapter, certain chapters, e.g. Chapter 8, will be easier to follow if you have some experience of data analysis or have read earlier chapters. Since the chapters stand alone, some material is covered more than once. All the procedures described in the book are indexed separately, allowing quick access to required information.

Examples

Annotated calculations are given to illustrate the use of procedures. These should be reasonably straightforward to follow. Where possible, the calculations have been set out so they can be performed easily by hand with a simple calculator, or with a spreadsheet program such as EXCEL. It is not possible or realistic to perform some procedures by hand, so I have shown how to do them using MINITAB, a general statistics package. Although I have chosen MINITAB, other packages, such as SPSS, could be used in its place.

Table of data types

The table of data types on page xvii attempts to relate the form of the data set to the range of possible procedures that might be used in its analysis. In an ideal world the statistical analysis should be planned *before* data collection (Chapter 1). Unfortunately, few people are perfect and we all operate in an imperfect world. It is very easy to collect too much data on too many things and then have to ask, What can I do with it? If you find yourself in this situation, the table may help you to match your data with possible analyses. But by far the best approach is to carefully plan your data collection and analysis from the outset.

Notes and Glossary

Included at the end of the book are a glossary and a section of chapter endnotes. The chapter endnotes, indicated by numbers e.g. [1] in the text, attempt to clarify points that some readers may find confusing. The glossary provides brief definitions and explanations of key statistical terms. To help readers with little knowledge of statistics and to allow the chapters to be read independently of each other, I have tried to make the glossary as inclusive as possible. The majority of statistical terms used in the book are covered in the glossary.

Data types and possible modes of analysis

Data table	Notes on data table	Examples of data sets	Possible analysis options
$\begin{bmatrix} x_1 \\ x_2 \\ \vdots \\ x_n \end{bmatrix}$	*Single-variable data set* Single column of values, one variable recorded from n sample units	Records of the biomass of a number of organisms	*Small n*: small sample size limits the options to simple descriptive statistics, e.g. measures of central tendency and dispersion (Box 1.3) *Large n*: the nature and shape of the distribution of x could be examined (Box 1.4)
		Records of the size or density of a species, or values of an environmental variable recorded from sample units at different locations or at different times	Pattern analysis: are the values clumped, regular or uniformly dispersed among the sample units? (Chapter 4)
		Number of species present in each sample unit	Measures of species richness (Chapter 2)
	Multiple-variable data set Each x refers to one of n different variables	Species abundance recorded in each sample unit; column represents a single sample in which n species are recorded	Measures of species or community diversity (Chapter 2) Species–area relationships and sample effort curves may be relevant (Section 1.3.1, Chapter 10)
$\begin{bmatrix} x_1 & y_1 \\ x_2 & y_2 \\ \vdots & \vdots \\ x_n & y_n \end{bmatrix}$	*Multiple-variable data set* Two columns of data; paired data, i.e. two variables, x and y, measured for each sample unit	x and y continuous variables (or ranks), e.g. wing and tail length or species abundance and temperature measured for n cases	Does the value of y change with x? Find out by using correlation analysis (Chapter 7) or linear regression (Chapter 10)
		x and y both binary (or one binary), e.g. presence/absence of two species (x and y) recorded in each of n sample units	Association and correlation (Chapter 7) Use y to characterise the values of x and produce a single index that summarises the variable x for a sample (Chapter 5)
		x and y are paired, but they refer to different variables, e.g. x is the abundance of 1 to n different species in a sample unit (or sample) and y is an index of shade tolerance for each of the n species	If the sample is large enough, association or correlation analysis may be applicable (Chapter 7) Weighted averages (Chapter 5)
		Demographic data sets: x is age of organisms and y is number or density	See Chapter 3

Data types and possible modes of analysis

Data table	Notes on data table	Examples of data sets	Possible analysis options
$\begin{bmatrix} x_1 & x_1 \\ x_2 & x_2 \\ \vdots & \vdots \\ x_n & x_n \end{bmatrix}$	*Multiple-variable data set* Two columns of data; rows are different variables and columns are different samples; variables x_1 to x_n are measured for two sample units (or samples); the data set is paired	Species abundance recorded at two sites, or n physical characteristics measured for two environmental samples	How similar are the two samples? Use descriptive measures of sample similarity (Chapter 6) Similarity may be measured by correlation (Chapter 7)
	Single-variable data set Two columns of data; the columns are different samples and the same variable (x) is measured for two samples, each containing n sample units	Head-to-tail lengths for n fish of the same species collected from two separate stream systems	Do sample averages or distributions differ? Compare means and distributions (Boxes 1.3 and 1.4). Small samples or non-normal data require non-parametric methods (Appendix 1.1). And see Chapter 10. How similar are the two samples? Use descriptive measures of sample similarity (Chapter 6)

Analysis of data matrices

Data matrices

Data matrices with more than two rows and two columns can be analysed in four ways:

1. Compare complete rows, row–row comparisons up and down the table
2. Summarise individual rows of data across the table
3. Compare complete columns, column–column comparisons across the table
4. Summarise individual columns of data down the table

Arrows show possible directions of analysis and comparison

Column data

Data table

Row data

Data table	Notes on data table	Examples of data sets	Possible analysis options
$$\begin{bmatrix} y_1 & x_1 & \cdots & x_1 \\ y_2 & x_2 & \cdots & x_2 \\ \vdots & \vdots & \cdots & \vdots \\ y_n & x_n & \cdots & x_n \end{bmatrix}$$	*Multiple-variable data set* More than two columns of data; columns are variables, rows are cases, i.e. sample units; data paired, one dependent variable y recorded along with several independent variables x for each of the n sample units	y is seabird survival following de-oiling; x may be various measures of the bird's precleaning health and the types of cleaning treatment. Data collected to study effects of bird health and cleaning treatment on survival	Looking for relationships between y and the x-variables. If individual x-variables are used to classify birds into different groups then see Chapter 10. But also look at the G-test and chi-squared procedures, along with non-parametric tests (Appendix 1.1) Correlation between variables (Chapter 7); the data set might also be summarised using multivariate methods (Chapter 8) Can the value of y be predicted from the x-values? Use multiple regression (Chapter 10)
$$\begin{bmatrix} x_1 & \cdots & x_1 \\ x_2 & \cdots & x_2 \\ \vdots & \cdots & \vdots \\ x_n & \cdots & x_n \end{bmatrix}$$	*Single-variable data set* More than two columns of data; columns are different samples Same variable is recorded for n sample units for more than two samples	The concentration of Zn in n soil sample units collected from six abandoned mine spoil sites Values for chlorophyll-a concentrations of leaves taken from n plants grown under four different light levels	Preliminary analysis, calculation of means and confidence limits (Boxes 1.3 and 1.4) Descriptive comparison and correlation on paired data (Chapters 6 and 7) Recommended approach is analysis of variance (Chapter 10); compare with non-parametric methods (Appendix 1.1)
	Multiple-variable data set More than two columns; data paired. Columns are samples (or sample units); rows are different variables Range of variables x_1 to x_n, measured for more than two samples	Species–community matrix, species (n) abundance or presence recorded at 20 sites Range (n) of water quality parameters measured at a number of different lakes Range (n) of morphological measurements made on 60 individual animals	*How similar are samples? Comparing rows or columns* For a small number of samples (3 to 4) use resemblance functions (Chapter 6) For more than a few samples use weighted averages (Chapter 5) for subjective analysis and ordination (Chapter 10) for objective analysis *Can the data set be split into groups?* For a small number of samples (3 to 4) use asemblance functions (Chapter 6) For more than a few samples use classification methods (Chapter 9)

Data table	Notes on data table	Examples of data sets	Possible analysis options
$$\begin{bmatrix} x_1 & \cdots & x_1 \\ \vdots & \vdots & \vdots \\ x_n & \cdots & x_n \\ z_1 & \cdots & z_1 \\ \vdots & \vdots & \vdots \\ z_m & \cdots & z_m \end{bmatrix}$$	*Multiple-variable data set* More than two columns; data paired. Data matrix partitioned; columns are samples (or sample units); rows x_1 to x_n are one set of variables; z_1 to z_m are a different set of variables	Species–community matrix, abundance or presence of n species (x-variables) recorded at 20 sites along with values for m environmental factors (z-variables)	By analysing part of the matrix it may be possible to investigate the relationships between individual x and individual z variables or a small subset of variables (Chapter 10) Attempt to relate both the top (x-part) and bottom (z-part) of the data matrix (Chapter 11)

Notes

1. In different data sets, columns and rows may represent either samples or variables. Read notes on data sets and description of examples carefully.
2. Data matrices may be transposed. For example a species–community matrix may be formed where sites are represented by columns and species by rows; alternatively the same data set may be presented with columns representing species and row sites.
3. With multiple-variable data sets, analysis may be carried out at the level of individual sample units, or at the levels of samples formed from groups of sample units.
4. Samples are composed of sample units. A site might be sampled by recording species presence in 20 randomly placed quadrats. In this case the sample consists of 20 random sample units. Each quadrat constitutes a sample unit. Data sets can often be analysed at both levels, sample and sample unit.
5. The complexity of the data sets and methods of analysis increase down the table, but remember that complex data sets can be broken down into smaller simpler sets and analysed in stages. To analyse a data set well, you don't always have to use the most sophisticated or complex methods available.
6. Chapter 3 covers analysis and summary of demographic and population data sets, including methods for estimating population density.
7. Chapter 5 has a range of descriptive methods for summarising simple and complex data sets.

PART ONE

Characterising Data Sets

Chapter One

Planning fieldwork and sampling regimes

Summary

Factors that should be considered during the planning of fieldwork are discussed. The need to formulate hypotheses and the importance of statistics in testing hypotheses are considered. Fundamental statistical terms are defined and procedures to describe data sets are presented. Procedures described include measures of central tendency, measures of data spread or dispersion, the setting of confidence limits and the calculation of percentage similarity. The importance and development of sampling schemes are considered in depth. The three key questions when sampling are (i) What constitutes a suitable sample unit? (ii) How many sample units are required? (iii) How should sample units be placed or selected? The chapter concludes by considering the particular problems associated with monitoring, i.e. sampling schemes designed to detect changes in the system being studied.

1.1 *Introduction*

Well designed, conducted and analysed field studies are fundamental to ecology and environmental science. To be of value, fieldwork must be carefully planned with data collected in an objective (i.e. unbiased) and systematic manner. Fieldwork should only be contemplated when the investigator has clear and unambiguous objectives that can be easily and simply articulated. The aimless collection of data has no place in ecology or environmental science. Field studies should aim to answer specific and well-formulated questions. Consider this question, Is the distribution of a species (e.g. a plant species or species of ground beetle) related to soil type and/or previous site management? Even such an apparently simple question can hide a considerable amount of complexity that must be considered carefully before any fieldwork is undertaken. The question needs to be refined. What is meant by soil type? Can soil type be defined and measured in a meaningful way in the field or should samples be taken and classified in the laboratory?

More important perhaps is whether a general measure of soil type is sufficiently precise for the nature and scale of the study. It is important to consider the spatial and temporal scale of a study early in the planning process. In this example, general soil types derived from a classification of soils might be an appropriate variable to investigate regional or national relationships between soils and species distribution. In such a large-scale study a wide range of soil types are likely to be encountered. In a small-scale study the number and range of soil types recorded might be extremely limited. If this were the case, even if the distribution of the species were closely associated with soil characteristics, attempts to relate species distribution to soil type would probably be unsuccessful. If a relationship exists it is unlikely be identified in a small-scale study unless the soil characteristics are described with sufficient precision. For example, it may be necessary to determine soil nutrients or other soil parameters, such as pH or water-holding capacity. This raises further issues. What are the most appropriate soil variables to measure and how? Similar issues are raised if consideration is given to the measurement and assessment of species distribution, and past and present site management. The questions can be refined in several ways.

Careful consideration of the objectives   If a study is commissioned by an outside body to assess the potential ecological impact of a development, or the consequences of a change in the management regime for a nature reserve, the investigator must ensure the planned study meets the requirements of the commissioning body. These requirements need to be defined clearly and understood by all those involved. The data required to determine whether the development will adversely affect the diversity of bird fauna in a neighbouring wood is very different from the data required to predict which species populations will decrease and by how much; it differs in both quality and quantity. One might expect the aims and objectives of applied studies to be more easily defined, and the subsequent fieldwork appropriately planned and conducted, but experience suggests this is frequently not the case (Green, 1979; Hellawell, 1991; Maher *et al.*, 1994).

Careful consideration of previous studies   Appropriate and achievable objectives are most likely to be set and decisions made when they are based on a sound knowledge of the system under study. An appreciation of the basic ecology and biology of a system will often help to initiate a study and to resolve issues raised during the design and conduct of a study; it also allows the results to be interpreted in a more rigorous manner.

Preliminary or pilot studies   Always consider conducting a pilot study. It should be simple in design and limited in scope; it should aim to identify key variables and to assess the feasibility of the main study. Pilot studies may be used to test proposed sampling regimes and to determine the minimum sample size required. The results of a pilot study can often be incorporated into the main study. If investigators are honest, most of their unpiloted studies could have been improved by an appropriate pilot.

Once the objectives of the study have been formulated as a set of suitable specific questions, they need to be translated into a working hypothesis. The working hypothesis is normally a refinement of the investigator's ideas into a formal statement (or series of statements) that reflect possible causal relationships and/or mechanisms linking relevant factors and variables together. From the working hypotheses it should be possible to produce one or more testable predictions. The hypotheses and associated predictions give purpose to the fieldwork or experimental work undertaken, which should be designed so the results of the study will allow the validity of the prediction(s) to be tested. The hypothesis and associated predictions should satisfy three criteria:

- They should be logical, i.e. based on sound observation and reasoning.
- Where several hypotheses and predictions are formulated, they should be consistent with each other.
- They should be concisely and precisely worded so the predictions can be readily tested against the results of the investigation.

The working or initial hypothesis is normally called the null hypothesis H_0. Because science proceeds conservatively, the null hypothesis should be framed in neutral terms that assume a relationship does not exist. Suppose a field study is undertaken to investigate whether the breeding success of a bird species is related to the abundance or type of ground vegetation. There may be several reasons why this relationship has been suggested: the vegetation might provide cover from predators, it might provide roosting sites, or it might act as a food source. But the reasons are not important when formulating the null hypothesis. If breeding success, the dependent or response variable (y), is related to the extent of plant cover, the independent[1] variable (x), then only two forms of the null hypothesis are possible, each of which has an associated alternative hypothesis H_a.

Difference hypotheses
- H_0: Breeding success *does not* differ between sites with different levels of plant cover.
- H_a: Breeding success *does* differ between sites with different levels of plant cover.
- A result consistent with H_0: Mean breeding success does not differ between two or more sites that have differing levels and/or types of vegetation cover. Accept H_0.
- A result inconsistent with H_0: Mean breeding success differs substantially between two or more sites that have different levels of vegetation cover. Reject H_0, provisionally accept H_a.

Trend hypothesis
- H_0: Breeding success *does not* vary with vegetation cover, i.e. there is no positive or negative trend between breeding and the level of vegetative cover.
- H_a: Breeding success *does* vary with vegetation cover, i.e. there is a positive or negative trend between breeding and the level of vegetative cover.
  - A result consistent with H_0: No trend is evident when breeding success is plotted against vegetation cover. Accept H_0.

- A result inconsistent with H_0: A positive trend is evident from a plot of breeding success against vegetation cover. Reject H_0, provisionally accept H_a.

If the results are not consistent with the null hypothesis, the null hypothesis is rejected and the alternative hypothesis is provisionally accepted. In some cases it may not be appropriate or possible to formulate explicit testable hypotheses. For example, the primary aim of a survey may be to establish the occurrence and abundance of the species present at a particular site. However, even here it is important that the data is collected in a systematic and objective way. The design and quality of the survey conducted will determine the value of the data collected and the potential range of uses it might be put to in future.

1.2 *The role of statistics*

To accept or reject the null hypothesis, judgements must be made about the extent of differences between dependent variables or whether the strength of any relationship between the x and y is sufficient to merit the rejection of the null hypothesis. These decisions are more easily made when quantitative data is available. Statistical analysis allows such judgements to be made in a quantifiable way. Statistics provides a set of objective procedures so that data can be efficiently summarised and values can be compared. Where the results of analysis suggest that the null hypothesis should be rejected, the use of statistics allows the reliability of this decision to assessed. This is the great value of statistics. In an ideal world, predictions would be tested and a hypothesis accepted or rejected with 100% certainty. Unfortunately, in biology, ecology and environmental sciences it is rarely possible to formulate the null hypothesis so it can be accepted or rejected in a simple yes or no manner. A decision has to be made on the balance of probabilities. Using appropriate statistics it is possible to calculate the exact probability that a decision is correct, allowing choices to be made in an informed manner. Some important statistical terms are defined in Box 1.1.

Confidence limits

By convention, in most scientific disciplines, the null hypothesis is rejected only if by doing so the probability of being wrong is less than or equal to 5% ($p \leq 0.05$), i.e. the chance of making a mistake is less than 1 in 20. Thus, the statement 'mean sample wing lengths of two populations of birds differ significantly at the 5% probability level' implies the likelihood that mean sample wing lengths do not differ, i.e. the likelihood they are the same, is less than 5%. Another way of expressing this is to say that we are 95% confident that the means do differ. Notice that we are not 100% confident; this is important. By accepting that the sample means are different, and rejecting the null hypothesis of equal means, we may make an error. Two types of error are possible.

Type I error   The null hypothesis is wrongly rejected (false positive). In the wing length example a type I error occurs if we conclude that mean wing lengths do differ when in fact they don't. The observed difference between mean wing length may be due to inadequate sampling and sampling error.

Type II error   The null hypothesis is wrongly accepted (false negative). In the wing length example, a type II error occurs if we conclude that mean wing lengths are the same when in fact the true population means are different. The apparent similarity between the means may reflect a lack of measurement precision and inadequate sampling.

Box 1.1   Some statistical terms

Accuracy A measure of the closeness of the sample statistic to the true population values (e.g. the accuracy of the sample estimate of density ($\hat{N}$) is equal to the difference between $\hat{N}$ and the true population density (N).

Bias A consistent over- or underestimate of the true population value. Bias most frequently results from inadequate or unrepresentative sampling, although some statistical procedures or data manipulations may introduce bias.

Error Difference between a statistic and the true population value. Errors may arise from many sources. For example, sampling errors and measurement or determination errors may contribute to the overall total error associated with a statistic. Individual errors are assumed to be independent and equally likely to be positive or negative, i.e. they are normally distributed about the true population value.

Parameter A known characteristic of a population (e.g. density).

Population The entire collection of individuals or potential sample units. The term 'population' has different meanings in statistics and biology. In a biological context it means a group of individuals or organisms (normally of the same species); in a statistical context it means all items of a particular type. The population of trees in a wood consists of every tree present. The population mean of tree height would be obtained by calculating the average tree height from measurements taken from every tree in the wood.

Precision A measure of the repeatability of a statistic; that is, the variation in the statistic obtained from replicated samples collected and treated in the same way. The smaller the range or variation between replicate sample estimates, the greater the precision.

Sample A collection of individuals or sample units drawn from the statistical population. The sample mean is the average of all the values recorded for each item (individual or sample unit) in the sample. For example, the sample mean of tree height might be obtained by calculating the mean of height measurements made on 50 randomly selected trees.

Statistic An estimator of a population parameter (e.g. the estimate of population density obtained from samples drawn from the population).

The probability of making a type I error is related to the probability of making a type II error. The probability, α, of making a type I error is determined by the significance level selected. If we decrease the significance level from 5% to 1% ($p = 0.01$), the probability of making a type I error is reduced to 1 in 100, i.e. the null hypothesis can be rejected with 99% confidence. However, by decreasing the likelihood of making a type I error, the probability, β, of wrongly accepting the null hypothesis (a type II error) is increased. There is always a trade-off between the probability of making a type I error and the probability of making a type II error. An efficient statistical method of data analysis should be conservative (low probability of making a type I error); powerful (low probability of making a type II error) and robust. A robust procedure or test is one that is not seriously affected by the particular characteristics of a data set; for example, a robust measure of the most typical wing length of a sampled population should not be unduly sensitive to extremely small or extremely large values. The performance of any statistical procedure applied to the results of a study will always be improved by increasing sample size (i.e. replication).

Adequate replication will reduce either type I errors, type II errors or perhaps both errors (Green, 1979).

Parametric or non-parametric?

The most frequently used statistical procedures are parametric. Parametric procedures require a limited number of parameters (e.g. the population mean and variance) to be estimated, these are then used to establish an appropriate sample distribution. In most cases the sample distribution is assumed to be normal. Once the data has been fitted to a particular distribution, the statistical properties of the distribution are used to make inferences about original data. In contrast, non-parametric or distribution-free procedures do not make assumptions about the distribution of the data – they impose considerably less stringent assumptions about the data and its underlying distribution. Given that field data seldom conforms completely to the requirements of traditional parametric statistics, one might expect that non-parametric procedures should be routinely used to analyse field data. Unfortunately, although non-parametric tests place fewer restrictions on the nature

---

Box 1.2   Variable types

Measured variables may be either continuous or discontinuous:

- Discontinuous variables take whole number values only.
- Continuous variables may take any value, including fractions.

Weight may be treated as a continuous variable or a discontinuous variable. If a typical measurement is recorded as 10.258 g, then weight be considered as a continuous variable. But if the measurements are recorded to the nearest whole gram, e.g. 10.258 g is recorded as 10 g, then weight is a discontinuous variable.

Variables may be measured on four scales:

- *Nominal scales* are where individuals or samples are classified as belonging to mutually exclusive categories, e.g. species, sex, colour, habitat type. Binary variables, coded 1 or 0, are one kind of nominal variable. In ecological studies, species presence or absence is a commonly encountered binary variable.

- *Ordinal scales* involve both classifying and ordering observations. Observations are classified into mutually exclusive categories which are ranked. For example, species abundance may be assessed subjectively as dominant, abundant, frequent, occasional and rare (the DAFOR scale). Ranking the classes from 1 (rare) to 5 (dominant) allows species abundance to be recorded on an ordinal scale; dominant species are recorded as 5, abundant as 4, frequent as 3, etc.

- *Interval scale* observations are ordered and grouped into non-overlapping but continuous intervals (units). The interval scale incorporates the classification and ordering of observations but it allows the difference between units of the scale to be determined.

- *Ratio scales* represent the highest level of measurement; they incorporate the properties of the interval scale but they also include zero. Observations are ordered along the real number line.

The mathematical properties of the interval and ratio scales are similar. If the scale intervals are sufficiently fine, interval scale data can often be approximated as a continuous variable.

of the data set, they are considerably less powerful, and their use incurs a greater risk of committing a type II error – wrongly concluding that the null hypothesis of no effect or difference is correct.

Green (1979) argues strongly that the tendency to retreat from the use of parametric statistics and embrace non-parametric procedures is misplaced. Parametric procedures are frequently more robust than commonly thought, and with adequate sampling, violations may be corrected by the use of appropriate transformation. The consequences of assumption violations have been extensively reviewed by Glass *et al.* (1972) and discussed by Green (1979). Sample size is important. Regardless of the underlying distribution of data, as sample size increases, deviations of the sample distribution from the normal become smaller (Box 1.3). The choice of procedures is partly governed by the type of variable recorded (Box 1.2); non-parametric procedures, unlike parametric procedures, can be used to analyse nominal or ordinal data sets.

As a rule, unless (i) data variables are ordinal or nominal, (ii) sample size is small and the underlying distribution is thought to be non-normal or (iii) the population distribution is extremely skewed, parametric procedures should be adopted. Throughout this book, both parametric and non-parametric procedures are presented as appropriate. However, when the classical statistical problems of comparing means and testing for the occurrence of linear trends, etc., are discussed, greater emphasis is placed on parametric statistical tests. For completeness, some commonly used non-parametric alternatives to *t*-tests, ANOVA and regression are given in Appendix 1.1. Some key statistical concepts and the normal distribution are reviewed in Box 1.3. Procedures for analysing and describing the sample distribution associated with a single group of numbers, i.e. a single-variable data set, are outlined in Box 1.4.

1.3 *Sampling schemes*

It is rarely possible to count or measure all individuals in a population, so a sample has to be taken. Based on an analysis of the sample, we infer characteristics and properties of the population as a whole. If the sample is unrepresentative, incorrect conclusions will be drawn about the nature of the population. Sampling is fundamental to environmental sciences and field biology. The selection of samples must allow valid generalisations to be made. Assuming that the objectives of the study have been clearly defined and appropriate response variables have been selected, three basic issues remain to be considered before a sampling scheme or frame can be developed: (i) What should be used as the sample unit? (ii) Replication, how many sample units should be used? (iii) Placement/selection, where should sample units be placed or samples taken from?

1.3.1 *The sample unit*

The objectives of the study and the nature of the system being studied will govern the choice of sample unit. Sample units may be arbitrary or natural. Examples of arbitrary sample units include quadrats, water samples of a fixed volume or insects caught in a trap over a fixed time interval. Examples of natural sample units include logs, rock pools, leaves, individual animals or plants (Table 1.1). Although the terms are often interchanged, samples and sample units are not the same. A sample is a collection of sample units. Thus a sample of woodland leaf litter macro-invertebrates might be obtained from searching through 10 sample units, each sample unit consisting of an equal volume of leaf litter, or the litter collected from equal areas of ground. In an array of traps placed in the same habitat, individual traps form the basic sample units of the study. In practice the sample units are often selected according

Box 1.3 Basic statistics

Notation

Particular data values are often identified using subscripts. For example, suppose that the weights of 8 mice are recorded as the variable x. Using subscripts we could identify the second and eighth values as x_2 and x_8. More generally we could specify the ith value as x_i. Values may be identified by more than one subscript; $Z_{1,6}$ could be used to identify the sixth value in the first row of a table containing values of the variable Z.

Subscripts provide a convenient shorthand and they allow the use of the sigma or summation symbol. $\sum x$ means the sum of all the x-values. Sometimes the meaning of $\sum x$ may be ambiguous. It is better to specify exactly which values are to be summed:

last value in the sequence to be added

$$\sum_{i=1}^{8} x_i = x_1 + x_2 + x_3 + x_4 + x_5 + x_6 + x_7 + x_8$$

first value in the sequence

$\sum x$ **means the sum of all the x-values**

The first value in the sequence need not be 1; it can be any $i < n$. More complicated calculations can be expressed a similar way:

$$G = \sum_{i=1}^{n} x_i \ln x_i$$

For each value of x, from 1 to n, the natural logarithm of x is taken then multiplied by the original value of x. The resulting values (1 to n) are then summed to give G.

A simple single-variable data set, e.g. n diameter (x_i) values obtained by measuring the size of n randomly selected limpet shells, can be described by calculating suitable measures of central tendency and measures of dispersion.

Measures of central tendency

Measures of central tendency attempt to summarise a data set by calculating a single 'typical' or representative value. The *arithmetic sample mean* is given by

$$\bar{x} = \frac{1}{n} \sum_{i=1}^{n} x_i$$

the population mean μ is obtained by replacing n, the sample size, with N, the total population size.
individual data values

a bar is the conventional symbol to indicate a sample mean

The mean is sensitive to outliers, i.e. extremely large and small values. To overcome this problem, a *trimmed mean* can be calculated. To calculate a 10% trimmed mean, the data is ordered and 10% of the original sample is removed from each end of the distribution. The mean is then calculated using the remaining 80% of values.

The *median* (m) is the middle value in a sequence of ranked values. Where the number of values is even, the mean of the middle pair of values is taken as the median.

The *mode* is the most frequent data value; the crude mode or modal class is the class in a frequency histogram (distribution) which contains the most observations. The mode may be used to describe qualitative data sets consisting of categories (not numerical values).

The mean is the best measure of central tendency for symmetrical distributions. Skewed distributions may be better described by the median, although suitable data

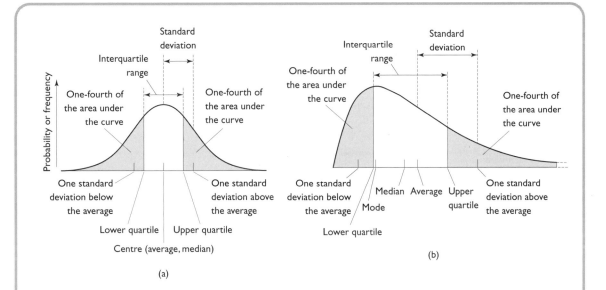

(a)

(b)

transformations (e.g. replacing x with $\log x$) will often remove the skewed nature of a distribution, allowing the mean to be used.

For perfectly symmetrical distributions the mean, median and mode are equal. If the distribution is skewed, the mean shifts in the direction of the skew (Figure 1). Of the three measures of central tendency, the mean is the only one that uses all the data – its value reflects all observations. A mean may also be combined with other means to produce an overall mean.

Measures of dispersion

Dispersion measures the spread or variability of data values; here are three ways to measure dispersion:

Sample variation (variance) $\qquad S^2 = \dfrac{1}{n-1} \sum_{i=1}^{n}(x_i - \bar{x})^2$

Sample standard deviation $\qquad S = \sqrt{S^2}$

Coefficient of variation $\qquad \mathrm{CV} = \left(\dfrac{S}{x}\right) \times 100$

The *population variance* and the *population standard deviation*, σ^2 and σ, are obtained by replacing $(n-1)$ with N, the total population size. The quantity $(n-1)$ is called the number of *degrees of freedom*. The sample standard deviation (S) provides a very useful summary of how the data values are spread about the mean, but its value depends on the scale and magnitude of the values used to calculate it. To overcome this problem, the *coefficient of variation* (CV), expressed as a percentage, is often used to compare the relative variability of different data sets.

The *range* of a data set is the difference between its largest and smallest values. The *interquartile range* is the difference between the lower quartile and the upper quartile.

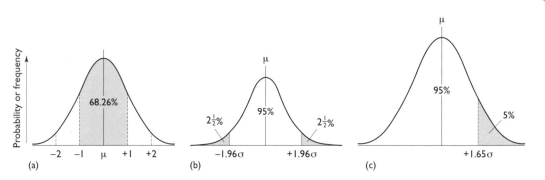

Figure 2 The normal distribution: (a) one standard deviation either side of the mean, (b) 5% in two tails, (c) 5% in the upper tail. Reprinted, with permission, from Siegel (1988).

It is a robust measure of variability. Data values are ranked, the median is then found and used to divide the data into two halves, upper and lower. The median of the lower half gives the lower quartile and the median of the upper half gives the upper quartile.

The normal distribution

Many data sets follow the bell-shaped normal distribution (Figure 2). Two parameters, the mean and standard deviation, are required to fit a normal distribution curve to a data set. The normal distribution is symmetrical about the mean. The mean marks the centre (peak) of the distribution, has a probability of 0.5 and provides an estimate of the most likely value. The proportion of observations either side of the mean is related to the standard deviation. One standard deviation either side of the mean, along the x-axis, encloses approximately 68.26% of all possible observations; 95% are contained within 1.96 standard deviations of the mean. These relationships between the probability of particular values and their distance from the mean (measured in units of standard deviation) hold for all normal distributions, regardless of whether they are narrow and tall (small standard deviation) or flat and broad (large standard deviation). This allows the probability of individual values or sets of values to be calculated, confidence limits to be set about means, and means to be compared. The general properties of the normal distribution, sample means, standard deviation and variance account for the power of *parametric* statistics.

Setting confidence limits

- Large samples ($n \geq 30$): 95% confidence limits are given by $\bar{x} \pm 1.96\sigma$ or $\bar{x} \pm 1.96S$; 95% of values are enclosed in the interval from $\bar{x} + 1.96S$ to $\bar{x} - 1.96S$.
- Small samples ($n < 30$): 95% confidence limits are given by $\bar{x} \pm t_{n-1}S$ where t_{n-1} is Student's t-value with $n - 1$ degrees of freedom at the 95% ($\alpha = 0.05$) confidence level for a two-tailed test (values obtained from tables).

Why t-values? For large samples, S and $\bar{x}$ provide reasonable estimates of the population standard deviation (σ) and mean (μ), allowing the required normal distribution to be specified. For small samples S and $\bar{x}$ may not be good estimates of σ and μ. The t-value acts as a correction factor for small sample size. For any sample size, the t-value required to set 95% confidence limits will be greater than 1.96 (as sample size tends to infinity, t tends to 1.96). Note that confidence limits based on S are used to determine whether individual values of x belong to the particular distribution characterised by S and $\bar{x}$. They are not for comparing or setting confidence limits about sample means.

Calculating the probability of an individual value

The probability associated with a value can be obtained from tabled z-scores and t-values. The z-scores transform data values to the *standard normal distribution* that has a mean of 0 and a standard deviation of 1:

$$z = \frac{x - \mu}{\sigma} \cong \frac{x - \bar{x}}{s} \qquad t = \frac{x - \bar{x}}{s}$$

used for small sample sizes

One- and two-tailed tests

Tests and confidence limits may be one-tailed or two-tailed. One-tailed tests are concerned with whether a particular value or statistic is above or below a specified limit. A 95% one-tailed upper confidence limit implies that 5% of all possible values may exceed this critical value. The usual 95% two-tailed procedure implies that 2.5% of all possible values will be above the upper limit and 2.5% below the lower limit.

The normal distribution and sample means

The importance given in statistics to the normal distribution rests on its ability to provide a good description of the properties of a wide range of data sets. In addition, if a population is repeatedly sampled, sample means are found to follow a normal distribution centred on the true population mean. It turns out that the standard deviation of the sample mean distribution, the standard error of the mean (SE), can be estimated from the standard deviation of a single sample. Repeated sampling is therefore not needed to determine the distribution of possible sample means if an adequate first sample is taken. This is an extremely useful property; it allows sample means to be compared and confidence limits to be constructed about them.

Confidence limits about sample means

The relevant equations are as follows:

$$SE = \frac{S}{\sqrt{n}}$$

$$\bar{x} \pm (1.96 \times SE)$$

$$\bar{x} \pm (t_{n-1} \times SE)$$

SE replaces S used in the formulae given above for setting limits about a single data set and is used to assess the probability that particular values are members of the distribution. For small samples, as before, 1.96 is replaced by the appropriate t-value.

Where the sampled population is normally distributed, it is perhaps not surprising that sample means should be normally distributed. However, the value of this relationship, expressed formally as the Central Limit Theorem, is increased tremendously by the fact that sample means are normally distributed regardless of the distribution for the population being sampled.

Central Limit Theorem

Consider the sum and the mean of a sample of n repeated independent observations $(X_1, X_2, \ldots, X_n)$ of a random variable with any probability distribution. For large n the mean and sum of X values will be approximately normally distributed. And $\bar{X}$ (the average of the n values) will be approximately normally distributed with mean μ and standard deviation $\sigma/\sqrt{n}$. In practice, generalisations based on the central limit theorem hold well for sample sizes of over 30 observations; but if the distribution of the population is badly skewed, the sample sizes should exceed 50.

Box 1.4 The shape of a distribution

There are many circumstances when it is useful to be able to describe the distribution of a single group of numbers. The most obvious approach is to inspect histogram plots of the data; alternatively, several measures or indices can be calculated that help to characterise the shape of the distribution. If the data set consists of a collection of n random observations of a single variable x, e.g. individual organism size, the distribution of organism size may be summarised by calculating the following parameters. The relevant formulae are given in Box 1.2.

- The mean ($\bar{x}$) and median (m) give the average or centre of the distribution.
- Variance, standard deviation (S) and interquartile range (IQ) provide measures of the variability in size.
- The coefficient of variation (CV) provides a dimensionless measure of variability, making it possible to compare the relative variability of data sets with different sized means.

Is the distribution normal? For symmetrical (bell-shaped) distributions the median and mean should be equal. For a normal distribution the interquartile range divided by the standard deviation should be approximately 1.3, and around 70% of the values should lie within one standard deviation either side of the mean.

Measures of asymmetry or skewness

- Pearson's coefficient of skewness:

$$\gamma = \frac{3(\bar{x} - m)}{S}$$

For a symmetrical distribution the mean and median are equal and $\gamma = 0$. When the distribution is positively skewed, mean > median and $\gamma > 0$. For a negatively skewed distribution, median > mean and $\gamma < 0$.

- Moment coefficient of skewness (third dimensionless moment about the mean, often simply called skewness).

$$g_3 = \frac{1}{S^3} \left(\frac{1}{n} \sum (x - \bar{x})^3 \right)$$

For a symmetrical distribution g_3 is equal to 0. For a positively skewed distribution $g_3 > 0$, i.e. a distribution with a long tail to the right. For a negatively skewed distribution with a tail to the left, $g_3 < 0$.

- Moment coefficient of kurtosis (fourth moment about the mean):

$$g_4 = \frac{1}{S^4} \left(\frac{1}{n} \sum (x - \bar{x})^4 \right)$$

For a normal distribution g_4 is equal to 0. Negative values indicate platykurtosis (flatness), positive values indicate leptokurtosis (pointedness).

Relationships between moments

The variance, coefficients of skewness and kurtosis are related. All are moments about the mean and they involve calculating residuals – the differences between individual values of x and the sample mean. The general formula for moments about the mean is

$$M_r = \frac{1}{n} \sum (x - \bar{x})^r \qquad g_r = M_r / S^r$$

The dimensionless form of the moment, g_r, is obtained by dividing M_r by S^r. When $r = 2$, M_2 equals the variance. Measures of skewness are obtained when $r = 3$, and kurtosis when $r = 4$.

- The Gini coefficient is an appropriate measure when interest centres on the degree of size inequality rather than the asymmetry of the distribution (Weiner and Solbrig, 1984):

$$G = \frac{\sum\limits_{i=1}^{n} \sum\limits_{j=1}^{n} (x_i - x_j)}{2n^2 \bar{x}}$$

The top line of the equation involves calculating the difference between each value of x and all remaining $n - 1$ values of x; these differences are summed for each x and then summed overall for all n values in the data set. The greater the inequality between data values, the greater the size of this sum and the greater the value of G. When there is no inequality, i.e. when all values are the same, $G = 0$.

to conventions born out of experience. When sampling vegetation, quadrats of $0.25\,\text{m}^2$ are frequently used to study low herb communities, quadrats of $1-4\,\text{m}^2$ are used to survey tall herb and low shrub communities, and quadrats of $4-25\,\text{m}^2$ have been used for tall shrub communities (Moore and Chapman, 1986; Goldsmith, 1991). For woodlands, $100\,\text{m}^2$ quadrats have been used to survey ground flora, with larger $2500\,\text{m}^2$ ($50\,\text{m} \times 50\,\text{m}$) quadrats being used to record woodland trees (Ferris-Kaan and Patterson, 1992).

Ideally the sample units should be the same, but this is not always possible. Weighted means and appropriate pooled estimates of variance should be used when values are combined

Table 1.1 Some sampling units (SUs) used in various fields of ecology and typical variables measured

Field	Measurement variable	Sampling unit
Population ecology	Abundance parameters (e.g. density)	Trapline, grid or flush transect
Physiological ecology	Organism response (e.g. photosynthesis)	Individual animal, plant or microbe
Behavioural ecology	Response parameters (e.g. feeding rate)	Individual animal, plant or microbe
Microbial ecology	Growth/decay parameters (e.g. loss of litter)	Petri dish or litter bag
Community ecology	Species abundances or presence/absence	Plot, quadrat or line transect

Two basic types of ecological data matrix: (a) species and environmental factor data measured in one location through time (a total of t observations, the SUs) and (b) species and environmental factor data measured on N SUs over space, i.e. at different locations in the landscape. Source: Ludwig and Reynolds (1988)

from different sample units (Sokal and Rohlf, 1995; Greenwood, 1996). A pilot study will often show whether a particular sample unit is appropriate. The optimum size for a sample unit will depend on the density of the subjects. Suppose the aim of a study is to determine the density of limpets on a rocky shore. It is decided to count the numbers of limpets occurring in each quadrat. The number of limpets recorded will clearly depend on the size of quadrats used and the density of limpets present. If a small quadrat is used and the limpets have a low density at the sampled sites, large numbers of zero and low counts will be obtained. Unless a very large number of quadrats are recorded, the limpet population will be undersampled. A more representative sample may be obtained by adopting a larger sample. A larger sample unit increases the total area of the site sampled, reduces the number of zero counts and allows a more representative sample of limpet population density to be obtained. The situation is further complicated if the distribution of limpets is either clumped or regularly dispersed throughout the habitat. Where species, other variables or traits are recorded on a presence or absence basis the results may be expressed as frequencies. If species A occurs in 35 out of 100 quadrats, the percentage frequency of A is 35%. Frequency values should ideally lie between 20% and 70%. Values below 20% suggest that the sample unit (e.g. quadrat) is too small and should be increased. The relationship between quadrat size, quadrat arrangement and the spatial distribution of organisms is discussed in Chapter 4.

This discussion has assumed that the sample consists of more than one sample unit. However, in some studies where habitats are considered to be homogeneous, one sample unit or a small number of sample units may be used. In large-scale regional vegetation surveys, sites are often chosen subjectively to ensure that all the major vegetation types are adequately sampled. Within each vegetation type, sample units are placed selectively within areas considered to be homogeneous and typical of the vegetation type. In this type of descriptive study, where a limited number of sample units are used, each sample unit must be large enough to ensure it is representative. The *minimum sample area* required for a representative sample may be estimated by plotting accumulative species number against quadrat size. The minimum sample area, defined as the smallest area sufficient to obtain an adequate and representative sample, is taken as the area at which the plotted curve flattens, or as the area in which 95% of all recorded species occur. The minimum sample areas vary between vegetation types (Figure 1.1).

This approach can be generalised to other situations where the primary aim of the study is to assess community composition; for example, minimum trapping effort or sample volume could be determined from plots of accumulative species number (richness) against sample effort or volume. Where many smaller sample units are used, plots of accumulative species number against either the sample unit number or the accumulative sum of sample unit size can be used to determine the minimum sampling effort needed to adequately sample species composition. This approach – using a few large, subjectively placed sample units – has historically been adopted for large-scale botanical surveys and community classification studies, particularly by the Continental school of plant 'phytosociology' (Kent and Coker, 1992). However, this approach has little to commend it. In most circumstances greater information and insight will be obtained from using more than one sample unit. If necessary, values obtained from using smaller sample units can be combined, and the variance between sample units can provide valuable information on spatial or temporal heterogeneity.

1.3.2 How many sample units should be used?

Graphical methods

The simplest way of estimating the most appropriate sample size is to plot the mean of the response variable against sample size (n), producing what is called a *sample effort curve*. Means are calculated as accumulative means – as sample size increases, the number of values used to calculate the mean increases. The first value plotted is simply the value recorded from the first sample unit, the second is the average for sample units 1 and 2, the third is the average for sample units 1, 2 and 3, and the process continues until all the available values have been used. Initially the mean value will vary greatly as new values are used in its calculation; but as sample size increases, the amount of variation will decrease and the value will stabilise. Once the mean has stabilised, increased sampling effort has little effect, i.e. it does not improve our estimate of the true population mean (Figure 1.2). For field surveys the point at which successive means vary by less that 10% is often selected as an appropriate sample size. Alternatively, estimates of variance, standard deviation, standard error of the mean or the confidence limits may be plotted (Box 1.2).

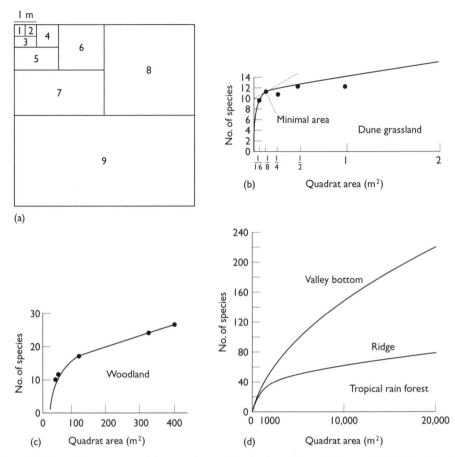

Figure 1.1 The species–area curve. (a) A system of nested plots for determining minimal area. (b) Minimal area for dune grassland in North Carolina is about 0.13 m². (c) Minimal area for an English woodland is about 100 m² (d) Minimal areas for two stands of tropical rainforest in Brunei are 1000 m² (a ridge) and 20 000 m² (a valley bottom). Parts (a) and (d) reprinted, with permission, from D. Mueller-Dombois and H. Ellenberg, 1974, *Aims and Methods of Vegetation Ecology*, copyright John Wiley and Sons, Inc., New York. Part (b) reprinted, with permission, from A.D. Smith, 1940, A discussion of the application of a climatological diagram, the hythergraph, to the distribution of natural vegetation types, *Ecology* **21**:184–91, copyright the Ecological Society of America. Part (c) reprinted from B. Hopkins, 1957, Patterns in plant community, *Journal of Ecology*, **45**:451–63, with permission of the British Ecological Society.

Some textbooks state that sample effort curves should be produced by combining randomly selected sample units. Samples of different sizes are obtained by randomly selecting n sample units from the total of m, where $n \leq m$; the mean or variance, etc., is calculated and plotted for each value of n. This procedure is not necessary if the sample units are randomly placed or selected. For random selection of the sample units, sample effort curves can be produced by combining sample unit values in the order they are collected. This allows sample effort curves to be readily produced in the field as the data is collected, allowing planned sampling schemes to be developed and modified rapidly as required. Although successive points will not be independent, this does not present a problem, as the resulting sample effort curves should only be used to estimate appropriate sample size, not to make statistical comparison between successive points.

Where interest centres on processes that are adequately summarised by a single response variable, the conventional sample effort curve approach works well. With complex processes

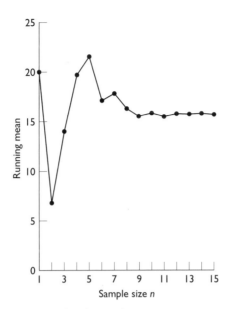

Figure 1.2 Sample effort curve based on a plot of accumulative means.

that are best described by measuring a set of response variables, sample effort curves can be cumbersome, with separate plots required for each variable. This type of problem is frequently encountered when sampling communities. One solution is to use the minimum area approach outlined above; species–area curves or sample effort curves are produced by plotting accumulative species number against sample effort (n). However, species richness is only one parameter of community structure. The adequacy of a community sample should not be judged on the recorded species numbers alone; relative abundance should also be considered. Based on calculating the similarity between successive samples, Streever and Bloom (1993) have proposed a solution to this problem. There are many similarity indices or sample resemblance functions; some of them are correlation coefficients. Resemblance functions allow the similarity between two multivariable samples to be quantified. All can be scaled so they are equal to 1.0 when the samples are identical and equal to 0 when the samples have nothing in common. Resemblance measures are discussed in detail in Chapter 6.

If two samples drawn from the same community are representative, we expect them to be similar. Both samples should contain the same range of species at similar levels of abundance. Samples based on small numbers of sample units are unlikely to be representative of the community as a whole, and are likely to differ substantially from one another, i.e. to have low similarities. As sampling effort increases, the samples will become more representative and sample similarity will increase. In their procedure, Streever and Bloom (1993) generated samples of size n by randomly selecting two sets of n sample units from the complete set of m sample units. The selected sample units were combined to form two samples of size n, the similarity between them was then calculated. For each value of n, the process was repeated 10 times, allowing a mean (and standard deviation) of sample similarity to be calculated. Mean sample similarity is then plotted against sample effort (n) to produce a *self-similarity curve* which approaches a plateau of 1.0 as sample effort increases and samples become increasingly similar. This procedure can be modified, allowing its application without the need to generate multiple random samples. The simplest procedure is to combine equal numbers of samples units into two non-overlapping samples that are then compared with each other. At $n = 1$ the first two sample units are compared; at $n = 2$ sample units 1 and 2 are combined and compared with a combined sample of 3 and 4; at $n = 3$ sample units 1, 2 and 3 are combined and compared with 4, 5 and 6, etc.

If necessary the process could be repeated using different combinations of sample unit to assess the robustness of the estimate of sample size. In practice this is unlikely to be necessary unless the system being studied is very heterogeneous. Although Streever and Bloom (1993) recommend the use of Morisitia's index of similarity, which Wolda (1981) found to be independent of sample size and diversity,[2] other indices are likely to perform equally well if not better. The percentage similarity index is recommended here (Chapter 6).

$$PS_{jk} = \left(\frac{2W}{A + B} \right) \times 100$$

$$A = \sum_{i=1}^{n} x_{ij}$$

A is the sum of species abundance values associated with sample j.

$$B = \sum_{i=1}^{n} x_{ik}$$

B is the sum of species abundance values associated with sample k.

$$W = \sum_{i=1}^{s} \min(x_{ij}, x_{ik})$$

W is the sum of the minimum abundance for species occurring in samples j and k.

Sample size and precision

In a study to investigate the impact of industrial river water extraction on fish populations, the mean sizes of fish trapped on the protective grille of a water intake pipe were randomly sampled. The weights of individual fish were measured and a mean calculated. In this case the basic sample unit is an individual fish. If initially 5 fish are weighed and a mean calculated, the process repeated and a second mean based on the weights of 5 new fish calculated, we would not be surprised if the two means differed. The difference will depend on the population variance of the fish weights. If the variance is low, i.e. all the fish have similar size, we would expect the means to be very similar; but if the variance is large, with fish of very different sizes occurring, it would be surprising if the means did not differ. If the sample size is increased from 5 to 15 fish, we would expect the means to be closer to each other and closer to the true population mean that would be obtained if all fish caught in the intake were weighed and used to calculate the mean. The difference or variance between sample means is due to sampling error, and it reflects the fact that fishes of different sizes are measured in each sample. When the sample size is small (i.e. 5) the occurrence of unusually large or small fish will have a marked effect on the mean. When the sample size is increased from 5 to 15, the influence of individual fish is reduced and the sample is more likely to be representative of the population as a whole. Thus, sampling error depends on the variance of the population being sampled and the size of the sample, i.e. the number of fish or the number of sample units forming the sample. Expressing these concepts more formally, the 95% confidence limits about a mean are given by

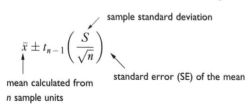

sample standard deviation

$$\bar{x} \pm t_{n-1} \left(\frac{S}{\sqrt{n}} \right)$$

mean calculated from
n sample units

standard error (SE) of the mean

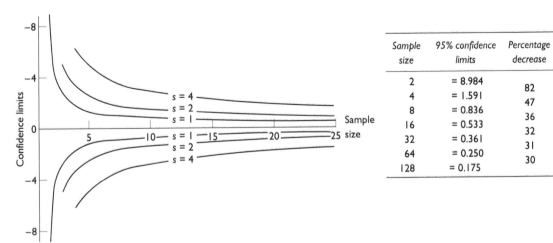

Figure 1.3 The decrease in 95% confidence limits with increasing sample size. The lines are drawn for different values of the standard deviation (s). Student's t-distribution has been used in calculating the confidence limits. As the sample size approaches infinity, all the confidence limits approach zero. Inset is a table of 95% confidence limits obtained by assuming $s = 1$. Reprinted, with permission, from Goldsmith (1991).

The t-value is a constant for a given sample size and probability level. Its value is obtained from tables of the Student's t-value distribution. It can be viewed as a correction factor for small sample sizes. For large samples size ($n \geq 30$) at the 95% probability level, t can be replaced by 1.96. For a sample size of 5 the appropriate t-value, with $5 - 1 = 4$ degrees of freedom and at the 95% probability levels, is 2.776. As n increases, t tends to 1.96. From the equation above it is clear that the width of the 95% confidence interval, a measure of the precision of the calculated mean, depends on two factors, the number of sample units (n) and the population variance, estimated by the sample standard deviation (S). Since it is not possible to alter the population variance, the precision of our estimate can only be increased by increasing the size of the sample; as n increases, the width of the confidence interval will decrease. For small samples, large reductions in sampling error are gained for small increases in n (Figure 1.3).[3] Using the relation between confidence intervals, t-values, n and s, it is possible to define the precision of a sample mean and to estimate the sample size required to achieve a given level of precision.

Measures of precision
The variance, standard error of the mean and 95% confidence limits (CL) all provide an indication of the precision of an estimate. The variance and the difference between the upper and lower confidence limits will be small with a good, i.e. precise, estimate of population size. Percentage relative precision (PRP) provides a simple approximate guide to the precision of an estimate. PRP is defined as the mean of the difference between the 95% confidence limits expressed as a percentage of the estimated parameter (e.g. the mean). Although confidence limits may be asymmetrical, the PRP is calculated as

$$PRP = \frac{(CL_2 - CL_1)/2}{\hat{N}} \times 100 = \frac{CL_2 - CL_1}{\hat{N}} \times 50$$

Here the parameter estimated from a sample is $\hat{N}$, the estimated population size; $\hat{N}$ may be replaced by an estimate of the mean of any response variable; CL_1, CL_2 are the upper and lower confidence limits.

Calculating the required sample size

The required level of precision, hence the sample size, will depend on whether the investigator wishes to detect a 5%, 15% or 30% difference between means. For a normally distributed population, the sample mean can be related to the true population mean using what is known as the *t*-distribution, where values of *t* are given by

Difference between the sample mean $\bar{x}$ and μ, the theoretical population mean, provides a direct measure of the precision of $\bar{x}$; the smaller the difference, the better $\bar{x}$ is as an estimate of μ.

$$t = \frac{\bar{x} - \mu}{\sqrt{S^2/n}} = \frac{\bar{x} - \mu}{S/\sqrt{n}}$$

standard error of the mean (SE) $= S/\sqrt{N}$

Although the equation above can be rearranged, allowing *n* to be calculated, little is gained without knowing the value of μ. However, it is possible to remove μ from the equation by expressing the difference, $\bar{x} - \mu$, in terms of the precision of $\bar{x}$. Suppose that the required level of precision is 10%, this implies that the sample mean should not differ from the true population mean, μ, by more than 10% or, expressed as a proportion, by 0.1 of $\bar{x}$. Thus the numerator in the above equation can be replaced by the sample mean multiplied by the proportional precision (p). The resulting equation can then be rearranged to allow the required sample size to be estimated:

$$t \cong \frac{p\bar{x}}{\sqrt{S^2/n}}$$
Equation for *t*.

$$t\sqrt{\frac{S^2}{n}} \cong p\bar{x}$$
Rearrange to bring *n* to the left-hand side.

$$t^2\left(\frac{S^2}{n}\right) \cong (p\bar{x})^2$$
Square both sides to remove the square root sign. Then divide through by t^2 and S^2, and rearrange to make *n* the subject.

$$n \cong \frac{t^2 S^2}{(p\bar{x})^2}$$
Equation to estimate the required sample size.

To apply this approach, the sample standard deviation, *S*, must be estimated from a pilot sample and an appropriate *t*-value chosen. Following an example given by Eckblad (1991), in a study to determine the population density of *Hexagenia* mayfly nymphs in the benthos of a backwater lake on the upper Mississippi River, an initial pilot study of 15 Ponar grab samples was made. The pilot sample mean for nymph density was 8.47, the sample variance (S^2) was 17.407. How many grab samples would be needed to estimate the mean population density within 10% of the true mean? To estimate this with 95% confidence the required *t*-value is 2.145 (*t*-value with 14 degrees of freedom at probability level 0.05). The required proportional precision (p) is 0.10, thus the appropriate sample size is

$$n \cong \frac{t^2 S^2}{(p\bar{x})^2} = \frac{(2.145)^2(17.409)}{(0.10 \times 8.47)^2} \cong 112$$

This method of estimating the required sample size will be most reliable when that data is normally distributed. However, because of the Central Limit Theorem[4] (Box 1.3), this procedure can be applied to non-normally distributed data; although where the distribution is strongly skewed, the formula should be used conservatively, i.e. the actual number of samples should exceed the calculated figure. Four points are worth noting:

- By rearranging the equation used to estimate sample size, the proportional precision of a sample mean can be estimated:

$$p = \frac{t\sqrt{S^2/n}}{\bar{x}} = \frac{t(\text{SE})}{\bar{x}}$$

For the example given above, the standard error of the mean (SE) = 1.08, t = 2.145 and the proportional precision of the pilot sample mean of 8.47 is given by (2.145)(1.08)/8.47 = 0.273.

- An alternative but related approach is to calculate the sample size required to ensure that the 95% confidence interval is less than some specified size E, i.e. $t(\text{SE}) < E$. This allows the minimum sample size to be calculated from

$$n > \frac{t^2 S^2}{E^2}$$

- If the population variance is known before the study, t-values may be replaced by 1.96 and t^2 approximated as 4.

- Separate calculations are required for every variable of interest, and the required sample sizes are likely to differ from one variable to another.

1.3.3 Replication and pseudoreplication

In order to assess the extent of sampling errors, the extent of spatial or temporal variation, or the effects of experimental treatments, sample units and associated measurements must be replicated. However, replicate sample units must be placed or selected so that the true extent of variation present in the population is encountered in the sample. Consider a large study site on a rocky shore. It is decided that the community composition of the site should be surveyed using 20 quadrats (sample units) of area $0.5\,\text{m}^2$, i.e. the sample consists of 20 replicated sample units. If the first sample unit is placed randomly, how should the remaining 19 sample units be placed? This is an important question. If all the sample units are grouped together – concentrated in only a small portion of the site – the sample will be biased, as a large part of the site will not be represented in the final sample. The community will appear to be more homogeneous than it actually is and sample errors (i.e. within-site variation) will appear to be small, giving the impression that a high level of precision has been achieved. This is an example of pseudoreplication (Hurlbert, 1984). The replicated sample units are not true replicates; the sample is effectively composed of 20 repeated measures from the same area, each replicate adds little information to the sample.

It is important to realise that a large number of replicates alone is not sufficient, it does not necessarily guarantee a representative sample. From a good sample it should be possible to generalise about the whole site (population) with confidence. To achieve a good sample, the whole study area should be adequately represented in the sample. In the present example this might most easily be achieved by the random placement of all of the sample units. The problem of pseudoreplication and how it may be avoided is illustrated in Figure 1.4 for a simple field experiment involving treated plots and control plots. In addition to the problems of pseudoreplication, sample units that are closely related, either spatially or temporally, are unlikely to be independent. Sample independence is a basic requirement of most statistical procedures. For this reason alone it is rarely wise to group the selection of sample units too closely to one another either in space or time.

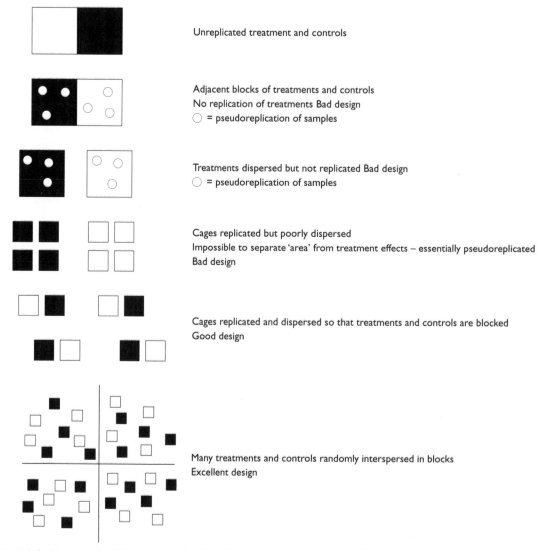

Figure 1.4 Replication in the field: good and bad designs. Reprinted, with permission, from Rafaelli and Hawkins (1996).

1.3.4 Placement and selection

Random sampling schemes

Sampling schemes can generally be described as random, regular or stratified random. In the vast majority of cases a random sampling or stratified random sampling is most appropriate. In a random sampling scheme each individual in the population or each point in the study area is equally likely to be selected or sampled. Random sampling has the advantage that sample units are more likely to be independent and the sample representative of the population or area as a whole. Individual sample units should ideally be selected using random numbers. Random numbers may be obtained from tables, or generated using a computer or small hand calculator. Where sample units correspond to individual organisms, they should be numbered or ordered in such a way that a random sequence or selection can be produced. In vegetation studies or other spatially based studies, random sampling points can be obtained relatively easily using randomly generated x and y coordinates. Where

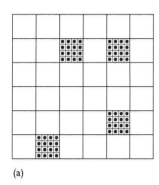 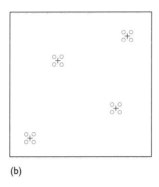 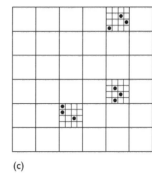

(a)   (b)   (c)

Figure 1.5 Cluster sampling: (a) cluster areas (the large squares) are chosen at random and all sample units (small squares) are sampled within each cluster; (b) points are chosen at random (+) and samples (○) are taken in a fixed pattern relative to each point; (c) major units (large squares) are randomly chosen and minor units (small squares) are sampled at random within each major unit. Reprinted, with permission, from Greenwood (1996).

fixed quadrats or sample plots form the basic sample units, random coordinates can be used to select their positions for their placement. This approach may be extended to transect-based studies (Greenwood, 1996), where random coordinates serve as the starting point for each transect. However, care should be taken not to assume that the sample units which may form part of a transect are random or independent. The results of each transect should be treated as a single replicate. Individual sample units that form part of a transect, e.g. regular points along a line transect or quadrats forming part of a belt transect, are not independent of each other. The problem of sample unit independence is encountered when sample units are clustered either in time or space.

Clustered random sampling schemes are sometimes employed where the location of the major sampling units is difficult or time-consuming (Figure 1.5). Consider the case where a large survey of the shrub and ground flora is planned in an area of dense tropical forest. Because of the large area to be surveyed and the limited resources available, it is decided to survey 50 m × 50 m squares of forest floor (the basic sample units) at each of 150 locations chosen from a 1 km grid map (1 km squares form the major sampling units). One approach would be to randomly locate the 150 major sampling units. The survey team would then make their way to the centre of each 1 km square, survey the vegetation within the 50 m × 50 m sample unit and then move on to the next map square to be surveyed. In this type of large-scale study, there may be considerable transport costs for travel between sample points, measured in terms of time and money. An alternative sampling scheme, where more than one sample unit is located in each randomly selected 1 km square, could reduce transport costs substantially.

One of the many possibilities would be to survey three sampling units (50 m × 50 m areas) within each of 50 randomly chosen 1 km map squares. Such a clustered sampling scheme has two advantages: (i) because the total area sampled within each map square is increased the precision of data at this level will be increased, and (ii) the amount of travelling between sampled sites will be substantially reduced. However, clustering also imposes several penalties. Because the clustered sample units are not independent, they must be treated as a single sample unit, reducing the effective sample size from 150 to 50 replicated sample units. And although the total area sampled remains the same, the number of 1 km squares of forest that are sampled is reduced by one-third. Which of these two sampling schemes is more efficient will depend on the relative magnitudes and scales of the variance in the forest vegetation. If at the scale of 1 km^2 plots the forest is relatively homogeneous, the clustered sampling scheme may be more efficient than a completely randomised scheme. Greenwood (1996) discusses clustered random sampling schemes in more detail and demonstrates how the results of a pre-liminary study may be used to choose between completely random sampling and different clustered sampling schemes.

Multi-level random sampling, an alternative to clustered sampling, reduces the problem of sample unit independence. The clustered sample units are allocated randomly within the major sample units (Figure 1.5). Greenwood (1996) states that, in terms of cost and overall precision, multi-level sampling schemes are intermediate between completely randomised schemes and clustered sampling schemes, and they are often superior to both. The data collected from a multi-level sampling scheme may be aggregated from the lowest level upwards. Suppose the aim of a study is to determine the density of a particular species of worm on an intertidal muddy shore. The total area of shore is estimated to be $150\,000\,\mathrm{m}^2$. Based on the results of a pilot survey, a two-layered sampling scheme is adopted, in which ten $2\,\mathrm{m} \times 2\,\mathrm{m}$ square quadrats (major sample units) are located randomly in the study area. Within each $2\,\mathrm{m} \times 2\,\mathrm{m}$ quadrat, three random $20\,\mathrm{cm} \times 20\,\mathrm{cm}$ (i.e. $0.2\,\mathrm{m} \times 0.2\,\mathrm{m}$) mud cores are taken. Individual mud cores form the basic or minor sample units of the study. The intensity of this sampling scheme can be assessed using four parameters:

M = number of major units available for sampling

m = number of major units actually sampled

U = number of minor units available for sampling within each major unit

u = number of minor units actually sampled

The *intensity of sampling* at both levels is given by the ratio of the actual units sampled to those available for sampling. Maximum sampling intensity occurs when these ratios equal 1.0, at which point all available sampling units are sampled. Note that sampling intensities can and will vary between levels; in general the higher sampling intensity should be reserved for the level with the highest variance. For the sampling scheme described, $M = 150\,000/(2 \times 2) = 37\,500$, $m = 5$, $U = (2 \times 2)/(0.2 \times 0.2) = 100$ and $u = 4$. For each quadrat, it is possible to calculate a mean and variance of the density of worms per core. The results can thus be summarised by 10 quadrat mean and variance values from which three further statistics can be calculated:

$\bar{\bar{x}}$ = overall mean, mean of the m individual quadrat means $(\bar{x})$

$S_{\bar{x}}^2$ = the variance of the m quadrat means $(\bar{x})$

S_m^2 = the mean of the variance values calculated for each of the m quadrats

After sampling the shore, suppose the following results were obtained: $\bar{\bar{x}} = 5.240$ worms per core, the variance of the means $(S_{\bar{x}}^2) = 5.392$ and the mean of the variances $(S_m^2) = 10.017$. Then the best estimate for the overall density of worms is given by $\bar{\bar{x}}$, which combines the results of both levels of sampling. The best estimate of the total number of worms present in the entire study area is given by $\bar{\bar{x}}MU$, which equals $5.240 \times 37\,500 \times 100 = 19.65 \times 10^6$ worms. Using the formula given by Greenwood (1996), the standard error and confidence limits about the mean and total number of worms is given by

$$\mathrm{SE}_{\bar{\bar{x}}} = \sqrt{\left(1 - \frac{m}{M}\right)\left(\frac{S_{\bar{x}}^2}{m}\right) + \left(1 - \frac{u}{U}\right)\left(\frac{S_m^2}{um}\right)}$$

This is based on the standard formula used to calculate a pooled estimate of variance for two samples of different sizes and variances.

$$\mathrm{SE}_{\bar{\bar{x}}} = \sqrt{\left(1 - \frac{10}{37\,500}\right)\left(\frac{5.392}{10}\right) + \left(1 - \frac{3}{100}\right)\left(\frac{10.017}{30}\right)} = 0.9289$$

The approximate 95% confidence limits are given by

value of t with $m(u - 1)$ d.f.

$$\bar{\bar{x}} \pm t \times \text{SE}_{\bar{\bar{x}}}$$

$$5.240 \pm 2.086 \times 0.9289$$

$$\text{UCL} = 3.30 \quad \text{(upper confidence limit)}$$

$$\text{LCL} = 7.18 \quad \text{(lower confidence limit)}$$

The standard error for the total number of worms is obtained by taking the calculated value for the overall mean, $\bar{x}$, and multiplying by *MU*. The same goes for the confidence limits.

In many cases, particularly when sampling animal populations, samples may not be truly random; often this is an unfortunate but unavoidable constraint of the methodology (e.g. trap type) or the system being studied. This problem is particularly marked in field studies of animal behaviour. Often the investigator can at best hope to obtain a sample that approximates to a random sample. When studying the behaviour of social animals, for perfectly valid practical reasons the researcher will often select large rather than small social groups. Even if observations within the selected groups are subsequently randomised, the sample of animals studied is not random and the results will be biased towards the behaviour of animals in large groups, and this may differ from the behaviour of animals in smaller groups. The results of such a study will be biased towards those individuals present in the largest groups. No matter how difficult it may be, it is important that investigators strive to ensure the sample is as unbiased and as representative as possible. Where this cannot be achieved, the extent and direction of possible biases should be openly acknowledged (and if possible quantified). Try to ensure that individual sample units (observations) are as independent as possible. Lehner (1996) points out that, when selecting individuals for a randomised experimental design or samples, a distinction should be made between random, haphazard and opportunistic samples:

- *Haphazard samples* are taken on an arbitrary basis. They may be measurements taken for individual animals which happen to be close to the observer, or observations made at times convenient to the researcher.

- *Opportunistic samples* are taken whenever behaviour occurs in any individual in the population being observed. Suppose a researcher is interested in a particular type of behaviour, an opportunistic sample would be obtained if records were only taken from individuals observed to demonstrate the behaviour pattern of interest. Such a sample would be unrepresentative of the population.

Although many studies contain an element of haphazard sampling, there is little excuse for sampling schemes which are entirely haphazard and which do not attempt to randomise observations or selection sample units.

Stratified random sampling
When the behaviour is rare or when the phenomenon of interest is rare, then opportunistic sampling is often employed; all individuals are observed but data is only collected from individuals encountered that demonstrate the phenomenon of interest. Although individual data records may be independent, such sampling schemes are not random. A more appropriate randomised sample would be obtained if the sample were grouped or stratified by sex or body size and an attempt made to sample randomly within each group or stratum. Where a large group of animals are being observed, e.g. geese in a field, the population could be stratified spatially using an imaginary grid or markers placed in the field (Lehner, 1996). Observation could then be randomised at two levels: observed grids and individuals within

grid squares. The chosen grid squares must be far enough apart to ensure that, between recordings, geese are unable to move from one observed grid to the next. If the animals are able to move between grids (strata) then the recordings will not be independent.

In many studies of animal behaviour, observation will be effectively stratified by time. An individual researcher is only able to directly observe and record the behaviour of a very limited number of individuals. Because of this, and to ensure that the study area or population is covered, available observation time is frequently divided into blocks. For example, as part of a pilot study, the number and behaviour of bumble bees occurring on randomly selected flower spikes are followed for 5 min, then a new flower spike is selected; the process is repeated until 12 flower spikes have been observed. Once the behaviour of bees has been observed for 60 min (12×5 min), the whole processes is repeated on randomly selected flower spikes of a second species of plant. For this sampling scheme, records may be considered as 'blocked' or stratified at three levels: individual flower spikes (the basic sample unit), species of flowering plant (the experimental unit of study) and two blocks of 60 min. Although the plants and individual flower spikes observed might have been randomly selected, the recording sequence was not. It is likely that, during the 2 h of the study, the behaviour of the bees would change in response to environmental changes (e.g. temperature) and previous behaviour (e.g. past feeding activity); similarly, the amount and availability of nectar might also be expected to change. Thus it would not be surprising to find that the visitation and feeding rates differed between the two species of plant.

Unfortunately, any recorded difference may have little to do with the relative attractiveness of the flowers to potential pollinators. Temporal changes in bee behaviour and flower nectar production (or availability) might be expected to occur during the two experimental periods. This experiment design can be improved by attempting to break the dependence of recordings made within each 60 min time block. The sequence of recordings could be completely randomised between all flower spikes for the two species. Or smaller sets of observations could be used, these blocks or sets of observations being either randomly allocated to each species of plant or alternated between species after randomly selecting the first species to be observed. The issues raised in this example have parallels with those involved in the design of manipulative experiments. The use of analysis of variance (ANOVA) to investigate blocked data is outlined in Chapter 10. Whichever sampling scheme is adopted, the value of the results obtained will undoubtedly be enhanced by extending the sampling beyond a 2 h period on a single day.

When sampling vegetation or spatially distributed phenomena, a completely randomised sampling scheme may undersample some areas of the study site. Not all random placements are equally good. There is a small but finite probability that randomly placed sample units may be concentrated in one part of the study area, hence the sample will be unrepresentative. This problem may be avoided by using a stratified random sampling scheme. The study area is divided into equal areas, called strata, and within each stratum the basic samples units are randomly placed (Figure 1.6). Suppose that vegetation present in a meadow is to be surveyed using a hundred $1 \, m^2$ quadrats. If the meadow is homogeneous, there is little to be gained by stratified sampling, so a completely randomised sampling scheme could be adopted. However, if the meadow is heterogeneous or suspected of being heterogeneous then a stratified sampling scheme should be adopted. The field might be divided into 4 equal compartments running from east to west, and 25 quadrats could be randomly located within each compartment (stratum). Such stratified sampling schemes are random but they ensure the whole site is adequately sampled. If compartments differ in size then the sampling effort or intensity should be varied accordingly, i.e. the number of sampling units per unit area should be the same; if 10 sample units are used to sample an area $100 \, m^2$ then 20 should be used to sample an area of $200 \, m^2$. The mean and variance may be calculated for each stratum and

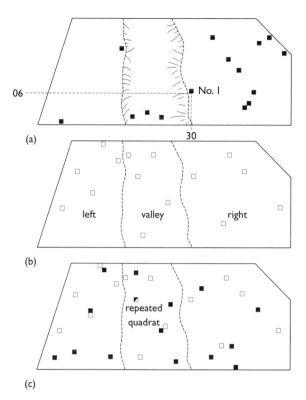

Figure 1.6 A diagrammatic nature reserve, with a valley running through it, on which a plant species is to be monitored by 15 quadrats. (a) The random selection of 15 quadrats based on a square grid over the reserve; the first quadrat is selected at grid coordinates (30, 06). (b) The reserve is now divided into three strata and five quadrats are located at random within each stratum; this is a stratified random sample. When monitoring or during repeated sampling, to avoid autocorrelation induced by the sampling scheme, each random selection in the three strata is used on only two successive occasions. Here the open squares show quadrats recorded in years 1 and 2, and the filled squares show quadrats recorded in years 2 and 3. Reprinted, with permission, from Goldsmith (1991).

ANOVA may be used to compare compartment values. If the compartments do not differ, the results may be combined. Stratified random sampling has three major advantages over a completely randomised sampling scheme:

- It can ensure that the whole study site is adequately represented in the sample.
- It allows the presence of differences between strata to be detected and quantified. This information can be valuable, and where strata conform to a grid or sections of a transect, the data may be presented using a map.
- Overall estimates based on stratified sampling have much greater precision than estimates based on a completely randomised design.

And three other points are worth noting:

- The strata or compartments need not be continuous.
- The choice of strata should be governed by the nature and aims of the study or by the results of a preliminary study. As long as there is some difference between the strata means, then stratification will be advantageous.
- The number of strata should not be such that the number of sample units per stratum becomes too small to adequately sample the stratum.

Regular sampling schemes

Regular sampling schemes, e.g. selecting every fifth animal or sampling at each grid intersection, are rarely justified. They are not random and are extremely unlikely to be representative. One problem is that the grid or sampling interval may coincide with natural regularities in the system being studied, so the sample will be highly biased. Because the samples are not random and the sample units are not independent, results cannot be subjected to statistical analysis; it is only possible to use descriptive statistics. In environmental studies there are only really two occasions where regular sampling schemes can be justified, for mapping and for investigating spatial patterns:

- *Mapping studies* are used when the primary aim is to map the occurrence or magnitude of a phenomenon. A regular sampling scheme helps to ensure that the entire area is surveyed and makes it easier to produce a map.

- *Spatial patterns* can be investigated using a regular sampling scheme as long as the null hypothesis assumes that the spatial pattern being investigated is random. This exception to the normal statistical requirement for a random sample is discussed in Chapter 4. Note that when different data sets are compared, the samples do have to be random.

Transects are a form of regular sampling frequently used in environmental fieldwork; two types need to be distinguished. In one type the transect is substituting for a more conventional sample unit. For example, in habitats such as dense forest it may be easier to walk 250 m counting the number of ant nests that lie within 5 m either side of the line, than to locate and search a random 50 m × 50 m plot. The transect forms the basic sample unit of the study, and the validity of the overall sample will depend on the number of transects and where they are placed. Transects, like quadrats, should be located randomly; but unlike the conventional square quadrat, they may be oriented in various ways. Orientation may be constant (e.g. always running in the same direction), systematically rotated or randomly oriented. Greenwood (1996) suggests that in most circumstances there is little benefit to be gained by choosing one orientation over another.

Related to this question and within the context of vegetation studies, Greig-Smith (1983) has discussed the relative merits of square and rectangular quadrats having the same area. Although some studies have suggested that rectangular quadrats perform best, in practice the differences are often trivial and square quadrats or sample plots are conventionally used. There are exceptions. A rectangular quadrat (or short transect) should be used in habitats or environmental systems known to be highly patterned or patchy at a scale similar to the size of a conventional sample square. The long side of the quadrat or the length of the transect should be at least 1.5 times the linear scale of the pattern. For example, the surface vegetation of mires (bogs) is often highly patterned. Species and microhabitat conditions vary over short distances. If the microhabitat conditions and plant species are strongly patterned at a scale of 50 cm, i.e. patches of approximately 50 cm diameter are evident, then a rectangular quadrat at least 1 m long (e.g. 25 × 100 cm), should be used in place of the conventional 50 cm × 50 cm quadrat. For small sample sizes in this type of patchy environment, rectangular quadrats are more likely to yield a representative sample. Individual sample units will always cut across any patch, ensuring that patch and non-patch are represented in the sample. With large random samples, the results obtained from square quadrats will be similar to the results from rectangular quadrats.

The use of transects can also be justified if there is an environmental gradient with a dominant direction and the study is concerned with describing or investigating its influence. In these situations the system may show marked zonation. For example, soil contaminants will

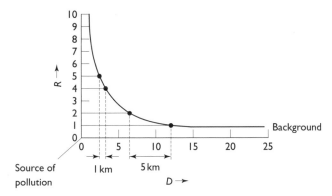

Figure 1.7 The typical exponential decline with distance (*D*) from a point source that is observed in responses (*R*) of biotic and abiotic samples to pollutant (concentrations and/or effects). Sampling sites have to be closer together near the source to detect the same change in *R*. Reprinted, with permission, from Hopkin (1993).

decrease in concentration with increasing distance from a point source of pollution; zones of concentration and environmental impact are likely to occur. A series of transects radiating away from the point source will allow the pattern of zonation to be identified and described. Because pollutant concentrations typically decline exponentially away from a point source, close to the source the distance between samples should be reduced (Figure 1.7). This will ensure that sampling intensity is highest where gradients in concentration are steepest. Coastal areas typically exhibit pronounced gradients in environmental conditions from inland sites towards the sea and transects are often used to describe the pattern of organism zonation down the shore profile. But these transect-based studies can only be descriptive; sample units placed along the transect are not independent or random and they will not be representative of the site as a whole. Only a small strip of the site will be sampled. If a transect study is chosen there are three guidelines to follow:

- A transect should only be used if it is evident that a pronounced environmental gradient exists.
- The transect should be oriented along the direction of the major gradient and at right angles to the supposed pattern of zonation.
- A belt transect should be used in place of line transects. The wider the belt transect, the more representative the samples.

If a transect or grid based sampling scheme is contemplated, an alternative stratified random sampling scheme should also be considered. A belt transect may easily be divided into a series of contiguous strata, each of which can be sampled randomly. By averaging the results from the sample units in each stratum, the results may be presented as a normal transect plot (e.g. species abundance against distance along the transect). In the vast majority of cases a stratified random sampling scheme will provide more information and prove to be more valuable than a transect-based study.

Recommendations

1. In the vast majority of studies, random or stratified random sampling schemes are the most appropriate and most efficient. Where several different variables are to be measured at each sample location, consider using a multi-level random sampling scheme. The basic units for sampling soils and vegetation have different sizes, so a multi-level random sampling scheme will be most appropriate to simultaneously sample

site soil and vegetation. The smaller soil sample units will be randomly located within the larger quadrats used to assess the vegetation, also randomly located.

2. Clustered random sampling should only be adopted after considering the results of an appropriate pilot study and only when it can be shown that clustering of sample units produces a substantial saving in sampling costs. Where clustered random sampling schemes are planned, consider using a multi-level random sampling scheme instead.

3. If there is evidence of variation within the study site, or between the members of the population being studied, then a stratified sampling scheme should be used.

4. Only in very specific situations, i.e. descriptive or mapping studies, should a regular sampling scheme be used. A guide to good sampling practice is provided in Box 1.5.

1.4 *Survey or monitoring?*

1.4.1 *Controlling for natural change*

Studies can often be considered as either surveys or monitoring. This distinction is important; survey data is collected once, whereas monitoring requires data to be repeatedly collected, often from the same location and over a long period of time. A survey sampling scheme must ensure that appropriate data is collected with sufficient precision to achieve the objectives of the study. Time, in terms of the frequency and number of recording events required, is not a factor that needs to be considered. Suppose that the heavy metal concentration of contaminated soils is to be surveyed at a number of sites. If the samples are collected and analysed in the same way, differences between site means and variance in metal concentrations will reflect the combined effects of sampling error, the spatial variation and the true differences in site contamination. The sampling regime must ensure that spatial variation and sampling errors do not prevent the detection of real differences in the levels of site contamination.

Further issues are raised if the study is extended to monitor the effectiveness of measures taken to reduce sources of contamination. The sampling scheme must now be able to distinguish real declines from the effects of spatial variation and sampling error. The situation is complicated by the fact that heavy metal concentrations in the soil may vary naturally. Depending on the bio-availability and environmental mobility of the metal, soil metal levels will fluctuate seasonally due to leaching, uptake by plants and the effects of soil bacteria on mobility (Hardman *et al.*, 1993). A monitoring programme that is completed within a year must control for seasonal variations. Problems of this type can be pronounced when monitoring community composition or the performance of an individual species over time. Habitats will be subject to a series of 'natural' changes, each of which needs to be controlled for; here are some such changes.

Seasonal and annual cycles

In long-term monitoring studies, the importance of seasonal effects may be reduced by sampling each year in the same 'biological' season, or at the same stage of population growth or species life cycle. Because weather patterns vary from year to year, it is rarely appropriate simply to sample at the same time each year. For some short-term studies, data on the normal extent of annual or seasonal variations may be sufficient to allow seasonal effects to be separated from trends. If long runs of data are available, some time trend analysis methods allow seasonal components to be identified and quantified. Alternatively, moving-average or running-average calculations can be used to remove seasonal effects and identify trends (Box 1.6).

Box 1.5   **A guide to good practice**

Ask yourself these questions

- Can the problem or reason for the study be clearly stated?
- Are the objectives sufficiently concise but adequately precise?
- Is it possible to identify a limited number of variables which should be measured or followed during the study?
- If the study is to involve experimental treatments, can suitable independent variables be chosen?

The choice of response and experimental variables will reflect existing knowledge and the investigator's conceptual model of the system. Carefully consider the validity of any assumptions implicit in the choice of variables.

Once the objectives of the study have been established, they should be translated into working hypotheses. For each of these hypotheses, a testable null hypothesis must be formulated. In order to test each hypothesis, a series of questions need to be answered:

- Will the data collected yield the information required to test the hypotheses?
- Is the study entirely descriptive?
- What are the most appropriate statistical procedures?
- The proposed statistical tests, are their assumptions likely to be met?
- What level of precision is required?

Ensure that the planned sampling scheme or experimental design incorporates the following attributes:

- Replicated samples or measurements from each combination of site, time, treatment and independent or experimental variables.
- Random selection and allocation of sample units.
- A suitable control (effects can only be detected with reference to a control).
- A pilot study.

The pilot study has several purposes:

- To establish that the appropriate sampling methodology or device (e.g. trap) has been chosen.
- To identify sampling device biases and assess sampling efficiency.
- To test that the most appropriate response variables have been selected and that they can be measured with sufficient precision.
- To establish sample unit size and number.

The results of the pilot study should be used to modify the planned investigation.

Once the data has been collected, it should be subjected to descriptive and exploratory analysis. Variable frequency histograms and plots of one variable against another (scattergrams) should be produced, means and standard deviations calculated and inspected. Exploratory analysis allows the general characteristics of the data set to be explored. It can also identify a need for transformations, the presence of outliers and occasionally an unsuspected relationship between variables. This preliminary phase of data analysis

▶

should allow appropriate statistical procedures to be selected, i.e. procedures with the required statistical power that match the characteristics of the data with the nature of the hypothesis being tested.

Additional advice for undergraduates and those embarking on field investigations for the first time

Keep a notebook In the same way that laboratory work requires the keeping of a detailed lab notebook, so it is good practice to keep a detailed and well-structured field notebook. Your field notes should contains sufficient information to allow the study to be repeated. Good field notes can save hours of wasted time when it comes to analysing and writing data collected often months ago.

Record data sensibly When recording data, write it in a form that is amenable to analysis. If you intend to store and analyse your data using a computer, make sure the format (and package) used to record the data is compatible with the format (and package) needed to perform the required statistical analysis. Having to re-enter data is tedious.

Read enough but not too much Although there is no substitute for background reading before a practical project, it is wise to strike a balance. In an effort to refine the aims and objectives of a study and decide on the most appropriate sampling method, it is all too easy to spend an excessive amount of time reading around a subject. Vast literatures are available on almost every subject and it is simply impossible to read it all. Be selective; try to identify key reviews and papers which relate closely to the proposed subject of your project. But remember, there is no substitute for practical experience.

Make it simple It is often more productive to conduct a series of simple studies than to attempt one complex study.

Use procedures you understand Don't become obsessed with attempting to select the 'right' statistical procedure. There is more than one way to analyse any data set. Each method places different restrictions on the data and accentuates different characteristics. Students often feel compelled to apply the most sophisticated techniques available. This is rarely warranted. It is better to apply procedures that you understand than to blindly apply advanced techniques that may not be appropriate and may give results which you cannot interpret with confidence.

Don't be scared of statistics The number of statistical tests is vast and ever increasing. The choice can be baffling. Rather than select what might be construed as the wrong test, it can be tempting, especially if you lack confidence in your mathematical ability, to avoid the use of statistics altogether. This is unfortunate and unnecessary. Most data sets can be reasonably well analysed using a limited tool kit of simple techniques. The basic tool kit includes being able to calculate means, variance and confidence limits; calculate percentage similarities (Chapter 1); calculate a diversity index or plot dominance diversity curves (Chapter 2); plot scattergrams and calculate a measure of correlation or association (Chapter 7). These are all very simple procedures that can be easily performed by hand with the aid of a small electronic calculator.

Evaluate your results objectively   If your findings don't match your expectations, don't dismiss them as being wrong. Check to ensure that your design and sampling procedures are sound; if they are, assume your findings are valid and attempt to interpret them accordingly.

Flawed studies can still be revealing   If you realise that your sampling was fundamentally flawed, don't panic! It is rare that the data will be completely worthless. Poorly collected data does not prevent the use of statistics; it simply means that inferences from the data to the population of all possible samples cannot be made without qualification. The study becomes essentially descriptive; statistics should be used simply to provide a quantitative description of the data. The results and conclusions can only be applied with confidence to that particular experiment or set of sampled locations. How much can be inferred from the study will depend on the design of the sampling scheme, the nature of the flaws and the system being studied. It is important to acknowledge the faults or suspected shortcomings of a study. Although they may prevent the work from being published in an academic journal, within the context of a student project, they should not be so damning. Even if it is impossible to accept or reject a hypothesis, it should be possible to conclude whether the results are consistent or inconsistent with the original hypothesis. No study is perfect, so learn from your mistakes and don't be discouraged.

Adjustment to historical changes

As with any form of fieldwork, monitoring should be undertaken for a specific purpose. The objective of the monitoring programme will determine both the spatial scale and length of study required. Monitoring may often be undertaken to establish the effectiveness of remedial site treatment or the success of a new habitat management regime. Here is an apparently simple example. A new grazing regime is introduced to increase the population of a rare butterfly species on a nature reserve. It is hoped the grazing regime will increase the abundance of the butterfly's food plant. To make an initial assessment, it is decided to monitor the abundance of the food plant. Over the next three seasons, following the change in management, the abundance of the food plant fails to increase. Can we conclude that the grazing regime has failed?

Unfortunately not; no conclusions can confidently be drawn from this study. It is possible that grazing has had no measurable impact on the abundance of the plant. In the absence of grazing, the abundance of the food plant may have remained unchanged. However, it is equally possible that, in the absence of grazing, the abundance of the food plant might have decreased or even increased. Such changes could be in response to some unknown past or current habitat conditions. Site vegetation may be recovering from a previous disturbance such as a past episode of overgrazing or severe summer drought. These problems of interpretation are less likely to occur if the study is well designed and includes an appropriate control site which is also monitored.

In this example to assess the extent of natural changes, the abundance of the food plant should ideally be monitored in two similar areas of the reserve, one subjected to the new management regime, the other a control site. Where control areas cannot be established, the site should be monitored before the change in management is implemented. The pre-impact monitoring should be long enough so that trends can be identified and a clear baseline established against which future changes can be judged.

Where control site or pre-impact monitoring is neither possible nor practical, the investigator must be able to justify the implicit assumption that site conditions were stable

Box 1.6 **Monitoring: a case study**

Following the installation of a series of weirs to control the flow of water through a valley mire complex at Thursley Common, in the UK, site managers were concerned that parts of the complex might be drying out, causing the vegetation change. As part of a three-year investigation of the ecology of the system, Dr Stephanie Greshon attempted to monitor changes in the vegetation.

A number of permanent rectangular 200 cm × 50 cm quadrats were established on the site. The vegetation in each quadrat was monitored using a regular array of 400 pins; all species in contact with each pin were recorded at each monitoring event. This allowed species absolute cover (species pin contacts per 400 pins) and species relative cover (species pin contacts divided by the total number of recorded pin contacts) to be measured very precisely. Because of the slow growth of mire vegetation, species abundance had to

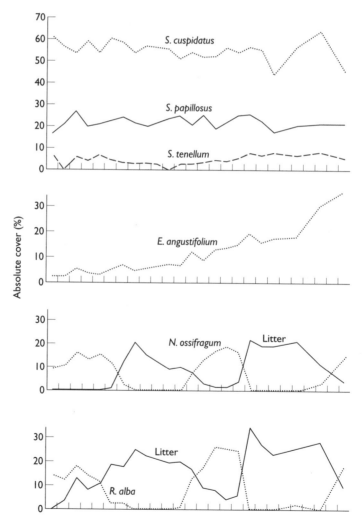

Figure 1 Phenology of eight plant species on Thursley West Bog during a period of approximately two years. Reprinted, with permission, from Greshon (1989).

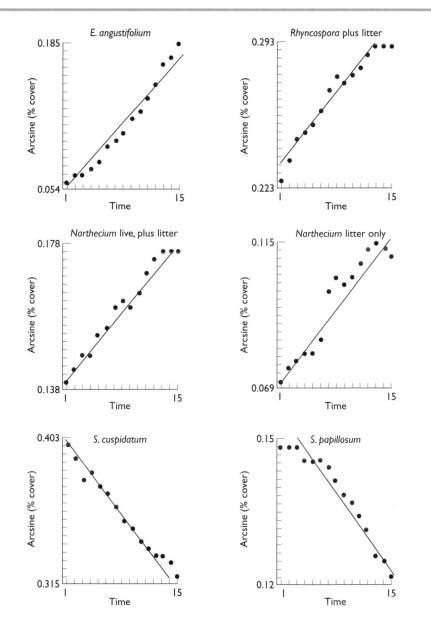

Figure 2 Species percentage abundance on the West Bog transect, arcsine transformed and plotted against time. Seasonal effects were removed from the data using moving averages. The horizontal axis represents 15 twelve-month periods from May 1985 to June 1987. Absolute percentage cover data was used in all plots except *shagnum cuspidatum* and *S. papillosum*, where relative cover data was used. Reprinted, with permission, from Greshon (1989).

be measured precisely if trends were to be detected in the time available. The vegetation was recorded at approximately monthly intervals between May 1985 and June 1987. Changes in the absolute percentage cover for key species present on West Bog are shown in Figure 1.

Although one species, *Eriophorum angustifolium* (cotton grass), appears to demonstrate a clear trend, it is difficult to discern any pattern among the other species. This is partly because any trend will be masked by seasonal effects. Seasonality was removed by calculating moving averages. Twelve-month moving averages of species abundance were calculated for the months 1–12, 2–13, 3–14, and so on, giving a total of 15 values for the study period of 26 months. When these averages are plotted in sequence, clear trends emerge (Figure 2).

The trends shown by species on the West Bog were consistent with an increase in the amount of standing water. On other parts of the mire complex, the observed trends were consistent with increased flow rates and channelling of water flows, causing the local level of the water table to increase in some parts of the mire and decrease in others (Greshon, 1989).

before the onset of monitoring and/or be able to demonstrate that the observed trends exceed any changes that might reasonably be expected to occur due to past events. In addition to short-term changes reflecting past disturbance events, habitats are also subject to changes as a result of the natural long-term process such as community succession. The impact of successional changes must be considered, particularly when planning long-term monitoring programmes.

Stochastic variation

Habitat and environmental conditions vary from day to day, month to month and year to year. The effects of environmental variations on the subject being monitored will contribute to the overall sampling error. The extent of this variation needs to be considered. In some ways the problem is analogous to those encountered in product quality control. A fixed manufacturing process produces a product that can be characterised by measuring a number of parameters. To be of an acceptable quality, each parameter must lie within certain strict limits. If these limits are exceeded, the manufacturing process must be modified so the goods produced are of an appropriate standard.

To ensure that an acceptable output is maintained, the manufacturing processes must be monitored. Production output must be regularly sampled, appropriate parameters measured and compared with desired values. The stability of the manufacturing process may be assessed by plotting the mean and standard deviation of parameter values against time to produce a control chart. The differences between sample means and standard deviations reflect sampling errors and stochastic (random) variations in the operation of manufacturing processes. These errors should be unbiased, i.e. unusually large and low values should be equally likely, and no trends should be evident in mean values. Trends are identified by runs of consecutive high or low mean values. Such trends may or may not be accompanied by a trend in the associated standard deviations – it is possible for trends in mean values to occur while the variance remains constant, or alternatively the variance may increase or decrease with or without changes in mean values.

Numerous techniques exist for analysing such data sets, many of which are supported by readily available general statistical packages such as SPSS and MINITAB. In the absence of runs of consecutive means above or below the long-term mean,[5] many of these procedures rely on comparing sample mean values with long-term parameter means and standard deviations. Unusual events or trends are identified by comparing successive sample means with an overall long-term mean. For this approach to be effective, the time sequence of

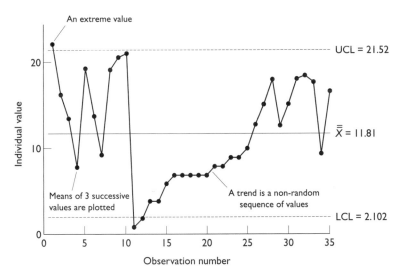

Figure 1.8 A basic control chart for hypothetical data.

the data run must be long enough to allow reliable estimates of the baseline mean to be made and appropriate limits to be set about the baseline mean. These limits are normally set as the approximate 95% confidence interval (Figure 1.8). By adopting these limits, stochastic or random variation is implicitly defined as the variation in parameter values or their mean which falls within the 95% confidence interval centred on the long-term mean or baseline value. Values outside this envelope of probability are considered to have some significance and perhaps some importance. Chapter 4 outlines how to apply the control chart approach for detecting spatial pattern.

1.4.2 What to measure and how often?

Monitoring, by its very nature, requires repeated sampling to be undertaken, and this immediately raises two questions. How frequently should samples be taken and what should be measured at each sampling episode? These are often difficult questions to answer, particularly if the aims of the monitoring programme are poorly defined or difficult to define. The objective of the study will influence the frequency and nature of the sampling undertaken. Consider the type of monitoring programme needed to assess the effects of climate change on community composition. At present the consensus of scientific opinion is that global climate patterns will shift because the burning of fossil fuels generates green-house gases, notably CO_2. The projected scenarios for northern temperate areas suggest somewhere between 1 and 2°C increase in average temperatures and changes in the amount and seasonal patterns of precipitation. In the United Kingdom it is expected that precipitation will increase by some 5–8% and become more seasonal, with a move towards drier summers and wetter, warmer winters.

Although considerable uncertainty surrounds climate change predictions, the main uncertainty does not centre on whether climate change will occur but when and at what rate. Even in the absence of climate changes, the increase in global ambient atmospheric CO_2 from a pre-industrial level of 275 ppm to the current level of around 360 ppm, and a projected level of 550 ppm by 2075, will affect the ecology of natural systems. Ambient atmospheric CO_2 levels affect the rate of plant photosynthesis. The rate of photosynthesis increases with CO_2, and this increase is particularly marked among C3-plants which are mainly found in temperate regions. The doubling of CO_2 from presents levels will increase C3-plant production by an average of approximately 30%; however, the size of the photo-synthesis increase varies between species and plant life stages. The range of responses is large. The production of some species is increased by over 130%, whereas other species show only a marginal increase, perhaps 5–10%.

The differential effects of CO_2 enrichment on plant growth will affect the balance of com-petition between plants, hence the species composition of plant communities. Whatever the forcing mechanism, be it climate change or CO_2 enrichment, ecological change seems likely to be gradual and continuous. Although sudden changes might occur, it is most probable that natural systems will change gradually, with species continuously adjusting their distribution and abundance in response to gradual changes in environmental conditions. Substantial changes in natural systems might become evident within decades (Greene, 1991; Solomon and Shugart, 1993). To detect and monitor the early onset of such long-term changes, yearly sampling would seem most appropriate. The monitoring programme would need to distinguish between 'natural' year-to-year variation and trends or significant shifts in the previous long-standing system norms. Data collection would need to be long-term and open-ended. Since the changes are likely to be relatively small, at least to start with, sampling and measurement must allow the response variable being monitored (e.g. species abundance) to be estimated precisely. Crude estimates of species abundance with large variances will not be sensitive enough to allow early changes to be identified. In other situations, where the impacts of disturbance or changes in management are likely to be large and of short duration, it will be more appropriate to perform frequent sampling at low resolution. All studies have limits on their duration and resources, so there will be a trade-off between the length of the study, the frequency of the sampling and the intensity of the sampling effort. These problems are consider in depth by Hellawell (1991) and Maher *et al.* (1994).

1.5 *Two worked examples*

1.5.1 *Percentage similarity between allele frequencies*

As part of a study into the occurrence of multiple paternity in natural populations of the live-bearing mosquitofish (*Gambusia holbrooki*) in Southern Carolina, data was collected on the frequency of genetic alleles at three loci. The molecular technique of PCR[6] was used to identify the occurrence of alleles at three loci among fish collected from two ponds (Zane *et al.*, 1999). A small portion of the data is presented in Table 1.2. The percentage similarity between the allele frequencies of the two fish populations is given by

$$PS_{jk} = \left(\frac{2W}{A+B} \right) \times 100 = \frac{2 \times 1.438}{3.0 + 2.96} \times 100 = 48.2$$

1.5.2 *Setting 95% confidence limits using MINITAB*

Using MINITAB to calculate the mean and standard deviation, the command **Describe C1.** is used to analyse the data stored in column 1. After analysis the data is printed out using the **Print** command. Both of these operations can be carried out via the menu options at the top of the screen. The data stored in C1 is a set of thorax lengths (mm) for 20 female fruit flies that have survived exposure to an endoparasitoid wasp by encapsulating the parasitoid larvae in the haemocoel. In addition to the mean and standard deviation needed to calculate the confidence limits, the trimmed mean, mode, lower (Q1) and upper (Q3) quartiles are also printed out (Boxes 1.3 and 1.4).

Table 1.2 PCR data for mosquitofish from two ponds

Locus	Allele (base pairs)	Allele frequency in two pond populations		Amount or frequency in common
		Fisher Pond	Fire Pond	
Mf-1	178	0	0.256	0*
	170	0.212	0.244	0.212
	162	0.394	0.005	0.005
	150	0.280	0.274	0.274
	138	0.114	0.171	0.114
Mf-6	247	0	0.460	0
	245	0.061	0.182	0.061
	243	0.167	0.068	0.068
	241	0.197	0.102	0.102
	233	0.075	0.198	0.075
	229	0.5	0	0
Mf-13	164	0.447	0.045	0.045
	163	0.023	0.017	0.017
	162	0.197	0.343	0.197
	160	0.076	0.011	0.011
	156	0.257	0.584	0.257
	Totals	$A = 3.0$	$B = 2.96$	$W = 1.438$

* minimum value entered in column, i.e. this allele frequency occurs in both populations

```
MTB > Describe C1.
```

Descriptive Statistics

```
Variable   N     Mean     Median    TrMean    StDev     SE Mean
Thorax L   15    1.0993   1.0965    1.0991    0.0528    0.0136
Variable   Minimum   Maximum   Q1       Q3
Thorax L   0.9997    1.2009    1.0655   1.1257
MTB > Print C1
```

Data Display

```
Thorax Length
 1.11479 1.04366 1.09733 1.09038 1.20088 1.16071 1.12352
 1.04105 1.12572 1.09648 0.99968 1.16997 1.08579 1.07380
 1.06553
MTB >
```

Calculate the 95% probability limits for the distribution:

Lower limit $= \bar{x} - t_{0.05,19}S = 1.0993 - (2.093 \times 0.0528) = 1.0993 - 0.1151 = 0.9842$

Upper limit $= \bar{x} + t_{0.05,19}S = 1.0993 + (2.093 \times 0.0528) = 1.0993 + 0.1151 = 1.2144$

value of t at $p = 0.05$ with d.f. $= 20 - 1$

We would therefore expect 95% of thorax lengths for fruit flies sampled from this population to lie between 0.9842 and 1.2144 mm. A value of 1.23 mm, which is outside these limits, would suggest that a fruit fly of this size probably does not belong to the population sampled, i.e. it is a very unusual value and should be rejected from the sample as an outlier.

Set 95% confidence limits about the sample mean

Lower confidence limit about the mean $= \bar{x} - t_{0.05,19}\mathrm{SE}$

$$= 1.0993 - (2.093 \times 0.0136)$$

$$= 1.0993 - 0.0285 = 1.0708$$

Upper confidence limit about the mean $= \bar{x} - t_{0.05,19}\mathrm{SE}$

$$= 1.0993 + (2.093 \times 0.0136)$$

$$= 1.0993 + 0.0285 = 1.1278$$

We would therefore expect, with a confidence level of 95%, that the means of samples drawn from the same population of female flies will lie between 1.0708 and 1.1278. If a mean of 1.3501 is obtained for a sample population of flies that has not been exposed to the endoparasitoid, we may conclude that *this* mean differs significantly from the first (it is significantly larger). But without knowing anything about the standard error and confidence limits associated with this second mean, it would be unsafe to conclude that the two populations differ. If the two sets of confidence limits do not overlap, we may conclude that the means differ significantly and that endoparasitoid infection significantly decreases the size of female flies.

Appendix 1.1

Some commonly used non-parametric procedures

Being based on ranked data, non-parametric procedures are relatively easy to understand and can be performed by hand with the aid of a basic calculator. All the procedures in this appendix replace original data values with rank values. Groups of values are compared by assuming that, in the absence of any real differences, similar numbers of high and low ranked values will occur in each group; unless differences exist, summed group ranks will be similar. When testing for the presence of trends between x and y, it is assumed that if they are correlated then either high ranks for x and y values will tend to occur together (positive correlation) or low ranked x-values will be associated with high y-ranked (negative correlation). Given a fixed number of values, hence a fixed number of ranks, it is normally possible to calculate the exact probability of any combination or sequence of ranks. This allows significance levels to be attributed to a particular set of ranks and the associated test statistics. Luckily the results of such calculations have been conveniently summarised in the tables of critical values for the test statistics.

Mann–Whitney U-test

A non-parametric equivalent of the *t*-test, the Mann–Whitney U-test is used to test for a significant difference between the medians of two groups.

1. Determine the group sizes:

   n_1 = number of values in group 1

   n_2 = number of values in group 2

2. If the two groups differ in size, n_1 denotes the size of the smallest group.

3. Rank the whole set of values; do not do the two groups separately:

   The lowest value is given rank 1

   Tied values are given the same average rank

4. Add the ranks for each group:

   R_1 = sum of rank values for group 1

   R_2 = sum of rank values for group 2

5. Calculate U_1 and U_2

$$U_1 = (n_1 \times n_2) + \left(\left(\frac{n_1(n_1 + 1)}{2} \right) \right) - R_1$$

$$U_2 = (n_1 \times n_2) + \left(\left(\frac{n_2(n_2 + 1)}{2} \right) \right) - R_2$$

Since $U_1 + U_2 = n_1 \times n_2$ the value of U_2 is also given by:

$$U_2 = (n_1 \times n_2) - U_1$$

The smallest value, either U_1 or U_2, is taken as the test statistic. Its value is compared with the critical values given in Table 1. For the null hypothesis of equal medians to be rejected, the calculated U-values must be *less* than the tabulated value for $p = 0.05$.

Table 1 Mann–Whitney U-test values (two-tailed test) $P = 0.05$

n_1 \ n_2	2	3	4	5	6	7	8	9	10	11	12	13	14	15	16	17	18	19	20
2							0	0	0	0	1	1	1	1	1	2	2	2	2
3			0	1	1	2	2	3	3	4	4	5	5	6	6	7	7	8
4			0	1	2	3	4	4	5	6	7	8	9	10	11	11	12	13	13
5		0	1	2	3	5	6	7	8	9	11	12	13	14	15	17	18	19	20
6		1	2	3	5	6	8	10	11	13	14	16	17	19	21	22	24	25	27
7		1	3	5	6	8	10	12	14	16	18	20	22	24	26	28	30	32	34
8	0	2	4	6	8	10	13	15	17	19	22	24	26	29	31	34	36	38	41
9	0	2	4	7	10	12	15	17	20	23	26	28	31	34	37	39	42	45	48
10	0	3	5	8	11	14	17	20	23	26	29	33	36	39	42	45	48	52	55
11	0	3	6	9	13	16	19	23	26	30	33	37	40	44	47	51	55	58	62
12	1	4	7	11	14	18	22	26	29	33	37	41	45	49	53	57	61	65	69
13	1	4	8	12	16	20	24	28	33	37	41	45	50	54	59	63	67	72	76
14	1	5	9	13	17	22	26	31	36	40	45	50	55	59	64	67	74	78	83
15	1	5	10	14	19	24	29	34	39	44	49	54	59	64	70	75	80	85	90
16	1	6	11	15	21	26	31	37	42	47	53	59	64	70	75	81	86	92	98
17	2	6	11	17	22	28	34	39	45	51	57	63	67	75	81	87	93	99	105
18	2	7	12	18	24	30	36	42	48	55	61	67	74	80	86	93	99	106	112
19	2	7	13	19	25	32	38	45	52	58	65	72	78	85	92	99	106	113	119
20	2	8	13	20	27	34	41	48	55	62	69	76	83	90	98	105	112	119	127

Source: Fowler *et al.* (1998)

Although the Mann–Whitney U-test is a non-parametric test and does not require the data to be normally distributed, it does require that the two groups should have the same shaped distribution. If either n_1 or n_2 is greater than 20, the z-test statistic should be used. For large samples, under the null hypothesis, U is approximately normal with mean $\frac{1}{2}n_1n_2$ and variance $\frac{1}{12}n_1n_2(n_1 + n_2 + 1)$, allowing z to be estimated from

$$z = \frac{U - \dfrac{n_1 n_2}{2}}{\sqrt{\dfrac{n_1 n_2 (n_1 + n_2 + 1)}{12}}}$$

Critical values of z:

Significance level	5% ($p = 0.5$)	1% ($p = 0.01$)	0.1% ($p = 0.001$)
Critical value of z	1.96	2.58	3.29

The null hypothesis of equal medians is rejected if the absolute value of z exceeds the tabulated critical value of z.

Kruskal–Wallis test

The Kruskal–Wallis test is a non-parametric equivalent of one-way ANOVA. It is used to test for significant differences between the medians of more than two groups, and it can be applied to data from a completely randomised experiment or a similar situation in which there are m independent samples of sizes $n_1, n_2, \ldots, n_m$.

1. Rank all the values (as in the U-test). The lowest value is given rank 1; tied values are given the same average rank.

2. Sum the ranks for each of the m samples $R_1, R_2, \ldots, R_m$.

3. Formulate predictions, i.e. alternative hypotheses; in each case the null hypothesis is that group medians do not differ.

There are two sorts of prediction:

- *General predictions* propose that the medians are heterogeneous, i.e. they are not all the same. Calculate the following test statistic:

$$H = \frac{12}{N(N+1)} \sum_{i=1}^{m} \frac{R_i^2}{n_i} - 3(N+1) \quad \text{where} \quad N = \sum_{i=1}^{m} n_i$$

N is the total number of values in the combined data set.

  H approximately follows the chi-squared distribution. Critical values of H can be obtained from tabulated χ^2-values with $m - 1$ degrees of freedom. Large values of H count against the null hypothesis of equal medians.

- *Specific predictions* are alternative hypotheses that specify the rank order of group medians. Predict which groups will have the largest or smallest medians and assign each median a rank coefficient (λ_i) in accordance with the specific prediction, i.e. the lowest prediction median is ranked 1 ($\lambda_1 = 1.0$) the highest is ranked m ($\lambda_m = m$).

Now calculate:

$$L = \sum_{i=1}^{m} \lambda_i R_i$$

$$E = \frac{1}{2}(N+1) \sum_{i=1}^{m} \lambda_i n_i$$

$$V = \frac{1}{12}(N+1)\left(N \sum_{i=1}^{m} \lambda_i^2 n_i - \left(\sum_{i=1}^{m} \lambda_i n_i\right)^2\right)$$

$$z = \frac{L - E}{\sqrt{V}}$$

• Critical values of z are given above. Large values of z count in favour of the predicted order of median values (i.e. rejection of the null hypothesis).

Friedman's test

Friedman's test is a non-parametric alternative to two-way ANOVA. It is used to test for significant differences between the medians of more than two groups, and it can be applied to data from a blocked randomised experiment or a similar situation in which there are m independent samples of sizes $n_1, n_2, \ldots, n_m$ subject to two types of treatment (each applied at more than one level). Suppose there are a blocks and m equal-sized samples (i.e. the total number of values would be given by $N = anm$ where n is the number of values in each sample).

1. Rank the observations *within* each block, and sum them to give the rank total for each treatment $R_1, R_2, \ldots, R_m$.

2. Calculate the test statistic:

$$M = \frac{12}{am(m+1)}\left(\sum_{i=1}^{m} R_i^2 - 3a(m+1)\right)$$

Large values of M count against the null hypothesis of no treatment differences. As with H, for large sample sizes the test statistic M approximately follows the chi-squared distribution. Critical values of M can be obtained from tabulated χ^2-values with $m - 1$ degrees of freedom.

Consider the case where the average hovering time for a hunting kestrel was recorded for 6 individual birds recorded over 5 three-week periods of observation. The investigator wishes to know whether average hovering times differ between individual kestrels. Individual kestrels constitute the m treatments, and the records grouped into 5 time periods constitute the blocks. Records for each kestrel occur once in each block. Table 2 ranks the recorded hovering times in each block (time period). The shortest hovering times in each block are given rank 1. Applying the formula:

$$M = \frac{12}{5 \times 6(6+1)} \times [(9^2 + 15^2 + 20^2 + 10^2 + 23^2 + 28^2) - 3 \times 5(6+1)] = 115.08$$

Critical values of M for different values of m and a may be obtained from Table 3. For large samples, χ^2-values with $m - 1$ degrees of freedom may be used. From tables, at the 5% probability level, the critical values are $M = 10.49$ and $\chi^2 = 11.070$ (d.f. $= 5$), so it is possible to reject the null hypothesis of no differences between the hovering times of individual kestrels, and with confidence.

Table 2 Ranked hovering times for kestrels 1 to 6

Time period ($a = 5$)	Ranked hovering times ($m = 6$)					
	1	2	3	4	5	6
1	1	3	4	2	5	6
2	2	4	5	1	3	6
3	2	3	4	1	6	5
4	3	1	2	4	6	5
5	1	4	5	2	3	6
Treatment R totals	9	15	20	10	23	28

Non-parametric two-way analysis of variance

A non-parametric version of two-way ANOVA may be performed by the repeated application of the Kruskal–Wallis procedure to suitably grouped data. For example, in a Scandinavian study on the impact of above-ground high tension cables on bird populations, the number of deaths attributable to birds colliding with cables was recorded along five random 1000 km sections of cable. Data was collected for two species, the willow ptarmigan and the black grouse (Table 4). Rank values for the complete data set. Replace the original data values with ranks. Sum the cell ranks to give cell R-values. Now test some predictions.

Compare columns   Does the mean or median number of kills vary from season to season? Sum cell R-values for the three treatment columns ($m = 3$) to give $R_1 = 155$, $R_2 = 177.5$ and $R_3 = 132.5$. Perform a Kruskal–Wallis test, calculating H_{col} using the formula given above, with $n_i = 10$ and $m = 3$. Check H against tabulated critical values of H_{col} or χ^2 with $m - 1$ degrees of freedom:

$$H = \frac{12}{N(N+1)} \sum_{i=1}^{m} \frac{R_i^2}{n_i} - 3(N+1) \qquad N = \sum_{i=1}^{m} n_i = 30$$

$$H_{col} = \frac{12}{30(31)} \left(\frac{155^2}{10} + \frac{177.5^2}{10} + \frac{132.5^2}{10} \right) - 3(31) = 1.23$$

d.f. $= 3 - 1 = 2$

The critical value is $\chi^2 = 5.991$ with d.f. $= 2$ and $p = 0.05$. The null hypothesis of no differences is accepted.

Compare rows   Does the mean or median number of kills differ from species to species? Sum cell R-values for each row and calculate H_{row}, with $n_i = 15$ and $m = 2$. Check H against tabulated critical values of H_{row} or χ^2 with $m - 1$ degrees of freedom:

$$H_{row} = \frac{12}{30(31)} \left(\frac{126.5^2}{15} + \frac{335.5^2}{15} \right) - 3(31) = 15.01$$

d.f. $= 2 - 1 = 1$

Table 3 Critical values for Friedman's test

α	m = 3				m = 4				m = 5				m = 6			
a	10%	5%	2%	1%	10%	5%	2%	1%	10%	5%	2%	1%	10%	5%	2%	1%
2	—	—	—	—	6.000	6.000	—	—	7.200	7.600	8.000	8.000	8.286	9.143	9.429	9.714
3	6.000	6.000	—	—	6.600	7.400	8.200	9.000	7.467	8.533	9.600	10.13	8.714	9.857	11.00	11.76
4	6.000	6.500	8.000	8.000	6.300	7.800	8.400	9.600	7.600	8.800	10.20	11.20	9.000	10.29	11.71	12.71
5	5.200	6.400	8.400	8.400	6.360	7.800	9.000	9.960	7.680	8.960	10.56	11.68	9.000	10.49	12.09	13.23
6	5.333	7.000	8.333	9.000	6.400	7.600	9.400	10.20	7.733	9.067	10.80	11.87	9.048	10.57	12.38	13.62
7	5.429	7.143	8.000	8.857	6.429	7.800	9.171	10.54	7.771	9.143	10.97	12.11	9.122	10.67	12.55	13.86
8	5.250	6.250	7.750	9.000	6.300	7.650	9.450	10.50	7.700	9.200	11.00	12.30	9.071	10.71	12.64	14.00
9	5.556	6.222	8.000	9.556	6.200	7.667	9.400	10.73	7.733	9.244	11.11	12.44	9.127	10.78	12.75	14.14
10	5.000	6.200	7.800	9.600	6.360	7.680	9.480	10.68	7.760	9.280	11.20	12.48	9.143	10.80	12.80	14.23
11	5.091	6.545	7.818	9.455	6.273	7.691	9.655	10.75	7.782	9.309	11.20	12.58	9.130	10.84	12.92	14.32
12	5.167	6.500	8.000	9.500	6.300	7.700	9.500	10.80	7.733	9.333	11.27	12.60	9.143	10.86	12.95	14.38
13	4.769	6.615	8.000	9.385	6.138	7.800	9.646	10.85	7.754	9.354	11.32	12.68	9.176	10.89	13.00	14.45
14	5.143	6.143	8.143	9.143	6.343	7.714	9.600	10.89	7.771	9.371	11.37	12.74	9.184	10.90	13.02	14.49
15	4.933	6.400	8.133	8.933	6.280	7.720	9.640	10.92	7.787	9.387	11.36	12.80	9.210	10.92	13.06	14.54
16	4.875	6.500	7.875	9.375	6.300	7.800	9.600	10.95	7.750	9.400	11.40	12.80	9.214	10.96	13.07	14.57
17	5.059	6.118	7.529	9.294	6.318	7.800	9.635	11.05	7.765	9.412	11.44	12.85	9.202	10.95	13.10	14.61
18	4.778	6.333	8.111	9.000	6.333	7.733	9.667	10.93	7.778	9.422	11.47	12.89	9.206	10.95	13.11	14.63
19	5.053	6.421	7.895	9.579	6.347	7.863	9.632	11.02	7.789	9.432	11.45	12.88	9.196	11.00	13.14	14.67
20	4.900	6.300	7.900	9.300	6.240	7.800	9.600	11.10	7.760	9.400	11.48	12.92	9.200	11.00	13.11	14.66
21	4.952	6.095	7.714	9.238	6.314	7.800	9.686	11.06	7.771	9.448	11.50	12.91	9.218	10.99	13.14	14.69
22	4.727	6.091	8.273	9.091	6.327	7.800	9.709	11.07	7.782	9.418	11.49	12.95	9.221	10.96	13.14	14.73
23	4.957	6.348	8.087	9.391	6.287	7.800	9.678	11.09	7.791	9.426	11.51	12.97	9.236	11.00	13.19	14.73
24	5.083	6.250	7.750	9.250	6.250	7.750	9.700	11.15	7.767	9.433	11.50	13.00	9.238	10.95	13.19	14.74
25	4.880	6.080	7.760	8.960	6.264	7.800	9.672	11.16	7.776	9.440	11.52	12.99	9.229	10.99	13.21	14.74
∞	4.605	5.991	7.824	9.210	6.251	7.815	9.837	11.34	7.779	9.488	11.67	13.28	9.236	11.07	13.39	15.09

Source: Neave (1979)

Table 4 Recorded bird casualties per 1000 km of high tension power cable

Species	Sep–Oct	Nov–Mar	Apr–May	Summed row R values, $n = 15$
Black grouse	259, 285, 200, 197, 265 (A1)	132, 186, 102, 125, 138 (B1)	104, 120, 80, 95, 102 (C1)	
Ranks	11, 12, 13.5, 16, 19 $R = 71.5$	3.5, 7, 8, 10 $R = 37.5$	1, 2, 3.5, 5, 6 $R = 17.5$	$71.5 + 37.5 + 17.5 = 126.5$
Willow ptarmigan	281, 262, 299, 283, 259 (A2)	880, 991, 1075, 1777, 750 (B2)	480, 503, 602, 420, 395 (C2)	
Ranks	13.5, 15, 17, 18, 20 $R = 83.5$	26, 27, 28, 29, 30 $R = 140$	21, 22, 23, 24, 25 $R = 115$	$83.5 + 140 + 115 = 338.5$
Summed column R values, $n = 10$	$71.5 + 83.5 = 155$	$37.5 + 140 = 177.5$	$17.5 + 115 = 132.5$	

The critical value is $\chi^2 = 3.841$ with d.f. $= 1$ and $p = 0.05$. The null hypothesis of no differences is rejected.

Interaction between row and column Is there an interaction between season and bird species? The H-value for the complete table, H_{tot}, is calculated by including each cell R-value in the calculation with $n_i = 5$. The number of degrees of freedom for H_{tot} is equal to the number of cells in the table minus $1 = 12 - 1 = 11$. The H-value for the interaction is obtained by subtraction: $H_{inter} = H_{tot} - H_{col} - H_{row}$. The number of degrees of freedom is also obtained by subtraction: d.f.$_{inter}$ = d.f.$_{tot}$ − d.f.$_{col}$ − d.f.$_{row}$.

$$H_{tot} = \frac{12}{30(31)}\left(\frac{71.5^2}{5} + \frac{37.5^2}{5} + \frac{17.5^2}{5} + \frac{83.5^2}{5} + \frac{140^2}{5} + \frac{115^2}{5}\right) - 3(31) = 27.25$$

$$H_{inter} = H_{tot} - H_{col} - H_{row} = 27.25 - 1.23 - 15.01 = 10.99$$

$$\text{d.f.}_{tot} = 11, \quad \text{d.f.}_{col} = 2, \quad \text{d.f.}_{row} = 1 \quad \text{(from above)}$$

$$\text{d.f.}_{inter} = 11 - 2 - 1 = 8$$

The critical value is $\chi^2 = 15.507$ with d.f. $= 8$ and $p = 0.05$. The null hypothesis of no interaction is accepted.

Specific contrasts or predictions For any table containing c cells there are generally $c - 1$ classes of contrasts which may be made. These contrasts between medians are specific and must be formulated in terms of particular inequalities from which the required coefficients (λ) can be obtained. Consider the prediction that black grouse deaths are greater than willow ptarmigan deaths; expressed formally this is equivalent to $(A1 + B1 + C1) > (A2 + B2 + C1)$. Moving all of the cell values to the right-hand side gives the inequality from which the coefficients are derived:

$$A1 - A2 + B1 - B2 + C1 - 1C2 > 0$$

λ for cell C2 $= -1$

$$+1A1 - 1A2 + 1B1 - 1B2 + 1C1 - 1C2 > 0$$

In this case the coefficient values are either $+1$ or -1. For other contrasts the coefficients may take fractional values. The prediction that the deaths associated with willow ptarmigan during Nov–Mar are greater than the average for all other cells, this would be equivalent to

$$B2 > (A1 + A2 + B1 + C1 + C2)/5 \quad \text{or}$$

$$+1B2 - 1/5(A1 + A2 + B1 + C1 + C2) > 0$$

Thus cell B2 has a coefficient of $+1$, all other cells have a coefficient of $-1/5$. As a check the coefficients should sum to zero.

Once the coefficients have been obtained for a contrast, L, E, V and the test statistic z are calculated using the formula given for the Kruskal–Wallis procedure.

Spearman's rank correlation

Spearman's rank correlation is a non-parametric equivalent of Pearson's moment correlation coefficient. Used to test for the presence of a trend, it is applied to paired data where, for each of n cases or sample units, two variables x and y are measured.

1. Rank the values of the first variable only then rank the values of the second variable only.
2. Correlate the two ranks using the parametric Pearson correlation.

If there are few tied ranks then follow this procedure:

1. For each pair of values $1, 2, \ldots, n$ subtract the second rank value from the first to give d_i, the difference in the ranks of x and y.
2. Calculate Spearman's correlation coefficient r_S:

$$r_S = 1 - \frac{6 \sum_{i=1}^{n} d_i^2}{n(n^2 - 1)}$$

$$t = r_S \sqrt{(n - 2)(1 - r_S)}$$

$$z = r_S \sqrt{n - 1}$$

3. Compare the calculated value of r_S with tabulated values.

To test the presence of any trend, positive or negative, use a two-tailed test. To test the presence of only one type of trend, use a one-tailed test. Exact tables are available for cases up to $n = 20$. In the absence of tables and for $n > 10$, the t-statistic is commonly used with d.f. $= n - 2$; for $n > 30$ the z-statistic of the standard normal distribution may be used. For large samples the sampling distribution of r_S is approximately normal with a standard error of $1\sqrt{n - 1}$, so 95% confidence limits can easily be set, $r_S \pm 1.96/\sqrt{n - 1}$.

Further reading

Barnard, C., Gilbert, F. and McGregor, P. (1993) *Asking Questions in Biology: Design, Analysis and Presentation in Practical Work*. Longmans, Harlow. Good but basic introduction to planning and undertaking project work.

Dytham, C. (1999) *Choosing and Using Statistics: A Biologist's Guide*. Blackwells, Oxford. Provides an introduction to traditional statistics, illustrated with example calculations using commonly available computer packages.

Fowler J., Cohen, L. and Jarvis, P. (1998) *Practical Statistics for Field Biology*, 2nd edn. John Wiley, Chichester. Good introductory text explaining the use of traditional statistics with emphasis on analysing field data.

Keith, H.L. (ed.) (1996) *Principles of Environmental Sampling*, 2nd edn. American Chemical Society, Washington, DC. An advanced text, particularly useful where samples are collected primarily for chemical analysis.

Manly, B.F.J. (1992) *The Design and Analysis of Research Studies*. Cambridge University Press, Cambridge. Provides a very readable and clear account of experimental design and analysis; introduces advanced statistical methods.

Raffaelli, D. and Hawkins, S. (1996) *Intertidal Ecology*. Chapman & Hall, London. Chapter 8 provides an excellent introduction to planning and undertaking fieldwork in intertidal habitats.

Seigel, A.F. and Morgan, C.J. (1996) *Statistics and Data Analysis: an Introduction*. John Wiley & Sons, New York. An excellent basic introduction to traditional statistics, it explains important concepts very simply and clearly; an underused book! If you are unhappy with statistics, this is worth looking at.

Underwood, A.J. (1997) *Experiments in ecology: their logical design and interpretation using analysis of variance*. Cambridge University Press, Cambridge. A comprehensive advanced text on experimental design.

Chapter Two

Community and sample diversity

Summary

This chapter is concerned with methods for measuring sample diversity or heterogeneity. A typical data set might record the abundance of all the species found within a sample. The diversity of such a sample will depend on the species richness, i.e. the number of species present, and on the species evenness, i.e. the relative abundance of the species present in the sample. The methods described in this chapter may be applied to other data sets of a similar form, e.g. the number and proportion of different land use categories in a given area. Four general approaches to the measurement of sample heterogeneity are considered: (i) measures of species richness; (ii) graphical methods, rank–abundance plots; (iii) distribution models, where the observed abundances of species or data categories are compared with those predicted by a particular distribution model; and (iv) indices of species diversity and evenness. The use of the statistical technique of jackknifing to estimate the species richness and its variance is also outlined.

2.1 *Introduction*

The term 'diversity' is commonly used in a range of contexts. Historically, particularly in the area of conservation it has been erroneously been linked with 'higher-order' community attributes, such as community stability and quality (Magurran, 1988; French, 1994; Begon *et al.*, 1996; Stiling, 1999). In practice, diversity is best viewed as describing sample heterogeneity or variability. In ecological studies, samples will frequently consist of information on the number and relative abundance of the species present. The diversity of the sample will depend on two distinct components, species richness and species evenness or equability. Species richness simply refers to the total number of species present. Evenness is concerned with the relative abundance of species. In a community with high evenness, many species will have similar levels of abundance, no single species being significantly more abundant (i.e. clearly dominant). Thus ecological communities may differ in terms of their species richness and evenness. A highly diverse community would be one containing a large number of species (high species richness) that are all similarly abundant (high evenness). Communities may differ in either or both of these attributes. For example, two communities may have the same number of species but different patterns of species abundance, hence different species diversity (Figure 2.1).

Diversity may be viewed as operating on a number of different scales (Southwood, 1978; Magurran, 1988):

- α-diversity corresponds to the diversity of species present in a habitat or community; most studies are concerned with α-diversity.

- β-diversity is concerned with the variation in diversity from one habitat (community) to the next; it may be viewed as a measure of the extent and rate of change in species richness and distribution along a gradient.

- γ-diversity is the species richness of a range of habitats in a geographical area.

The methods described in this chapter are mainly concerned with assessing the α-diversity of samples. The assessment of β diversity is also covered. As defined above, γ-diversity simply equates to the species richness of an area containing a range of habitats. If the γ-diversity is estimated from samples then the procedures used for the assessment of α-diversity may be appropriate. Otherwise γ-diversity may be derived from published area and national species lists. The relationship between species richness and sample area is discussed in the context of deciding the minimum area that should be surveyed in Chapter 1, and in terms of relating species richness to true island or habitat island area in Chapter 10. Although poorly defined, the term 'biodiversity' or 'biological diversity' has become widely used by environmentalists, conservationists and ecologists. Gaston (1998) presents 10 different definitions of biodiversity and discusses whether it is a measurable entity. Although species richness is sometimes treated as synonymous with biodiversity, it is not. Biodiversity is concerned with the 'variety of life' measured at levels below and above the species, including ecological diversity which can be viewed as including niches, habitats, ecosystems, landscapes, bioregions and biomes (Heywood, 1995). Species richness and diversity represent only one level in this hierarchy. Although procedural examples presented in this chapter are primarily concerned with measuring species diversity they can equally be viewed as general measures of sample richness and/or heterogeneity. The use of diversity indices for measuring species niche breadth is outlined in Chapter 5. All that is required is a data set consisting of a number of distinct classes or entities with known frequency or abundance.

Four distinct methods may be used to assess species diversity; each is covered in turn. The easiest procedures to use are those described in Sections 2.2 and 2.4.

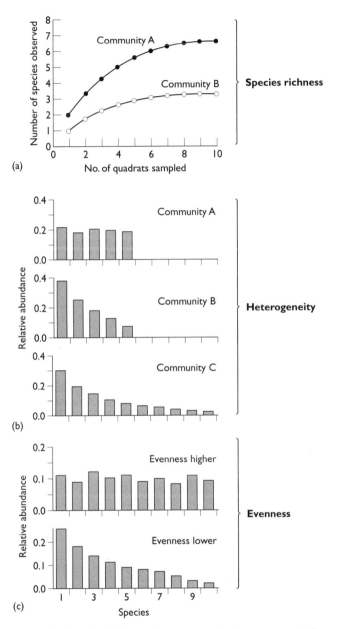

Figure 2.1 Concepts of species diversity. (a) *Species richness:* community A has more species than community B so it has a higher species richness. (b) *Heterogeneity:* community A has the same number of species as community B but the relative abundances are more even, so by a heterogeneity measure, A is more diverse than B. Community C has the same abundance pattern as B but it has more species, so it is more diverse than B. (c) *Evenness:* when all species have equal abundances in the community, evenness is maximal. Reprinted, with permission, from Krebs (1999).

- Species richness measures
- Graphical methods
- Species abundance models
- General indices of species diversity and evenness.

2.2 Measures of species richness

The simplest measure of species richness is the total number of species (S) present in a sample of individuals or found in an area. However, since sample size (i.e. the total number of individual organisms captured or the area searched) frequently varies, even when attempts are made to standardise the search effort, S can at best only be used as a crude measure of community species richness. Comparisons between communities are more easily made if the results are expressed as *species densities*; that is, the average number of species present in a standard-sized sample or area, e.g. the average number of species per 100 or 1000 individuals. In botanical studies the number of species per square metre has frequently been used as a measure of community species richness.

The number of species recorded will clearly increase with sample size. The more individuals captured or the larger the area searched, the greater the number of species likely to be encountered. Species density values merely mask the problems of unequal sample size and should not be used if sample size or sampling effort differs substantially between the study sites. To overcome problems of unequal sample size, two approaches may be adopted. Indices of species richness may be calculated or statistical procedures may be used to estimate the number of species one would expect to find in a random sample of a given size, $E(S_n)$.

2.2.1 Indices of species richness

Two indices of species richness are commonly described, the Margalef (1958) index

$$R_1 = (S - 1)/\ln n$$

and the Menhinick (1964) index

$$R_2 = S/\sqrt{n}$$

where S = the total number of species recorded in the sample
n = sample size, i.e. the total number of individuals present in the sample
$\ln n$ = the natural logarithm of n, $\log_e n$

Suppose 34 species of insect were found in a sample of 634 individuals, then

$$R_1 = (34 - 1)/\ln 634 = 33/6.452 = 5.115$$
$$R_2 = 34/\sqrt{634} = 1.35$$

Both of the indices assume a simple and constant relationship between S and n; effectively they are proportionality constants relating S to n. This can readily be seen by rearranging the formula above to make S the subject of the equations. For Margalef's index $S - 1 = R_1 \ln n$ and for Menhinick's index $S = R_2\sqrt{n}$. Because these simple relationships between S and n will seldom if ever be found (Ludwig and Reynolds, 1988), the use of these indices cannot be justified.

2.2.2 Expected number of species in a sample

If sample sizes differ substantially, measures of community richness may be obtained using a procedure know as rarefaction. This allows the investigator to estimate the number of species to be expected in community samples of an equal size. Alternatively, where multiple samples have been obtained from each community, a jackknife or bootstrap estimate of S may be obtained.

Rarefaction

The method of rarefaction was originally proposed by Sanders (1968) and developed by Hurlbert (1971). Rarefaction allows us to estimate the number of species expected in a random sample of individuals taken from a collection. Hurlbert (1971) showed that the expected number of species in a sample of n individuals is given by

$$E(S_n) = \sum_{i=1}^{S} \left(1 - \binom{N - N_i}{n} \Big/ \binom{N}{n} \right)$$

where $E(S_n)$ = expected number of species in a random sample of n individuals

S = total number of species in the sample

N_i = number of individuals of species i in the original sample

N = total number of individuals in the sample $\sum N_i$

n = number of individuals present in the chosen standardised sample size

$\binom{N}{r}$ = the mathematical shorthand for a combination – the number of different possible combinations of r objects that can be randomly formed from a collection of N, with $N > r$

The value of $\binom{N}{r}$ can be obtained from the formula:

$$\binom{N}{r} = \frac{N!}{r!(N-r)!}$$

where $r!$ is r factorial; $r! = r \times (r-1) \times (r-2) \times \cdots \times 3 \times 2 \times 1$, so $5! = 5 \times 4 \times 3 \times 2 \times 1 = 120$.

A worked example is given in Box 2.1, from which it is clear that even for simple data sets the calculation can be very tedious. If $E(S_n)$ is calculated for a series of increasing sample sizes, rarefaction curves can be produced (Figure 2.2) which show how the expected number of species increases with sample size. Although rarefaction can be very useful and has been used extensively, particularly in aquatic studies, there are some important ecological restrictions (Ludwig and Reynolds, 1988; Krebs, 1999). The method assumes that the species within the community samples are randomly dispersed with respect to individuals of the same and other species. In practice they may be clumped (Chapter 4) and they may be both positively and negatively associated (Chapter 7). Krebs (1989) suggests that the only practicable remedy to this problem is to use large representative samples. The use of a large sample ($n \geq 30$) also permits the variance of $E(S_n)$ to be estimated using a formula developed by Heck *et al.* (1975) and this allows confidence limits to be put around $E(S_n)$:

$$V(S_n) = \binom{N}{n}^{-1} \left[\sum_{i=1}^{S} \binom{N - N_i}{n} \left(1 - \binom{N - N_i}{n} \Big/ \binom{N}{n} \right) \right.$$

$$\left. + 2 \sum_{i=1}^{S-1} \sum_{j=i+1}^{S} \binom{N - N_i - N_j}{n} - \binom{N - N_i}{n} \binom{N - N_j}{n} \Big/ \binom{N}{n} \right]$$

Rarefaction should only be used to compare samples of the same type, that is samples composed of organisms having the same broad taxonomic groups obtained using the same sampling procedures. Normally n is chosen to be equal to the size of the smallest sample (Magurran, 1988). Ideally the sampled communities should have the same basic underlying species abundance pattern (Peet, 1974). It should not be used to extrapolate beyond the size of the sample. It is only possible to extrapolate if an underlying statistical distribution is known and shown to adequately fit the data (see Section 2.4, particularly Section 2.4.4).

Box 2.1   Rarefaction

Following a simple example given by Krebs (1999), if 4 species are found in a collection of 42 individuals, the rarefaction procedure could be used to calculate the number of species one might expect to find in a sample of 30 individuals, $E(S_{30})$. In this case $n = 30$, $N = 42$ and $S = 4$. If the species abundances are 21, 16, 3, 2 then $N_1 = 21$, $N_2 = 16$, $N_3 = 3$ and $N_4 = 2$ (note $N = \sum N_i = 21 + 16 + 3 + 2 = 42$). We have $n = 30$ and $N = 42$, now we substitute for each N_i ($i = 1, 2, 3, 4$) and sum to obtain $E(S_{30})$:

$$E(S_n) = \sum_{i=1}^{S} \left(1 - \binom{N - n_i}{n} \Big/ \binom{N}{n} \right)$$

For $i = 1$ we have

$$1 - \binom{42 - 21}{30} \Big/ \binom{42}{30}$$

Now $\binom{42 - 21}{30} = \binom{21}{30} = \dfrac{21!}{30!\,(21 - 30)!}$

By definition this is equal to 0. The factorial of a negative number $(21 - 30)! = -9!$ has no meaning. It is not possible to form a combination of 30 objects from 21.

In all cases where $N - N_i < n$ the combination will be undefined and therefore equal to 0. This is a useful point to remember as it as can speed up the calculations. We also have

$$\binom{42}{30} = \frac{42!}{30!\,(42 - 30)!} = \frac{42!}{30!\,12!} = 1.0158 \times 10^{10}$$

Substituting into our original expression:

$$1 - \binom{42 - 21}{30} \Big/ \binom{42}{30} = 1 - \frac{0}{1.1058 \times 10^{10}} = 1$$

For $i = 2$ $\quad 1 - \binom{42 - 21}{30} \Big/ \binom{42}{30} = 1 - \dfrac{0}{1.0158 \times 10^{10}} = 1$

For $i = 3$ $\quad 1 - \binom{42 - 3}{30} \Big/ \binom{42}{30} = 1 - \binom{39}{30} \Big/ \binom{42}{30}$

$$= \frac{39!}{30!\,(39 - 30)!} \frac{1}{1.1058 \times 10^{10}}$$

$$= 1 - \frac{2.1192 \times 10^8}{1.1058 \times 10^8} = 0.981$$

For $i = 4$ $\quad 1 - \binom{42 - 2}{30} \Big/ \binom{42}{30} = 1 - \binom{40}{30} \Big/ \binom{42}{30}$

$$= \frac{40!}{30!\,(40 - 30)!} \frac{1}{1.1058 \times 10^{10}}$$

$$= 1 - \frac{8.4766 \times 10^8}{1.1058 \times 10^8} = 0.932$$

Summing the results for $i = 1$ to 4:

$$E(S_n) = 1 + 1 + 0.981 + 0.923 = 3.90$$

Thus the expected number of species to be found in a sample of 30 individuals is 3.90.

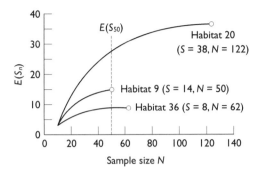

Figure 2.2 Rarefaction curves for three avian habitats showing the expected number of species as a function of sample size. Adapted from James and Rathburn (1981).

Jackknife estimates of S

The jackknife method of parameter estimation is a relatively recent development that allows the mean and variance of a parameter to be estimated. It is a non-parametric method, making no assumptions about the underlying statistical distribution of the data; more details are given in Chapter 5. The method involves initially calculating the parameter of interest using all the original data from the n replicate samples. The following steps are then undertaken:

1. Recombine the original data omitting one of the n replicates.

2. Using the recombined data, calculate the parameter of interest and the corresponding pseudovalue, $\phi = nS - (n - 1)S_t$, where $n =$ the original sample size, $S =$ the original statistical estimate based on the complete data set, $S_t =$ the recalculated parameter of interest in which one sample has been omitted.

3. Repeat steps 1 and 2, calculating pseudovalues for each combination of data in which one replicate value is omitted in turn.

4. Estimate the mean and standard error of the parameter of interest from the resulting pseudovalues.

Heltshe and Forrester (1983a,b) have shown how the jackknife method may be used to estimate species richness from quadrat data. The data is initially reduced to a record of species presence and absence, from which is obtained the number of **unique species**, i.e. species that occur in only one quadrat. The jackknife estimate of the number of species is then given by

$$S^* = s + \left(\frac{n-1}{n}\right)k \quad \text{and} \quad \text{var}(S^*) = \frac{n-1}{n}\sum j^2 f_j - \frac{k^2}{n}$$

where $S^* =$ jackknife estimate of species richness
$S =$ observed total number of species present in all n quadrats
$n =$ total number of quadrats sampled
$k =$ number of unique species
$f_j =$ number of quadrats containing j unique species $(j = 1, 2, 3, \ldots, S)$

The jackknife estimate of species richness tends to be positively biased – it overestimates the number of species present in the community. However, this degree of bias is usually less than the degree to which species richness is commonly underestimated from the observed data (Heltshe and Forrester, 1983b). Looking closely at the equation for estimating S^*, Krebs (1999) points out that as the number of unique species (k) approaches the total number of species (S) present in the data set, the estimate of S tends to a maximum value of $2S$. So if the number of rare, unique species is large, this procedure cannot be used (Krebs, 1999).

2.2.3 Measurement of β-diversity

Measures of β-diversity are based on either assessing species turnover along an environmental gradient or the extent of variation in species diversity among the communities or habitats in the study area. In practice, different distinct samples are often treated as if they constitute different habitats or communities. The intuitive argument behind this approach is that low between-sample variation in diversity will occur in uniform areas of low β-diversity and conversely high sample variation will occur in areas of high β-diversity. Two simple indices reflect these two approaches:

$$\text{Whittaker's index} \qquad \beta_W = \frac{S}{\alpha - 1}$$

$$\text{Wilson and Shmida's index} \quad \beta_T = (G + L)/2\alpha$$

where S = the total number of species recorded
α = the average number of species recorded in each sample
G = the number of species gained along the gradient
L = the total number of species lost along the gradient

The first sample, or a small group of samples, at the start of the gradient, is used as the threshold or base set of species; losses and gains are assessed with reference to this base set.

Both of the indices have been shown to perform well (Wilson and Shmida, 1984). Where species turnover along a gradient is involved, β_T is the more appropriate index to use. Several alternative approaches have been used, including the use of similarity indices (Chapter 6) to compare the species composition of samples (Magurran, 1988). As with the indices of β-diversity, the focus of these approaches is variation in species richness. An alternative and equally valid approach would be to examine the variation between samples or along a gradient using a general measure of species diversity, e.g. the Shannon–Wiener diversity index (Section 2.5).

2.3 Graphical methods

Once a series of samples have been collected, it rapidly becomes apparent that communities differ not only in their species richness but also in their patterns of species abundance. Not all species are equally abundant. Some species occur frequently in the sample whereas others occur only rarely. Differences in species abundance can be readily seen graphically by plotting species frequency against abundance or by producing a species rank–abundance plot. In frequency–abundance plots, the number of species at each abundance level is plotted against abundance; an example is given in Figure 2.3. Clearly in this study the vast majority of species (around 115) are represented in the sample by only one individual. This type of graph can easily be produced where samples consist of collections of discrete individual organisms that can be sorted into different species. In plant studies, where species abundance is often measured as percentage cover, the situation is a little more complicated. Now the x-axis needs to be divided into equal-sized percentage cover classes. The resulting graph now depicts the number of species present at a given level of cover. Although such plots summarise the distribution of species abundance values, the range of values on the x-axis is curtailed, since the maximum cover value is 100%. Hence these plots are not strictly comparable with the standard frequency abundance plots described above. If plant cover values have been

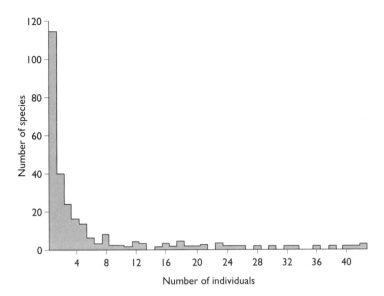

Figure 2.3 Not all species have equal numbers of individuals. This graph shows the relationship between number of species and number of individuals for beetles in flood refuse from the River Thames. The majority of species are represented by only a single individual but a few species are very abundant. Reprinted, with permission, from Magurran (1988).

obtained using a point quadrat (Chapter 1), an alternative would be to plot the number of species against the total number of contacts recorded for each species.

In vegetation studies there has been a tradition of plotting the $\log_{10}$ (species abundance) against the rank of the species in the sample, where the most abundant species is given the rank of 1 (Whittaker, 1965). Species of equal abundance are given consecutive numbers, e.g. 5, 6, 7; average rank values are *not* given. When the graph is plotted, it will form a horizontal section for the equally abundant species 5, 6 and 7. These graphs are known as dominance–diversity or rank–abundance plots. They are a valuable way of summarising community data sets. The length of the line reflects the species richness of the sample, and the slope of the line reflects the community evenness. A steep, short line indicates a community with low species richness and low evenness. Linear regression is rarely performed but it may be used to give a quantitative description of the plots, allowing slopes to be compared. The species composition can also be shown by labelling the plotted points. Plotting data for several communities on the same graph makes comparisons much easier (Figure 2.4).

2.4 *Distribution models*

Once a suitable plot has been produced, no further analysis may be required. But if community diversity is central to the aims of the study, the investigator may wish to describe the pattern of species abundance in more detail. If the entire species abundance distribution can be described by a distribution model characterised by a limited number of parameters, then sample comparison should become relatively straightforward. In essence this approach is analogous to summarising normally distributed measurements (e.g. body weights) by their mean and standard deviation. Once the mean and standard deviation of a sample have been obtained, their values can be compared with the means and standard deviations of other samples. This approach works and is appropriate because the shape of a normal distribution

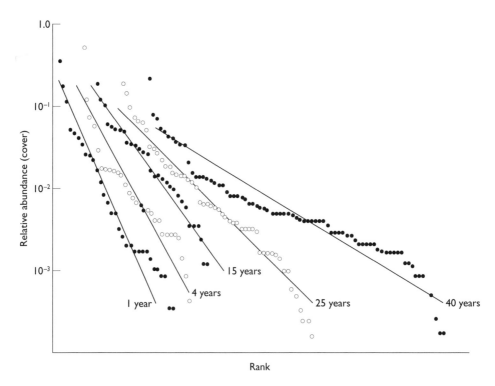

Figure 2.4 Rank–abundance relationships of successional plant communities of a deciduous forest, representing five ages after abandonment. Note the progressively shallower slope of the superimposed geometric series model in older communities. Adapted from Bazzaz (1975).

curve depends on only two parameters, the mean and standard deviation. Thus, if a simple distribution can be found which fits the observed pattern of species abundance, then in theory it should be possible to objectively describe and compare community samples. This approach has the advantage of using all the data collected, not only information on the number of species but also their abundance. And if species abundance is related to resource availability, then the fitted model (distribution) may tell us something about the way in which key community resources are partitioned between species (Magurran, 1988; Tokeshi, 1993; Stiling, 1999).

Four main models have been proposed, the lognormal distribution, the geometric series, the logarithmic or log series and MacArthur's broken stick model (Magurran, 1988). The broken stick model is really of historical interest only and it will not be considered further. Of the distributions discussed in this chapter, only the geometric series is derived solely from a theoretical model of species abundance; the other distributions provide empirical descriptions only. Although the lognormal distribution was originally proposed by Preston (1948) as a good empirical description of a wide range of data sets, a theoretical interpretation is possible (May, 1975). The models represent a progression from communities dominated by a few abundant species to more diverse, species-rich communities. Each has a characteristic shape when plotted as a rank–abundance curve (Figure 2.5; Whittaker, 1977). The geometric series (niche pre-emption hypothesis) is frequently the most appropriate model for low diversity communities dominated by a limited number of abundant species. As species equitability (evenness) and species richness increase, the log series and lognormal distributions provide a better description. In high diversity communities the species abundance often follows a lognormal distribution.

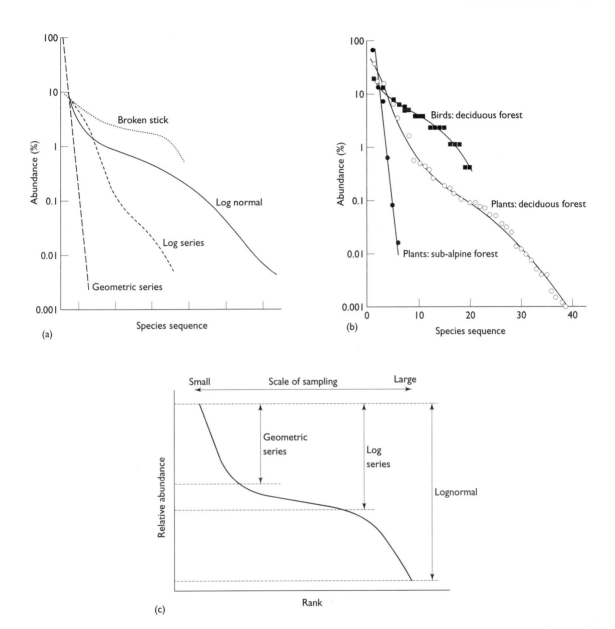

Figure 2.5 Rank–abundance data plotted on a log scale: (a) hypothetical and (b) real data. (c) Nested relationship between the models (excluding the broken stick model). Parts (a) and (b) reprinted, with permission, from Magurran (1988); part (c) reprinted, with permission, from Tokeshi (1993).

2.4.1 Fitting distribution models to observed data sets

Three major steps
Produce a species rank–abundance plot Inspection of the resulting curve allows the most appropriate distribution to be selected. If the shape of the plot is linear, the geometric series or log series model should be adopted. If species richness is low and the slope of the line is steep, i.e. the community is dominated by only a few species, the geometric series should initially be tried. Otherwise the lognormal distribution should be adopted.

Table 2.1 Insect count data

Abundance of species (no. of individuals per species)	1	2	3	4	5	6	7	9	10	11	21	28	33	120
Frequency of species (no. of species)	32	8	9	2	3	3	3	2	1	2	1	1	1	1

Estimate the distribution parameters   Once an appropriate model has been selected, distribution parameters are estimated using the observed data.

Test the goodness of fit for the distribution model   Once estimates of the model distribution parameters have been obtained, expected values may be calculated. With the geometric series, it is usual to generate the expected number of individuals for the ith most abundant species in the community. The log series and lognormal models allow the expected number of species at any given level of abundance to be calculated. In both cases the model's goodness of fit is assessed by statistically comparing the expected values generated by the fitted equation with appropriate observed values. The model is rejected if the discrepancy between the two sets of values is statistically significant.

A sample data set

The following sections introduce the distribution models and show how to estimate parameters. In each case an attempt has been made to fit the distribution to the same simple data set taken from Ludwig and Reynolds (1988). The data consists of insect counts obtained by combining the catches from 14 sweep-net samplings from a grassland community (Table 2.1). The total number of species is $S = 69$ and the total number of individuals present in the sample is $N = 389$. The adequacy of each model is also discussed.

Testing goodness of fit

The goodness of fit for a distribution is typically assessed by calculating a series of expected values that are then compared with the corresponding observed values. The smaller the difference between the two sets of values, the greater the confidence in the adequacy of the distribution. The extent of this difference has traditionally been assessed using the chi-squared procedure. The test statistic X^2 follows a chi-squared distribution and is calculated using the formula

$$X^2 = \sum \frac{(O - E)^2}{E}$$

where O = observed values
E = expected values
$\sum$ = summation over all pairs of O and E values

Values of X^2 are compared with tabulated values of χ^2 at an appropriate probability level (normally $p < 0.05$) and for the correct number of degrees of freedom (d.f.). The number of degrees of freedom is *not*, as frequently stated, equal to $(a - 1)$, one less than the number of classes (a) in the summation. Additional degrees of freedom are lost where use is made of the original data to estimate the parameters used to calculate the expected values (Sokal and Rohlf, 1987). One degree of freedom is lost for every parameter estimated directly from the original data. Thus, when testing the fit of the models described in this chapter, the appropriate value for the degrees of freedom is $a - 3$ (since in each case the original data is used to estimate two parameters). If X^2 is greater than the tabulated value of χ^2, the null hypothesis that there is no significant difference between the expected and observed frequencies is rejected. A more reliable alternative to the standard chi-squared procedure is the log-likelihood ratio or G-test (Sokal and Rohlf, 1987; Fowler *et al.*, 1998). This test should be used as a matter of course in place of the chi-squared procedure. The G-test and chi-squared procedures are computationally similar. The same rules apply for calculating the number of degrees of freedom. Both test statistics, G and X^2, follow a chi-squared distribution. G is calculated from

$$G = 2 \sum O \ln(O/E)$$

These tests do not perform well if expected values are small. To avoid this problem, classes with low E values should be grouped with adjacent classes. The resulting combined E values should exceed 3 if $a \geq 5$ or 5 where $a < 3$ (Sokal and Rohlf, 1987). Observed values must be similarly grouped to match the newly created classes. Williams' continuity correction factor is also routinely applied when the sample size is small. The correction factor reduces the value of G, making the test more conservative, reducing the likelihood of rejecting the null hypothesis that the observed and expected values do not differ. Williams' correction factor is $1 + (a^2 - 1)/6n\nu$, where ν is the degrees of freedom of the G-test and n is equal to the sample size. The adjusted value of G is obtained from, $G_{\mathrm{adj}} = G/(\text{correction factor})$. The effect of the correction factor on the size of G decreases rapidly as the sample size increases.

The chi-squared procedure does have one potential advantage over the G-test. If some observed values are zero, it is not possible to calculate G because the log of the ratio (O/E) cannot be evaluated as $O/E = 0$, and $\ln 0$ is undefined. Since logarithms are not used during the calculation of X^2, this problem does not occur when using the chi-squared procedure. It may most easily be avoided by combining adjacent classes to remove observed values equal to zero before attempting to carry out the G-test.

Some care is needed when interpreting a non-significant goodness-of-fit test, i.e. where the null hypothesis is to be accepted. The lack of a significant difference between observed and expected values cannot be taken as proof that the theoretical assumptions of the model actually apply to a community. A good fit alone does not vindicate the ecological assumptions of a model. For example, Harvey and Godfray (1987) have shown that a lognormal species abundance distribution need not follow from the lognormal distribution of resource use. Often more than one model is capable of providing a reasonable fit to a given data set. At best it can be said that a particular model provides an adequate description of the data, if the distribution of species abundance values is consistent with the assumptions made by the model.

2.4.2 *The geometric series*

The geometric model, also known as the niche pre-emption model, describes the pattern of species distribution that will occur if each species pre-empts a constant proportion (k) of some limiting available resource. The most abundant species is assumed to pre-empt a proportion k of the initial amount of the limiting resource; the same proportion of the amount remaining $(1 - k)$ is then used by the second most abundant species, i.e. $k(1 - k)$; the third species takes k of what remains, i.e. $k^2(1 - k)$. The process continues until all S species have been accommodated and the resource completely partitioned among the species present. The resulting abundance of the ith most abundant species is given by

$$n_i = NC_k k(1 - k)^{i-1} \quad \text{with} \quad C_k = (1 - (1 - k)^S)^{-1}$$

where n_i = the number of individuals in the ith species
N = the total number of individuals in the sample

The amount of resource available, hence the abundance of successive species, decreases rapidly by a constant proportion k. For communities that conform to the geometric series, the log rank–abundance graph (Figure 2.5) will be linear. These communities will typically be species poor and dominated by a few abundant species.

Fitting the geometric series
Estimate k   An estimate of k is obtained by iteratively attempting to balance the equation

$$\frac{N_{min}}{N} = \left(\frac{k}{1-k}\right)\left(\frac{(1-k)^S}{1-(1-k)^S}\right)$$

where N_{min} = the number of individuals in the least abundant species
N = the total number of individuals in the sample
N_{min}/N = the proportional abundance of the rarest species

An initial value of k is guessed at by inspection and substituted into the equation. If the equation does not balance, the value of k is changed slightly and the process repeated until the left-hand side (LHS) and right-hand side (RHS) balance. If LHS > RHS the value of k should be decreased; if LHS < RHS the value of k should be increased. If the initial value of k is a good estimate, a balanced equation will be achieved rapidly. The value of k must lie between 0 and 1.0. Its value will decrease as the number of species present in the sample increases; that is, the more diverse the community, the smaller the value of k. Using the data set described above, $N = 389$, $N_{min} = 1$, $S = 69$, take 0.1 as an initial estimate of k and substitute into the equation:

$$\frac{1}{389} = \frac{0.1}{1-0.1}\left(\frac{(1-0.1)^{69}}{1-(1-0.1)^{69}}\right)$$

$$0.002\,5707 = 7.74 \times 10^{-5}$$

Clearly the observed value of N_{min}/N is far larger than the calculated value based on $k = 0.1$, i.e. LHS $\gg$ RHS; the value of k should be decreased. The complete process is summarised in Table 2.2.

Table 2.2 Fitting the geometric series

No. of attempts	Value of k	Value of LHS, i.e. N_{min}/N	Value of RHS	LHS < RHS increase k	LHS > RHS decrease k	RHS ≈ LHS terminate
1	0.1	0.002 5707	0.000 0774		yes	
2	0.05	0.002 5707	0.001 5738		yes	
3	0.025	0.002 5707	0.005 4129	yes		
4	0.03	0.002 5707	0.004 3075	yes		
5	0.04	0.002 5707	0.002 6502	yes		
6	0.0405	0.002 5707	0.002 5814			yes

Estimate C_k   Using the estimate of k obtained above, C_k may be calculated directly from the relationship

$$C_k = (1 - (1 - k)^S)^{-1} = (1 - (1 - 0.0405)^{69})^{-1} = (1 - (0.9595)^{69})^{-1}$$

$$= 1/0.942\,309 = 1.061\,223$$

Estimate expected values   Expected values may be calculated from the original equation for the geometric series using the estimated values of k and C_k:

$$n_i = NC_k k(1 - k)^{i-1}$$

Thus the expected number of individuals of the most abundant species in the sample, i.e. the first species, will be

$$n_1 = 389 \times 1.061\,223 \times 0.0405 \times (1 - 0.0405)^{1-1}$$

$$= 389 \times 1.061\,223 \times 0.0405 \times (0.9595)^0 = 16.7190 \qquad (x^0 = 1)$$

Repeating the calculation for the 20th most abundant species

$$n_{20} = 389 \times 1.061\,223 \times 0.0405 \times (1 - 0.0405)^{20-1}$$

$$= 16.7190 \times (0.9595)^{19} = 7.62$$

The actual observed values for n_1 and n_{20} are 120 and 4 respectively (Figure 2.6, Table 2.3).

Assessing goodness of fit

Expected species abundances are calculated from the estimated parameters. Together with the observed values, they are shown in Table 2.3. Notice that the observed abundances and corresponding expected values for species 43 to 69 have been combined. This has been done to ensure that expected values do not fall below 3, which would reduce the reliability of the G-test. The value of G is easily obtained by manipulating the initial two left-hand columns, C2 and C3. The sum of the final column (C6) multiplied by 2 gives the required value of G, which in this case is equal to 370.198. The number of classes (rows) in the table is equal to 43. Since the original data was used to estimate k and C_k, G has $43 - 3$ degrees of freedom. The tabulated χ^2-value at $p < 0.05$ with d.f. $= 40$ is 55.758. Since the calculated test statistic G greatly exceeds this value, the null hypothesis is rejected. It can be concluded that the observed species abundances do not follow the geometric series.

The inadequacy of the geometric model is clear from Figure 2.6. Magurran (1988) suggests that the goodness of fit for the geometric model may be assessed using linear regression to test for a linear rank–abundance plot. However, this approach cannot be recommended. Despite the clearly curved nature of the rank–abundance plot, the fitted regression line provides a significant fit (Figure 2.6). And under certain circumstances, this approach may fail to distinguish between the geometric series, which always produces a linear rank–abundance plot, and the log series, which occasionally generates a linear rank–abundance plot.

2.4.3 Log series distribution

Fisher *et al.* (1943) first suggested that the logarithmic series could be used to describe the distribution of individuals among species in community samples. The series may be

Table 2.3 Calculation of G-test statistic for fitted geometric model

(C1) Species	(C2) O	(C3) E	(C4) O/E	(C5) ln(O/E)	(C6) O ln(O/E)
1	120	16.72	7.177 034	1.970 886	236.5063
2	33	16.04	2.057 357	0.721 422	23.806 92
3	28	15.39	1.819 363	0.598 487	16.757 62
4	21	14.76	1.422 764	0.352 602	7.404 634
5	11	14.17	0.776 288	−0.253 23	−2.785 55
6	11	13.6	0.808 824	−0.212 17	−2.333 92
7	10	13.05	0.766 284	−0.2662	−2.662 03
8	9	12.52	0.718 85	−0.3301	−2.970 93
9	9	12.01	0.749 376	−0.288 52	−2.596 64
10	7	11.52	0.607 639	−0.498 17	−3.487 22
11	7	11.05	0.633 484	−0.456 52	−3.195 64
12	7	10.61	0.659 755	−0.415 89	−2.911 21
13	6	10.18	0.589 391	−0.528 67	−3.171 99
14	6	9.77	0.614 125	−0.487 56	−2.925 34
15	6	9.37	0.640 342	−0.445 75	−2.674 52
16	5	8.99	0.556 174	−0.586 67	−2.933 37
17	5	8.63	0.579 374	−0.545 81	−2.729 03
18	5	8.28	0.603 865	−0.504 41	−2.522 03
19	4	7.94	0.503 778	−0.685 62	−2.742 48
20	4	7.62	0.524 934	−0.644 48	−2.577 93
21	3	7.31	0.410 397	−0.890 63	−2.671 89
22	3	7.01	0.427 96	−0.848 73	−2.546 18
23	3	6.73	0.445 765	−0.807 96	−2.423 89
24	3	6.46	0.464 396	−0.767 02	−2.301 05
25	3	6.19	0.484 653	−0.724 32	−2.172 97
26	3	5.94	0.505 05	−0.6831	−2.049 29
27	3	5.7	0.526 316	−0.641 85	−1.925 56
28	3	5.48	0.547 445	−0.602 49	−1.807 48
29	3	5.25	0.571 429	−0.559 62	−1.678 85
30	2	5.04	0.396 825	−0.924 26	−1.848 52
31	2	4.83	0.414 079	−0.8817	−1.763 4
32	2	4.64	0.431 035	−0.841 57	−1.683 13
33	2	4.45	0.449 438	−0.799 76	−1.599 51
34	2	4.27	0.468 384	−0.758 47	−1.516 93
35	2	4.099	0.487 924	−0.7176	−1.435 19
36	2	3.93	0.508 906	−0.675 49	−1.350 98
37	2	3.774	0.529 942	−0.634 99	−1.269 98
38	1	3.621	0.276 167	−1.286 75	−1.286 75
39	1	3.47	0.288 184	−1.244 15	−1.244 15
40	1	3.333	0.300 03	−1.203 87	−1.203 87
41	1	3.1689	0.315 567	−1.153 38	−1.153 38
42	1	3.069	0.325 839	−1.121 35	−1.121 35
43–69	27	49.02	0.550 796	−0.596 39	−16.1026

$$\sum O \ln(O/E) = \qquad 185.099$$
$$G = 2 \sum O \ln(O/E) = \qquad 370.198$$

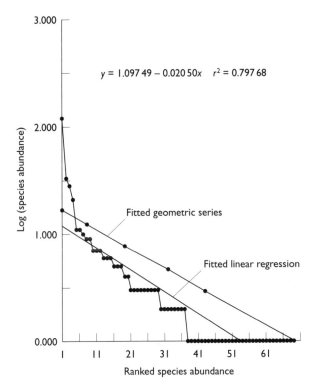

Figure 2.6 Rank–abundance (dominance–diversity) plot of insect catch data; the fitted regression is significant at $p < 0.001$.

written as

$$\alpha x, \quad \frac{\alpha x^2}{2}, \quad \frac{\alpha x^3}{3}, \quad \frac{\alpha x^4}{4}, \quad \cdots, \quad \frac{\alpha x^n}{n}$$

$$\underbrace{\qquad}_{\substack{\text{number of species in} \\ \text{the sample represented} \\ \text{by one individual}}} \qquad \underbrace{\qquad}_{\substack{\text{number of species in the} \\ \text{sample represented by} \\ n \text{ individuals}}}$$

where α and x are constants normally estimated from the observed data. Each term in the sequence gives the expected number of species in the sample represented by n individuals. The log series sums to $\alpha \ln(1 - x)$, and this equals S, the total number of species in the sample. Here the series is constrained by the variables S and N, where N is the total number of individuals in the sample (Southwood, 1978). The relationship between them is

$$S = \alpha \ln(1 + N/\alpha)$$

The values of α, known as the α-diversity index, have been widely used as a direct index of diversity (Taylor, 1978; Magurran, 1988). Kempton and Taylor (1974a,b) have shown that, as an index of diversity, α discriminates effectively between samples. They found that, in comparison with other measures of diversity, α was less sensitive to variation in sample size and was relatively insensitive to changes in the abundance of either rare or common species. Its value is principally determined by species of intermediate abundance.

Fitting the log series distribution requires estimates of two parameters, x and α. An estimate of x is obtained by iteratively attempting to balance the equation

$$\frac{S}{N} = \frac{1-x}{x}(-\ln(1-x))$$

Table 2.4 Relation between values of x and the average number of units per group (N/S) in samples from populations distributed according to the logarithmic series

x	N/S	x	N/S	x	N/S
0.50	1.000	0.97	9.214	0.9990	144.6
0.60	1.637	0.980	12.53	0.9992	175.1
0.70	1.938	0.985	15.63	0.9994	224.5
0.80	2.483	0.990	21.47	0.9996	319.4
0.85	2.987	0.991	23.38	0.9998	586.9
0.90	3.909	0.992	25.68	0.999 90	1 086
0.91	4.198	0.993	28.58	0.999 95	2 020
0.92	4.551	0.994	32.38	0.999 990	8 696
0.93	4.995	0.995	37.48	0.999 995	16 390
0.94	5.567	0.996	45.11	0.999 9990	71 430
0.95	6.340	0.997	57.21	–	–
0.96	7.458	0.998	80.33	–	–

Source: The table is reproduced from Krebs (1999), who used data from Williams (1964).

Based on the observed values of S and N an initial crude estimate of x may be obtained from Table 2.4. This is then substituted into the equation above. If the value on the right-hand (RHS) side of equation exceeds value on the left-hand side (LHS), then the value of x is increased slightly. The process is then repeated. If the converse is true, i.e. LHS > RHS, the value of x is decreased slightly and the process is repeated. The process is stopped once the equation is balanced; the value of x that achieves balance is taken as the final estimate. Once a value for x has been obtained then α is estimated from the relationship $\alpha = N(1 - x)/x$.

Fitting the log series distribution
Estimate x

Total number of individuals in the sample, $N = 389$

Total number of species in the sample, $S = 69$

$N/S = 389/69 = 5.6377$

Using this value, refer to Table 2.3 to obtain an initial estimate of $x = 0.94$. Attempt to obtain a more accurate estimate of x using the iterative procedure:

$$\frac{S}{N} = \frac{1-x}{x}(-\ln(1-x))$$

Substituting $x = 0.94$ into the equation gives

$$\frac{69}{389} = \frac{1-0.94}{0.94}[-\ln(1-0.94)]$$

$$0.177\,377\,89 = 0.179\,5794$$

Since LHS < RHS the value of x is increased and an attempt is made to balance the equation. The results are summarised in Table 2.5.

Table 2.5 Fitting the log series distribution

No. of attempts	Value of x	Value of LHS, i.e. N/S	Value of RHS	LHS < RHS increase x	LHS > RHS decrease x	RHS ≈ LHS terminate
1	0.94	0.177 377 892	0.179 5794	yes		
2	0.9401	0.177 377 892	0.179 5582	yes		
3	0.941	0.177 377 892	0.177 4525	yes		
4	0.9415	0.177 377 892	0.176 3840		yes	
5	0.941 25	0.177 377 892	0.176 9187		yes	
6	0.941 05	0.177 377 892	0.177 3458		yes	
7	0.941 025	0.177 377 892	0.177 3992	yes		
8	0.941 0375	0.177 377 892	0.177 3725			yes

Estimate α Calculate α from the best estimate of x obtained in the previous step:

$$\alpha = N\frac{1-x}{x} = 389\frac{1-0.941\,0375}{0.941\,0375} = 24.3735$$

Anscombe (1950) provides a formula that allows the variance of α to be estimated for samples:

$$V(\alpha) = \frac{0.693\,147\alpha}{\left(\ln\left(\dfrac{x}{1-x}\right) - 1\right)^2} = \frac{16.894\,42}{(1.890\,372)^2} = 4.728$$

For what appears to be little significant gain, the iterative estimation of x can be excessively time-consuming. Using the first crude estimate of $x = 0.94$ to obtain a value of α gives 24.8298, which is not greatly different from the value obtained above. However, two things should be noted. Firstly, the effects of x on the calculated value of α will depend on the size of N; the larger the value of N, the greater the sensitivity of the estimated α to small changes in x. Secondly, if expected species frequency values are to be generated, and used to test the goodness of fit for the log series, then small differences in α can become important. If there is no intention to calculate expected species frequencies α is used as an index of community diversity – an approximation of its values may be obtained directly from Figure 2.7.

Calculate expected values   The expected number of species represented in a sample by a particular number of individuals may be calculated directly from the log series using the estimated values of x and α. The expected number of species present in the sample with one individual is given by αx. The number of species with two individuals is given by $\alpha x^2/2$ and the number with n individuals is $\alpha x^n/n$. Thus the expected number of species present in a sample with four individuals is

$$\frac{\alpha x^4}{4} = \frac{24.3735(0.941\,0375)^4}{4} = 4.778$$

The statistical comparison of expected and observed values may be used to test whether the log series provides an appropriate descriptive model of the observed data set.

Assessing goodness of fit

The log series generates the expected number of species at every level of abundance, i.e. the expected number of species in the sample with 1, 2, 3, 4, ... individuals. In practice, species

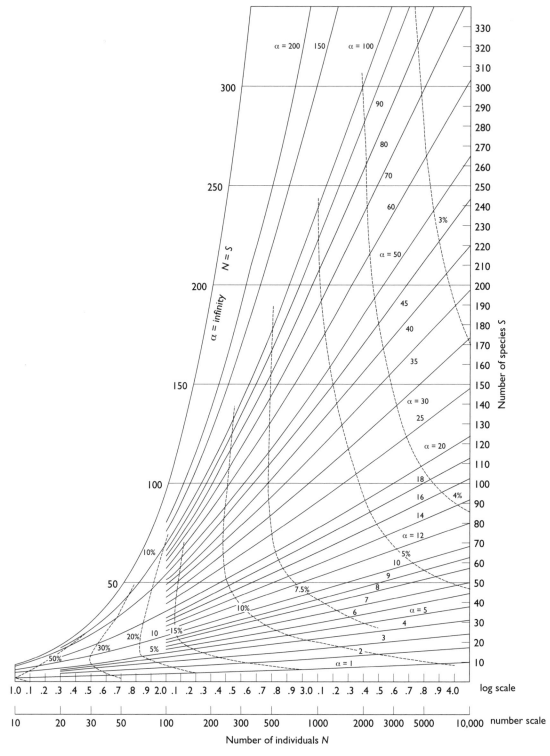

Figure 2.7 Nomogram for determining the index of diversity (α) for the number of species (S) and the number of individuals (N). The standard errors contain only the component of variation due to sampling. Adapted from Williams (1947).

Table 2.6 Expected frequencies are compared with observed frequencies until the expected frequency has decreased to 3

(C1) No. of individual per species (n)	(C2) Observed frequency (O) of species with n individuals	(C3) Expected frequency (E) of species with n individuals, $\alpha x^n / n$	(C4) O/E	(C5) $\ln(O/E)$	(C6) $O \ln(O/E)$
1	32	22.19	0.692 1875	−0.367 898	−11.772 736
2	8	10.10	0.792 0792	−0.233 094	−1.864 752
3	9	6.13	1.468 1892	0.384 029	3.456 261
4	2	4.19	0.477 3269	−0.739 553	−1.479 106
5	3	3.05	0.983 6065	−0.016 529	−0.049 587
6	3 ⎫	(Total = 45.66,			
7	3 ⎪	69 − 45.66 = 23.24)			
9	2 ⎪				
10	1 ⎪				
11	2 ⎬ 45.66	23.34	1.956 2982	0.671 054	30.640 323
21	1 ⎪				
28	1 ⎪				
33	1 ⎪				
120	1 ⎭				
Totals	69	69			18.930403

at certain abundance levels may not occur in the sample. For example, no species occur in the present data set at an abundance of 12 individuals. But if the data followed the fitted log series, one would expect there to be approximately one species $(\alpha x^{12}/12 = 0.690)$ in the sample with 12 individuals. In this case the discrepancy $(0 - 0.690)$ is minor, but in some data sets where species at low abundance levels are underrepresented in the sample, the effects can be large and may invalidate the procedure. The key point is that *all* possible expected values must be compared with observed species frequency, even when the observed frequency is 0, i.e. species at that abundance level are absent from the sample. To overcome this problem, Magurran (1988) groups species into abundance classes (octaves) in the same way as when fitting the lognormal distribution, and species abundance doubles in successive classes (Section 2.4.4). There is little to be gained from this. The expected value for every species frequency included in each octave still has to be calculated and summed for over the complete range of the class. The amount of effort required to achieve this can be considerable. Consider the sixth octave in Table 2.7, containing species with between 16 and 32 individuals. Although only two species in the data set fall into this range (abundance 21 and 28), the expected frequencies for all species abundance values between 16 and 32 must still be calculated. In practice this approach is frequently not necessary. The problem can generally be avoided if abundance levels are *not* grouped until expected species frequencies approach 3, where grouping becomes appropriate. Starting at the lowest species abundance level, expected values are calculated in turn and compared with the observed frequencies. Where species at a given abundance level do not occur in the sample, the observed value is recorded as 0. The process continues until the expected frequency decreases to 3, then all remaining values are grouped together. The final expected value is obtained by subtraction. This approach ensures that the degrees of freedom available to the test are not reduced by excessive aggregation of abundance levels. The procedure is illustrated in Table 2.6.

The value of G is obtained by doubling the sum of the final column (C6), which is generated from columns C2 and C3 that contain the observed and predicted values. The final value of G is thus 37.86, with $6 - 3$ degrees of freedom. The tabulated χ^2 value with 3 d.f. at $p < 0.05$ of 7.815 is considerably less than the calculated value of $G = 37.86$. The null hypothesis that the expected and observed distribution of species abundance values do not differ is rejected. The discrepancy between the expected and observed frequency is too large to occur by chance. Therefore, the log series does not provide an appropriate model of the data set. The values in C6 suggest that the fitted log series substantially underestimates the frequency of species present at the lowest and highest abundance levels (Figure 2.6).

2.4.4 The lognormal distribution

Species abundance data has frequently been found to follow a lognormal distribution. A variable z is lognormally distributed if the logarithms of z follow a normal distribution, that is the values of $\log z$ are normally distributed. The lognormal distribution was first applied to species abundance data sets by Preston (1948). It was subsequently found to provide a good description for a wide range of data sets (Sugihara, 1980). Although initially used as an empirical model, its use has been justified on theoretical grounds. The validity and relevance of these justifications remains a topic of debate. A lognormal pattern of species abundance may result from the complex patterns of species and community interactions. Alternatively it may simply arise from the statistical properties of large numbers and the operation of the central limit theorem (May, 1975; Sugihara, 1980; Minshall et al., 1985). One consequence of the central limit theorem (Box 1.3) is that, in large complex systems, variables affected by many randomly varying independent factors will tend to follow a normal distribution. Thus, given that communities are complex systems and species abundance values are affected by an array of factors, a lognormal distribution might be expected.

The lognormal distribution is given by

$$S(R) = S_0 \, e^{-a^2 R^2}$$

where S_0 = the number of species present in the modal octave, i.e. the octave (abundance) class containing the largest number of species

      $S(R)$ = the number of species in the Rth octave, i.e. the number of species in the Rth abundance class

      a = a measure of the spread or dispersion of the distribution

      e = 2.171 828, the base of the natural logarithm

If S_0 and a are known, the number of species in any abundance class (octave) can be calculated. Estimates of S_0 and a may be obtained while attempting to fit the lognormal distribution to the observed data set. Because ecological samples are rarely complete – part of the community always remains unsampled – fitting the lognormal distribution is a difficult and complex process. The number of species recorded depends on the diversity of the community being sampled and the size of the sample. Initially only the most abundant species will be recorded. If sample size is increased, additional species will be encountered; and the larger the sample, the greater the likelihood of recording rare species. But no sample will be complete; some rare species with low abundance will fail to be recorded, effectively being hidden from the investigator. Thus, to model observed species abundance patterns using the lognormal distribution, a truncated lognormal distribution must be fitted. It is the truncated nature of the distribution that introduces the difficulty (Hughes, 1986). The method outlined below uses an example given by Ludwig and Reynolds (1988). Although relatively simple, it provides reasonably good estimates of S_0 and a. A clear account of a more accurate and complex procedure can be found in Krebs (1999). For most cases the method described here will be adequate.

Fitting a truncated lognormal distribution

Express the observed frequencies in octaves   Following Preston (1948), species abundance values are rescaled into classes so that each successive class (octave) represents a doubling of species abundance. This is equivalent to expressing species abundance values as logarithms to base 2. Species with an abundance value of 0 to 1 are placed in the first octave; the second octave contains species with abundance values between 1 and 2; the third octave between 2 and 4; and the fourth octave between 4 and 8. The process is continued until all the species have been allocated to an octave. Since these classes are not mutually exclusive, how should we treat species on the boundary of neighbouring classes? Do we group species with an abundance of 4 individuals in the third octave (2–4) or the fourth octave (4–8)? The solution is to share the species between neighbouring octaves; half the species occurring on a boundary are allocated to the lower octave and half to the upper octave. For example, of the 32 species in the sample with one individual, 16 are placed in the first octave and 16 are placed in the second octave; the second octave will also contain half of the 8 species present in the sample with 2 individuals. Once the species have been allocated, the modal octaves should be evident (Table 2.7).

Calculate the octave R-values   Once species abundance values have been allocated to appropriate octaves, each octave is numbered (i.e. given an R-value) and values of R^2 and $\ln S(R)$ are calculated (Table 2.7). Allocating R-values to individual octaves is easily done once the modal octave has been identified. The lognormal distribution requires a clear modal octave. If no clear modal octave is present, analysis should be stopped and the lognormal distribution rejected as a suitable model for the data. The modal octave is given an R-value of 0; octaves above it are numbered 1, 2, 3, etc., and octaves below it are numbered $-1, -2, -3$, etc. Mathematically $R = \log_2(n_i/n_0)$, where n_i is equal to the number of species in the ith octave, and n_0 is the number of species in the modal octave. For the modal octave, n_i and n_0 will be equal, so $(n_i/n_0) = 1.0$ and since the $\log_2 1 = 0$ the values of R for the modal octave will equal 0.

Table 2.7 The road-medium insect count data arranged in octaves

Octave	Number of individuals per species	R	R^2	Observed $S(R)$	$\ln S/R$
1	0–1	−1	1	16	2.77
2	1–2	0	0	20	3.00
3	2–4	+1	1	14	2.64
4	4–8	+2	4	10	2.30
5	8–12	+3	9	5	1.61
6	16–32	+4	16	2	0.69
7	32–64	+5	25	1	0.00
8	64–128	+6	36	1	0.00

Source: Ludwig and Reynolds (1988)

Estimate the parameters An approximation of the parameter a may be obtained from

$$a = \sqrt{\frac{\ln(S_0)/S(R_{max}))}{R_{max}^2}}$$

where S_0 = the observed number of species in the modal octave, here 20

R_{max} = the R-value of the octave most distant from the modal octave; if two octaves are most distant from the modal octave (e.g. $R_{max} = \pm 4$), then both values of R_{max} should be used to provide two separate estimates which are then averaged to give the final value

$S(R_{max})$ = the observed number of species in the octave most distant from the modal octave (i.e. the R_{max} octave)

We have $R_{max} = 6$ so $R_{max}^2 = 36$, $S(0) = 20$, $S(R_{max}) = 1$; therefore

$$\ln(S(0)/S(R_{max})) = \ln(20/1) = \ln 20$$

$$a = \sqrt{\frac{\ln 20}{36}} = 0.29$$

The value of S_0 to be used in the lognormal equation

$$S(R) = S_0\,e^{-a^2 R^2}$$

can be taken as the observed number of species in the modal octave, $S(0)$, here 20. An alternative estimate based on the properties of the normal distribution may be obtained from

$$S_0 = \exp(w + a^2 \bar{R}^2)$$

where w = the mean of $\ln S(R)$

$\bar{R}^2$ = the mean of octave R^2-values

From Table 2.7, $w = 1.63$ and $\bar{R}^2 = 11.5$, so

$$\exp(x) = e^x S_0 = \exp(1.63 + (0.29)^2 11.5) = 13.42$$

Thus the parameter estimates for the lognormal distribution describing the data set are $a = 0.29$ and $S_0 = 13.42$.

Calculate the expected values Using the estimated values of a and S_0, expected values of $S(R)$ may be calculated using the original equation for the lognormal distribution, $S(R) = S_0 e^{-a^2 R^2}$. For example, the expected number of species in the second octave is

$$S_2 = 13.42e^{-0.29^2 \times 2^2} = 13.42e^{-0.3364} = 13.42 \times 0.714\,34 = 9.59$$

The goodness of fit of the lognormal distribution specified by the estimated parameters, a and S_0, is assessed by statistically comparing the observed and expected numbers of species in each octave. This procedure is described below.

Assessing goodness of fit
The goodness of fit of the lognormal model is easily assessed. Because abundance values are grouped into octaves, the numbers of expected and observed classes are limited, reducing the complexity of the calculations involved. Using the fitted parameters, $a = 0.29$ and $S_0 = 13.42$, the expected number of species in each octave $S(R)$ are calculated from the standard model equation, $S(R) = S_0 \exp(-0.292 R^2)$. Expected and observed $S(R)$ values are compared using the G-test (Table 2.8).

Table 2.8 Comparing observed and expected $S(R)$ using the G-test

Octave	R	Observed $S(R)$	Expected $S(R)$	O/E	$\ln(O/E)$	$O\ln(O/E)$
1	−1	16	12.3	1.300 813	0.262 989	4.207 831
2	0	20	13.4	1.492 537	0.400 478	8.009 551
3	1	14	12.3	1.138 211	0.129 458	1.812 413
4	2	10	9.6	1.041 667	0.040 822	0.408 22
5	3	5	6.3	0.793 651	−0.231 11	−1.155 56
6	4	2	3.5	0.571 429	−0.559 62	−1.119 23
7	5	1	1.7	0.588 235	−0.530 63	−0.530 63
8	6	1	0.6	1.666 667	0.510 826	0.510 826
Totals	–	69	59.7	–	–	12.143 42

$$G = 2\sum O\ln(O/E) = 2 \times 12.1434 = 24.267$$

The number of octaves in this example is 8, thus G has $8 - 3$ degrees of freedom. The calculated value of $G = 24.267$ is above the tabulated χ^2 value of 11.070 ($p < 0.05$, d.f. $= 5$) and the null hypothesis is rejected. It is concluded that the truncated lognormal description does not provide an adequate description of the observed data set. Note that if the chi-squared procedure is used instead of the G-test, the test statistic $X^2 = 5.57$, implies that the null hypothesis should be accepted. This difference in the outcome of the two test procedures illustrates the greater power of the G-test.

This result is interesting. It is clear from an inspection of the table that the lognormal model with parameter values $a = 0.29$ and $S_0 = 13.42$ underestimates the number of species in the community, particularly species with low abundance. However, comparison of the G-values obtained when testing the fit of the geometric, the log series and the lognormal distributions would suggest that the lognormal distribution provides the best description of the data. It is possible that the sample does follow a lognormal distribution but with different parameter values. In fact, this is the case. Using a computer program that allows iterative substitution to refine estimates of a and S_0, Ludwig and Reynolds (1988) were able to show that the data follows a lognormal distribution with parameters $a = 0.305$ and $S_0 = 15.9$.

2.4.5 *Using the lognormal distribution to estimate species richness*

If the lognormal distribution provides an adequate description of the data, it is possible to extend the analysis and use the fitted curve to estimate the theoretical total number of species (S^*) present in the community (i.e. community species richness):

$$S^* = \frac{1.772\,454}{a}S_0$$

Suppose we assume that the community data analysed above is adequately described by the lognormal distribution with $a = 0.29$ and $S_0 = 13.42$, then an estimate of total community species richness is given by

$$S^* = \frac{1.772\,454}{0.29} \times 13.42 = 82.02$$

When this is compared with the 69 species found in the sample, it suggests that an increase in sample size would substantially increase the number of species obtained. For many cases $a = 0.2$, allowing the entire lognormal distribution to be specified by one parameter, S_0, and approximate estimates of S^* to be made (Krebs,1999). It is possible to estimate species richness using this approach, because the fitted curve can be used to extrapolate beyond the observed range of values to give an estimate of S^* for the 'complete' community sample.

2.5 *General diversity and evenness*

An alternative to species abundance models for assessing community diversity is to calculate diversity indices based on the proportional abundance of species. Of the many available, Simpson's index and the Shannon–Wiener index have been widely used. In comparison with abundance models, diversity indices are easily calculated and have the advantage of making no assumptions about the underlying distribution or processes determining the abundance of species. Southwood (1978) refers to them as non-parametric measures of diversity. Of the two indices, the Shannon–Wiener index is the more sensitive to changes in the number and abundance of rare species, and Simpson's index is more sensitive to changes in the more abundant species (Peet, 1974). The interpretation of diversity indices can be problematic; different numbers of species and combinations of abundance values can give rise to the same index value. Diversity indices should be considered simply as descriptive statistics that provide a quantitative description (or summary) of sample heterogeneity.

2.5.1 *Shannon–Wiener index* (H')

Theoretically the Shannon index requires that the sample is both random and representative, i.e. it contains all species (Pielou, 1975); however, it is less sensitive to sample size than many other diversity measures. The index is normally calculated from

$$H' = -\sum p_i \ln p_i$$

the importance value of the *i*th species ($\sum p_i = 1$); for plants this is equivalent to the relative percentage cover value of the species expressed as a proportion; for animals or count-based data $p_i = n_i/N$, where n_i is the number of individuals of species *i*, and *N* is the total number of individuals in the sample

since the logarithm of each proportional p_i will be negative, this negative sign ensures that the final index has a positive value

The importance values for each species in the sample are calculated, logged then multiplied by themselves; the resulting values are then summed for all S species in the sample. A worked example set out as a spreadsheet calculation is given in Box 2.2. Although originally calculated using logs to base 2, any base may be used but natural logs are most common. For large samples, if natural logarithms are used the variance of H' may be estimated from

$$\text{var}(H') = \frac{\sum p_i (\ln p_i)^2 - (\sum p_i \ln p_i)^2}{N} + \frac{S - 1}{2N^2}$$

Once $\text{var}(H')$ values have been estimated, samples may be compared using Student's *t*-test (Hutcheson, 1970):

$$t = \frac{H_1' - H_2'}{\sqrt{\text{var}(H_1') + \text{var}(H_2')}}$$

Box 2.2   Species diversity indices

Data collected from a point-quadrat survey (Chapter 3) of grassland vegetation at Box Hill in southern England. The data was obtained from 20 randomly placed quadrat frames each with 10 pins. n_i = number of pin contacts recorded for species i, N = total number of contacts recorded for all species.

Species	S	n_i	$p_i = n_i/N$	p_i^2	$\ln p_i$	$p_i \ln p_i$
Galium verum (lady's bedstraw)	1	76	0.242 812	0.058 957	−1.415 47	−0.343 69
Rubus fruticosus agg. (bramble, blackberry)	2	55	0.175 719	0.030 877	−1.738 87	−0.305 55
Plantago lanceolata (ribwort plantain)	3	44	0.140 575	0.019 761	−1.962 01	−0.275 81
Galium saxatile (heath bedstraw)	4	24	0.076 677	0.005 879	−2.568 15	−0.196 92
Poterium sanguisorba (salad burnet)	5	23	0.073 482	0.0054	−2.610 71	−0.191 84
Holcus lanatus (Yorkshire fog, grass)	6	22	0.070 288	0.004 94	−2.655 16	−0.186 62
Teucrium scorodonia (wood sage)	7	14	0.044 728	0.002 001	−3.107 15	−0.138 98
Origanum vulgare (marjoram)	8	12	0.038 339	0.001 47	−3.2613	−0.125 03
Crepis capillaris (smooth hawksbeard)	9	8	0.025 559	0.000 653	−3.666 76	−0.093 72
Pastinaca sativa (wild parsnip)	10	8	0.025 559	0.000 653	−3.666 76	−0.093 72
Veronica chamaedrys (germander speedwell)	11	8	0.025 559	0.000 653	−3.666 76	−0.093 72
Brachypodium sylvaticum (false brome, grass)	12	6	0.019 169	0.000 367	−3.954 44	−0.0758
Clinopodium vulgare (wild basil)	13	4	0.012 78	0.000 163	−4.359 91	−0.055 72
Festuca ovina agg. (sheep's fescue, grass)	14	4	0.012 78	0.000 163	−4.359 91	−0.055 72
Glechoma hederacea (ground ivy)	15	4	0.012 78	0.000 163	−4.359 91	−0.055 72
Lotus corniculatus (common birdsfoot trefoil)	16	1	0.003 195	1.02E − 05	−5.7462	−0.018 36
Totals		313	1.0	0.132 113		−2.306 92

Notes:
$\ln S = \ln 16 = 2.772 59 = H_{max}$
Shannon–Weiner index of evenness is $\mathcal{J} = H'/\ln S = 2.30692/2.777259 = 0.832$.
Log rank–abundance plots are produced by plotting $\log_{10}(p_i \times 100)$ on the y-axis against the species rank on the x-axis.
$\sum p_i \ln p_i = -2.30692$, $-\sum p_i \ln p_i = 2.30693 = H'$.
$\sum p_i^2 = $ Simpson's index of dominance (D).
$1 - D = $ Simpson's index of diversity $= 1 - 0.132\,113 = 0.867$

with degrees of freedom given by

$$\text{d.f.} = \frac{(\text{var}(H_1') + \text{var}(H_2'))^2}{\text{var}(H_1')^2/N_1 + \text{var}(H_2')^2/N_2}$$

where N_1 and N_2 are the total numbers of individuals in samples 1 and 2, and H_1' and H_2' are the respective Shannon–Wiener diversity values. This approach is only valid if the samples are truly random, and this is rarely true in practice (Poole, 1974; Krebs, 1988). However, if replicated samples are taken from each community, the independent estimates of H' obtained from each sample will be normally distributed (Taylor, 1978), allowing comparison between communities using standard statistical procedures. For each community an estimate of the true diversity $^*H'$ can be obtained from the grand mean of sample H' values. Alternatively the technique of jackknifing may be applied (Section 2.2.2; Zahl, 1977; Geogoire, 1984). Schlesinger *et al.* (1994) used this technique to examine long-term changes in the tree diversity of permanent forest plots in Orange County, Indiana (USA).

The Shannon–Wiener index was originally developed in information theory, as a measure of information content or uncertainty. Within an ecological context, it measures the amount of uncertainty associated with the identity of a randomly selected individual (Margalef, 1958; Krebs, 1999). If a community has low species richness and is largely dominated by one species, the identity of a randomly selected individual has a low degree of uncertainty and the associated value of H' will be low. In a community with high species richness and evenness, there is a large degree of uncertainty associated with the identity of a randomly selected individual or species of plant growing at a randomly selected point. In practice the main justification for using the Shannon–Wiener index should be based on empirical not theoretical grounds. The index has proved to be a good robust general index of diversity, its values being influenced by species evenness and richness. When the sample contains only one species ($S = 1$), $H' = 0$. The values of H' increase with S, but they rarely exceed 5.0. For any sample, the theoretical maximum of H' is equal to $\ln S$. This corresponds to the values of H' obtained when all species are equally abundant, i.e. the sample has maximum evenness. This allows the Shannon–Wiener index to be used to derive a measure of sample evenness $J = H'/\ln S$, which ranges from 0 to 1 (Pielou, 1975, 1977).

The exponential form of the Shannon–Wiener index, N_1, is equal to the number of equally common species that would be required to produce the same diversity as H':

$$N_1 = e^{H'}$$

where $e = 2.71838$
$\qquad H' =$ the Shannon–Wiener index calculated using natural logs

A worked example is given in Box 2.2.

2.5.2 Simpson's index (D)

Simpson's index is easily calculated using the formula

$$D' = 1 - D \quad \text{where} \quad D = \sum p_i^2$$

the importance values of the ith species, or for count-based data $p_i = n_i/N$, where n_i is the number of individuals of species i and N is the total number of individuals in the sample

Here D is actually an index of dominance, with the range 0 to 1, and it gives the probability that two individuals drawn randomly from a sample will belong to the same species. The maximum value of 1 occurs when samples contain individuals that all belong to the same species. By subtracting D from 1 an index of diversity is obtained whose values will also range from 0 to 1. In this case the maximum value of 1 will occur when all individuals belong to different species. Some confusion exists in the literature over what is meant by Simpson's index. This confusion can be avoided if the various forms of the index are named consistently, following Krebs (1999):

$$D = \sum_{i=1}^{S} p_i^2$$
Simpson's index or Simpson's index of dominance; ranges from 0 to 1.

$$1 - D$$
Simpson's index of diversity; ranges from 0 at low diversity to $1(1 - 1/S)$.

$$\frac{1}{D}$$
Simpson's reciprocal index; an index of diversity that ranges from 1 to S.

A worked example set out as a spreadsheet calculation is given in Box 2.2. The variance associated with Simpson's index may be obtained using the jackknife (Section 2.2.2; Routledge, 1980; Heltshe and Forrester, 1985).

2.5.3 *Evenness indices and the family of diversity indices*

Hill (1973) has suggested a relationship between the limited number of diversity indices which have an ecological interpretation; they can be seen as part of a series based on the equation

$$N_A = \sum p_i^{1/(1-A)}$$

where N_A is the diversity number and A gives the order of the number ($A = 0, 1, 2$, etc.). According to Hill, the first three number diversity indices are the most useful and they provide a basis for calculating indices of evenness:

$A = 0$ $\quad N_0 = S$ $\qquad$ where S is the total number of species in the sample

$A = 1$ $\quad N_1 = e^{H'}$ $\qquad$ the exponential version of the Shannon–Wiener index

$A = 2$ $\quad N_2 = 1/D$ $\qquad$ the reciprocal of Simpson's index of dominance

And here are the evenness indices:

$$E_1 = \frac{\ln N_1}{\ln N_0} = \frac{H'}{\ln S}$$

This corresponds to the *J* index described above and is equal to the ratio between the maximum possible values of *H'* given S species and the actual *H'* obtained

$$E_2 = \frac{N_1}{N_0}$$

Sheldon (1969) exponential version of E_1

$$E_3 = \frac{N_1 - 1}{N_0 - 1}$$

Heip (1974)

$$E_4 = \frac{N_2}{N_1}$$

Hill (1973). This index gives the ratio of very abundant species to less abundant species

$$E_5 = \frac{N_2 - 1}{N_1 - 1}$$

Hill's modified ratio has the property of approaching 0 as a single species become dominant (in these circumstances E_4 approaches 1).

An evenness index should ideally be independent of species richness. Indices E_1, E_2 and E_3 are sensitive to S, especially where the richness of the sample (community) is low. The addition of one rare species to the sample has a large effect on the values of these indices. So where these three indices are used, the value of S should be given. Indices E_4 and E_5 are not sensitive to S, which appears in both the numerator and denominator, cancelling out its effects on the final values. Hill's modified ratio, E_5, has been shown to approach 0 as one species becomes increasingly dominant in the sample; in this respect it performs better than E_4. Camargo (1993) has recently proposed a new index that involves summing the absolute differences between all pairs of species divided by S:

$$C = 1 - \left(\sum_{i=1}^{S} \sum_{j=i+1}^{S} \left[\frac{|p_i - p_j|}{S} \right] \right) .$$

The index has the advantage that it is unaffected by species richness or by rare species in the sample.

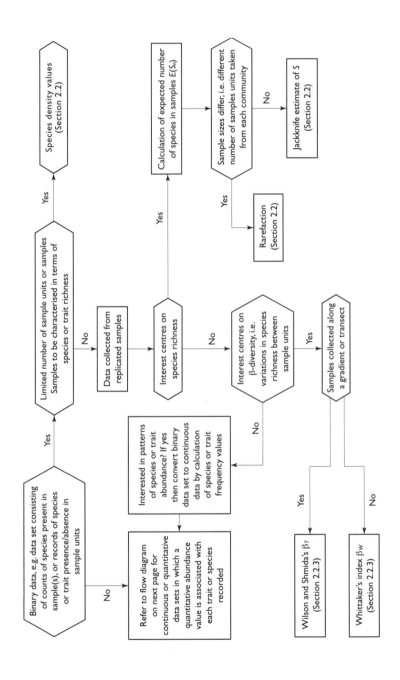

2.5.4 *The use of diversity indices*

Diversity indices, particularly the Shannon–Wiener index, have been widely used in ecological and environmental studies. They have been used to measure the impact of pollution on community structure. Although their uncritical use in studies of this type may be dangerous, in conjunction with information on the species composition of the community, they can provide a useful aid to the monitoring and assessment of communities. The Shannon–Wiener index has also been used to examine the 'diversity' of landscapes (Farina, 1998).

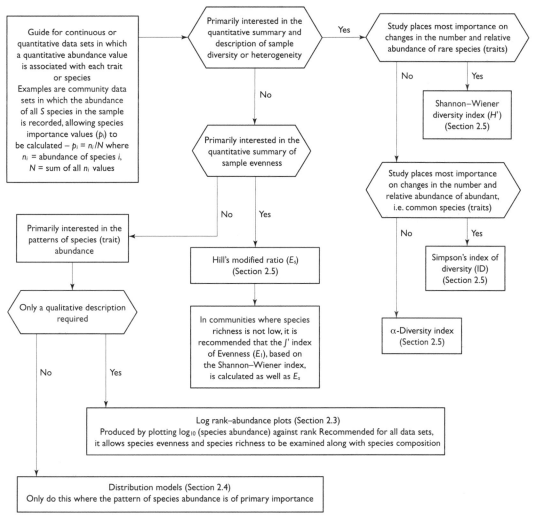

Notes
1. If comparisons are to be made between samples, e.g. communities, then the samples must be random.
2. Where species or trait abundance values are available, log rank–abundance plots are recommended.
   This is particularly important if the distribution of species abundance is to be modelled; the shape of the rank–abundance plots will help with the initial choice of distribution model.
3. Species ranks may be compared using the non-parametric Mann–Whitney *U*-test or Spearman's rank correlation (Appendix 1.1)
4. The Shannon–Wiener Index (*H'*) should be used routinely; Simpson's diversity index should be viewed as a secondary index.
   The α-diversity index may be determined directly from Figure 2.7, which requires only the total number of species (*S*) and individuals (*N*) in the sample. For botanical studies where species abundance is measured as percentage cover (Chapter 3), *N* has no real meaning unless each pin contact is treated as equivalent to an individual. Relative cover values ($p_i/\Sigma p_i$) may be used directly in the Shannon–Wiener index and Simpson's index.

In this type of study the proportional abundance of species (p_i) is replaced by the proportional abundance of habitat types or landscape forms. In this context the index provides a measure of landscape diversity. These studies also use an index of dominance (ID), which measures the deviation of H' from its maximum possible value for that data set:

$$\text{ID} = H_{\text{max}} + \sum_{i=1}^{k} p_i \ln p_i = H_{\text{max}} - H'$$

where p_i = the proportion of the study area occupied by landscape type i
       H_{max} = the maximum possible landscape diversity $\ln K$
       K = the number of different landscape types recognised in the study

Here the diversity indices are being used solely as useful descriptive measures of sample heterogeneity.

2.6 *Recommendations*

The methods presented in this chapter are concerned with assessing sample (heterogeneity). Data sets may be community data sets (species abundance by samples) where the analysis is primarily concerned with assessing species richness and diversity (α-diversity). However, the methods described may also be applied to other forms of data, e.g. landscape types. The choice of method will be governed by the aims of the study and the type of data. Data sets may be binary, e.g. counts of species presence, or they may be continuous (quantitative), recording the abundance of each species (entity) in each sample unit. A guide to the appropriate choice of procedure is given in the flow diagrams on pages 80 and 81. The data may result from either a single or replicated set of sample units. Samples may be either regular or random. However, random samples should be used if at all possible, and random samples must be used if estimates of species richness (S) or indices of diversity are to be calculated and compared between communities.

Further reading

- Krebs, C.J. (1999) *Ecological Methodology*, 2nd edn. Addison Wesley Longman, Menlo Park, CA. Provides a detailed account of distribution-based methods.
- Ludwig, J.A. and Reynolds, J.F. (1988) *Statistical Ecology: A Primer on Methods and Computing*. John Wiley, Chichester. Provides a clear and concise treatment of how to calculate diversity indices and distribution-based methods
- Magurran, A.E. (1988) *Ecological Diversity and Its Measurement*. Croom Helm, London. Provides a very readable account of diversity and its measurement. Contains many example data sets and calculations.
- Stiling, P. (1999) *Ecology: Theories and Applications*, 3rd edn. Prentice Hall, Englewood Cliffs, NJ. Chapters 15, 16 and 17 provide a good undergraduate-level synthesis of the subject's theoretical basis, its relevance to ecology and our understanding of ecological communities.

Chapter Three

Estimating population size and population parameters

Summary

This chapter is divided into two parts. The first part, Sections 3.2 to 3.5, is concerned with the problems of assessing species abundance and estimating population size. The second part, Sections 3.6 to 3.9, covers the estimation of key population life table parameters. Topics covered in the first half of the chapter include direct counting of populations and the use of quadrat, transect and plotless sampling methods for estimating population abundance. Indirect indices of population abundance are considered, along with methods based on animal capture, mark and release. Section 3.5 outlines some methods for estimating microbial population size. Many of the methods covered may be generalised to cover other situations where there is a need to estimate the number or density of a particular entity. The second half of the chapter describes how to construct population life tables. Methods for comparing cohort survival and mortality rates are presented. In order to calculate key population parameters and construct life tables, data is required on the number of individuals surviving through time, e.g. estimates of population density at monthly intervals for a 10 month period. Alternatively some population statistics may be calculated where the age structure of the population is known or can be established.

3.1 *Introduction*

Total counts of individuals present in a population are the most direct way of assessing the abundance or density of a population. However, total counts are rarely practical as large areas often need to be surveyed, which can be time-consuming and costly, and individual animals may easily be missed or counted more than once. If total counts are not used, population size must be estimated from sample counts or from indirect methods such as those based on the capture, marking, release and subsequent recapture of marked animals. If sample counts are to be used, three questions need to be considered: What are the sample units to be used? How many are needed? How should they be placed or selected? These questions are discussed in Chapter 1. The first part of the present chapter focuses on the various procedures and calculations used to obtain indirect estimates of population size. The second looks at the calculation and comparison of population life table parameters. Although this chapter does not consider the practical problems associated with estimating population abundance, note that the number and density of individuals is rarely the most appropriate measure of plant abundance. Unlike the vast majority of animals, plants are plastic. Individual plants of the same age may vary considerably in size; thus, simple counts are of limited value if they fail to include differences in plant size and biomass. And because many plants species undergo vegetative propagation (asexual reproduction), it can be difficult to identify individual plants (Hutchings, 1997), making direct counts of individuals difficult if not impossible. For these reasons, measures of percentage plant cover based on point or pin quadrat surveys provide the most reliable non-destructive measure of plant abundance (Box 3.1).

3.2 *Point and transect estimates*

The number of animals seen by an observer standing at a point will depend on the surrounding density of animals and their visibility. The higher the density, the greater the number of animals likely to be observed. Assuming the visibility of animals decreases exponentially with distance from the sample point, an estimate of density can be obtained from the number of animals observed within and outside two zones centred on the sample point. This approach can be extended to line transects. An observer walks along a line and records the number of animals observed within and beyond a set distance either side of the line. Line transects have been used for surveying vegetation. A measure of the abundance of the particular species is given by the proportion of the transect line intercepted by the species (i.e. the length of line passing over the species as a ratio of the total length of the transect), or the number of plants which the line intercepts. Muttlak and Sabooghi-Alvandi (1993) discuss how estimates of variance and measures of the overlap between plant species may be obtained using the line intercept method. For plants or sessile organisms, nearest-neighbour distances and point-to-individual distances may also be used to estimate density. These methods are normally known as plotless sampling methods and form the basis of several procedures used to investigate the spatial pattern of individuals; Chapter 4 gives more details. The equations associated with these point and transect estimates of abundance are given in Box 3.2.

3.3 *Indices of population abundance*

Where the direct counting of the population is not possible, indirect indices of population size must be used. The number of road kills per kilometre, the density and freshness of faecal deposits or animal tracks might be used as an index of population size. Similarly, the number of animals seen while walking a set distance or transect, or caught in an array of

Box 3.1 **Estimating plant abundance**

Frequency

The presence or absence of species A is recorded in m randomly located quadrats. If the species occurs in n quadrats, species frequency is given by

$$f_A = n/m$$

There are three points to note:

- Species frequency is a measure of the probability that a random quadrat will contain the species.
- Frequency values depend on the size of the quadrat, so it should always be quoted.
- The number of successes, i.e. quadrats containing species A, follows a binomial distribution. The confidence limits for the proportion of successes (in this case f_A) out of m binomial trials is given by

$$f_A \pm z_c \sqrt{\frac{f_A(1 - f_A)}{m}}$$

For $m \geq 30$, $z_c = 1.96$ to give the 95% confidence interval, otherwise the appropriate t-value should be used.

Estimates of percentage cover

For large-scale surveys the percentage cover of plant species present in a quadrat may be estimated by eye. This is very subjective and it is not a particularly accurate method. Scaling crude estimates of percentage cover can reduce the extent of variation between recording events and observers. Several schemes are commonly used; Table 1 gives details of the Braun–Blanquet and Domin scales. Similar scales have been used to assess the abundance of intertidal organisms (Table 2).

Table 1 The Braun–Blanquet and Domin cover scales

Value	Braun–Blanquet	Domin
+	<1% cover	A single individual. No measurable cover
1	1–5% cover	1–2 individuals. No measurable cover. Individuals with normal vigour
2	6–25% cover	Several individuals but less than 1% cover
3	26–50% cover	1–4% cover
4	51–75% cover	4–10% cover
5	76–100% cover	11–25% cover
6		26–33% cover
7		34–50% cover
8		51–75% cover
9		76–90% cover
10		91–100% cover

Source: Chalmers and Parker (1986)

Table 2 Abundance scales for use on rocky shores[a]

1 Algae
E More than 90% cover
S 60–89% cover
A 30–59% cover
C 5–29% cover
F Less than 5% cover but zone still apparent
O Scattered plants, zone indistinct
R Only one or two plants present

2 Lichens and *Lithothamnion*
E More than 80% cover
S 50–79% cover
A 20–49% cover
C 1–19% cover
F Large scattered patches
O Widely scattered patches, all small
R Only one or two small patches present

3 Small barnacles and small winkles
E 500 or more $0.01\,\mathrm{m}^{-2}$
S 300–499 $0.01\,\mathrm{m}^{-2}$
A 100–299 $0.01\,\mathrm{m}^{-2}$
C 10–99 $0.01\,\mathrm{m}^{-2}$
F 1–9 $0.01\,\mathrm{m}^{-2}$
O 1–99 m^{-2}
R Less than $1\,\mathrm{m}^{-1}$

4 Limpets and large winkles
E 20 or more $0.1\,\mathrm{m}^{-2}$
S 10–19 $0.1\,\mathrm{m}^{-2}$
A 5–9 $0.1\,\mathrm{m}^{-2}$
C 1–4 $0.1\,\mathrm{m}^{-2}$
F 5–9 m^{-2}
O 1–4 m^{-2}
R Less than $1\,\mathrm{m}^{-1}$

5 Large barnacles *Balanus perforatus*
E 300 or more $0.01\,\mathrm{m}^{-2}$
S 100–299 $0.01\,\mathrm{m}^{-2}$
A 10–99 $0.01\,\mathrm{m}^{-2}$
C 1–9 $0.01\,\mathrm{m}^{-2}$
F 1–9 $0.1\,\mathrm{m}^{-2}$
O 1–9 m^{-2}
R Less than $1\,\mathrm{m}^{-2}$

6 Dogwhelks, topshells and anemones
E 10 or more $0.1\,\mathrm{m}^{-2}$
S 5–9 $0.1\,\mathrm{m}^{-2}$
A 1–4 $0.1\,\mathrm{m}^{-2}$
C 5–9 m^{-2}, locally sometimes more
F 1–4 m^{-2}, locally sometimes more
O Less than $1\,\mathrm{m}^{-1}$, locally sometimes more
R Always less than $1\,\mathrm{m}^{-1}$

7 Mussels and piddocks (score holes)
E More than 80% cover
S 50–79% cover
A 20–49% cover
C 5–19% cover
F Small patches, covering less than 5% of the rock surface
O 1–9 individuals m^{-2}; no patches
R Less than one individual m^{-2}

8 Tube worms such as *Pomatoceros*
A 50 or more tubes $0.01\,\mathrm{m}^{-2}$
C 1–49 tubes $0.01\,\mathrm{m}^{-2}$
F 1–9 tubes $0.1\,\mathrm{m}^{-2}$
O 1–9 tubes m^{-2}
R Less than 1 tube m^{-2}

[a] This is the modified version produced by Dr Keith Hiscock of the Field Studies Council's Oil Pullution Research Unit. It uses quadrats of three sizes: $1\,\mathrm{m}^2$, $0.1\,\mathrm{m}^2$ and $0.01\,\mathrm{m}^2$.
Key to letters: E = extremely abundant, S = superabundant, A = abundant, C = common, F = frequent, O = occasional, R = rare, N = absent.

Point quadrat estimates of cover

Experience shows that the subjective errors associated with estimating percentage cover decrease when smaller quadrats are used. With point or pin quadrats, the subjective judgements are removed completely; the observer has only to record whether the plant species is in contact with the point or pin (Figures 1 and 2).

Various frame designs have been tried; a commonly used system consists of a linear array of 10 'pins' separated by 5 cm which can be lowered into the vegetation. Absolute cover values are obtained by dividing the total number of contacts recorded for a species

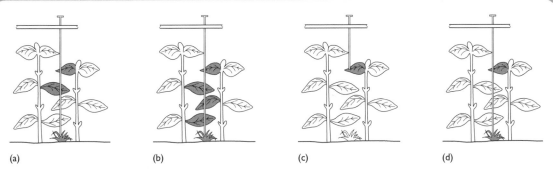

Figure 1 Collecting data with a point frame. Shading indicates the hits made by the tip of the pointer: (a) score the first hit on each individual to measure relative numbers of each species; (b) score all hits to measure total cover; (c) score only the first hit to measure canopy shading; (d) score the first hit on each 'species' to measure cover. Reprinted, with permission, from Chalmers and Parker (1986).

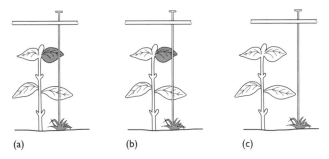

Figure 2 Collecting presence/absence data using a point frame. Shading indicates the hits that should be recorded: (a) both species, (b) only the tall species, (c) only the short species. Reprinted, with permission, from Chalmers and Parker (1986).

by the number of pins or points. Relative cover values are obtained by dividing the number of contacts recorded for a species by the total number of contacts recorded for all species. The accuracy of the estimates varies with the pin diameter (accuracy increases as pin diameter decreases). Point quadrats and other methods of estimating plant abundance are discussed in depth by Greig-Smith (1983) and Moore and Chapman (1986).

pitfall traps, is an index of population size. To be useful, the population index must relate directly to the actual density of the population. In a perfect world the index should be validated and, if possible, calibrated against known or independent estimates of population size. This is especially important where the index does not involve the recording of seen or trapped individuals. In the field, data must be collected in a consistent and rigidly standardised manner. The trapping and search efforts must be fixed. Where subjective judgements are required, efforts should be made to use clear and unambiguous criteria; this is particularly important where more than one observer is involved in collecting the data. As with any form of field data, indices derived from replicated random sampling schemes will generally be most reliable and informative. But very often random sampling is not possible. For example, collecting replicate random samples of road-kill counts is not possible since road networks are not random. A stratified random sample might be achieved by treating particular roads as strata and sampling at random locations or sections along each road. The fact that it may not be possible to sample in a completely random manner need not be particularly

Box 3.2   Point and transect estimates

Point transect method

The estimate of density (Figure 1) is given by

$$D = \frac{n_1 + n_2}{\pi r^2 m} \ln\left(\frac{n_1 + n_2}{n_2}\right)$$

Biddy *et al.* (1985) counted the number of willow warblers (*Phylloscopus trochilus*) seen over 5 min within and beyond 30 m of 326 replicated points in a conifer plantation; 421 birds were recorded within 30 m of the sample point, 504 beyond. Using this data we have

$$D = \frac{421 + 504}{\pi(30)^2 326} \ln\left(\frac{421 + 504}{504}\right) = 6.09 \times 10^{-4}\,\text{m}^{-2} = 6.09\,\text{ha}^{-1}$$

Unbounded transect

- The point transect equation may be generalised and applied to unbounded line transects:

$$D = \frac{n_1 + n_2}{2rl} \ln\left(\frac{n_1 + n_2}{n_2}\right)$$

  where *l* is the length of the line.

- Eberhardt's (1978) non-parametric estimate of density is given by

$$D = \frac{3n_1 - n_2}{4lr}$$

  Its precision is improved by increasing the value of *r*, but accuracy is enhanced by choosing small values of *r* (Seber, 1982).

POINT TRANSECT   LINE TRANSECT

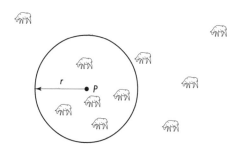

P = one of the *m* points
n_1 = number of animals seen within distance *r* of sample point *P*
n_2 = number of animals seen beyond distance *r* of sample point *P*

Figure 1 The theory behind transects.

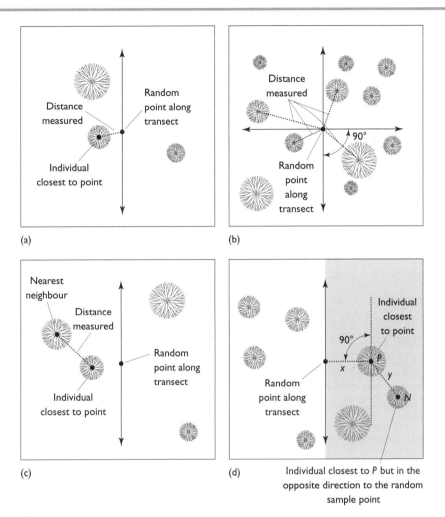

(a)

(b)

(c)

(d)

Individual closest to *P* but in the opposite direction to the random sample point

Figure 2 Sample points may be random points within the sample area or random points along a transect. Here are four distance methods: (a) nearest individual, (b) point-centred quarter, (c) nearest neighbour, (d) T-square. Reprinted and modified, with permission, from M.G. Barbour, J.H. Burk and W.D. Pitts, 1987, *Terrestrial Plant Ecology*, 2nd edn, Benjamin/Cummings, Menlo Park, CA.

Plotless sampling estimates of density

Plotless methods can be useful where population density is low and individuals sparse. Then it is often not practical to construct sample plots or use quadrats. Plotless sampling may be centred on randomly located points, or on points randomly located along a transect which crosses the sample area (Figure 2).

Nearest-individual method

Select m random points and for each one record the distance (r) to the nearest individual. The mean of r is then used to estimate the density:

$$D = 1/(2\bar{r})^2$$

Point-centred quarter method

Select m random points; take the area surrounding each point and divide it into four quadrants; record the distance (r) from the point to the nearest individual in each quadrant. These four values are averaged for each sample point, and the mean of these averages for all m sample points (R) is used to estimate the density:

$$D = 1/R^2$$

Nearest-neighbour distance

Select m random points; for each random point, choose the individual nearest to it and measure the distance (r) from that individual to its nearest neighbour. The mean of all m nearest-neighbour distances is used to estimate the density:

$$D = 1/(1.67\bar{r})^2$$

T-square method

Select m random points. Measure the distance (x) to the nearest individual (P) from the sample point. Take the area surrounding the sample point and divide it in two by a line at right angles to a line joining the sample point and the first individual (P). Now select a second individual (N) that is nearest the original sample point but in the opposite half of the sample area to the first individual (P). Measure the distance (y) from N to the sample point. The totals of x and y are then used to estimate the density:

$$D = \frac{m^2}{2.828 T_x T_y} \quad \text{with} \quad T_x = \sum_{i=1}^{m} x_i, \quad T_y = \sum_{i=1}^{m} y_i$$

Advantages and disadvantages

Estimates given by these methods are biased if the distribution of individuals is not random. The direction of bias differs between methods. When individuals are aggregated (clumped), procedures based on nearest-neighbour distances overestimate the density whereas those based on object-to-individual distances underestimate the density. The converse is true where individuals are regularly distributed. The T-square method is the most robust (Greenwood, 1996).

The precision of the estimates improves with sample size. The T-square method requires a minimum of 10 random points. As a rule of thumb, the other procedures require around 50 distance measures. Smaller sample sizes may sometimes provide good estimates of density. A suitable sample size may be derived by plotting a graph of estimated density against sample size; minimum sample size is then taken as the point where the estimate of density stabilises (Chapter 1). Krebs (1999) presents alternative forms of these plotless methods and discusses how to set confidence limits.

With all these procedures it is important that all distances are measured in the same units; if distances are measured in metres, the estimates of density will be given in individuals per square metre.

important as long as the limitations of the data are appreciated. It would not be appropriate to extrapolate from an estimate of population density based on the number of individuals observed from a car travelling along a road to areas distant from or between roads. In addition to the inherent sampling constraints, it is probable that the behaviour of the animals, hence the likelihood of them being seen, will be affected by the presence of the road and the density of traffic. Similar arguments apply to counts of animals made along paths and other landscape features.

3.4 *Capture-based population estimates*

3.4.1 *Mark–recapture methods*

The basis of mark–recapture methods is deceptively simple (Figure 3.1). The population is initially sampled, all captured individuals (n_1) are marked in some way and then they are released back into the population. The population is sampled for a second time; of the n_2 individuals captured during the second sampling, some (m_2) will be marked. If both groups of animals, marked and unmarked, mix freely within the population and are equally likely to be caught, the size of the population can be estimated by assuming that the ratio of marks (m_2) to non-marks in the second sample (n_2) is the same as the ratio of the marked

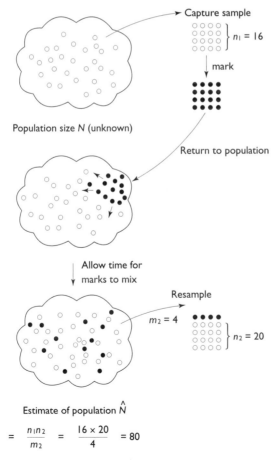

Figure 3.1 Estimating population size using a mark–recapture method.

individuals (n_1) to the total population N. That is,

$$\underset{\text{size of second sample}}{\underset{\nearrow}{\overset{\text{size of first sample}}{\overset{\swarrow}{\frac{m_2}{n_2} = \frac{n_1}{N}}}}} \qquad N = \frac{n_1 n_2}{m_2}$$

size of first sample

size of second sample   number of marks recovered

This is the foundation of the Lincoln index or Petersen estimate of population size (Box 3.3). This form of the Lincoln index tends to overestimate the size of the population, but the bias may be largely removed when $m_2 > 7$ by using

$$\hat{N} = \frac{(n_1 + 1)(n_2 + 1)}{m_2 + 1} - 1$$

A minor modification to this equation allows it to be used for estimating the population size where individuals in the second sample (n_2) are 'sighted' rather than captured (Bailey, 1952). Here the second sample is effectively taken with replacement; individuals may be recorded more than once. This type of situation arises when a sample of the population is taken, marked or identified in some way, returned to the population, and then later observed when the number of marked or identified individuals (m_2) among the total number of individuals observed (n_2) is recorded. In this situation an estimate of the population size is given by

$$\hat{N} = \frac{n_1(n_2 + 1)}{m_2 + 1}$$

There are various ways in which confidence limits about the Petersen estimate of population size may be set. If the proportion of recapture marks (p) in the second sample, i.e. m_2/n_2, is greater than 0.1, limits about p may be read directly from charts of binomial distribution 95% confidence limits (Appendix 3.1). Where p is less than 0.1, i.e. the recapture of a marked individual is a rare event, confidence limits about the number of animals recaptured m_2 may be set using tables of confidence limits for the Poisson frequency distribution (Appendix 3.2). If $p > 0.1$ and the number of recaptured marks is greater than 50, a normal approximation may be used. Fowler *et al.* (1998) provide a simple formula for crude estimates of the standard error (SE) of N which can be used to set confidence limits:

$$\text{SE} = \sqrt{\frac{n_1^2 \times n_2(n_2 - m_2)}{m_2^3}}$$

Alternative normal approximations are given in Box 3.3.

Now consider a study of vole populations. At the start of the year, 60 animals were caught, marked and released. In the second sample, taken shortly afterwards, 50 voles were captured and 25 of them had marks. Using the formula,

$$\hat{N} = \frac{(n_1 + 1)(n_2 + 1)}{m_2 + 1} - 1 = \frac{(60 + 1)(50 + 1)}{25 + 1} - 1 = \frac{3111}{26} - 1 = 118.65$$

$$p = \frac{m_2}{n_2} = \frac{25}{50} = 0.5$$

Since $p > 0.1$ the binomial distribution may be used to set confidence limits about p. From Appendix 3.1 the lower limit for p with a sample size of 50 (n_2) is approximately 0.355, and

Box 3.3 **Mark–recapture: the theory**

Lincoln index or the Petersen method

Estimate of population size is given by

$$\hat{N} = \frac{(n_1 + 1)(n_2 + 1)}{m_2 + 1} - 1$$

where n_1 = number marked and released
n_2 = total number caught when the population is resampled
m_2 = number of marked individuals present in the second sample

If $m_2 < 8$ the estimate of N is biased. For $m_2 > 50$ reasonably accurate 95% confidence limits are given by

$$Cl_1 = w_1/n_1 \qquad Cl_2 = w_2/n_1$$

where

$$w_1, w_2 = p \pm \left[1.96 \sqrt{\frac{p(1-p)(1-m_2/n_1)}{n_2 - 1}} + \frac{1}{2n_2} \right]$$

and $p = m_2/n_2$ is the proportion of marked individuals in the second sample.

If samples are large, Blower *et al.* (1981) recommend a simpler approximation to obtain the 95% confidence limits. This involves calculating the limits about the proportion (p) of marks recovered in the second sample n_2:

$$\pm 1.96 \sqrt{\frac{p(1-p)}{n_2}}$$

Using the basic formula (in the text):

$$\frac{m_2}{n_2} = \frac{n_1}{N} \quad \text{and} \quad N = \frac{n_1 n_2}{m_2} = \frac{n_1}{p}$$

The upper confidence limit about the estimate of N is obtained by dividing n_1, the number of animals originally captured, marked and released, by the lower limit of p. The lower limit of N is obtained by dividing n_1 by the upper limit of p.

The Schnabel method

Preliminary calculations:

$$M_i = \sum_{j=1}^{i-1} u_j, \quad A = \sum_{i=1}^{S} n_i M_i^2, \quad B = \sum_{i=1}^{S} m_i M_i, \quad C = \sum_{i=1}^{S} m_i^2/n_i$$

where S = number of samples
n_i = number of animals captured in the ith sample
m_i = number of marked animals in the ith sample
$u_i = n_i - m_i$ is the number of unmarked animals in the ith sample

Note that for the first sample, when $i = 1$, $m_i = 0$, $M_i = 0$ and $u_i = n_i$. The estimate of population size is given by

$$\hat{N} = A/B$$

▶

and 95% confidence limits by

$$\frac{A}{B \pm t_{s-2}\sqrt{(AC - B^2)/(S - 2)}}$$

Where t_{s-2} is Student's t-value for $S - 2$ degrees of freedom at the 5% significance level.

Bailey's triple catch method

In order to distinguish between captured and marked individuals on each occasion, two different marking procedures must be used. An estimate of population size is given by

$$\hat{N} = \frac{n_2 R_{13}}{R_{23}} + R_{12}$$

where R_{12} = the number of individuals that were marked in the first sample and recaptured in the second sample

R_{23} = the number of individuals that were marked in the second sample and recaptured in the third sample

R_{13} = the number of individuals that were marked in the first sample and recaptured in the third sample

n_2 = the total number of individuals captured on the second sampling occasion

the upper limit is 0.65. Using the basic formula for the Petersen estimate:

$$N = \frac{n_1 n_2}{m_2} = n_1 \frac{1}{p}$$

Expressing the formula in terms of n_1 and p.

$$p_{ll} = 0.355$$

Lower 95% confidence limit for p, used to calculate the upper limit for **N**.

$$\hat{N}_{ul} = 60 \frac{1}{0.335} = 179.10$$

$$p_{ul} = 0.65$$

Upper 95% confidence limit for p, used to calculate lower limit for **N**.

$$\hat{N}_{ll} = 60 \frac{1}{0.65} = 92.30$$

Thus, early in the year before breeding, the population of voles was estimated[1] to be 119 with upper and lower approximate 95% confidence limits of 179 and 92. When the population was resampled later in the year, after the breeding season, 164 animals were initially caught, marked and released. On recapture 183 voles were caught, but only 15 had marks. Estimating the population size as before:

$$\hat{N} = \frac{(n_1 + 1)(n_2 + 1)}{m_2 + 1} - 1 = \frac{(164 + 1)(183 + 1)}{15 + 1} - 1 = 1896.5$$

$$p = \frac{m_2}{n_2} = \frac{15}{183} = 0.0824$$

Since $p < 0.1$ the confidence limits are set using the Poisson distribution. From Appendix 3.2, the lower and upper 95% confidence limits for $m_2 = 15$ are 8.102 and 23.762. Using these two values for m_2, the corresponding upper and lower limits for N may be calculated as follows:

$$\hat{N}_{ul} = \frac{(164+1)(183+1)}{8.102+1} - 1 = 3335.53 \qquad \text{upper 95\% confidence limit for } N$$

$$\hat{N}_{ll} = \frac{(164+1)(183+1)}{23.762+1} - 1 = 1225.07 \qquad \text{lower 95\% confidence limit for } N$$

So in the study area, the population of voles has increased from around 119 at the start of the year to 1896 at the end of the breeding season; this represents an apparent per capita population increase or dilution of $1896/119 = 15.932$. However, without additional information on the movement of voles into and out of the study area, it is impossible to say whether this is an over- or underestimate of the population growth rate. Note also that we have not distinguished between male voles and female voles.

If the mark and recapture process is repeated, the number of marked individuals in the population will increase. If the process is continued long enough, all individuals in the population will be marked and the proportion of captured animals marked will be 1.0. This is the basis of the Schnabel method of estimating population size, in which the population is repeatedly sampled and all captured individuals are marked and returned to the population. The time between repeated samplings must be sufficient to allow the marked individuals to mix within the population, and the sampling effort should be the same throughout the study. An estimate of population size is obtained either by calculation (Box 3.3) or by plotting the proportion of marked individuals recovered against the cumulative number of captured and marked individuals (Figure 3.2). The plotted line should be drawn through the origin. The validity of the assumptions behind the mark–recapture model of the populations can be assessed from the graph. If the model is valid, the plotted points should lie along a line from the origin to the point where y (the proportion of marks in the samples) equals 1.0 and $x = \hat{N}$, the calculated estimate of the population size (Box 3.3). If a linear graph is not produced, the estimate is likely to be biased. The fit of the model may be tested formally by performing a goodness-of-fit test. A simpler alternative to the Schnabel method is provided by Bailey's triple catch method (Box 3.3), which requires the population to be sampled on three occasions only.

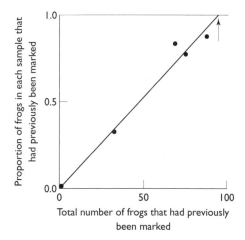

Figure 3.2 The Schnabel method has been applied to a population of cricket frogs; the arrow indicates the estimated population size. The frogs were sampled over five successive days. Reprinted, with permission, from Sutherland (1996).

A single estimate of population size is usually of limited value. Where multiple estimates of population size are made, it is possible to estimate both mortality and recruitment. At the start of first time interval, the population size (N_1) is estimated and n_1 marked individuals are released into the population. At the end of the first time interval, a second estimate of the population (N_2) is made, along with an estimate of the number of marked individuals that are still present (sm_2). An estimate of the number of surviving marks (sm) is made by assuming that the proportion (p) of marked individuals recovered when estimating N_2 reflects the proportion of surviving marks in the whole population. Thus the total number of surviving marks is given by pN_2. Between the two sampling events, the population may have increased ($N_2 > N_1$), decreased ($N_2 < N_1$) or remained the same ($N_2 = N_1$). In contrast, the number of marked individuals can only decrease between sampling events; unmarked individuals cannot become marked individuals. The extent of decline will depend on the mortality rate (and emigration rate), thus the survival rate (S) of marked animals is given by

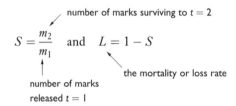

$$S = \frac{m_2}{m_1} \quad \text{and} \quad L = 1 - S$$

number of marks surviving to $t = 2$

the mortality or loss rate

number of marks
released $t = 1$

If the survival rate of the marked individuals is assumed to apply to all members of the population, whether marked or unmarked, the expected population size at the start of the second time interval will be given by the product SN_1. The difference between the expected size and estimated size, known as the dilution (D), will depend on the amount of recruitment and immigration that occurred during the first time interval:

$$D = N_2 - SN_1 \quad \text{and} \quad d = D/N_1 \quad \longleftarrow \quad \text{the rate of dilution}$$

Worked examples of mark–recapture calculations are given in Box 3.4.

3.4.2 Removal methods

Continued removal

An estimate of population size can be obtained by repeatedly removing animals from the population. At each sampling episode, captured animals are removed from the population. As more animals are removed, the size of the population will decline and the number caught at each sampling episode will decrease. If the number of animals caught at each sampling episode is plotted against accumulative catch size, an estimate of the original population size can be obtained by extrapolating the graph to the point where the number of animals caught is equal to zero (Figure 3.3). A very crude estimate of the population size may be obtained from just two sampling events (Chalmers and Parker, 1986). S_1 individuals are captured and removed from the population, which is then resampled. If S_2 individuals are captured at the second sampling event, the population size can be estimated from

$$\hat{N} = \frac{S_1^2 - S_2}{S_1 - S_2}$$

For these methods to work, a constant sampling or trapping effort should be used on each sampling episode. More accurate methods do exist for estimating population abundance from animal removal, but they use much more complicated mathematics (Hirst, 1994).

Box 3.4   **Mark–recapture: examples**

First sampling event estimate of population at $t = 1$		Second sampling event estimate of population at $t = 2$	
Sample 1	Sample 2	Sample 3	Sample 4

Sample 1	Sample 2	Sample 3	Sample 4
Number of animals captured and marked is $n_1 = 150$	Total number of animals caught is $n_2 = 145$ Number of marks in second sample is $m_2 = 55$	Number of animals captured and marked is $n_1 = 180$ Number of marks from $t = 1$ recaptured $= 20$	Total number of animals caught is $n_2 = 200$ Number of marks in second sample is $m_2 = 80$

$$\hat{N}_1 = \frac{(n_1 + 1)(n_2 + 1)}{m_2 + 1} - 1$$

$$= \frac{(150 + 1)(145 + 1)}{55 + 1} - 1$$

$$= \frac{151 \times 146}{56} - 1 = 392.68$$

$$\hat{N}_2 = \frac{(180 + 1)(200 + 1)}{80 + 1} - 1$$

$$= \frac{181 \times 201}{81} - 1$$

$$= 448.15$$

Using the Blower *et al.* (1981) method for estimating approximate 95% confidence limits about the population estimate, based on calculating limits about the proportion of marks in the recaptured sample

$p \pm 1.96\sqrt{[p(1 - p)]/n_2}$

p = proportion of marks in the second sample

$p = 55/145 = 0.3793$

$p \pm 1.96\sqrt{[0.3793(1 - 0.3793)]/145}$

$p \pm 1.96(0.040\,29)$

$0.3793 \pm 0.078\,98$
Upper limit $p = 0.458\,28$
Lower limit $p = 0.300\,32$

p = proportion of marks in the second sample

$p = 80/200 = 0.4$

$p \pm 1.96\sqrt{[0.4(1 - 0.4)]/200}$

$p \pm 1.96(0.034\,64)$

$0.4 \pm 0.067\,89$

Upper limit $p = 0.467\,89$
Lower limit $p = 0.332\,10$

Calculation of 95% confidence limits about estimate of population size using basic formula $\hat{N} = n_1/p$

Lower limit $= 150/0.458\,28 = 327.31$
Upper limit $= 150/0.300\,32 = 499.47$

Lower limit $= 200/0.467\,89 = 427.45$
Upper limit $= 200/0.332\,10 = 602.22$

Calculation of survival rate and population dilution rate
Assume that the proportion of the originally marked individuals recaptured in sample 3 reflects the proportion of surviving marks in the population as a whole. Then the number of marks present at sampling event 3 is given by

$$\left(\frac{20}{180}\right)\hat{N}_2 = 0.1111 \times 448.15 = 49.79$$

Original number of marks released following their capture during sampling event 1 is 150. Estimate of mark survival is
$S = 49.79/150 = 0.3319$
Estimate of animals surviving from $t = 1$ to $t = 2$ is given by $SN_1 = 0.3319 \times 392.68 = 130.33$
Dilution $D = 448.15 - 130.33 = 317.82$
Dilution rate $D/N = 317.82/392.68 = 0.809$
This is equal to the net increase per capita due to emigration and reproduction

Index manipulation method

Index manipulation provides a simple way of estimating the size of a population from indirect indices of population size. An index of population size is obtained (I_1), a known number of animals are then removed (C) and a second index obtained (I_2). If the population is closed then the removal of animals will cause the index to decrease. The difference between

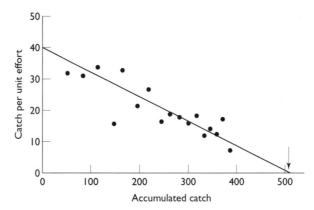

Figure 3.3 The removal method has been applied to black rat catches in 70 houses; the arrow indicates the estimated population size. The rats were caught over 18 days. Reprinted, with permission, from Sutherland (1996).

I_1 and I_2 will depend on the size of the original population N and the numbers of individuals removed:

$$\hat{N} = \frac{I_1 C}{I_1 - I_2}$$

Following Eberhardt (1982) the standard error in the estimate of population size can be derived from

$$p = (I_1 - I_2)/I \qquad q = 1 - p$$

$$\text{var}(\hat{N}) \approx \hat{N}^2 \left(\frac{q}{p}\right)^2 \left(\frac{1}{I_1} + \frac{1}{I_2}\right)$$

$$\text{SE}(\hat{N}) \approx \sqrt{\text{var}(\hat{N})}$$

where p is an estimate of the proportion of the population removed and q is an estimate of the proportion remaining after C animals have been removed.

Change-of-ratio method
Where the individuals of a population can be divided into distinct classes (e.g. males and females, juveniles and adults, or different coloured morphs) the change-of-ratio method can be used to estimate population size. Let one class of individual be labelled x and the proportion of class x individuals in the original population p_1. The population is then manipulated by either removing or adding C_x individuals of type x and C_y individuals of type y. The total number of individuals removed or added, C, equals $C_x + C_y$. Following manipulation the proportion p_2 of type x individuals in the population must be estimated. The size of the population before the manipulation is estimated from

$$\hat{N} = \frac{C_x - p_2 C}{p_2 - p_1}$$

When animals are added to the population then C is positive; when animals are removed then C is negative. The population must be closed and the time interval between surveys must be short.

3.4.3 *Assumption behind capture-based methods*

All the capture-based sampling methods we have described make the following assumptions:

- All animals in the population can be caught and are equally likely to be caught. Whether these conditions are met will depend on the behaviour of animals, e.g. whether trap-happy or trap-shy animals occur in the population, and on the type, number and placement of traps. The choice of trapping procedure must be considered carefully. If traps are poorly placed, if the number of traps is too small, or if the traps are inappropriate, the probability of capture will differ between individuals.
- Where the method involves more than one trapping event, the population is sampled under the same conditions and with the same trapping effort. If the behaviour or distribution pattern of the population varies during the day, or with weather conditions, each sampling event must, as far as possible, be conducted under the same conditions and at the same time of day.
- The populations are closed during the period of study used to estimate the population size. During this period there must be no gains (births or immigration) or losses (deaths or emigration).

Methods which involve the marking and recapture of individuals also have these requirements:

- Marks are not lost; that is, the marks or labels used to indicate an animal has previously been caught are not lost or worn off.
- Marking does not affect the mortality or behaviour of marked individuals.
- The marked individuals mix freely (randomly) with the unmarked individuals. This is only likely to occur when the marked individuals are a truly representative sample of the original population and sufficient time is allowed following release for the marked individuals to disperse and mix.

The procedures presented here and alternatives, including methods for open populations, are described in detail by Blower *et al.* (1981), Seber (1982), Pollock *et al.* (1990) and Greenwood (1996). Practical details on the trapping and sampling of populations may be found in Southwood (1978) and Sutherland (1996). Improvements and new procedures for estimating population size are continually being developed. An alternative to the capture–mark–release methods is the plant–capture method recently developed by Laska and Meisner (1993). Marked individuals are added to the population (planted) and an estimate of population size is derived from the number subsequently captured. For this method to work, sufficient plants must be available and, apart from the mark used to identify them, they must be indistinguishable from members of the original population. Where this can be achieved, it has the advantage of requiring only a single capture event.

3.5 *Estimating microbial population size*

Because of their small size and their large diversity, estimating the microbial population associated with any habitat is extremely difficult. Three general approaches have been used: direct observation and counts, plate counts, and most-probable-number estimates. The direct observation and counting of microbes such as bacteria requires suitable samples to be obtained (normally a water suspension of microbes); sometimes stained, the samples are then mounted, examined under a microscope and counted. If the volume of the sample counted is known, an estimate of the population density can be made. The method does have advantages. In theory at least, the procedure is non-selective, i.e. all of the microbial organisms observed can be counted directly (Byrd and Colwell, 1992). However, obtaining suitable representative samples can be difficult and the method is very time-consuming.

Plate counts and most-probable-number (MPN) estimates are selective methods. They both involve the culturing of the organisms present in the original sample. All culture conditions will be selective, favouring the growth of some species over others. This can be an advantage where interest centres on one particular type of organism with specific growth conditions. For example, faecal coliform contamination of water samples can be tested by incubating cultures at a temperature of 44.5°C. At this temperature, the faecal coliforms can grow but not the non-faecal coliforms. Evidence of growth, e.g. gas production in a liquid lactose broth culture, provides a positive test for the presence of faecal coliforms (Atlas and Bartha, 1998). The plate count method for bacteria involves inoculating agar plates with suitably diluted samples. The plates are then incubated and the numbers of colonies that develop are counted.

A range of dilutions must be used to ensure the colony density for at least some dilution can be accurately counted. It is assumed that every bacterium present in the sample spread or poured on to the agar plate will give rise to a single colony. For example, an estimate of the viable microbial population of a soil might be obtained by the following outline procedure (Clark 1965):

1. A water suspension is prepared by mixing 10 g of fresh sieved soil with 95 ml of sterilised distilled water and glass beads (to ensure good mixing). After shaking for 10 min, 10 ml of the suspension is removed and added to 90 ml of sterilised water, giving an initial 10^{-2} dilution.

2. From this 10^{-2} dilution a series of dilution is prepared down to 10^{-7}.

3. For each dilution from 10^{-5} to 10^{-7}, 1 ml of the diluted suspension is added to five replicated freshly poured agar medium plates (the medium must be suitable for the growth of soil microbes).

4. The agar plates are incubated for 10 to 14 days at a constant temperature of 25°C or 30°C.

5. If plates have more than 300 colonies, the dilution has been too low; if plates have fewer that 30 colonies, the dilution has been too high. The dilution that has a colony density of between 30 and 300 is selected and the number of colonies is counted for each replicate. These values are used to obtain the number of bacteria present in the initial suspension.

After following this procedure at the 10^{-6} dilution, suppose that the five replicate plate colony counts are 105, 122, 108, 95 and 100. Taking the mean, 106, and multiplying by the dilution factor (10^6), gives a total count of 106×10^6 bacteria per gram of fresh soil. If the dry matter content of the soil is 0.8 g per gram of moist soil, this value corresponds to 106/0.8 million = 132 million bacteria per gram of dry soil.

Most-probable-number estimates
The most-probable-number (MPN) estimate procedure allows the population density to be estimated without actual cell or colony counts and has similarities to the removal method of estimating population size (Section 3.4.2). It involves the progressive dilution of the original suspension and the culturing of the diluted samples. The dilution is continued until evidence of growth is only found on some, not all of the replicate cultures. At the start of the dilution process, the concentration of cells in suspension will be high enough to ensure that every replicate culture will be inoculated with cells. As the sample is progressively diluted, the

number of cells in each inoculum will decrease. Eventually the concentration of cells in the diluted suspension will be so small that some cultures will receive no cells, and after incubation they will show no evidence of microbial growth. At this dilution the suspension can be modelled by imagining a well-mixed set of coloured balls, a small number of yellow balls (bacteria, e.g. 10) and a larger number of white balls (e.g. 90).

If the balls are randomly distributed among 10 containers in equal lots of 10, it is very unlikely that each container will receive one yellow ball. Some containers will receive more than one and others will receive none. It is possible to calculate the probability of a container receiving no yellow balls and hence the expected number of containers which receive yellow balls. Clearly, this will depend on the total number of yellow balls present (bacteria), the number of balls randomly placed in each container (size of the inoculum) and the number of containers (culture plates). The probability calculations required to estimate the number of yellow balls in the original set form the statistical basis of MPN (Cochran, 1950). Knowing the dilution factor, the volume of diluted suspension added, and the number of replicates that receive at least one bacterium and therefore score positively for growth, it is possible to calculate the most probable number of viable cells. Halvorson and Ziegler (1933) provide a general equation which allows the MPN to be calculated on the basis of the number of positive and negative cultures in three successive dilutions. The subscripts 1, 2 and 3 refer to the first, second and third dilutions.

$$a_1 n_1 + a_2 n_2 + a_3 n_3 = \frac{a_1 p_1}{1 - e^{a_1 X}} + \frac{a_2 p_2}{1 - e^{a_2 X}} + \frac{a_3 p_3}{1 - e^{a_3 X}}$$

where a_1, a_2, a_3 = the quantities or relative quantities of the original sample in the inoculum applied

n_1, n_2, n_3 = the numbers of tubes or plates inoculated

p_1, p_2, p_3 = the numbers of tubes or plates showing growth

X = the most probable number of organisms in the quantity of inoculum added in the second dilution

e = 2.718.

Multiplying X by the dilution factor gives the most probable number of organisms in the original sample. Solving the above equation for X is tedious and in practice MPN values are obtained from tables. The tables provided in Appendix 3.3 allow the MPN and 95% confidence limits to be obtained where five replicated tubes or plates are used per dilution and where the dilution ratio is 10. Suppose that after incubation the results were as shown in Table 3.1.

From Appendix 3.3, with $p_1 = 5$, $p_2 = 3$ and $p_3 = 1$ the tabulated value for X is 1.1. Multiplying this by the dilution factor, 10^7, gives an MPN of 11 million in the original sample. A factor of 3.30 for the calculation of 95% confidence limits for a dilution ratio of 10 and 5 culture tubes is obtained from the second table. The upper limit is obtained

Table 3.1 Results after incubation

Dilution	Number of positive replicates (out of 5)
10^{-5}	5
10^{-6}	3
10^{-7}	1
10^{-8}	0

by multiplying the MPN by this factor, the lower limit by dividing:

Upper limit $= 11 \times 3.3 = 360$ million viable cells

Lower limit $= 11/3.3 = 3.3$ million viable cells

Notice that more accurate determinations of MPN (i.e. narrower confidence limits) are obtained by decreasing the dilution ratio and increasing the number of replicate cultures. The estimate is most sensitive to changes in the dilution ratio; little is gained by increasing the number of replicates beyond five. A dilution ratio of 10 and five replicates at each level represents a suitable compromise that gives reasonable accuracy with a manageable number of cultures. One of the major advantages of MPN is that it can be generalised to any group of micro-organisms that can be cultured and the occurrence of growth easily scored. Colonies need not be counted. In liquid cultures, growth may be indicated by changes in turbidity or, in the case of phytoplankton, by the presence of chlorophyll (Atlas and Bartha, 1998). The general MPN approach has potential applications outside of microbiology. There are three important aspects to consider: Are the organisms or items of interest dispersed throughout a medium? Can they be easily diluted by mixing with an inert material and partitioned into replicated samples? Can the presence or growth of the organisms be easily scored? If all three answers are yes then MPN is worth considering.

3.6 *Life table analysis*

Population data is often summarised in the form of a life table. Depending on the nature of the data, two types of life table can be produced: a cohort life table or a static life table. Cohort life tables are produced when the fate and performance of a group of individuals born at the same time (i.e. a cohort) are followed throughout their entire lifespan. From such demographic studies, the age at the first reproductive episode, the number of reproductive episodes and the age at death will be known for each individual in the cohort. The reproductive output, i.e. the number of offspring produced by the individuals of the cohort, might be recorded directly during the study or it might be estimated from knowledge of the reproductive biology of the species. Unfortunately, particularly for long-lived species, it is not always possible to collect cohort data; relationships between age and mortality must be deduced from the age structure of the population and the resulting life table a static life table.

The basic life table calculations for static and cohort life tables are the same. The data is arranged into columns (Table 3.2). The first column, headed x, refers to the age interval and the second column, headed n_x, refers to the number of individuals alive at the start of age interval x. From these columns are calculated the survivorship (l_x), i.e. the proportion of the original cohort alive at start of age interval x, and the number of individuals dying during age interval (d_x).[2] These are in turn used to calculate the age-specific mortality rate (q_x), which is equal to the probability of an individual dying in a particular age class. The corresponding probability of an individual surviving from the beginning to the end of the age class, p_x, is given by $1 - q_x$. The k-factor or killing factor, k_x, is another measure of mortality which is frequently calculated and has the advantage of being additive:

individual age class or life stage *k*-factor values

$$K = k_1 + k_2 + \cdots + k_I = \sum_{i=1}^{I} k_i$$

total cohort or generation mortality

Table 3.2 Outline of life table calculations concerned with mortality and survival

Age class x (e.g. years)	Number of individuals alive (n_x)	Survivorship $(l_x = n_x/n_0)$	Number dying during age interval $(d_x = n_x - n_{x+1})$	Age-specific mortality rate $(q_x = d_x/n_x)$	$log_{10} n_x$	Killing power $(k_x = log_{10} n_x - log_{10} n_{x+1})$
0	250	250/250 = 1.0	250 − 120 = 130	130/250 = 0.52	2.397 94	2.397 94 − 2.079 18 = 0.318 76
2	120	120/250 = 0.48	120 − 75 = 45	45/120 = 0.375	2.079 18	2.079 18 − 1.875 06 = 0.204 12
3	75	75/250 = 0.3	75 − 55 = 20	20/75 = 0.267	1.875 06	1.875 06 − 1.740 36 = 0.134 70
4	55	55/255 = 0.22	55 − 0 = 55	55/55 = 1.0[a]	1.740 36	b
5	0	0/250 = 0	–	–	–	$\sum k_x = 0.657\,58$[c]

[a] Since all individuals die during this time interval q_x, the probability of mortality is 1.0.
[b] This cannot be calculated because log 0 is undefined.
[c] $\sum k_x$ is the total generation mortality.

The total cohort or generation mortality (K) is obtained by summing the k-factor values for each age class. This additive property is particularly useful where total generation mortality and life stage or age class k-factor values are obtained for several cohorts. By correlating k-factor values against total generation mortality, it is possible to assess the relative contribution of each to the overall population mortality. Correlations between total population density, cohort life stage or age class density and total cohort mortality and individual k-factors can provide evidence of dependent mortality. The loss of potential progeny may also be viewed as a mortality factor. The k-factor for reduced fecundity is equal to log_{10}(potential fecundity) − log_{10}(actual fecundity). By incorporating reductions in fecundity within a k-factor analysis, reproductive performance can be analysed in a similar way to other forms of mortality that occur during the lifespan of an individual (Figures 3.4 and 3.5).

If data is available on the number of offspring produced by individuals in each age class, a fecundity schedule can be produced. The column m_x contains age-specific fecundity or birth rate values which are equal to the average number of female offspring produced by a female of age x (Table 3.3). Notice that m_x is defined in terms of females only. For many species, population size and growth are governed by the number, age and status of female animals present, so life tables are frequently constructed for females only. Where a life table includes age-specific fecundity values, the net reproductive rate (R_0) can be calculated from

$$R_0 = \sum l_x m_x$$

equals the average number of offspring produced by an individual throughout its entire life

Notice that the influence of mortality on recruitment is incorporated through the inclusion of cohort survivorship values (l_x). The total number of offspring produced depends on the number of cohort members surviving to each age class and the average number of offspring produced by females of that age. For an annual species, i.e. one that completes its life cycle within one year, R_0 corresponds to R, the net annual rate of population increase. A stable population size will occur when $R = 1.0$; if $R > 1.0$ the population will increase and if $R < 1.0$ the population will decrease. For populations with overlapping generations, R_0 is effectively the generation rate of increase and the calculation of R is a little more complex. The mean generation time (T_c), which can be defined as the average age of the parents of all the offspring produced by cohort members (Gotelli, 1998), needs to

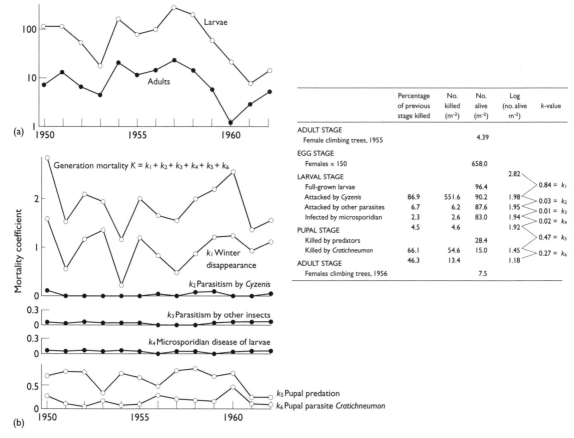

	Percentage of previous stage killed	No. killed (m⁻²)	No. alive (m⁻²)	Log (no. alive m⁻²)	k-value
ADULT STAGE					
Female climbing trees, 1955			4.39		
EGG STAGE					
Females × 150			658.0		
LARVAL STAGE				2.82	
Full-grown larvae			96.4		0.84 = k_1
Attacked by *Cyzenis*	86.9	551.6	90.2	1.98	0.03 = k_2
Attacked by other parasites	6.7	6.2	87.6	1.95	0.01 = k_3
Infected by microsporidian	2.3	2.6	83.0	1.94	0.02 = k_4
	4.5	4.6		1.92	
PUPAL STAGE					0.47 = k_5
Killed by predators			28.4		
Killed by *Cratichneumon*	66.1	54.6	15.0	1.45	0.27 = k_6
	46.3	13.4		1.18	
ADULT STAGE					
Females climbing trees, 1956			7.5		

Figure 3.4 Winter moths in Wytham woods near Oxford, 1950–62: (a) population fluctuations for larvae and adults; (b) changes in mortality, expressed as k-values, for the six mortality factors in the accompanying life table. The biggest contribution to change in the generation mortality comes from changes in k_1, winter disappearance, which is the key factor for this population. Reprinted, with permission, from Varley *et al.* (1973).

be calculated:

$$T_c = \frac{\sum xl_xm_x}{\sum l_xm_x} = \frac{\sum xl_xm_x}{R_0}$$

age of cohort

In order to estimate R, we need to briefly consider the process of population growth. Taking the simplest model of population growth, the size of the population next year will depend on the number of individuals present this year and the average number of offspring produced per individual; in mathematical terms:

$$N_1 = N_0R$$

$$N_2 = N_1R = (N_0R)R = N_0R^2$$

$$N_3 = N_2R = (N_0R^2)R = N_0R^3$$
$$\vdots$$
$$N_T = N_0R^T$$

Repeated application of this simple model leads to the generalised equation.

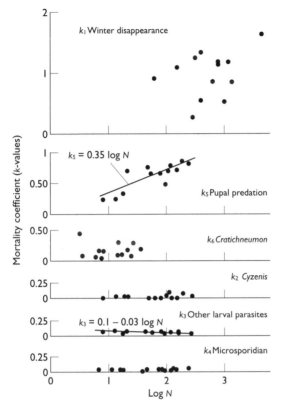

Figure 3.5 Relationship of winter moth mortality coefficients to population density. The *k*-values for the different mortalities are plotted against the population densities of the stage on which they acted. k_1 and k_6 are density independent and quite variable; k_2 and k_4 are density independent but constant; k_3 is inversely density dependent and k_5 is strongly density dependent. Reprinted, with permission, from Varley *et al.* (1973).

Where the generation rate of increase (R_0) and the generation time (T_c) are known, the size of the population after one complete generation is given by

$$N_T = N_0 R_0$$

Using the general equation we obtained above, we can write a second equation for the same population in terms of the annual rate of increase (R) and the generation time (T_c):

$$N_T = N_0 R^{T_c}$$

By comparing these two equations, it is clear that

$$N_T = N_0 R_0 = N_0 R^{T_c} \quad \text{and} \quad R_0 = R^{T_c}$$

Taking natural logarithms of both sides:

$$\ln R_0 = T_c \ln R$$

$$\ln R = \frac{\ln R_0}{T_c}$$

equal to the intrinsic rate of increase (r), the constant in $dN/dt = rN$, the differential equation for population growth

Table 3.3 Outline of life table calculations concerned with reproduction and population increase

Age class x (e.g. years)	Number of individuals alive (n_x)	Survivorship (l_x)	Average number of female offspring (m_x) produced by a female aged x	Contribution ($l_x m_x$) of each age class to R_0	$x l_x m_x$
0	250	1.0	0	0	0
2	120	0.48	125	60	120
3	75	0.3	300	90	270
4	55	0.22	175	38.5	154
5	0	0	–	0	0
				$R_0 = \sum l_x m_x = 248.5$	$\sum x l_x m_x = 544$

R_0 is the average number of offspring produced by an individual throughout its entire life

Estimate of mean generation time $\quad T_c = \dfrac{\sum x l_x m_x}{\sum l_x m_x} = \dfrac{544}{R_0} = \dfrac{544}{248.5} = 2.189$

Estimate of the intrinsic rate of increase $\quad r = \ln R = \dfrac{\ln R_0}{T_c} = \dfrac{\ln 248.5}{2.189} = 2.5196$

r is the rate parameter in the differential equation for exponential growth, which describes the potential growth of a population under unrestricted conditions. i.e. $dN/dt = rN$

$R = e^r$ is the net annual rate of population increase; when $r = 2.5196$ then $R = 12.423$. The difference equation for exponential growth is $N_{t+1} = RN_t$. In many texts R is represented by λ

In this example, since R is very large, the population is clearly capable of rapid increases of the type shown by crop pests such as aphids

This equation is only an approximation but generally performs well. A more detailed but readable account of the calculations may be found in Begon *et al.* (1996).

Life tables are normally based on population data organised by age; the fates of individuals are described using distinct age classes, often of equal length. But they may be constructed for data organised around life stages (egg, larva, first instar, etc.) which may not be of equal duration. Alternatively, individuals may be classified by size groups then analogous calculations are based on the probability that individuals survive from one size class to the next and the average number of offspring produced by individuals within a given size class. In this case, although a measure analogous to R_0 can be calculated and interpreted as average cohort offspring production, the calculations of T_c and R are largely meaningless. In order to apply life table analysis to such data, mortality between size classes must occur and individuals should only be capable of moving between size classes in one direction, e.g. individuals may increase in size only, and mortality must occur. Where these constraints are met, individual size is effectively a surrogate measure of age.

3.7 *Relating age to mortality*

The overall relationship between age and mortality can be seen from cohort survivorship curves produced by plotting the logarithm of either the number of individuals surviving (n_x) or l_x-values against age (x) or time (t). The plotted n_x and l_x values are often scaled so that the first value at $x = 0$ or $t = 0$ is 1000. This can be achieved by plotting log $1000 l_x$ in place of l_x-values; it has the advantage of aiding comparisons between cohorts of different initial sizes and also avoids the need to plot negative logarithms. Where the number of survivors of a mixed aged population is plotted against time, the resulting curves are called depletion curves. Three hypothetical survivorship curves are recognised (Figure 3.6). Type I curves occur where survivorship is initially high, decreasing rapidly

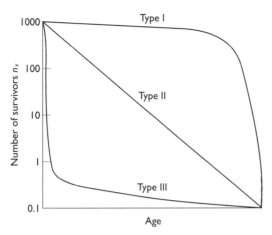

Figure 3.6 Hypothetical survivorship curves. Type I includes man, mammals and higher animals, often with parental care of young. Type II includes some birds and some invertebrates such as hydra. Type III includes some insects and many lower organisms with pelagic juvenile stages, such as benthic invertebrates, molluscs, oysters and fishes. Reprinted, with permission, from Stiling (1999).

in later life. This form of survivorship curve is associated with humans and other organisms that invest heavily in the parental care and the provisioning of a limited number of young. In contrast, type III survivorship curves are characteristic of species that produce large numbers of offspring but invest little in the protection and support of individual offspring; as a consequence, mortality is high during the early stages of life. Examples include many species of fish such as salmon and cod, and some annual plant species that produce many very small seeds. The straight line of the type II survivorship curves implies that the risk of mortality is constant throughout the life cycle. Examples includes many herbaceous perennials in stable habitats and, once fledged, many bird species also have type II survivorship curves. In practice, survivorship curves may fall anywhere between the two extremes of type I and type III.

Linear regression (Chapter 10) can be used to fit particular models of cohort decline to survivorship curves. Two models that have frequently been used are the exponential decay model and the power function model. The exponential model assumes a constant rate of mortality providing a quantitative description of type II survivorship curves. Where natural logarithms are used to plot the survivorship curve, the slope of the plot is equal to the decay constant of the exponential model. The exponential model allows the patterns of survival to be quantified in term of cohort half-lives, the time required for the size of the cohort to halve (Waite, 1984). Cohort half-lives are analogous to the decay half-lives of radionuclides; both assume that the underlying processes, mortality and the decay of atoms, occur at a constant rate. The power function models a situation where the rate of mortality is not constant but decreases with age; this pattern of mortality corresponds more closely to type III survivorship.

Exponential model $\quad n_t = n_0 e^{-ct} \quad$ Plot $\quad \ln n_t = \ln n_0 - ct$

Power function model $\quad n_t = n_0 t^{-b} \quad$ Plot $\quad \ln n_t = \ln n_0 - b \ln t$

where $\quad c =$ the decay constant for the exponential model
$\quad b =$ the decay constant for the power function model

Where linear regression is used to describe survivorship data, a significant linear relationship does not necessarily confirm that the model under test provides the best description of the process. For example, it had been assumed that the exponential model adequately described the mortality of seeds within the soil seed bank. Rees and Long (1993) reanalysed several classic data sets on the survival of buried viable seeds in soil seed banks and found that models in which the mortality was age dependent provided superior descriptions of the data. Fox (1993) provides a detailed description of several alternative models of 'failure events' that can be used to describe survivorship data where failure equates to organism death. The statistical procedures for testing goodness of fit are described in Chapter 2.

3.8 *Cohorts and life table parameters*

Several methods allow statistical comparisons to be made between cohort and life table parameters (Hutchings *et al.*, 1991; Stewart, 1994). In any given age class an individual may be either successful (alive) or unsuccessful (dead). If all individuals are initially equally likely to reach age x, and the success or failure of particular individuals is independent, then the number surviving to a given age class will follow a binomial distribution. The number of deaths will follow a multinomial distribution. Estimates for the variance of key life table parameters based on these assumptions are given in Table 3.4. Confidence limits may be set for life table parameters by using tabulated confidence intervals for the appropriate binomial distribution, or where the age class is sufficiently large (e.g. more that 50 individuals), the confidence limits can be calculated by assuming a normal distribution.

The hypothesis that the patterns of mortality shown by two or more cohorts are the same can be tested using the chi-squared test or the G-test. These tests provide flexible, robust and straightforward methods for analysing cohort data. The basic approach is outlined by Stewart (1994) and described below. A more sophisticated but closely related procedure, developed from a method presented by Pyke and Thompson (1986, 1987), is described by Hutchings *et al.* (1991). The null hypothesis that the cohort age-specific mortality rates are equal is easily tested. For example, if the survivorship of three cohorts is followed over a period of six age classes, the data collected can be presented as a simple contingency table with 3 rows (r), 6 columns (c) plus associated marginal column and row totals (Table 3.5). Using the normal method for analysing frequency values arranged in an $r \times c$ contingency table:

Table 3.4 Definition of life table parameters and estimates of variance

Symbol and definition	Estimate of parameter	Variance estimator
n_x = number of survivors at the beginning of age class x	observed number	$n_0 l_x (1 - l_x)$
d_x = number of deaths occurring in age class x	$d_x = n_x - n_{x+1}$	$\dfrac{d_x}{n_0}(n_0 - d_x)$
l_x = probability of an individual of the original cohort surviving to the beginning of age class x	$l_x = n_x / n_0$	$\dfrac{l_x}{n_0}(1 - l_x)$
p_x = probability that an individual who survived to the beginning of age class x will survive to age class $x + 1$	$p_x = n_{x+1} / n_x$	$\dfrac{p_x q_x}{n_x}\left(1 + \dfrac{1}{n_x} - \dfrac{1}{n_0}\right)$
q_x = probability that an individual who survived to the beginning of age class x will die in age class x ($q_x = 1 - p_x$)	$q_x = d_x / n_x$	$\dfrac{p_x q_x}{n_x}\left(1 + \dfrac{1}{n_x} - \dfrac{1}{n_0}\right)$

Table 3.5 Contingency table of d_x values, the number of deaths in each class for three cohorts

Cohort (rows)	Age classes (x)						Row totals (RT$_r$)
	0	*1*	*2*	*3*	*4*	*5*	
1	130	25	25	12	6	5	203
2	120	30	15	15	10	9	199
3	94	37	23	20	12	14	200
Column totals (CT$_x$)	344	92	63	47	28	28	602 (G)

1. Expected values are calculated for each cell of the table from the row, column and grand total. Expected values for row r and column $c = $ (sum of row r) × (sum of column c)/(grand total, G). The expected value for row 2 and column 3 of the table is

$$E_{23} = RT_2 \times (CT_3/G) = 199 \times \frac{47}{602} = 15.54$$

2. For each cell the difference between the observed value (O) and expected value (E) is calculated, squared and then divided by the expected value. For row 2 and column 3 we have

$$\frac{(O - E)^2}{E} = \frac{(15 - 15.54)^2}{15.54} = 0.0114$$

The size of this term, the residual, depends on the difference between the observed and expected cell values, and it reflects the contribution of this difference to the final X^2-value. Dividing the squared difference between observed and expected values by the expected cell value ensures that the final X^2-value is not unduly influenced by cells with large numerical values where larger deviations are likely to occur.

3. To obtain the test statistic X^2, all the values calculated in step 2 are summed for the complete table: $X^2 = \sum (O - E)^2/E$.

4. The degrees of freedom of X^2 are equal to (number of rows $- 1$) × (number of columns $- 1$) $= 2 \times 5 = 10$.

5. The calculated X^2 is compared with tabulated values of χ^2 (Appendix 3.2). If the value of X^2 exceeds the value of χ^2, the null hypothesis of equal mortality rates is rejected. If the value of X^2 is less than the value of χ^2, the null hypothesis is accepted.

This procedure is easily performed using MINITAB. The contingency table is entered as a series of columns of equal length. The required command can be entered directly as

MINITAB session window prompt.

```
MTB> CHISQUARE C1-C6
```

columns containing the data

Alternatively the **Chi-Square Test** option can be selected from the options listed under **Tables** obtained by selecting **Stat** on the main menu. Using this procedure to analyse the data set above produces the following output:

```
MTB > ChiSquare C1-C6.
```

Chi-Square Test

Expected counts are printed below observed counts

This reveals low expected values which may invalidate the test.

	C1	C2	C3	C4	C5	C6	Total
1	130	25	25	12	6	5	203
	116.00	31.02	21.24	15.82	9.44	9.44	
2	120	30	15	15	10	9	199
	113.71	30.41	20.83	15.54	9.26	9.26	
3	94	37	23	20	12	14	200
	114.29	30.56	20.93	15.61	9.30	9.30	
Total	344	92	63	47	28	28	602

```
ChiSq = 1.690 + 1.169 + 0.664 + 0.935 + 1.255 + 2.090 +
        0.347 + 0.006 + 1.630 + 0.019 + 0.060 + 0.007 +
        3.601 + 1.355 + 0.205 + 1.232 + 0.782 + 2.372 = 19.417
```

Allows the contribution of each cell to be seen; values are arranged in the same order as the original table. The first six values correspond to row 1 of the contingency table.

```
df = 10, p = 0.037
MTB >
```

The probability level for $X^2 = 19.417$ with d.f. $= 10$ is $p = 0.037$; this is lower than $p = 0.05$ (i.e. the 5% significance level) so the null hypothesis can be rejected and the alternative hypothesis that the mortality rates differ between the three cohorts is accepted. The results of the chi-squared test can be unreliable if expected cell values are ≤ 5.0; where this occurs, small values should be pooled so that at least 80% of the cells in the table have expected values ≥ 5.0. Where pooling is required, only adjacent cells should be pooled; and where several possible pairs of cells can be pooled, those that minimise differences between the marginal totals should be selected. The power of the test is greatest when the marginal totals are approximately equal (Kendall and Stuart, 1973). The analysis can be refined by partitioning the contingency table into subtables that are then analysed. In the most extreme case, an $r \times c$ table may be divided into $(r-1)(c-1)$ contingency tables, each one 2×2 and with a single degree of freedom, and each one uncorrelated with the others (Stewart, 1994). However, the table should be partitioned carefully and with due consideration given to the biology and ecology of the species being studied. Where multiple tests are undertaken, it increases the danger of committing a type I error – wrongly rejecting the null hypothesis. This problem is discussed further in Chapters 7 and 10. It should be clear from the example that the chi-squared test and the related *G*-test are extremely versatile and may be applied in many situations where count data can be arranged in a contingency table.

3.9 *Recommendations*

Estimating population size and density

The appropriate method for estimating population size depends on the nature of the species, the habitat in which the work is being conducted and the aims of the study. This makes it difficult to give specific recommendations, and only general guidance will be given here. Methods involving the capture of animals should only be undertaken when the investigator is certain that the anticipated level of trapping will not cause undue stress to the individuals caught and will not endanger local populations. Where capture-based methods are selected, a pilot study should be undertaken to determine the required trapping or sampling effort. This is particularly important with capture–mark–release methods. These procedures can be very time-consuming, costly and yield hardly any valuable information if insufficient animals are captured. Krebs (1999) provides a detailed discussion of these and related problems.

Without detailed information derived from either capture-based studies or direct observations of individuals, estimates of mortality rates and the construction of cohort life tables will not be possible. Indirect measures of species abundance, e.g. point and transect methods, may often be the most appropriate. Similarly, if reliable information can be obtained on the age structure of a population, the possibility of producing a static life table should be considered. Because of their dependence on the spatial distribution of individuals, plotless sampling methods should be used with care. If a plotless sampling procedure is chosen the T-square procedure is recommended (Box 3.3). The flow diagram below summarises the sequence of decisions required to select an appropriate procedure for estimating species abundance. Where the organism or items of interest are dispersed throughout a medium that can be easily diluted by mixing with an inert material and partitioned into replicated samples

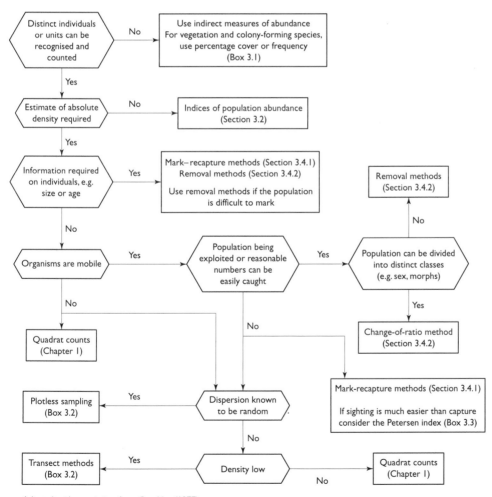

Adapted, with permission, from Caughley (1977)

in which the presence or growth of organisms can be easily scored, then the general MPN approach is worth considering (Section 3.5).

Analysis of cohort data

Where life table parameters are presented, the variance should be estimated and presented as either confidence limits or standard deviations. This is important. Parameter variance provides information on the reliability of estimated parameters, allows judgements to be made on whether observed differences between age class and cohorts may be significant; furthermore, the extent of variance may also be of direct biological or ecological interest. Not only is it of interest to know which life stages hold the greatest probability of mortality, it is also of interest to know which is the stage where the probability of mortality is most variable among members of the population. When differences between cohorts are to be tested, the tests are best carried out on d_x-values, i.e. the number of individuals dying during age class x; l_x-values will be highly dependent on one another and therefore not as useful (Stewart, 1994). Unless it is a primary aim, detailed modelling of survivorship curves is rarely warranted.

Appendix 3.1

The 95% confidence limits for a binomial distribution

Upper and lower 95% confidence limits for a population proportion. Confidence limits are read off the y-axis for an observed value of p on the x-axis. Sample sizes are marked on the contour lines. Reprinted, with permission, from N. Chalmers and P. Parker, 1986, *The OU Project Guide: Fieldwork and Statistics for Ecological Projects*, Field Studies Council, Taunton.

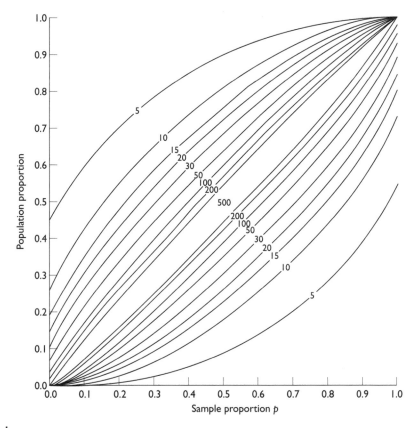

Figure 1

Appendix 3.2

Confidence limits for a Poisson frequency distribution

Given the number of organisms observed (x), this table provides the upper and lower limits from the Poisson distribution. Do not use this table unless you are sure the observed counts are adequately described by a Poisson distribution. When $x > 100$ use the normal approximation:

95% confidence limits of x

$$\text{Lower limit} = x - 0.94 - 1.96\sqrt{x - 0.02}$$
$$\text{Upper limit} = x + 1.94 + 1.96\sqrt{x + 0.98}$$

99% confidence limits of x

$$\text{Lower limit} = x - 0.99 - 2.576\sqrt{x + 0.33}$$
$$\text{Upper limit} = x + 2.99 + 2.576\sqrt{x + 1.33}$$

Appendix 3.2 Table

	95%		99%			95%		99%	
x	Lower	Upper	Lower	Upper	x	Lower	Upper	Lower	Upper
0	0	3.285	0	4.771	25	16.768	36.030	13.793	40.373
1	0.051	5.323	0.010	6.914	26	16.77	37.67	15.28	41.39
2	0.355	6.686	0.149	8.727	27	17.63	38.16	15.28	42.85
3	0.818	8.102	0.436	10.473	28	19.05	39.76	16.80	43.91
4	1.366	9.598	0.823	12.347	29	19.05	40.94	16.80	45.26
5	1.970	11.177	1.279	13.793	30	20.33	41.75	18.36	46.50
6	2.613	12.817	1.785	15.277	31	21.36	43.45	18.36	47.62
7	3.285	13.765	2.330	16.801	32	21.36	44.26	19.46	49.13
8	3.285	14.921	2.906	18.362	33	22.94	45.28	20.28	49.96
9	4.460	16.768	3.507	19.462	34	23.76	47.02	20.68	51.78
10	5.323	17.633	4.130	20.676	35	23.76	47.69	22.04	52.28
11	5.323	19.050	4.771	22.042	36	25.40	48.74	22.04	54.03
12	6.686	20.335	4.771	23.765	37	26.31	50.42	23.76	54.74
13	6.686	21.364	5.829	24.925	38	26.31	51.29	23.76	56.14
14	8.102	22.945	6.668	25.992	39	27.73	52.15	24.92	57.61
15	8.102	23.762	6.914	27.718	40	28.97	53.72	25.83	58.35
16	9.598	25.400	7.756	28.852	41	28.97	54.99	25.99	60.39
17	9.598	26.306	8.727	29.900	42	30.02	55.51	27.72	60.59
18	11.177	27.735	8.727	31.839	43	31.67	56.99	27.72	62.13
19	11.177	28.966	10.009	32.547	44	31.67	58.72	28.85	63.63
20	12.817	30.017	10.473	34.183	45	32.28	58.84	29.90	64.26
21	12.817	31.675	11.242	35.204	46	34.05	60.24	29.90	65.96
22	13.765	32.277	12.347	36.544	47	34.66	61.90	31.84	66.81
23	14.921	34.048	12.347	37.819	48	34.66	62.81	31.84	67.92
24	14.921	34.665	13.793	38.939	49	36.03	63.49	32.55	69.83

Appendix 3.2 Continued

	95%		99%			95%		99%	
x	*Lower*	*Upper*	*Lower*	*Upper*	*x*	*Lower*	*Upper*	*Lower*	*Upper*
50	37.67	64.95	34.18	70.05	80	62.81	99.17	58.35	105.66
51	37.67	66.76	34.18	71.56	81	63.49	99.17	60.39	106.12
52	38.16	66.76	35.20	73.20	82	64.95	100.32	60.39	107.10
53	39.76	68.10	36.54	73.62	83	66.76	101.71	60.59	108.61
54	40.94	69.62	36.54	75.16	84	66.76	103.31	62.13	110.16
55	40.94	71.09	37.82	76.61	85	66.76	104.40	63.63	110.37
56	41.75	71.28	38.94	77.15	86	68.10	104.58	63.63	111.78
57	43.45	72.66	38.94	78.71	87	69.62	105.90	64.26	113.45
58	44.26	74.22	40.37	80.06	88	71.09	107.32	65.96	114.33
59	44.26	75.49	41.39	80.65	89	71.09	109.11	66.81	114.99
60	45.28	75.78	41.39	82.21	90	71.28	109.61	66.81	116.44
61	47.02	77.16	42.85	83.56	91	72.66	110.11	67.92	118.33
62	47.69	78.73	43.91	84.12	92	74.22	111.44	69.83	118.33
63	47.69	79.98	43.91	85.65	93	75.49	112.87	69.83	119.59
64	48.74	80.25	45.26	87.12	94	75.49	114.84	70.05	121.09
65	50.42	81.61	46.50	87.55	95	75.78	114.84	71.56	122.69
66	51.29	83.14	46.50	89.05	96	77.16	115.60	73.20	122.78
67	51.29	84.57	47.62	90.72	97	78.73	116.93	73.20	124.16
68	52.15	84.67	49.13	90.96	98	79.98	118.35	73.62	125.70
69	53.72	86.01	49.13	92.42	99	79.98	120.36	75.16	127.07
70	54.99	87.48	49.96	94.34	100	80.25	120.36	76.61	127.31
71	54.99	89.23	51.78	94.35					
72	55.51	89.23	51.78	95.76					
73	56.99	90.37	52.28	97.42					
74	58.72	91.78	54.03	98.36					
75	58.72	93.48	54.74	99.09					
76	58.84	94.23	54.74	100.61					
77	60.24	94.70	56.14	102.16					
78	61.90	96.06	57.61	102.42					
79	62.81	97.54	57.61	103.84					

Source: Reprinted, with permission, from Crow and Gardner (1959).

MPN values and confidence limits

Most probable numbers for use with tenfold dilutions and five tubes per dilution

Appendix 3.3 Table I

p_1	p_2	Most probable number for indicated values of p_3					
		0	1	2	3	4	5
0	0	–	0.018	0.036	0.054	0.072	0.090
0	1	0.018	0.036	0.055	0.073	0.091	0.11
0	2	0.037	0.055	0.074	0.092	0.11	0.13
0	3	0.056	0.074	0.093	0.11	0.13	0.15
0	4	0.075	0.094	0.11	0.13	0.15	0.17
0	5	0.094	0.11	0.13	0.15	0.17	0.19
1	0	0.020	0.040	0.060	0.080	0.10	0.12
1	1	0.040	0.061	0.081	0.10	0.12	0.14
1	2	0.061	0.082	0.10	0.12	0.15	0.17
1	3	0.083	0.10	0.13	0.15	0.17	0.19
1	4	0.11	0.13	0.15	0.17	0.19	0.22
1	5	0.13	0.15	0.17	0.19	0.22	0.24
2	0	0.045	0.068	0.091	0.12	0.14	0.16
2	1	0.068	0.092	0.12	0.14	0.17	0.19
2	2	0.093	0.12	0.14	0.17	0.19	0.22
2	3	0.12	0.14	0.17	0.20	0.22	0.25
2	4	0.15	0.17	0.20	0.23	0.25	0.28
2	5	0.17	0.20	0.23	0.26	0.29	0.32
3	0	0.078	0.11	0.13	0.16	0.20	0.23
3	1	0.11	0.14	0.17	0.20	0.23	0.27
3	2	0.14	0.17	0.20	0.24	0.27	0.31
3	3	0.17	0.21	0.24	0.28	0.31	0.35
3	4	0.21	0.24	0.28	0.32	0.36	0.40
3	5	0.25	0.29	0.32	0.37	0.41	0.45
4	0	0.13	0.17	0.21	0.25	0.30	0.36
4	1	0.17	0.21	0.26	0.31	0.36	0.42
4	2	0.22	0.26	0.32	0.38	0.44	0.50
4	3	0.27	0.33	0.39	0.45	0.52	0.59
4	4	0.34	0.40	0.47	0.54	0.62	0.69
4	5	0.41	0.48	0.56	0.64	0.72	0.81
5	0	0.23	0.31	0.43	0.58	0.76	0.95
5	1	0.33	0.46	0.64	0.84	1.1	1.3
5	2	0.49	0.70	0.95	1.2	1.5	1.8
5	3	0.79	1.1	1.4	1.8	2.1	2.5
5	4	1.3	1.7	2.2	2.8	3.5	4.3
5	5	2.4	3.5	5.4	9.2	16	–

Source: Reprinted, with permission, from Cochran (1950).

Factors used when calculating the confidence limits for the MPN count

Appendix 3.3 Table 2

Number of tubes per dilution (n)	Factor for 95% confidence limits with indicated dilution ratios			
	2	4	5	10
1	4.00	7.14	8.32	14.45
2	2.67	4.00	4.47	6.61
3	2.23	3.10	3.39	4.68
4	2.00	2.68	2.88	3.80
5	1.86	2.41	2.58	3.30
6	1.76	2.23	2.38	2.98
7	1.69	2.10	2.23	2.74
8	1.64	2.00	2.12	2.57
9	1.58	1.92	2.02	2.43
10	1.55	1.86	1.95	2.32

Source: Reprinted, with permission, from Cochran (1950).

Appendix 3.4

Critical values for the chi-squared distribution

Appendix 3.4 Table

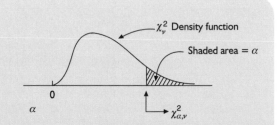

ν	.995	.99	.975	.95	.90	.10	.05	.025	.01	.005
1	0.000	0.000	0.001	0.004	0.016	2.706	3.843	5.025	6.637	7.882
2	0.010	0.020	0.051	0.103	0.211	4.605	5.992	7.378	9.210	10.597
3	0.072	0.115	0.216	0.352	0.584	6.251	7.815	9.348	11.344	12.837
4	0.207	0.297	0.484	0.711	1.064	7.779	9.488	11.143	13.277	14.860
5	0.412	0.554	0.831	1.145	1.610	9.236	11.070	12.832	15.085	16.748
6	0.676	0.872	1.237	1.635	2.204	10.645	12.592	14.440	16.812	18.548
7	0.989	1.239	1.690	2.167	2.833	12.017	14.067	16.012	18.474	20.276
8	1.344	1.646	2.180	2.733	3.490	13.362	15.507	17.534	20.090	21.954
9	1.735	2.088	2.700	3.325	4.168	14.684	16.919	19.022	21.665	23.587
10	2.156	2.558	3.247	3.940	4.865	15.987	18.307	20.483	23.209	25.188
11	2.603	3.053	3.816	4.575	5.578	17.275	19.675	21.920	24.724	26.755
12	3.074	3.571	4.404	5.226	6.304	18.549	21.026	23.337	26.217	28.300
13	3.565	4.107	5.009	5.892	7.041	19.812	22.362	24.735	27.687	29.817
14	4.075	4.660	5.629	6.571	7.790	21.064	23.685	26.119	29.141	31.319
15	4.600	5.229	6.262	7.261	8.547	22.307	24.996	27.488	30.577	32.799
16	5.142	5.812	6.908	7.962	9.312	23.542	26.296	28.845	32.000	34.267
17	5.697	6.407	7.564	8.682	10.085	24.769	27.587	30.190	33.408	35.716
18	6.265	7.015	8.231	9.390	10.865	25.989	28.869	31.526	34.805	37.156
19	6.843	7.632	8.906	10.117	11.651	27.203	30.143	32.852	36.190	38.580
20	7.434	8.260	9.591	10.851	12.443	28.412	31.410	34.170	37.566	39.997
21	8.033	8.897	10.283	11.591	13.240	29.615	32.670	35.478	38.930	41.399
22	8.643	9.542	10.982	12.338	14.042	30.813	33.924	36.781	40.289	42.796
23	9.260	10.195	11.688	13.090	14.848	32.007	35.172	38.075	41.637	44.179
24	9.886	10.856	12.401	13.848	15.659	33.196	36.415	39.364	42.980	45.558
25	10.519	11.523	13.120	14.611	16.473	34.381	37.652	40.646	44.313	46.925
26	11.160	12.198	13.844	15.379	17.292	35.563	38.885	41.923	45.642	48.290
27	11.807	12.878	14.573	16.151	18.114	36.741	40.113	43.194	46.962	49.642
28	12.461	13.565	15.308	16.928	18.939	37.916	41.337	44.461	48.278	50.993
29	13.120	14.256	16.147	17.708	19.768	39.087	42.557	45.772	49.586	52.333
30	13.787	14.954	16.791	18.493	20.599	40.256	43.773	46.979	50.892	53.672

Appendix 3.4 Table

ν	.995	.99	.975	.95	.90	.10	.05	.025	.01	.005
31	14.457	15.655	17.538	19.280	21.433	41.422	44.985	48.231	52.190	55.000
32	15.134	16.362	18.291	20.072	22.271	42.585	46.194	49.480	53.486	56.328
33	15.814	17.073	19.046	20.866	23.110	43.745	47.400	50.724	54.774	57.646
34	16.501	17.789	19.806	21.664	23.952	44.903	48.602	51.966	56.061	58.964
35	17.191	18.508	20.569	22.465	24.796	46.059	49.802	53.203	57.340	60.272
36	17.887	19.233	21.336	23.269	25.643	47.212	50.998	54.437	58.619	61.581
37	18.584	19.960	22.105	24.075	26.492	48.363	52.192	55.667	59.891	62.880
38	19.289	20.691	22.878	24.884	27.343	49.513	53.384	56.896	61.162	64.181
39	19.994	21.425	23.654	25.695	28.196	50.660	54.572	58.119	62.426	65.473
40	20.706	22.164	24.433	26.509	29.050	51.805	55.758	59.342	63.691	66.766

For $\nu > 40$, $\chi^2_{\alpha,\nu} \doteq \nu \left(1 - \dfrac{2}{9\nu} + z_\alpha \sqrt{\dfrac{2}{9\nu}} \right)^3$

Source: Reprinted with the permission of the trustees of *Biometrica* from E.S. Pearson and H.O. Hartley (eds), 1966, *The Biometrica Tables for Statisticians*, Vol. 1, 3rd edn.

Further reading

Blower, J.G., Cook, L.M. and Bishop, J.A. (1981) *Estimating the Size of Animal Populations*. Allen & Unwin, London.

Chalmers, N. and Parker, P. (1986) *The OU Project Guide: Fieldwork and Statistics for Ecological Projects*. Field Studies Council, Taunton.

Krebs, C.J. (1999) *Ecological Methodology*, 2nd edn. Addison Wesley Longman, Menlo Park, CA.

Sutherland, W.J. (ed.) (1996) *Ecological Census Techniques: A Handbook*. Cambridge University Press, Cambridge.

Chapter Four

Investigating spatial patterns

Summary

An understanding of pattern, the non-random distribution of entities (individuals) or events in time or space, is often fundamental to a study. This chapter presents methods that allow the occurrence of pattern to be detected and described. From the practical viewpoint of collecting data, it describes methods suitable for three basic sampling schemes: random quadrat samples (Section 4.3), non-random regular or contiguous sampling schemes (Section 4.4) and plotless sampling schemes (Section 4.5). In each case methods are presented for the analysis of binary (presence/absence) and continuous data sets. From a mathematical viewpoint, the methods involve either a comparison of the ratio of the sample mean and variance, or the analysis of ordered sequences or the distances between individuals or events. The use of descriptive and graphical procedures is outlined in Section 4.2.

4.1 *Introduction*

The identification and study of pattern are fundamental to environmental sciences and ecology. In the introduction to his seminal work, *Geographical Ecology*, MacArthur (1972) states:

> *To do sciences is to search for repeated patterns, not simply to accumulate facts, and to do the science of geographical ecology is to search for patterns of plant and animal life that can be put on a map.*

In practice MacArthur's influence extended well beyond the simple search for patterns in the spatial distributions of plants and animals, encompassing the study of pattern in the structure of communities, resource partition and utilisation. These later concepts, resource partition and utilisation, are linked to the idea and measurement of species niche and niche overlap, and they have played an important role in the development of ecology, particularly animal ecology (Kingsland, 1985; Begon *et al.*, 1996). Partly because of the sessile nature of plants, the study of spatial pattern has historically played a central role in botanical and geographical studies. However, these two topics of spatial pattern and resource utilisation are related. To a plant, space is a resource. Plants compete for space, and its occupation provides access to the other resources, e.g. light, water, soil nutrients (Silvertown and Lovett Doust, 1993).

Why should the detection of pattern be considered so important? Science assumes that the natural world is the result of a limited number of processes, some of which are known, others remain to be discovered and understood. The outcome of these processes is an apparently ordered or at least partially predictable world. We do not live in a completely chaotic world, pattern is evident all around us. The detection of non-random patterns is in part a confirmation of this. Non-random patterns have to be detected and described before the processes behind them can be explained.

The measurement of niche and niche overlap is explored in Chapter 5. This chapter is concerned with some of the methods available for the detection and description of spatial patterns. Although these methods are described in the context of analysing spatial pattern, many can be applied to the analysis of any sequential data, including time series. This chapter does not attempt to deal with the growing number of studies on the modelling of spatial patterns; a rigorous introduction to this area is given by Haining (1990), and Buckland and Elston (1993) provide a good example on how to model the spatial distribution of wildlife.

4.1.1 *Sampling*

Data for pattern analysis may be obtained from discrete sample units that may be natural, e.g. leaves, or artificial (arbitrary) such as quadrats. The information recorded from each sample unit will depend on the aims of the study. Depending on what is recorded, three types of data may be collected.

- Binary data, e.g. the presence or absence of a species
- Count data, e.g. the number of individuals present
- Continuous data, where the abundance of the species is recorded as a continuous variable, e.g. biomass or the percentage cover of the species (in plants studies)

Although some of the methods described in this chapter were originally developed to analyse count-based data, all of them can also be used to analyse continuous data. Data may be recorded for more than one variable or species at each sample unit or sample point; the analysis of each variable may then be conducted separately. The simultaneous joint analysis of patterns for more than two species or variables (i.e. multivariate analysis) is described in Chapters 8 and 9.

If the aim of the analysis is solely to detect the occurrence of a non-random distribution, i.e. the presence of a pattern, sample units need not be randomly selected. Where the null hypothesis is that the species is randomly distributed, there is little to be gained from the random selection of sample units. However, if the extent of deviation from random is to be assessed, or if different data sets are to be compared, sample units must be randomly selected. This also applies to the study of species association, where the null hypothesis is that the species are distributed independently of one another (Greig-Smith, 1983, Ch. 7). Bouxin (1991) states 'it is now clear that the random siting of sample units is not well adapted to pattern analysis'. Although the systematic or regular placement of sample units limits statistical analysis of the data, non-random placement allows the scale of the pattern to be investigated or at least described relatively easily. Pattern in vegetation has often been studied using transects or blocks of contiguous sample units (Figure 4.1). These sampling designs allow the values recorded from neighbouring sample units to be combined and treated as new sample units. Data obtained from a transect consisting of 32 contiguous quadrats may be rearranged by combining pairs of quadrats to give 16, which in turn may be rearranged to give 8 blocks each consisting of 4 quadrats. If each set of values is analysed in turn, the occurrence and intensity of pattern may be investigated at each of the block sizes. The use of a transect also allows the 'direction of pattern' to be investigated. For example, in habitats where there is a pronounced environmental gradient, such as a salt marsh, species may be

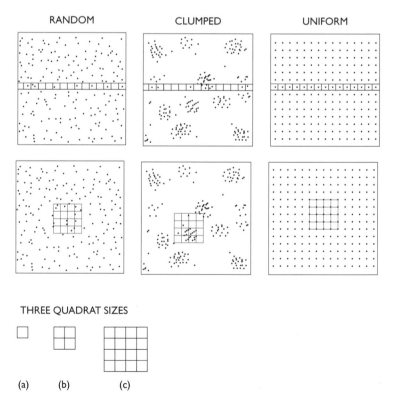

Figure 4.1 The upper diagram shows a transect and a square grid of quadrats used on random, clumped and uniform (regular) distributions. The lower diagram shows quadrats increasing in area by a factor of 4.

randomly distributed across the gradient but markedly clumped or regularly distributed along transects running in the direction of the major environmental gradient. With random placement the scale of pattern can only be investigated by repeating a study using quadrats of different sizes.

Besides collecting data from discrete sample units, several plotless methods also exist; they are based on analysis of these properties:

- Nearest-neighbour distance measured between randomly selected points and individuals or between individuals
- The spacing of points (or individuals) along a 'line' or narrow transect
- Polygons constructed around points or individuals

4.1.2 Some mathematical considerations

Number sequences
Whatever the combination of sampling scheme and sample units, the resulting data set can be presented as a sequence of numbers. If only presence and absence are recorded, the sequence will consist of a mixed string of 0s (absence) and 1s (presence). Where counts or other measures of abundance are recorded, a clumped or pattern distribution will be reflected in the values of the sequence. For data obtained from non-random samples, e.g. quadrats arranged along a transect, the order of values in the sequence as well as the variance of values is important. If clumping occurs, we would expect to find high values and low values clustered together. If the underlying distribution is regular or uniform, high and low values should be more evenly dispersed along the sequence. If the data is randomly distributed, i.e. no pattern is present, the occurrence of each value is completely independent of any other value.

Figure 4.1 shows three clear patterns of spatial distribution: random, regular and clumped. If each of the patterns is sampled using a quadrat of size (a), each time recording the number of points present, then we expect to obtain the following results.

Regular distribution   The number of points recorded in each quadrat varies relatively little from the overall mean; each quadrat contains similar numbers of points. For example, the sequence of 20 quadrat densities sampled from a regular (uniform) distribution of 45 individuals might be

$2, 3, 3, 3, 2, 1, 1, 2, 2, 3, 3, 2, 4, 2, 1, 2, 2, 2, 3, 2$

sequence mean $= 2.25$ sample variance $= 0.618$

variance $<$ mean

The extreme case is variance $= 0$, when each quadrat contains the same number of points.

Clumped distribution   The number of points recorded in each quadrat varies considerably from the overall mean; some quadrats outside of a clump would contain none or very few, whereas quadrats in a clump contain many. For example, the sequence of 20 quadrat densities sampled from a clumped (aggregated) distribution of 45 individuals might be

$0, 6, 5, 0, 1, 0, 0, 0, 4, 0, 0, 9, 0, 8, 0, 2, 0, 0, 6, 4$

sequence mean $= 2.25$ sample variance $= 9.355$

variance $>$ mean

Random distribution   The number of points recorded varies equally above and below the mean. For example, the sequence of 20 quadrat densities sampled from a random distribution of 45 individuals might be

$$2, 6, 3, 0, 0, 3, 3, 2, 2, 1, 3, 4, 3, 4, 0, 3, 2, 1, 2, 1$$

sequence mean $= 2.25$ sample variance $= 2.303$

variance $\cong$ mean

Note that in each case the mean density of points is the same, only the variance differs. Similar results would be obtained for both random and non-random placements of quadrats. These observations suggest that pattern may be detected by comparing the sample mean and variance; this is indeed the case. For a random distribution the values follow a Poisson distribution, which is characterised by the mean being equal to the variance. Writing σ^2 for the variance and μ for the mean, we have the following results:

- Random: $\sigma^2 = \mu$, a property of the Poisson distribution
- Clumped: $\sigma^2 > \mu$, a property of the negative binomial distribution
- Regular: $\sigma^2 < \mu$, a property of the positive binomial distribution

By using a distribution model with the appropriate properties, expected values may be calculated and then compared with the observed values. The extent of the differences between predicted values and observed values can be used to assess the pattern of distribution. In practice the most commonly used methods adopt the null hypothesis of a random distribution, often using the Poisson distribution to generate expected values. However, several authors suggest that the uniform distribution provides a more appropriate null hypothesis (Bouxin, 1991; Smallwood, 1993). Pielou (1977) points out that, besides the commonly used distributions (given above), other distributions may be equally appropriate.

The results obtained from sampling the clumped distribution in Figure 4.1 will depend on the size of the quadrat. As quadrat size approaches the average size of the clumps, moving from (a) to (b), variation in the number of points recorded will increase. Maximum variation will occur when the quadrat size is equal to the scale of the clumps. This means the quadrat size must be stated clearly when reporting the results of any study on pattern. The dependence of variance on sample unit size can be exploited to investigate the scale of clumping. Note that patterning may occur at many different scales within the same study site. For example, a species may demonstrate a clumped distribution at one scale, but within a clump individuals may be randomly or regularly distributed. A range of 'mixed' patterns may occur, each operating at different spatial or temporal scales. The detection and description of such mixed patterns is not possible when only one sample unit size is used. Where complex patterning is thought to exist, use a range of sample unit sizes and sampling schemes. Kershaw and Looney (1983) provide a good introduction to the different scales of pattern in vegetation, explaining how and why they occur.

4.1.3 A guide to the methods

The procedures in this chapter are only a small selection of those available. They should make it possible to analyse the majority of data sets encountered in ecological and environmental studies. The appropriate method will depend on the chosen sampling scheme and the nature of the data. Patterns may also be investigated by measuring the distances between points or individuals. Whether the sampling scheme is random or regular does not necessarily

Table 4.1

Sample unit placement	Data type	Methods (relevant sections)	Comments
Random	Counts and continuous variables	Distribution methods (4.3)	Poisson model normally most appropriate (4.3.1) Insensitive unless reasonably large sample sizes, i.e. >50. For small sample sizes use index of dispersion (4.3.4)
		Descriptive measures of the centre and dispersal of points (4.2.2)	Graphical method for describing the centre of distribution of points defined by x and y coordinates
Regular: sequential, time or transect series	Counts	Graphical analysis of ordered sequences of numbers (4.2.1)	Can be used to analyse presence and absence data
Regular: sequential, time or transect series	Binary and count data	Non-parametric procedures for the analysis of sequences (4.4.4)	
Regular: sequential, time or transect series and contiguous schemes	Counts and continuous variables	Non-parametric procedures for the analysis of sequences (4.4.4) The analysis of contiguous quadrats (4.4)	Range of methods
Plotless sampling	Continuous variables (distances)	Plotless sampling schemes (4.5)	

determine which methods can or cannot be used. Some methods may be applied to more than one type of data. But when using a regular or contiguous arrangement of sample points, the sequence of recorded values can contain important information on the scale of pattern. Data collected from randomly placed sample points must not be treated as an ordered sequence. A general guide to the selection of procedures is given in Table 4.1.

4.2 *Graphical and descriptive methods*

4.2.1 *Ordered sequences of numbers*

The statistical properties of random sequences provide a simple method for the detection of pattern. Using the example given by Harsch (1991), consider a sequence of numbers with values that range from 0 to 6. A random sequence may be generated from a random string of 0s and 1s that have been summed for *non-overlapping* blocks of six digits. Moving along the line in one direction and considering each value in turn, a series of jumps or transitions from one value to the next will be encountered (0 to 1, 0 to 2, etc.). The frequency of each transition may be summarised in a correlogram (Table 4.2). The mean jump for each value of x (each row) is obtained by multiplying the size of the jump by its frequency, summing the results for each row and dividing by the frequency of x (i.e. the row

Table 4.2 Correlograms produced for two sequences of numbers: (upper) constructed from a random sequence of numbers with values ranging from 0 to 6; (lower) produced from a non-random sequence constructed by summing overlapping sextets of random 0s and 1s. Adapted from Harsch (1991).

from digit x	to digit y 0	1	2	3	4	5	6	frequency $f(x)$	mean jump $j(x)$
0	–	–	1	3	2	–	–	6	+3.17
1	1	1	17	19	10	3	3	54	+2.06
2	2	9	33	61	41	12	3	161	+1.11
3	3	20	62	78	45	16	2	226	−0.12
4	–	16	32	48	25	7	5	133	−1.08
5	–	7	12	12	8	5	1	45	−2.11
6	–	1	4	5	2	2	1	15	−2.80

from digit x	to digit y 0	1	2	3	4	5	6	frequency $f(x)$	mean jump $j(x)$
0	3	3	–	–	–	–	–	6	+0.50
1	3	29	22	–	–	–	–	54	+0.35
2	–	22	80	59	–	–	–	161	+0.23
3	–	–	59	115	52	–	–	226	−0.03
4	–	–	–	52	56	25	–	133	−0.20
5	–	–	–	–	25	13	7	45	−0.40
6	–	–	–	–	–	7	8	15	−0.47

total $f(x)$):

$$\text{mean } j(x) = \sum \frac{f(x,y)(y-x)}{f(x)}$$

where $f(x,y)$ is the frequency of jumps from x to y, $(y-x)$ is the size of the run, and $f(x)$ is the frequency of value x in the sequence.

Consulting the upper correlogram in Table 4.2 and working along the row from left to right, the mean jump for $x = 0$ is

$$j(0) = \frac{1 \times (2-0) + 3 \times (3-0) + 2 \times (4-0)}{1+3+2} = \frac{19}{6} = +3.17$$

The lower correlogram in Table 4.2 has been produced in the same way from a second number sequence, this time generated by summing overlapping blocks of six random 1s or 0s. In each case the overlap was the same: digits 1 to 6 summed, then 2 to 7, 3 to 8, etc. The resulting sequence of numbers will again vary from 0 to 6, but it will no longer be truly random. Each value will be largely dependent (5/6) on the previous number. Inspection

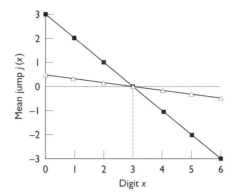

Figure 4.2 The fitted line crosses $j(x) = 0$ when $x = 3.0$; this is the value of the sequence mean. Reprinted, with permission, from Harsch (1991).

of these two correlograms shows that the non-random sequence of numbers exhibits a restricted range of transitions (jumps).

If the mean jump $j(x)$ is plotted against the value of the first digit, a straight line is produced for each set of data. In both cases the fitted line crosses the horizontal axis when x equals the sequence mean, here 3.0, and marks the point where the mean jump is zero (Figure 4.2). Where the sequence is random, the slope of the fitted line is $R = 1.0$. If the numbers are not independent of one another then $R < 1.0$. In the second sequence $R = 1/6$, which indicates that the sequence is not random and provides a measure of the degree of independence between successive values. As the distribution of values becomes more uniform, the slope of the line will decrease and the range of x-values will become progressively constricted. A clump distribution will produce a non-linear plot and the line will tend to zigzag, certain jumps being considerably more frequent than others. This method provides an easy, if time-consuming, way of testing for randomness in any data set which may be represented as an ordered number sequence. Many types of phenomena may be summarised in this way, e.g. the occurrence and magnitude of events in time or the sequence of particular amino acids coded as numbers. If required, the value of R may be determined and tested for significant deviation from 1.0 using linear regression (Chapter 10).

4.2.2 *Descriptive measures of the centre and dispersal of points*

Geographers routinely use a number of simple descriptive statistics to summarise spatial data (Ebdon, 1985; Burt and Barber, 1996). Many of these procedures deserve wider application. Given a list of values (x_i to x_n) we are generally happy to use the mean m ($m = \sum x_i/n$) and the standard deviations ($s^2 = \sum (x - m)^2/(n - 1)$) to measure the central tendency and dispersal (spread) of values (Box 1.3). The mean centre of distribution (c.o.d.) for a collection of points may be obtained by simply calculating the mean x-coordinate and the mean y-coordinate (Figure 4.3). This approach may be extended to include values of variables measured at each point to give a weighted mean centre of distribution. For example, suppose that the abundance of a species was recorded at a number of mapped points. The weighted mean centre of species distribution is obtained by calculating the mean x-coordinate and mean y-coordinate, each multiplied by an appropriate weighting factor, here species abundance. The resulting weighted mean represents the centre of species distribution and

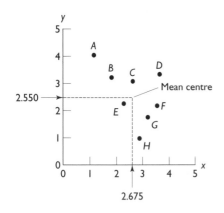

Point	Coordinates	
	x	y
A	1.2	4.0
B	1.8	3.2
C	2.7	3.0
D	3.7	3.2
E	2.3	2.2
F	3.6	2.1
G	3.2	1.7
H	2.9	1.0
n = 8	$\Sigma x = 21.4$	$\Sigma y = 20.4$

$$\bar{x} = \frac{21.4}{8} = 2.675 \qquad \bar{y} = \frac{20.4}{8} = 2.550$$

Coordinates of mean centre are 2.675, 2.550

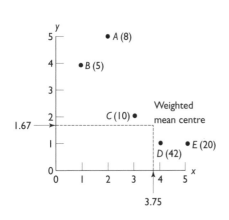

Point	Coordinates		Weight	Weighted coordinates	
	x	y	(w)	xw	yw
A	2	5	8	16	40
B	1	4	5	5	20
C	3	2	10	30	20
D	4	1	42	168	42
E	5	1	20	100	20
			85	319	142

$$\bar{x}_w = \frac{\Sigma xw}{\Sigma w} = \frac{319}{85} = 3.75$$

$$\bar{y}_w = \frac{\Sigma yw}{\Sigma w} = \frac{142}{85} = 1.67$$

Coordinates of weighted mean centre are 3.75, 1.67

Figure 4.3 The mean centre of distribution (c.o.d.) for a collection of points may be obtained by calculating the mean *x*-coordinate and the mean *y*-coordinate (top). The process may be adapted to calculate a weighted mean c.o.d. Reprinted, with permission, from Burt and Barber (1996).

abundance:

Coordinates of mean c.o.d.

$$\bar{x} = \sum_{i=1}^{n} \frac{x_i}{n} \qquad \bar{y} = \sum_{i=1}^{n} \frac{y_i}{n}$$

Coordinates of weighted mean c.o.d.

$$\bar{x}_w = \sum_{i=1}^{n} \frac{w_i x_i}{w_i} \qquad \bar{y}_w = \sum_{i=1}^{n} \frac{w_i y_i}{w_i}$$

where x, y = the *x* and *y* coordinates of point *i*
  w_i = the weighting factor for point *i*
  $\bar{x}, \bar{y}$ = the mean values of *x* and *y*

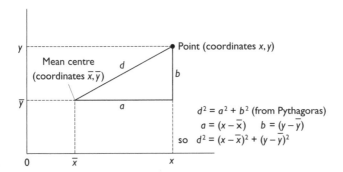

Figure 4.4 Using Pythagoras's theorem to calculate distances from coordinates.

The dispersion of points may be assessed by calculating the mean of the distances between the centre of the distribution and each individual point. Where the distance between the mean centre and each point is unknown, the relevant distances may be calculated from coordinate values using Pythagoras's theorem (Figure 4.4):

$$\text{Standard distance} = \sqrt{\frac{1}{n}\sum_{i=1}^{n} d_i^2}$$

$$= \sqrt{\frac{1}{n}\sum_{i=1}^{n}(x_i - \bar{x})^2 + (y_i - \bar{y})^2} \qquad \text{(from coordinates)}$$

where d_i is the distance from the mean centre of distribution to point i, $\bar{x}$ and $\bar{y}$ are the coordinates of the mean centre. By replacing the x_i, y_i values with their corresponding weighted values $(x_i w_i, y_i w_i)$ and $\bar{x}, \bar{y}$ with the coordinates of the weighted mean centre, a corresponding weighted standard distance can be calculated. Alternatively the standard deviation of x and y values may be used to assess the spread of points. Standard distances may be depicted as circles about the mean centre. Similarly, the standard deviation of x and y may be used to draw an ellipse about the mean centre, the axes of the ellipse being parallel to the x and y axes. In practice the dispersion of points about the mean centre will be best represented by a deviational ellipse that is not oriented parallel to the x and y axes. Ebdon (1985) describes how deviational ellipses can be derived by transposing and rotating the axes so that the long axis of the ellipse is oriented along the direction of maximum dispersion.

4.3 *Distribution methods*

4.3.1 *Poisson series: random pattern* $(\sigma^2 = \mu)$

The Poisson distribution provides a model for discrete random processes that can be used to generate a series of expected values. These values may then be compared with observed values using standard goodness-of-fit tests such as the *G*-test and the chi-squared test. If the observed and expected values differ significantly, the null hypothesis of a random distribution is rejected.

Expected values are calculated using the Poisson series:

$$p(0) = e^{-m}, \quad p(1) = m^1\frac{e^{-m}}{1!}, \quad p(2) = m^2\frac{e^{-m}}{2!}, \quad \cdots, \quad p(x) = m^x\frac{e^{-m}}{x!}$$

$x!$ is x factorial, e.g. $4! = 4 \times 3 \times 2 \times 1$

where $p(x)$ = the probability of a sample unit containing x individuals

[For example, $p(0)$ = the probability of a sample unit containing no individuals, $p(1)$ the probability of a sample unit containing 1 individual, $p(2)$ the probability of containing 2.]

m = the overall mean, i.e. the total number of counts divided by the number of sample units

$e = 2.718\,18$

Expected counts are obtained by multiplying the appropriate probabilities, $p(x)$ values, by the total number of sample units, N. Thus the expected number of sample units containing two records is $E(2) = p(2)N$. Notice that e^{-m} occurs in all the terms as a constant. Once the first term in the series, $p(0)$, has been calculated, the other terms may be easily generated from it by using the recurrence relationship $p(x) = (m/x)p(x-1)$. For example, $p(6) = (m/6)p(5)$. This relationship allows the required probabilities to be calculated easily using a hand calculator. Alternatively, expected values may be generated directly using MINITAB. The use of the Poisson series is illustrated in Box 4.1.

4.3.2 Negative binomial distribution: clumped pattern ($\sigma^2 > \mu$)

The negative binomial distribution is frequently used to model clumping. If a data set follows the negative binomial distribution, individuals are clumped rather than randomly distributed. To test the goodness of fit, expected values must first be calculated. The expected probabilities for sample units containing x records is given by

$$p(x) = \left(\frac{m}{m+k}\right)^x \left(\frac{(k+x-1)!}{x!\,(k-1)!}\right)\left(1 + \left(\frac{m}{k}\right)\right)^{-k}$$

This is not the most friendly of equations! However, $p(x)$ values can be obtained relatively painlessly. Notice that the formula requires only two parameters, k and m, to be known. As with the Poisson series, m is simply the overall sample mean, i.e. the mean number of individuals per sample unit. Parameter k measures the degree of clumping; the smaller the value of k, the more clumped the distribution. As the extent of clumping increases, k tends to 0. When $k > 8$ it indicates that the distribution is approaching a Poisson distribution, i.e. random. The size of k is related to the variance (S^2) and mean (m) of the data set (Southwood, 1978):

$$\frac{\sqrt{S^2}}{m} = \sqrt{\frac{1}{k} + \frac{1}{m}}$$

Notice that this is the formula for the coefficient of variation, $CV = S/m$.

The value of k may be estimated using various methods. An accurate estimate of k can be obtained using an iterative method described in Southwood (1978) and Ludwig and Reynolds (1988). However, a good approximation, adequate in most cases, may be obtained from the sample mean (m) and variance (S^2):

$$k = \frac{m^2}{S^2 - m}$$

Once k and m are known, the $p(x)$ values can be obtained by using a calculation scheme from Fowler *et al.* (1998):

$$p(x) = \frac{k + (x-1)}{x} Fp(x-1)$$

where F is a constant equal to $m/(m+k)$.

Box 4.1   **Poisson and negative binomial distributions**

Nereis diversicolor is a common intertidal polychaete worm found in the sands and muds of the middle and lower seashore. It is normally associated with brackish water and found on the muddy shores, especially where freshwater seepage occurs. In a study of the distribution of *N. diversicolor* the number of individuals in 50 randomly located sediment cores, 15 cm in diameter and 30 cm deep, was recorded. The Poisson and negative binomial series were used to examine the distribution of the species:

Total number of worms	90
Number of sediment cores (N)	50
Mean density of worms per core (m)	1.80
Variance of worm density (s^2)	2.856

Since $s^2 > m$ the binomial distribution may be rejected as a suitable model. The question is now whether the difference between s^2 and m is sufficient to allow the rejection of the Poisson distribution and whether the negative binomial distribution provides an adequate model of the data.

Calculating the expected $p(x)$

Poisson distribution

The $p(x)$ values may be calculated using the relationship $p(x) = (m/x)p(x-1)$, where the value $p(0)$ needed to initiate the sequence is equal to e^{-m}. Alternatively they may be generated easily using MINITAB. In this case the required MINITAB commands are as follows:

```
MTB > PDF C1;          ←— C1 contains the list of x-values, 1 to 8
SUBC> Poisson 1.80.    ←— specifies mean of required distribution
K      P(X = K)
0.00 0.1653
1.00 0.2975
2.00 0.2678
3.00 0.1607
4.00 0.0723
5.00 0.0260
6.00 0.0078
7.00 0.0020
8.00 0.0005
```

The command can be obtained from the *Calc* pull-down menu. Select *Probability Distributions* followed by the *Poisson* option. The mean, m = 1.80, is then entered as requested.

output of probability values used for the Poisson distribution

Negative binomial distribution

Calculate values for k, F and $p(0)$:

$$k = m^2/(s^2 - m) = (1.80)^2/(2.856 - 1.80) = 3.068$$

$$F = m/(m + k) = 1.80/(1.80 + 3.068) = 0.3698$$

$$p(0) = (1 + m/k)^{-k} = (1 + 1.80/3.068)^{-3.068} = 0.2426$$

Table 1 Goodness-of-fit test for Poisson and negative binomial models

Number of worms present in sample x	Observed number of sediment cores O(x)	Poisson model $p(x)$			Negative binomial model $p(x)$		
		Expected probability of cores with x worms, $p(x)$	Expected number of sediment cores, $E(x) = p(x) \times 50$	$(O - E)^2/E$	Expected probabilities of cores with x worms, $p(x)$	Expected number of sediment cores, $E(x) = p(x) \times 50$	$(O - E)^2/E$
0	18	0.1653	8.265	11.466	0.2626	13.13	1.806
1	1	0.2975	14.875	12.942	0.2752	13.76	11.833
2	17	0.2678	13.39	0.973	0.2070	10.35	4.273
3	7	0.1607	8.035	0.133	0.1293	6.465	0.044
4	3						
5	2	0.1087	5.435	0.451	0.1259	6.295	0.079
6	2						
>6	0						
Totals	50	1.0	50	$25.965 = \chi^2$ (d.f. = 3)	1.0	50	$18.037 = \chi^2$ (d.f. = 3)

Using the recurrence relationship

$$p(x) = \frac{k + (x - 1)}{x} F p(x - 1)$$

$p(0) = 0.2626$

$p(1) = 3.068 \times 0.3698 \times 0.2426 = 0.2752$

$p(2) = ((3.068 + 1)/2) \times 0.3698 \times 0.2752 = 0.2070$

$p(3) = ((3.068 + 2)/3) \times 0.3698 \times 0.2070 = 0.1293$

$p(4) = ((3.068 + 3)/4) \times 0.3698 \times 0.1293 = 0.0725$

Calculation ended here to avoid low expected values less than 5, $p(4)N = 0.0725 \times 50 = 3.625$.

$p(> 4) = 0.0534$ (by summing the above probabilities and subtracting from 1.0)

These values are used to calculate the expected values for sediment cores containing x worms (Table 1).

Calculating the index of dispersion (ID)

Calculate values for ID, χ^2 and d.

$$\text{ID} = S^2/m = 2.856/1.80 = 1.587$$

$$\chi^2 = \text{ID}(N - 1) = 1.587(50 - 1) = 77.747$$

$$d = \sqrt{2\chi^2} - \sqrt{2(N - 1) - 1} = \sqrt{2 \times 77.747} - \sqrt{(2 \times 49) - 1}$$

$$= \sqrt{155.494} - \sqrt{97} = 2.620$$

Therefore $d > 1.96$ and the null hypothesis is rejected. The distribution of worms is significantly clumped or aggregated.

The χ^2-value obtained for the Poisson model is highly significant ($p < 0.005$), allowing the null hypothesis to be rejected. The d-value obtained from calculating the index of dispersion, also indicates that the distribution of *N. diversicolor* among sediment cores is not random but clumped. Here both methods lead to the same conclusion, but this is not always the case. Greig–Smith (1983) describes circumstances where the two methods may yield different results; and because of this, Ludwig and Reynolds (1988) stress the need to use more than one method of analysis. Although the distribution of individuals is clumped, the significant χ^2 obtained for the fit of the negative binomial distribution ($p < 0.005$) indicates that this distribution does not provide a suitable model for the data set.

The values of $p(0)$ required to initiate the series is obtained from

$$p(0) = (1 + m/k)^{-k}$$

Thus to fit the negative binomial distribution, the sample mean and variance are first calculated and then used to estimate k and the factor F. The probability of a sample unit containing no individuals $p(0)$ is then calculated. The probabilities $p(1), p(2), \ldots, p(x)$ are obtained by multiplying the previous probability by the factor F and $(k + x - 1)/x$.

The expected numbers of sample units with $0, 1, 2, 3, \ldots, x$ individuals are obtained by multiplying the corresponding $p(x)$ values by N, the total number of sample units (e.g. the number of quadrats containing four individuals is $E(4) = p(4)N)$). These values may be compared with observed values using the standard goodness-of-fit tests (e.g. χ^2 and G). A worked example is given in Box 4.1.

The use of the negative binomial distribution to investigate pattern has been criticised. L.R. Taylor *et al.* (1978, 1979a) state that, although the negative binomial distribution provides a good description for a large number of data sets, a better description is often obtained from Taylor's power law (Section 4.3.1). They also state that k cannot be interpreted in any meaningful biological way. The use of k as a measure of aggregation suffers from two problems. Firstly, the variance of k varies with density (m) in a complex way. Secondly, although Waters (1959) correctly pointed out that $1/k$ tends to zero for a random distribution, this does not necessarily imply a random distribution; other factors may cause $1/k \to 0$ (L.R. Taylor *et al.*, 1979a).

4.3.3 The binomial distribution: uniform pattern ($\sigma^2 < \mu$)

The binomial distribution may be used to model uniformly distributed data, i.e. data sets for which the sample mean (m) is greater than the sample variance (S^2). As with the negative binomial distribution, two parameters need to be determined, k and ρ.

$$k = \frac{m^2}{m - S^2} \qquad \rho = \frac{m}{k}$$

This formula for k is the same as with the negative binomial distribution except that the order of S^2 and m is reversed, so the denominator is positive and therefore k is positive. This is necessary since $S^2 < m$ in a uniform distribution.

In this case k is equivalent to the highest number of records (individuals) that could be found in a sample unit and ρ is the probability that any point in a sample unit is occupied by an individual. The probability, q, that any point within a sampling unit is not occupied is $1 - p$. Once k and p have been estimated, expected probability values are calculated using the formula

$$p(x) = \frac{k!}{x!(k-x)!} \, p^x q^{(k-x)}$$

The expected number of individuals per sample unit is obtained by multiplying the appropriate probability value by N, the total number of sample units. Alternatively, expected values may be generated directly using MINITAB. These values are then compared with the observed frequency values. If the observed frequency and the expected frequency do not differ significantly, accept the null hypothesis that the data values are uniformly distributed according to the binomial distribution. A worked example is given in Box 4.1.

4.3.4 Index of dispersion

Several simple indices of dispersion have been based on the distribution models outlined above and the corresponding relationships between the sample variance and the mean. The simplest and most widely used is the mean–variance ratio, which is also known as the index of dispersion (ID):

$$\text{ID} = S^2/m$$

where $S^2 =$ the sample variance

        $m =$ the sample mean

If sample values are randomly distributed, i.e. they follow the Poisson distribution, S^2 and m should be equal and $\text{ID} = 1.0$. Significant departures from unity imply that the distribution is not random. $\text{ID} > 1.0$ suggests that values are clumped or aggregated, and $\text{ID} < 1.0$ implies a degree of overdispersion or a regular distribution. For small sample sizes $(N < 30)$ the significance of departures from unity may be tested using the chi-squared statistic:

$$\chi^2 = \text{ID}(N - 1)$$

where N is the number of sample units.

The interpretation of the resulting χ^2-value requires a little care:

- If χ^2 with $N - 1$ degrees of freedom falls between the tabulated values at the 0.975 and 0.025 probability levels, the null hypothesis of a random Poisson distribution with $S^2 = m$ is accepted.
- If χ^2 with $N - 1$ degrees of freedom is greater than the tabulated value at the 0.975 probability level, the null hypothesis is rejected, and a clumped or aggregated distribution is indicated, $S^2 > m$.
- If χ^2 with $N - 1$ degrees of freedom is less than the tabulated values at the 0.025 probability level, the null hypothesis is rejected and a regular or overdispersed distribution is indicated, $S^2 < m$.

Consider the critical values for χ^2 with d.f. $= 19$ (Table 4.3). The chart in Appendix 4.1 can be used instead of χ^2-tables. This clearly indicates the zones of χ^2-values associated with random, clumped and regular patterns. For $N > 30$ it is possible to use an alternative test statistic which follows a normal distribution:

$$d = \sqrt{2\chi^2} - \sqrt{2(N-1) - 1}$$

Table 4.3 Critical values for χ^2 with d.f. = 19

$p =$	0.005	0.025	0.05	0.9	0.95	0.975	0.999	0.995
χ^2	6.844	8.907	10.117	27.204	30.14	32.852	36.191	38.582
	Regular	→	←		Random distribution	→	←	Clumped

If $|d| \leq 1.96$ the null hypothesis is accepted; $d < -1.96$ suggests a regular distribution and $d > 1.96$ implies a clumped distribution.

The value of the index of dispersion (ID), or the mean–variance ratio, ranges from a minimum of 0 for a perfectly uniform distribution to a maximum of n, the total number of individuals in a sample at maximum clumping (i.e. all individuals occur in a single quadrat). David and Moore (1954) have proposed an index of clumping (IC) where $IC = ID - 1$. The index of clumping equals 0 for a random distribution, -1 when there is maximum regularity and $n - 1$ when there is maximum clumping. Although the index of dispersion (ID) is an extremely useful way of testing for pattern, and can be easily applied to a range of data sets, it is affected by the total number of individuals in the complete sample. To overcome the dependence of ID on n, R.H. Green (1966) suggests scaling the index (dividing through by $n - 1$) to provide a new index (GI) which allows the degree of clumping to be more easily assessed:

$$GI = \frac{(S^2/m) - 1}{n - 1} = \frac{ID - 1}{n - 1}$$

Green's index takes a value of 1.0 at maximum clumping, 0 for a random distribution and $-1/(n - 1)$ for a perfectly uniform distribution. The related indices of mean crowding and patchiness are described in Section 4.4.2.

4.3.5 Taylor's power law

Taylor has shown that, for many species, the sample variance (S^2) and mean (m) are related in an apparently simple and fixed way (L.R. Taylor, 1961; L.R. Taylor *et al.*, 1978). The relationship follows the power law; S^2 and m are linearly related when logarithms are taken:

$$S^2 = am^b$$

$$\log S^2 = \log a + b \log m$$

If Taylor's power law holds, plotting $\log S^2$ against $\log m$ will produce a straight line; the intercept on the vertical axis is equal to $\log a$ and the slope of the line is equal to b. The constant b has been viewed as a true population statistic, describing an intrinsic property of the spatial distribution of the population in a particular environment (L.R. Taylor, 1961; Southwood, 1978). The value of b varies with the pattern of the distribution and can be considered as an index of aggregation; $b = 1$ for a random distribution (i.e. $S^2 = m$), $b \to 0$ as the distribution becomes more regular, $b \to \infty$ as the distribution becomes clumped or aggregated. The constant a has no obvious simple interpretation but appears to be related to the nature and scale of the sampling scheme. However, if the distribution is random then $\log a$ should equal zero; that is, the line should go through the origin, so when $m = 1$, $S^2 = 0$.

To apply Taylor's power law, repeated random sampling is required. Values of m and S^2 for each sample must be calculated, logged and plotted. The value of the constants a and b, along with the model's overall goodness of fit, may be determined using linear regression.

If $\log a = 0$ and $b = 1.0$ the distribution is random; if $\log a \neq 0$ and $b > 1.0$ the distribution is clumped; if $\log a \neq 0$ and $b < 1.0$ the distribution is regular. It is therefore necessary to test whether the intercept is equal to zero and whether the slope is equal to 1.0.

To test whether $\log a = 0$

The standard error of the intercept of a regression line (SE_{int}) on the y-axis at $x = 0$ is given by

$$SE_{int} = \sqrt{S_y^2 \left(\frac{1}{n} + \frac{\overline{x^2}}{\sum x^2} \right)}$$

where $\overline{x^2}$ is the mean of x^2. Here each value of x corresponds to the logarithm of a sample mean. S_y^2 is the variance for all the values plotted on the y-axis, and each value plotted on the y-axis is the logarithm of a sample variance. SE_{int} is used to set confidence limits about the intercept; if 0 is outside the interval, it can be taken that the intercept differs significantly from zero (Sokal and Rohlf, 1987).

Uses of Taylor's power law

Taylor's power law has been successfully used to analyse many data sets (L.R. Taylor *et al.*, 1978, 1979a). By using the relationship to analyse data sets collected from distant sampling stations or data collected at single sampling points through time, Taylor's power functions have also been used to examine large-scale spatial pattern and the stability of populations (L.R. Taylor *et al.*, 1979b, 1980; A.D. Taylor, 1992).

Since Taylor's power law describes the relationship between the variance (S^2) and the mean (m) of a distribution, it has been used to determine the optimum sample size (Pringle and Giliomee, 1992) and appropriate transformation (Section 10.2.4) of the data before statistical analysis (Boag *et al.*, 1994). Where the data set fits the power relationship and the value of the parameter b is known, the following transformation will stabilise the population variance:

$$z = x^{1-b/2}$$

where x is the untransformed data value and z is the transformed value.

4.4 *Analysing contiguous quadrats*

The grouping of contiguously arranged quadrats provides a method for investigating the scale of pattern. Consider a data set consisting of species presence, density or abundance records obtained from a transect of 48 contiguously arranged quadrats. Neighbouring quadrats may be combined (values added together) repeatedly to give values for 24 sample units, each consisting of two smaller quadrats, i.e. of block size 2. This process may be continued to give 12 sample units of block size 4, then 6 of block size 8, and so on. Data collected from a square grid of quadrats may also be blocked in a similar way (Figure 4.1).

4.4.1 *Pattern analysis, analysis of variance in blocks (Block quadrat method)*

One approach to analysing counts and continuous data sets would be to calculate the mean–variance ratio for each block size in turn (Section 4.3.4). However, an alternative procedure, commonly known as pattern analysis, is claimed to be more efficient (Greig-Smith, 1952; Goodall, 1954). It uses a modified analysis of variance to partition the total amount of variance present in the data between the different block sizes. In practice, Pielou (1974) has shown that the results obtained (i.e. the relative amount of variance apparently associated with each block size) are the same as if the mean–variance ratios are calculated for each block size (Pielou, 1974). The procedure, as outlined below and in Table 4.4, is relatively straight-forward:

Table 4.4 The arrangement of the original data and its blocking in the calculation of blocked quadrat pattern analysis

	Block size					
	1	2	4	8	16	32
	$\dfrac{\sum x_1^2}{1}$	$\dfrac{\sum x_2^2}{2}$	$\dfrac{\sum x_4^2}{4}$	$\dfrac{\sum x_8^2}{8}$	$\dfrac{\sum x_{16}^2}{16}$	$\dfrac{\sum x_{32}^2}{32}$
SS =	$\dfrac{\sum x_1^2}{1} - \dfrac{\sum x_2^2}{2}$	$\dfrac{\sum x_2^2}{2} - \dfrac{\sum x_4^2}{4}$	$\dfrac{\sum x_4^2}{4} - \dfrac{\sum x_8^2}{8}$	$\dfrac{\sum x_8^2}{8} - \dfrac{\sum x_{16}^2}{16}$	$\dfrac{\sum x_{16}^2}{16} - \dfrac{\sum x_{32}^2}{32}$	
d.f. =	16 $(32 - 1 - 15)$	8 $(16 - 1 - 7)$	4 $(8 - 1 - 3)$	2 $(4 - 1 - 1)$	1 $(2 - 1)$	0
MS =	$\dfrac{SS}{16}$	$\dfrac{SS}{8}$	$\dfrac{SS}{4}$	$\dfrac{SS}{2}$	$\dfrac{SS}{1}$	

Transect of 32 basic units

1. For each block size the values are squared and summed to give $\sum x_i^2$, where i is the block size and corresponds to the number of basic sample units (e.g. quadrats) combined to produce each block size; x_i are the values recorded in each sample units at block size i.

2. Each of the $\sum x_i^2$ values is divided by the corresponding block size to give $(\sum x_i^2)/i$.

3. The sum of squares (SS) for each block size is then obtained by subtracting successive $(\sum x_i^2)/i$ terms from each other:

$$SS_1 = \frac{1}{1}\sum x_1^2 - \frac{1}{2}\sum x_2^2 \quad SS_2 = \frac{1}{2}\sum x_2^2 - \frac{1}{3}\sum x_3^2$$

$$SS_3 = \frac{1}{3}\sum x_3^2 - \frac{1}{4}\sum x_4^2 \quad \ldots$$

4. The degrees of freedom associated with each block size are then calculated. For block size n, d.f. = (number of values at block size $n - 1$) − (number of values at block size $n + 1$) − 1. Thus if there are 48 sample units of block size 1, d.f. = 48 − 24 − 1; for block size 2, d.f. = 24 − 12 − 1.

5. To obtain the mean of the squares (MS), usually called the mean square, the sum of squares (SS) is divided by the appropriate d.f. value. An MS value is calculated for each block size.

6. The MS values are then plotted against block size.

The MS values provide an estimate of the variance associated with each block size. Peaks in the plot of MS against block size are said to indicate the intensity of clumping and scale of pattern; the peak block size corresponds to the average scale of clumping. More than one peak may occur if clumping occurs at several scales, e.g. clumps within clumps. A flat, low plot suggests that the species is uniformly or regularly distributed. Depending on how the quadrats have been blocked, i.e. as a square grid or as a transect, peak MS values provide information on the mean area of clumping or the mean dimension for the scale of clumping (Kershaw, 1973).

Linking factors and covariance analysis
This form of analysis has historically been known as pattern analysis. Although originally developed to analyse density values, it can be used to analyse other measures of species abundance (e.g. local frequency and cover values). The method may be extended to investigate the relationships between pairs of species or environmental factors. Similar pattern analysis graphs, with peak variances at the same block size, suggests that either a direct relationship exists between the two variables or the operation of some unknown common factor, e.g. variation in habitat microclimate. The extent of the correlation between the two variables may be described by calculating the correlation coefficient (r), between the two variables at each block size (Chapter 7). The values of each variable, a and b (e.g. species A and B), are added together for each sample unit; they are then blocked and analysed as described above. The variance of the combined variables (V_{a+b}) is given by the corresponding MS value. From the rules for combining variances (Kershaw, 1961):

$$V_{a+b} = V_a + V_b + 2C_{ab} \qquad r = C_{ab}/\sqrt{V_a V_b}$$

where V_a and V_b are the variances of a and b; they can be estimated from the MS values obtained using separate pattern analysis of each variable. C_{ab} is the covariance between a and b.

Values of r or covariance (C_{ab}) are plotted against block size. Positive values of r (i.e. large C_{ab}) suggest that the distributions of the two variables vary in a similar way with changes in scale. Negative values of r suggest that the variables respond differently with changes in scale. If the two variables are distributed independently of each other, the expected values of r and C_{ab} are zero. Although Goldsmith *et al.* (1986) suggest that the significance of r may be tested, this cannot be justified since the estimates of variance at each block size are not independent (see below). Whether C_{ab} or r is plotted against block size, it is instructive to plot V_{a+b} against block size. This is particularly useful when examining the segregation and aggregation of species (Chapter 7). If a and b are both species, the plot of V_{a+b} provides information about the distribution of individuals regardless of species (Dale and Powell, 1994).

The two-termed local quadrat method

In the original procedure, before analysis the data is blocked by pairing neighbouring quadrats. Block sizes increase by a factor of 2. This blocked-quadrat method is inefficient, since it loses any information on patterns at uneven block sizes (e.g. 3, 5, 7). To avoid this, Hill (1973) proposed the two-term local quadrat variance method. Here the blocks are formed by sequentially adding the neighbouring quadrat values to each other to give non-overlapping block sizes of 1, 2, 3, 4, etc. (Figure 4.5). Ludwig and Reynolds (1988) give a formula for the direct calculation of block variance for quadrats arranged in a contiguous transect, where N is the total number of quadrats and x_i is the values recorded in the ith quadrat. Each squared term is divided by the number of values enclosed in brackets.

Variance block size 1

$$= \left(\frac{1}{N-1}\right)\left(\tfrac{1}{2}(x_1 - x_2)^2 + \tfrac{1}{2}(x_2 - x_3)^2 + \cdots + \tfrac{1}{2}(x_{N-1} - x_N)^2\right)$$

Variance block size 2

$$= \left(\frac{1}{N-3}\right)\left(\tfrac{1}{4}(x_1 + x_2 - x_3 - x_4)^2\right.$$
$$\left. + \tfrac{1}{4}(x_2 + x_3 - x_4 - x_5)^2 + \cdots + \tfrac{1}{4}(x_{N-3} + x_{N-2} - x_{N-1} - x_N)^2\right)$$

The variances for higher block sizes are calculated by extended analogous equations. The first term has the form $1/(N - b - 1)$ where b is the block size.

Paired-quadrat variance method

In the paired-quadrat variance method, blocked data is obtained by combining pairs of quadrats at different spacings (Goodall, 1974; Ludwig and Goodall, 1978). The block sizes correspond to the distances that separate the combined quadrats. At spacing level 1, each uncombined quadrat is treated as a separate value. At spacing 2, neighbouring contiguous quadrats are combined: 1 and 2, 2 and 3, 3 and 4, etc. At spacing 3, each of the paired quadrats is separated by one quadrat: quadrats 1 and 3 are combined, then 2 and 4, 3 and 5, 4 and 6, 5 and 7, etc. The process is continued and the spacing between the pairs of quadrats is extended by 1 at each stage (Figure 4.5). The resulting plots of the variance against spacing level provide information on the grain of pattern present, i.e. the spacing between patches of individuals. Ludwig and Reynolds (1988) give the following formulae to calculate the variance at each spacing level for quadrats arranged in a contiguous transect:

Spacing level 1

$$= \left(\frac{1}{N-1}\right)\left(\tfrac{1}{2}(x_1 - x_2)^2 + \tfrac{1}{2}(x_2 - x_3)^2 + \cdots + \tfrac{1}{2}(x_{N-1} - x_N)^2\right)$$

BELT TRANSECT OF CONTIGUOUS QUADRATS

1	2	3	4	5	6	7	8

GRID OF CONTIGUOUS QUADRATS

1	2	3	4
5	6	7	8
9	10	11	12

Blocked quadrat method	Block size	Quadrats		Block size	Quadrats
BQV	1	(1) (2) (3) (4) (5) (6) (7) (8)		1	(1) (2) (3) (4) (5) (6) (7) (8)
	2	(1,2) (3,4) (5,6) (7,8)		2	(1,2) (3,4) (5,6) (7,8) or (1,5) (2,6) (3,7) (4,8)
	4	(1,2,3,4) (5,6,7,8)		4	(1,2,3,4) (5,6,7,8) or (1,2,5,6) (3,4,7,8)
TTLQV	1	(1) (2) (3) (4) (5) (6) (7) (8)		1	(1) (2) (3) (4) (5) (6) (7) (8)
	2	(1,2) (3,4) (5,6) (7,8)		2	(1,2) (3,4) (5,6) (7,8) or (1,5) (2,6) (3,7) (4,8)
	3	(1,2,3) (4,5,6)		3	(1,2,3) (5,6,7) or (1,2,5) (6,7,3) or
	4	(1,2,3,4) (5,6,7,8)			(2,3,4) (6,7,8) or (3,4,8) (2,6,7)

Paired quadrat method	Spacing	Quadrats		Spacing	Quadrats
PQV	1	(1) (2) (3) (4) (5) (6) (7) (8)		1	(1) (2) (3) (4) (5) (6) (7) (8)
	2	(1,2) (2,3) (3,4) (4,5) (5,6) (6,7) (7,8)		2	(1,2) (2,3) (3,4) (5,6) (6,7) (7,8)
	3	(1,3) (2,4) (3,5) (4,6) (5,7) (6,8)			or (1,5) (2,6) (3,7) (4,8) (1,6) (2,5) (2,7) (6,3) (3,8) (7,4)
	4	(1,4) (2,5) (3,6) (4,7) (5,8)		3	(1,3) (2,4) (5,7) (6,8)
	5	(1,5) (2,6) (3,7) (4,8)			or (1,7) (2,8) (5,3) (6,4)
	6	(1,6) (2,7) (3,8)			or (1,9) (2,10) (3,11) (4,12)
	7	(1,7) (2,8)			or (1,11) (3,9) (4,10) (2,12)
				4	etc.

Figure 4.5 How to obtain blocked data in the paired-quadrat variance method.

Spacing level 2

$$= \left(\frac{1}{N-2}\right)\left(\tfrac{1}{2}(x_1 - x_3)^2 + \tfrac{1}{2}(x_2 - x_4)^2 + \cdots + \tfrac{1}{2}(x_{N-2} - x_N)^2\right)$$

Spacing level 3

$$= \left(\frac{1}{N-3}\right)\left(\tfrac{1}{2}(x_1 - x_4)^2 + \tfrac{1}{2}(x_2 - x_5)^2 + \cdots + \tfrac{1}{2}(x_{N-3} - x_N)^2\right)$$

where N is the total number of quadrats and x_i is the value recorded in the ith quadrat. The equation for spacing level 1 is the same as the equation for blocked quadrats with block size 1. The variances for higher spacing levels are calculated using analogous equations. The first term has the form $1/(N - s)$ where s is the spacing level.

Note that these formulae cannot be applied directly to data sets obtained from blocking quadrats arranged in a grid. When quadrats are arranged in a grid, they may be combined in several ways (Figure 4.5). Quadrats arranged in a belt transect can only be grouped by combining either adjacent quadrats or quadrats at some set distance along the transect. But in a grid, a quadrat may be combined with up to eight neighbours, four adjacent to the sides and four on the diagonals (touching the quadrat at the corners). Not all of these combinations are equivalent. The range of possible combinations provides the investigator with a subtle method for examining variations in pattern. However, care must be taken when deciding how quadrats are blocked. The blocking procedure must be consistent at each blocking size.

Problems associated with these methods

The pattern analysis methods outlined above, and the numerous variations that exist, all suffer from two fundamental problems:

- The precision of estimated block size variances decreases with block size. As the block size increases, the number of values available to estimate the variance at each block size rapidly becomes smaller, reducing the reliability of the estimated block variance.

- Estimates of block size variances are not independent, hence statistical comparisons cannot be made between block size variances.

A partial solution to the first problem is simply to limit the block size to a maximum of $N/10$. If this is done then the variance estimates will still be based on unequal sample sizes, but the estimate of variance at the largest block size will be based on at least 10 values. The second problem is more difficult to solve. The problem of non–independence arises from the procedure of combining values into blocks. Where sample sizes are large ($N > 200$) the paired-quadrat method may generate independent estimates of variance if quadrat pairs are randomly selected (without replacement) at different spacing levels (Goodall, 1974; Ludwig and Reynolds, 1988). An approach advocated by Ludwig and Goodall (1978) is to randomly partition the data set into two subsets. One set is used to identify block sizes associated with peak variance. The second subset is then used to test the significance of the variance at these block sizes *only*. However, to completely overcome the problem, each peak variance should be assessed using a separate subset of data. To make this approach work, it requires very large data sets which can be partitioned into subsets of sufficient size. Attempts have been made to infer the statistical significance of block variances by comparing them with variances generated from simulated random distributions of points. For example, by analysing 1000 trials of randomly distributed points in an $n \times n$ square grid of quadrats, Dale and Powell (1994) found that the variance $E[V_r]$ was approximately equal to $2X/3n^2$, where X is the total number of points distributed in the grid. As one would expect for a random distribution, $E[V_r]$ varied little with block size. They suggest, based on the central limit theorem, that the variance will be approximately normally distributed.

The contiguous arrangement of quadrats also generates problems. Pielou (1974) points out that a row or grid of quadrats is a single entity. A set of N quadrats arranged in a row or a square grid is only one of an infinite number of sets that could be sampled in an area. An arrangement of N contiguous quadrats represents a sample size of 1, not N. Observations on pattern – based on the analysis of a single row or grid of quadrats – will provide no information on the variability of the results or how representative they are. The only solution to this problem is to replicate both the sampling and analysis.

Given the inherent problems of sampling and analysis, procedures based on the analysis of variance of blocked data should only be treated as descriptive or exploratory. Despite these shortcomings Bouxin (1991), who provides a detailed review of pattern analysis, considers the contiguous arrangements of quadrats to be the most effective sampling method currently available for investigating the scale of pattern. Bouxin suggests that future developments will come from the application of non-parametric models of distribution and Monte Carlo test procedures to assess the model's goodness of fit and the significance of any indices derived from the chosen distribution model.

4.4.2 Indices of pattern intensity

Since analysis of variance of blocked data should only be used as a tool (see above), an alternative is to calculate Lloyd's (1967) index of mean crowding and the patchiness at each block size:

$$\text{Index of mean crowding} \quad m^* = m + (S^2/m - 1)$$

this corresponds to David and Moore's (1954) index of clumping (IC) based on the mean–variance ratio (Section 4.3.4)

As before, m is equal to the mean density and m^* is equal to the mean number of other individuals per individual present in a quadrat at that block size; m^* measures the density or intensity of clumping at the scale of the block size. Once m^* has been calculated, an index of patchiness may be obtained:

$$\text{Index of patchiness} \quad P^* = \frac{m^*}{m} = 1 + \frac{1}{k}$$

The term $1/k$ provides another measure of the distribution of individuals among sample units. Where the data follows a negative binomial distribution, the index is related directly to k, the parameter of the negative binomial distribution (Section 4.3.2). Where the distribution does not fit the negative binomial distribution, $1/k$ should be interpreted simply as the proportion by which mean crowding exceeds mean density.

Although these indices are described in terms of species or point densities, as with the block variance procedures, an alternative measure of abundance may be used. This approach simply involves plotting indices, based on the mean–variance ratios against block size. As before, the presence and height of any peaks reflect the intensity and scale of pattern. However, since block size mean–variance ratio (ID), m^* and P^* values may be readily interpreted (unlike MS values), this approach can provide a more meaningful description of the data and it is advocated here.

4.4.3 Correlogram analysis: Autocorrelation analysis

Where data sets consist of an ordered sequence of values, as with data obtained from contiguously arranged quadrats, it is possible to calculate a series of correlation coefficients between the values $x_1, x_2, x_3, \ldots, x_{n-s}$ and values s units farther along the sequence, $x_{1+s}, x_{2+s}, x_{3+s}, \ldots, x_n$. The value of s is called the lag. Each serial coefficient, r_s, is a measure of the degree of interdependence between any observation and the corresponding observation s units along the sequence. Once calculated, a correlogram is produced by plotting serial correlation coefficients against the lag. This procedure is more commonly known as autocorrelation and is frequently used to detected temporal pattern in time sequence data. The plotted correlogram is often called an autocorrelation function (ACF). If the original sequences of values are random, serial correlation values should be low and the correlogram plot should show no consistent trend. Over a long random sequence, the autocorrelation coefficients should equal zero. High autocorrelation values and the presence of a consistent trend in the correlogram plot imply the presence of a non-random distribution.

Autocorrelation analysis may be performed by calculating the correlation coefficient (Chapter 7) between values separated by an appropriate lag. MINITAB provides the command **LAG**, which allows a series of sequences with appropriate lags to be easily generated from the original data. For example, suppose that column C1 contains the original sequence of values, the command **LAG 2 C1 C2** generates a sequence of lag 2 from the values in C1 and places them in column C2. The analysis may be completed by correlating the values stored in C1 and C2 using the command **CORRELATE C1 C2**.

Although this procedure is straightforward, it is tedious to repeat it for each lag size. Fortunately, the process can be performed in one step for all the required lag sizes using the procedures supported by MINITAB for time series analysis. MINITAB also allows partial autocorrelation to be undertaken. The partial autocorrelation at lag s measures the strength of autocorrelation of lag s, allowing for the effects of autocorrelation at short lag lengths (Brown and Rothery, 1993). Many other statistical packages (e.g. SPSS) also support these procedures and allow a correlogram to be produced automatically. A worked example using MINITAB is given below. Two points should be noted:

- The number and size of lags is limited by the length of the original sequence of values. As the size of the lag increases, the number of values available to be correlated decreases by s, the size of the lag. As a default for small data sets ($n < 250$ values) MINITAB[1] normally sets the maximum number of lags as equal to $n/4$. Thus if $n = 100$ the lag size will vary from 1 to 25. At the largest lag size, the number of values available for calculating the autocorrelation is $100 - 25 = 75$. With small data sets, care must be taken to ensure that sufficient values exist to allow the reliable calculation of the correlation coefficient. Pielou (1974) suggests that the largest lag should be set to equal no more than 10% of n.

- Autocorrelation coefficients are not independent, so statistical significance should not be attributed to an individual value. The sampling distribution of the autocorrelation coefficients is extremely complex and beyond the scope of this book; for a more detailed introduction see Brown and Rothery (1993). One generalisation is important and can be presented here; for a random sequence the autocorrelation coefficients should be distributed with a mean of zero and a variance of $1/n$. Thus 95% confidence limits will be approximately $\pm 2/\sqrt{n}$. By plotting these limits about zero on a correlogram, points departing significantly from the random model may be identified. Some statistical packages support more advanced methods that allow the significance of autocorrelation coefficients to be assessed.

The autocorrelation graphs in Figure 4.6 were produced using an early version of MINITAB. Three data sets, each containing 40 values, were analysed; REG a regular sequence of increasing and decreasing numbers formed by repeating 0 2 4 6 8 6 4 2 0; RAN a random sequence of numbers; OX,2 the densities of *Chrysanthemum leucanthemum* (ox-eye daisy) plants recorded from a contiguous transect of forty 20 cm × 10 cm quadrats on a north-facing calcareous grassed bank in southern England. In each case the autocorrelation was performed using the command **MTB > ACF C1**. Here C1 represents the column number or name in which the data is stored. This command may also be executed by selecting the **Stat** option at the top of the screen, followed by the **Time Series** and **Autocorrelation** options. The default number of lags was set at $\sqrt{n} + 10$.

The regular cyclic pattern of clumping present in the REG data set is clearly evident in Figure 4.6a. High serial correlation coefficients are present at lags 1, 4, 9 and 13. The lack

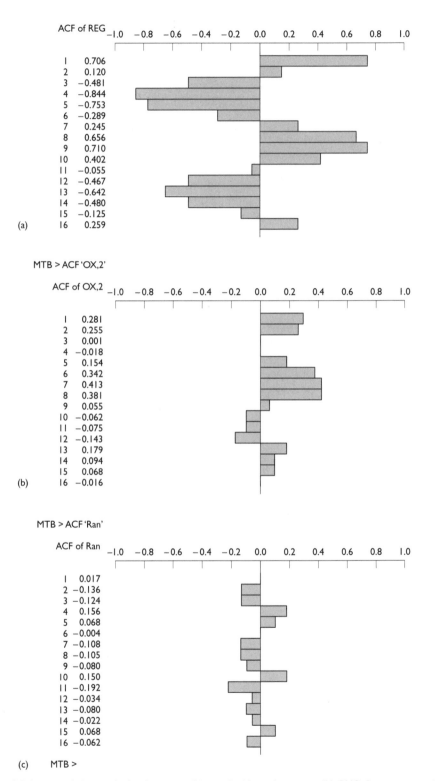

Figure 4.6 Autocorrelation graphs for the ox-eye daisy study: (a) regular pattern, (b) OX,2 shows some positive correlation at lags 6, 7 and 8, (c) random pattern.

of any significant autocorrelation for the RAN data set is also clearly shown (Figure 4.6c). Regardless of lag, all serial correlation coefficients for this data set are less than 0.2. In comparison, the autocorrelation diagram for the OX,2 data set suggests there is a degree of dependence (positive correlation) between the density of plants in the quadrats at lags 6, 7 and 8 (Figure 4.6b).

4.4.4 Non-parametric procedures for analysing sequences

Non-parametric tests do not require the data to follow a normal distribution. They are considered to be robust procedures, i.e. not strongly influenced by the particular characteristics of a data set. However, they tend to be less sensitive to the detection of pattern than parametric tests, which assume that the data values follow a normal distribution.

Runs or randomisation test
Where results may be summarised as a sequence of binary records, e.g. the presence or absence of a species at equally spaced points along a transect or records from contiguous quadrats, the non-parametric numbers-of-runs test can be used to test for randomness. If the results are clumped, the sequence will contain runs of recorded presence (+) interspersed with negative records (−). But if the results are regularly dispersed, positive records should be equally spaced along the sequence, separated by groups of negative records. The number of runs may be used to test for a departure from a random distribution.

A run is simply a sequence of neighbouring records of the same type:

```
                                                             9       12
      - - - - - + + + + + + - - - + + + + - - - - - - - - - + + + + + + - - - - - + - - + + + + - - + + + + +
Runs  1         2            3     4       5                 6        7    8  10  11
```

In this sequence there are 12 runs, i.e. 12 changes of sign, and the species occurs at 28 of the 53 sample points. The expected number of runs for a random distribution, $E(R)$, and the variance, $V(R)$, may be calculated exactly:

$$E(R) = \frac{2n_1 n_2}{n_1 + n_2} + 1 = \frac{2n_1 n_2}{N} + 1$$

$$V(R) = \frac{2n_1 n_2(2n_1 n_2 - n_1 - n_2)}{(n_1 + n_2)^2(n_1 + n_2 - 1)} = \frac{2n_1 n_2(2n_1 n_2 - n_1 - n_2)}{N^2(N - 1)}$$

where n_1 is the number of positive records and n_2 is the number of negative records; $n_1 + n_2$ is equal to N, the total number of records in the sequences. With $n_1, n_2 \geq 20$ the sampling distribution closely approximates to a normal distribution, and significant departure from randomness may be tested by calculating the standard normal deviate, z:

$$z = \frac{R - E(R)}{\sqrt{V(R)}}$$

If $|z| > 1.96$ then the number of runs differs significantly from random at the 5% probability level ($p < 0.05$), and the null hypothesis that the species is distributed randomly along the sequence is rejected. Significant positive z-values, $R > E(R)$, indicate regularity, negative z-values, $R < E(R)$, indicate clumping. For small samples, where n_1 and n_2 lie between 2 and 20, the upper and lower numbers of runs at the 5% probability level can be read directly from the tables in Appendix 4.2.

For the sequence given above, $N = 53$, $n_1 = 28$ and $n_2 = 25$; therefore

$$E(R) = \frac{2(28 \times 25)}{53} + 1 = 27.415$$

$$V(R) = \frac{2(28 \times 25)[2(28 \times 25) - 28 - 25]}{53^2(53 - 1)} = 12.910$$

$$z = \frac{R - E(R)}{\sqrt{V(R)}} = \frac{12 - 27.415}{\sqrt{12.90}} = -4.2919$$

Since $|z| > 1.96$ the null hypothesis of randomness is rejected. The negative sign indicates that the distribution of the species is clumped. Quantitative or continuous data sets may be analysed using this method by classifying values into two distinct classes. For example, if the abundance of a species along a transect is recorded, the data can be divided into two groups if records are scored as $+$ or $-$. Quadrats in which the abundance is greater than the mean are scored $+$; the remaining quadrats, where species abundance is below average, are scored $-$.

MINITAB runs test

MINITAB supports two versions of the runs test described above. The **RUNS** procedure performs a non-parametric two-sided runs test on a sequence of values stored as a column of values. The procedure can be set by the user to test two distinct but related hypotheses: that the number of runs above or below the median of the sequence is consistent with a random sequence of values; or that the number of runs above or below a level K is consistent with a random sequence. With K set to 1 the randomness of a sequence of presence and absence is effectively tested.

```
MTB > Runs 'OX,2'.
```

'OX,2' is a column heading; it contains the densities of *Chrysanthemum leucanthemum* (ox-eye daisy) plants recorded in 40 contiguous 20 cm × 10 cm quadrats. The transect was on a north-facing calcareous grassed bank in southern England.

The test is conducted by selecting the **Stat** menu then the **Nonparametrics** option and finally **Runs Test**. The default option analyses runs above and below the median.

```
Runs Test                        Output
OX,2
K = 2.1750 Median of values
The observed number of runs = 10
The expected number of runs = 16.9500
11 Observations above K   29 below
    The test is significant at 0.0050
```

The results of the test indicate that ox-eye daisy plants are not distributed randomly along the transect. Compare this result with the autocorrelation analysis carried out on the same data set and described in Section 4.4.3. Both suggest that the distribution of plants along the transect is not random.

Later editions of MINITAB provide **%RRUN**, a more sophisticated version of the runs test which performs one-sided tests and plots the data so that runs above and below the median (or mean) can be seen. This form of the test is normally used for product quality control. Typically, samples from a particular part of a production line are measured, generating a sequence of values. If the process is stable, values will vary only slightly, and the

Table 4.5 The runs test is able to distinguish four conditions

Test for randomness	Condition	Indications
Number of runs about the median	More runs observed than expected Data values fluctuate about the median; few values near the median	Data from two populations, i.e. a mixture, suggesting values influenced by presence of two or more processes operating at different levels
Number of runs about the median	Less runs observed than expected	Clustering of data, i.e. data values aggregated within the sequence
Number of runs up or down	More runs observed than expected Data values oscillate up and down rapidly along the sequence	The process is oscillating, i.e. the distribution of values is regularly dispersed, with runs of high values separated by runs of low values
Number of runs up or down	Less runs observed than expected Data contains few runs; sequences are characterised by long run of values above or below the median	There is a trend in the sequence values

pattern of variation should be random about the mean or median. Many of the data sets met in ecological studies are analogous to this situation, as they are ordered sequences of values separated by time or distance. As before, the basis of the test is to compare the number of runs above or below the median (or mean) with the expected number assuming a random distribution. The test statistic approximates to the standard normal distribution. The procedure also examines the numbers and lengths of runs up and down, i.e. above and below the median (or mean), allowing the presence of trends and clustering to be determined. The test procedure is able to distinguish four conditions present in a data set (Table 4.5).

Here is a **%RRUN** analysis of the ox-eye daisy data. The output is given in Figure 4.7. Further details of the method may be found in the MINITAB reference manual.

```
MTB > %Rrun ;              Command for test.
SUBC> Csub 'OX,1' 1;
SUBC> Medians.            Csub gives the location of data (OX,1) and stipulates that each
                          value is to be treated as a single value (1), i.e. the data is not to
                          be grouped and runs are to be identified with reference to the
                          median of the data.
```

This procedure can also be run by selecting the **Stat** menu then **Quality Tools** and finally **Run Chart**. The analysis suggests that a significant degree of clustering is present along with a significant trend. An apparent trend is due to the long right-hand tail of quadrats that contained no plants or very few plants (Figure 4.7). Here the trend should probably be considered as an artefact of the specific location and ending of the transect. A longer or shorter transect or a transect located in a different position might not give the same result for the presence of a trend, or indeed significant clustering (clumping).

Turning point analysis

Pielou (1974) describes a non-parametric method for analysing sequential data obtained from the contiguous arrangement of quadrats as used in pattern analysis (Section 4.4.1). This

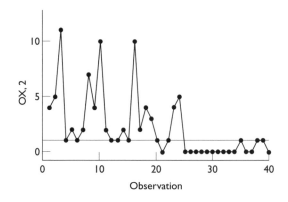

Number of runs about median	12.0000	Number of runs up or down	20.0000
Expected number of runs	20.2000	Expected number of runs	26.3333
Longest run about median	16.0000	Longest run up or down	10.0000
Approx p-value for clustering	0.0031	Approx p-value for trends	0.0075
Approx p-value for mixtures	0.9969	Approx p-value for oscillation	0.9925

Figure 4.7 Run chart for OX,2.

method has a wide range of possible applications and is similar to the number-of-runs test. It is based on the detection of turning points, i.e. local peaks or troughs in species abundance. Three consecutive numbers are needed to define a turning point. Comparing one number in the sequence with the next, there are three possible outcomes: the next number is smaller, the two numbers are the same, the next number is larger. For the numbers 1, 2, 3 there are only 6 possible sequences.[2] Two of them do not contain a turning point:

1 2 3
3 2 1

And four of them do contain a turning point:

1 3 2
2 1 3
2 3 1
3 1 2

Thus, the probability that three randomly arranged numbers contain a turning point is $4/6 = 2/3$. Since the first and last numbers in a sequence cannot be turning points, the expected number of turning points in a random sequence of N numbers is

$$E(\tau) = \tfrac{2}{3}(N - 2)$$

The variance of τ can be calculated (Kendall and Stuart, 1966) and used to give a standardised measure of sequential dependence, T (Pielou 1974):

$$V(\tau) = \frac{16N - 29}{90} \qquad T = \frac{E(\tau) - \tau}{\sqrt{V(\tau)}}$$

Both of these methods may be applied to blocked data. But as discussed in Section 4.4.1, the blocks are not independent. This means the results cannot be used to assess the significance at a particular block size of apparent departures from a random distribution.

4.5 *Plotless sampling schemes*

In addition to being used to estimate density (Chapter 1), several plotless sampling measures have been suggested for detecting pattern (Diggle, 1983). The majority of these methods depend on measuring the distances between pairs of nearest neighbours, or measuring the distance between a randomly selected point and its nearest neighbour. Ludwig and Reynolds (1988) provide a very clear and concise commentary on these methods and they recommend the use of the T-square index of spatial pattern.

4.5.1 *T-square index of spatial pattern*

In this procedure N random or regular[3] sample points are selected. At each sampling point, the distance from the selected point to the nearest relevant neighbour (1) is recorded (distance x), then the distance (y) from this individual to its nearest neighbour (2) in a direction *away* from the original sample point is recorded. This sampling scheme is sometimes known as a T-square sampling, because the second selected individual (2) should always be above an imaginary perpendicular line at point 2, which forms a T-shape (Figure 4.8). Based on these distance measures, it is possible to calculate an index $C = A/N$ with

$$A = \sum_{i=1}^{N} \frac{x_i^2}{x_i^2 + \frac{1}{2}y_i^2}$$

where x_i and y_i are the corresponding paired distance values for sample point i.

If the distribution of individuals is random then $E(x^2) = \frac{1}{2}E(y^2)$ and C should equal $\frac{1}{2}$. E stands for the expected value; in this case $E(x^2) \equiv$ mean of x^2. For a random distribution the mean of the distance x squared should equal half the mean of the distance y squared. If the distribution of individuals is uniform then $E(x^2) < \frac{1}{2}E(y^2)$ and $C < \frac{1}{2}$. If the distribution of individuals is clumped then $E(x^2)\frac{1}{2} < E(y^2)$ and $C > \frac{1}{2}$.

Since the index C is approximately normally distributed with a variance estimated by $1/12N$ (Ludwig and Reynolds, 1988), significant departures of C from the expected values

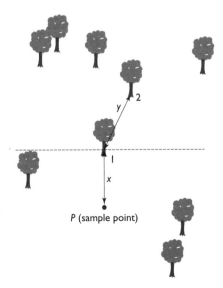

Figure 4.8 T-square sampling.

of 0.5 can be tested by calculating z-values:

$$z = \frac{C - 0.5}{\sqrt{1/12N}}$$

i.e. the difference between the recorded and expected values of C, divided by the estimated standard deviation of C. Although small sample sizes are not recommended, a t-statistic could be used instead where $N < 30$.

4.5.2 Sample point to individual index of spatial pattern

An alternative index proposed by Johnson and Zimmer (1985) is based on analysing only the sample point to individual distances (x). The index of dispersion (I) is calculated using the formula

$$I = (N + 1) \sum_{i=1}^{N} (x_i^2)^2 \Big/ \left(\sum_{i=1}^{N} x_i^2 \right)^2$$

For a random distribution $I = 2.0$; for a uniform distribution $I < 2.0$; and for a clumped distribution $I > 2.0$. For large sample sizes, I tends towards a normal distribution with a variance estimated by $4(N - 1)/(N + 2)(N + 3)$. As with the T-square index, significant departures from the expected values of I can be tested by calculating a z-value:

$$z = \frac{I - 2}{\sqrt{4(N - 1)/(N + 2)(N + 3)}}$$

In both cases if $|z| > 1.96$ (at $p = 0.05$) the null hypothesis that the distribution of distances reflects a random pattern can be rejected. Positive values of z, i.e. $I > 2.0$ (or $C > 0.5$), imply a clumped distribution. Negative values of z, i.e. $I < 2.0$ (or $C < 0.5$), suggest that the distribution is uniform. See Box 4.2.

4.5.3 The Clark and Evans index: nearest-neighbour distance

An alternative plotless sampling method proposed by Clark and Evans (1954) has been extensively used in both ecology and geography (Ebdon, 1985; Burt and Barber, 1996). In this method the nearest-neighbour distance (r) is recorded for *every individual* in the sample unit. The total number of individuals (N) in the sampled area must be known, from which the density (D) may be calculated. The expected mean nearest-neighbour distance $E(r)$, assuming the individual points are randomly dispersed in the sampled area, is compared with the measured mean nearest-neighbour distance. The procedures can be divided into three stages:

1. Calculate the observed mean nearest-neighbour distance $r_O = \sum r/N$. Some nearest neighbours occur outside the study area but they must still be recorded. If nearest neighbours outside the study area are excluded, the method is biased (Sinclair, 1985).

2. Calculate the density of individuals in the sample unit, $D = N/A$, where A is the area of the area being sampled. Both r and A must be measured in the same basic units, i.e. if A is measured in square metres, then r must be measured in metres.

3. Calculate the expected mean nearest-neighbour distance under the null hypothesis of a random distribution, $E(r) = 1/2\sqrt{D}$.

Box 4.2   Spatial pattern: calculating C and I

Table 1 outlines the calculations required for a hypothetical data set consisting of the recorded distance from 15 random sample points to the nearest ant nest (x) and the distance from that nest to its nearest neighbour in the direction away from the sample point. Distances are measured in metres. The calculations were performed using an EXCEL spreadsheet. The data, point-to-individual distances (x) and nearest-neighbour distances (y) were entered into the first two columns (C1 and C2). The subsequent columns across the table were then generated in turn and summed as required. Using the values generated in the table, the T-square index (C) and sample point-to-individual index (I) can be calculated for the spatial patterns.

T-square index (C)

We have

$$C = \frac{A}{N} = \frac{9.276\,952}{15} = 0.6185$$

A is obtained by summing column C8. C is greater than 0.5, suggesting that the distribution of ant nests is clumped or aggregated. Now test for a significant departure from the

Table 1 Ant nest data: using Excel to find A

C1 Random sample point (i)	C2 Point-to-individual distance (x_i)	C3 Nearest neighbour distance (y_i)	C4 x_i^2	C5 $(x_i^2)^2$	C6 $\frac{1}{2}y_i^2$	C7 $x_i^2 + \frac{1}{2}y_i^2$	C8 C4/C7
1	3.4	5.6	11.56	133.6336	15.68	27.24	0.424 376
2	4.5	2.3	20.25	410.0625	2.645	22.895	0.884 473
3	1.2	6	1.44	2.0736	18	19.44	0.074 074
4	4.5	7.3	20.25	410.0625	26.645	46.895	0.431 816
5	1.7	1.2	2.89	8.3521	0.72	3.61	0.800 554
6	6	6.7	36	1296	22.445	58.445	0.615 964
7	2.5	4.5	6.25	39.0625	10.125	16.375	0.381 679
8	7	2.3	49	2401	2.645	51.645	0.948 785
9	7.25	4.7	52.5625	2762.816	11.045	63.6075	0.826 357
10	8.9	2	79.21	6274.224	2	81.21	0.975 372
11	6.7	1.9	44.89	2015.112	1.805	46.695	0.961 345
12	2.3	1.5	5.29	27.9841	1.125	6.415	0.824 63
13	6.7	4	44.89	2015.112	8	52.89	0.848 743
14	2	6.1	4	16	18.605	22.605	0.176 952
15	1.25	5.25	1.5625	2.441 406	13.781 25	15.343 75	0.101 833

$$\sum x_i^2 = 380.045 \qquad 17\,813.94 = \sum (x_i^2)^2 \qquad\qquad A = 9.276952$$

$$\left(\sum x_i^2\right)^2 = 144434.2$$

expected value of C for a random distribution:

$$z = \frac{C - 0.5}{\sqrt{1/12N}} = \frac{0.6185 - 0.5}{\sqrt{1/(12 \times 15)}} = \frac{0.1185}{0.0745} = 1.589$$

Since z is not greater than 1.96 we conclude that the distribution of y does not differ significantly from random.

Point-to-individual index (I)

We have

$$I = (N + 1) \frac{\sum\limits_{i=1}^{N} (x_i^2)^2}{\left(\sum\limits_{i=1}^{N} x_i^2\right)^2} = (15 + 1) \frac{17\,813.95}{144\,434.2} = 1.973$$

I equals 1.973, close to the expected value of 2 for a random distribution. For completeness the minor departure from 2 can be tested:

$$z = \frac{I - 2}{\sqrt{4(N-1)/[(N+2)(N+3)]}} = \frac{1.973 - 2}{\sqrt{196/[17 \times 18]}} = -0.034$$

Since the absolute value of z is much lower than the critical value of 1.96, we can conclude

The test statistic R is calculated as the ratio of r_0 to $E(r)$, i.e. $R = r_0/E(r)$:

- If the distribution of individuals is random then $r_0 = E(r)$ and $R = 1.0$
- If the distribution of individuals in regular then $r_0 > E(r)$ and $R > 1.0$
- If the distribution of individuals is clumped then $r_0 < E(r)$ and $R < 1.0$

Theoretically the value of R may range from 0 for a clumped distribution to a maximum of 2.1496 for a uniform distribution where each individual is spaced evenly as far apart as possible. Significant departures of R from 1.0 may be tested by performing a z-test:

$$z = \frac{r - E(r)}{SE(r)} \qquad SE(r) = \frac{0.261\,36}{\sqrt{ND}}$$

where $SE(r)$ is the standard error of $E(r)$.

If $z > |1.96|$ the null hypothesis that the individual points are randomly distributed may be rejected at the $p = 0.05$ probability level. Basing the analysis on nearest-neighbour distances is very much an arbitrary choice. Second or third nearest neighbours could be used instead and might generate different results. The expected distances from an individual to its kth nearest neighbour ($k = 1, 2, 3, 4, 5$) and the associated standard errors are given by Thompson (1956), who also presents an alternative test for departures from randomness (Table 4.6). Thompson's test is based on the chi-squared distribution and can be used for any rank of nearest neighbour:

$$\chi^2 = 2\pi D \sum_{i=1}^{N} r_i^2 \qquad (\text{d.f.} = 2Nk)$$

Table 4.6 Thompson's nearest-neighbour distances

	Nearest neighbour				
	First	Second	Third	Fourth	Fifth
Expected nearest neighbour distance (r_i)	$\dfrac{0.5}{\sqrt{D}}$	$\dfrac{0.75}{\sqrt{D}}$	$\dfrac{0.9375}{\sqrt{D}}$	$\dfrac{1.0937}{\sqrt{D}}$	$\dfrac{01.23\,305}{\sqrt{D}}$
Standard error of expected distance (SE(r))	$\dfrac{0.2614}{\sqrt{ND}}$	$\dfrac{0.2723}{\sqrt{ND}}$	$\dfrac{0.2757}{\sqrt{ND}}$	$\dfrac{0.2774}{\sqrt{ND}}$	$\dfrac{0.2812}{\sqrt{ND}}$

N = number of individuals in the sample unit or study area; A = area of sample unit or study area; D = density of individuals in the sample unit or study area, $D = N/A$.

where D = population density, N/A
  r_i = distance from individual i to its kth nearest neighbour
  k = the rank of neighbour
  N = the number of individuals for whom nearest-neighbour distances were measured
  $\pi = 3.141\,59$

Large significant χ^2-values indicate a uniform distribution whereas small significant values indicate a clumped distribution:

- If χ^2 falls between the tabulated values at the 0.975 and 0.025 probability levels, the null hypothesis of a random distribution is accepted.
- If χ^2 is less than the tabulated value at the 0.975 probability level, the null hypothesis is rejected, and a clumped or aggregated distribution is indicated.
- If χ^2 is greater than the tabulated values at the 0.025 probability level, the null hypothesis is rejected and a regular or overdispersed distribution is indicated.

For large samples with too many degrees of freedom for the χ^2-tables, use the normal approximation $z = \sqrt{2\chi^2} - \sqrt{4Nk - 1}$.

4.5.4 Nearest-neighbour analysis of linear patterns

A modified form of nearest-neighbour analysis can be applied to linear data sets. This method could be used to tested for the clustering of individuals recorded along a transect or among data points recorded along linear land features, e.g. signs of otter (*Lutra lutra*) activity along a river bank, wildlife deaths along a road, or blackbird (*Turdus merula*) nests along a length of hedge. Along a hedge section of total length L, the nearest-neighbour distances between nests could be measured and used to calculate r_O, the observed nearest-neighbour distance. By computer simulation Pinder and Witherick (1975) have shown that if points are randomly distributed along a line, the expected distance (r_E) between neighbouring points is approximately given by

$$r_E = 0.5\left(\frac{L}{N-1}\right)$$

where L is the length of the transect and N is the number of data points.

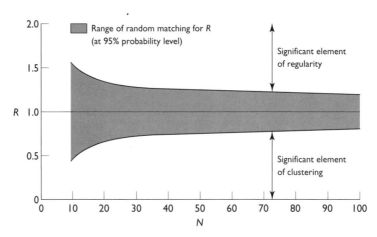

Figure 4.9 The range of random matching in a linear situation. Reprinted, with permission, from Pinder and Witherick (1975).

A test statistic (R) is calculated as the ratio of the expected (r_E) to the observed (r_O) mean nearest-neighbour distance. By analysing repeated simulations of random point distributions, Pinder and Witherick (1975) were able to plot the 95% confidences limits about $R = 1$, the value associated with a random distribution (Figure 4.9). The diagram may then be used to test for pattern using $N = 10$ to $N = 100$.

This method is capable of further modification. In some situations it may not be necessary to measure the absolute distances between neighbouring points. The illustration used by Hammond and McCullagh (1978) is an investigation into the clustering of shop types along a linear main street. In this case the distance between similar types of shop can be measured in terms of the number of shops between two shops of the same kind; L is the total number of shops along the main street. The expected and observed mean nearest-neighbour distances are calculated and the test performed as before. It is not hard to imagine analogous sets of ecological data which might be analysed in a similar way, although they could be analysed just as effectively using the randomisation runs test (Section 4.4.4).

4.5.5 Polygon analysis

Although nearest-neighbour distances are the most frequently used parameter to describe the pattern of points in a two-dimensional space, several other measurements can be used. One approach that generates several useful measures of spatial distribution is the construction of continuous polygons around each point. Voronoi or Thiessen polygons may be drawn around each point relatively easily using the following procedure (Figure 4.10).

1. Join all points to all neighbouring points (dashed lines).
2. Bisect each line drawn in step 1.
3. Join the lines drawn in step 2 to form polygons around each point.

To bisect a line, find its midpoint then draw a line through the midpoint at $90°$ to the original line. Performed by hand this process can be cumbersome, but it is easily accomplished on most computer-based geographic information systems (GIS) or with mapping programs. Alternatively a computer algorithm is available (P.J. Green and Sibson, 1978). Once the polygons have been constructed, the map of points effectively becomes divided into territories or areas centred on each point. The shape and area of the polygons will depend on

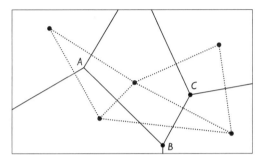

Figure 4.10 Conversion of point data to areal data. Reprinted, with permission, from Burt and Barber (1996).

the distribution of points. For example, a uniform distribution of points might be expected to yield regular-shaped and similar-sized polygons. In the past, to test for a non-random pattern, the observed distribution of polygon area was compared with an expected distribution derived from the Poisson distribution (Vincent *et al.*, 1976). Unfortunately, as Hutchings and Discombe (1986) point out, this is a flawed approach because individual polygons cannot be independent of one another; they provide an alternative approach. From a large number of computer simulations of random point distributions, they were able to generate cumulative probability distributions for seven measures of polygon shape and size. Of these, polygon area and mean neighbour distance[4] proved to be most valuable for detecting the occurrence of both regular and clumped distributions. Polygon perimeter length and displacement[5] were particularly sensitive to clumping, and the distribution of nearest-neighbour distances was sensitive to regularity.

Hutchings and Discombe presented their results as a series of graphs and tables giving the cumulative probability frequencies of each polygon parameter (*y*) against the cumulative percentage of parameter range (*x*). The *x*-axis is obtained by rescaling the parameter values so they range from 0 to 100 (i.e. expressing them as a percentage of the largest value obtained), and then dividing this into a number of equal-sized classes (Hutchings and Discombe used 100). Because the results are presented as percentages they can be used to analyse data sets containing different densities of points and on different spatial scales. The cumulative probability values provided for each parameter allow an envelope to be drawn which contains 95% of all possible values likely to be generated by a random distribution of points. There are five requirements when using these graphs to test for pattern:

- Edge points, i.e. points with polygons constrained by the edge of the plot, must be excluded.
- The range of the recorded parameter values must be rescaled to a maximum value of 100. That is, each value is divided by the largest value recorded and expressed as a percentage.

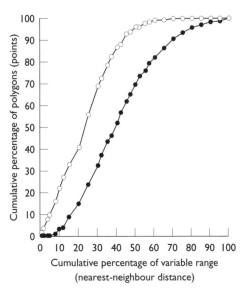

Figure 4.11 The 95% confidence envelope of nearest-neighbour distances for a random distribution: (△) upper bound, (▲) lower bound.

- The rescaled percentage values are divided into equal-sized classes. The number of classes will depend on the density of points.
- The cumulative percentage frequency for each class is calculated and plotted against the percentage parameter values.
- If an observed cumulative frequency plotted on the graph falls outside the 95% confidence envelope for a random distribution, the points may be assumed to differ significantly from random.

The values needed to plot cumulative probability graphs are given in Appendix 4.3. Values for nearest-neighbour distance are plotted in Figure 4.11.

The results of Hutchings and Discombe (1986) make it easy to analyse point and derived polygon distributions. Where the mapped points represent individuals, individual performance can be related to polygon area (Hutchings and Waite, 1985). This analysis of spatial polygons can provide a basis for model development (Czaran and Bartha, 1992). Although the construction of polygons and the calculation of polygon parameters may require access to either GIS or specialist computer programs, the method can be easily applied to conventional nearest-neighbour distance and mean neighbour distance. Then it offers an attractive alternative to other 'plotless' methods described above. It does not require any particular sampling scheme to be adopted and it appears to be appropriate for a wide range of data sets.

4.6 *Recommendations*

The general range of possible methods is outlined in the introduction to this chapter. It is not possible to offer detailed recommendations. The analysis and description of pattern is a complex process and is best done by adopting more than one approach.

The sampling scheme must be selected with care. The key question is whether the investigator wishes simply to determine whether a non-random pattern is present. If this is the case then a random or regular sampling scheme may be adopted and the methods described in Section 4.3 can be followed. If the sample size is small (<30) it is a good idea to calculate the indices of dispersion (Section 4.3.4) and pattern intensity (Section 4.4.2). With large samples the data may be fitted to a specific distribution model. In most circumstances the Poisson model is appropriate (Section 4.3.1). This approach is not recommended unless the sample size is above 50. It is important to consider the effects of sample unit size. Remember that the likelihood of detecting a non-random pattern will depend on the size of the chosen sample units.

If the central aim of the study is to investigate pattern at different spatial scales, adopt a contiguous or regular placement of sample units. This allows sample unit values to be analysed as an ordered sequence (Sections 4.4.4, 4.4.5 and 4.5.4) or as blocked values. The traditional blocked-variance method of patterns analysis (Section 4.4.1) and subsequent modifications have little to commend them. Once the blocking regime has been chosen, a more flexible strategy is to calculate the variance, plus the indices of dispersion and pattern intensity, directly for each set of blocked values. It seems there is nothing to be gained from subjecting them to a modified analysis of variance. When analysing data obtained from contiguously arranged quadrats, remember that each arrangement represents only a single sample of 1.

With the exception of the polygon-based procedure (Section 4.5.5) all of the plotless sampling methods in Section 4.5 have been widely used. Ludwig and Reynolds (1988) strongly recommend the index of spatial pattern (Section 4.5.1) . Methods based on polygons have yet to be widely used, largely because it is difficult to construct the polygons around the points. But this need not be a major obstacle, as demonstrated in this chapter.

Appendix 4.1

Critical regions of χ^2 for detecting pattern

Critical values for the chi-squared test of the dispersion index (I) for $\alpha = 0.05$ and $n < 101$. Large values of χ^2 indicate an aggregated pattern, small values indicate a uniform pattern. Reprinted, with permission, from Krebs (1999).

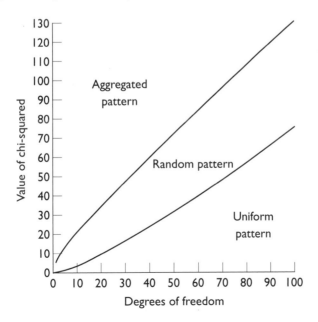

Appendix 4.2

Critical values for *r* in the runs test

Critical values for *r* in the runs test for n_1 or n_2 from 2 to 20. Any calculated value of *r* less than or equal to the values given in the upper table or greater than or equal to the values given in the lower table, is significant at the 0.05 level. Reprinted, with permission, from F.S. Swed and C. Eisenhart, 1943, Tables for testing randomness of grouping in a sequence of alternatives, *Annals of Mathematical Statistics*, **14**:83–86.

Appendix 4.2 Table

n_1 \ n_2	2	3	4	5	6	7	8	9	10	11	12	13	14	15	16	17	18	19	20
2											2	2	2	2	2	2	2	2	2
3				2	2	2	2	2	2	2	2	2	3	3	3	3	3	3	3
4			2	2	2	3	3	3	3	3	3	3	3	4	4	4	4	4	4
5		2	2	3	3	3	3	3	4	4	4	4	4	4	4	4	5	5	5
6		2	2	3	3	3	3	4	4	4	4	5	5	5	5	5	5	6	6
7		2	2	3	3	3	4	4	5	5	5	5	5	6	6	6	6	6	6
8		2	3	3	3	4	4	5	5	5	6	6	6	6	6	7	7	7	7
9		2	3	3	4	4	5	5	5	6	6	7	7	7	7	8	8	8	
10		2	3	3	4	5	5	5	6	6	7	7	7	7	8	8	8	8	9
11		2	3	4	4	5	5	6	6	7	7	7	8	8	8	9	9	9	9
12	2	2	3	4	4	5	6	6	7	7	7	8	8	8	9	9	9	10	10
13	2	2	3	4	5	5	6	6	7	7	8	8	9	9	9	10	10	10	10
14	2	2	3	4	5	5	6	7	7	8	8	9	9	9	10	10	10	11	11
15	2	3	3	5	5	6	6	7	7	8	8	9	9	10	10	11	11	11	12
16	2	3	4	4	5	6	6	7	8	8	9	9	10	10	11	11	11	12	12
17	2	3	4	4	5	6	7	7	8	9	9	10	10	11	11	11	12	12	13
18	2	3	4	5	5	6	7	8	8	9	9	10	10	11	11	12	12	13	13
19	2	3	4	5	6	6	7	8	8	9	10	10	11	11	12	12	13	13	13
20	2	3	4	5	6	6	7	8	9	9	10	10	11	12	12	13	13	13	14

n_1 \ n_2	2	3	4	5	6	7	8	9	10	11	12	13	14	15	16	17	18	19	20
2																			
3																			
4				9	9														
5			9	10	10	11	11												
6			9	10	11	12	12	13	13	13	13								
7				11	12	13	13	14	14	14	14	15	15	15					
8				11	12	13	14	14	15	15	16	16	16	16	17	17	17	17	17
9					13	14	14	15	16	16	16	17	17	18	18	18	18	18	18
10					13	14	15	16	16	17	17	18	18	18	19	19	19	20	20
11					13	14	15	16	17	17	18	19	19	19	20	20	20	21	21
12					13	14	16	16	17	18	19	19	20	20	21	21	21	22	22
13						15	16	17	18	19	19	20	20	21	21	22	22	23	23
14						15	16	17	18	19	20	20	21	22	22	23	23	23	24
15						15	16	18	18	19	20	21	22	22	23	23	24	24	25
16							17	18	19	20	21	22	22	23	23	24	25	25	25
17							17	18	19	20	21	22	23	23	24	25	25	26	26
18							17	18	19	20	21	22	23	24	25	25	26	26	27
19							17	18	20	21	22	23	23	24	25	26	26	27	27
20							17	18	20	21	22	23	24	25	25	26	27	27	28

Appendix 4.3

Polygon parameters

Upper and lower values of the envelopes illustrating cumulative percentage frequency histograms of various polygon parameters for 100 simulations of 500 randomly positioned points.

Appendix 4.3 Table I

Cumulative percentage of variable range	Area		Perimeter		Displacement		Eccentricity		Nearest neighbour distance		Mean neighbour distance	
	Lower value	Upper value	Lower value	Upper value	Lower value	Upper value	Lower value	Upper value	Lower value	Upper value	Lower value	Upper value
1	0.23	1.63	0.23	0.95	0.23	1.37	0.23	0.70	0.24	1.90	0.23	0.48
2	0.23	2.56	0.23	1.19	0.23	2.32	0.23	1.16	0.46	3.75	0.23	0.95
3	0.23	4.20	0.23	1.90	0.23	2.63	0.23	1.16	0.47	6.09	0.23	1.18
4	0.23	4.93	0.23	2.38	0.71	4.26	0.23	1.40	0.47	7.96	0.23	1.87
5	0.71	6.34	0.23	2.86	1.16	6.27	0.23	1.40	0.47	9.84	0.23	2.12
6	0.72	8.45	0.23	3.33	1.63	8.85	0.23	1.40	0.47	11.94	0.23	2.36
7	0.96	9.86	0.23	3.33	2.37	10.05	0.23	1.63	1.40	14.29	0.24	3.05
8	1.20	13.37	0.23	4.05	2.84	11.81	0.23	1.63	1.43	16.39	0.24	4.23
9	2.16	16.43	0.23	4.76	3.31	14.18	0.23	2.09	2.62	17.80	0.24	4.46
10	2.88	19.81	0.23	5.26	4.50	17.26	0.23	2.09	3.33	22.25	0.24	5.16
11	4.33	22.95	0.23	6.70	4.74	20.48	0.23	2.12	4.29	24.82	0.24	6.10
12	5.29	25.76	0.23	8.33	6.01	23.13	0.23	2.33	4.29	27.40	0.24	6.57
13	6.01	28.88	0.23	9.29	6.40	26.67	0.23	2.39	7.00	29.04	0.70	7.44
14	7.69	34.50	0.24	9.52	7.82	30.24	0.23	2.83	8.87	31.62	0.70	8.60
15	8.89	39.67	0.24	11.19	9.95	31.67	0.23	3.37	9.26	33.02	0.72	9.30
16	11.30	42.72	0.24	13.33	10.90	35.71	0.23	3.37	10.26	35.13	0.72	10.70
17	12.50	46.95	0.24	14.76	12.09	38.57	0.23	3.61	11.59	36.07	0.72	13.26
18	14.90	50.94	0.48	15.48	13.57	41.09	0.23	3.61	12.11	37.47	0.96	14.65
19	16.35	54.23	0.48	16.67	14.93	43.81	0.23	4.53	13.30	39.34	1.20	15.58
20	18.27	57.51	0.72	19.76	15.95	47.03	0.23	4.77	15.20	41.05	1.68	17.67
21	19.71	60.09	0.72	22.38	17.38	50.12	0.23	5.25	17.87	43.44	1.92	19.30
22	23.32	62.21	0.96	24.52	18.81	52.49	0.23	5.25	19.81	46.78	2.64	21.40
23	24.76	65.49	0.96	27.38	20.00	54.52	0.23	5.90	20.51	50.36	2.88	24.42
24	25.96	69.01	0.96	28.33	21.67	57.72	0.47	6.13	22.57	54.42	3.37	25.35
25	27.88	71.60	1.44	29.76	23.57	59.62	0.47	6.84	23.75	56.09	4.33	27.91
26	30.77	74.16	1.92	30.95	24.76	63.66	0.47	6.92	25.42	60.14	5.29	30.70
27	32.45	77.03	2.16	31.90	27.14	66.75	0.47	7.64	27.27	62.05	5.77	32.79
28	34.38	81.10	2.64	33.10	28.10	69.36	0.47	8.35	30.40	64.44	5.77	34.65
29	37.50	82.54	3.13	34.76	29.52	71.97	0.47	9.07	31.83	65.87	7.21	36.51
30	40.63	83.73	4.09	38.10	31.43	75.53	0.94	9.79	32.54	69.21	7.45	38.14

Appendix 4.3 Table I Continued

Cumulative percentage of variable range	Area		Perimeter		Displacement		Eccentricity		Nearest neighbour distance		Mean neighbour distance	
	Lower value	Upper value	Lower value	Upper value	Lower value	Upper value	Lower value	Upper value	Lower value	Upper value	Lower value	Upper value
31	42.79	85.41	4.57	40.71	33.81	76.96	0.94	10.02	34.50	70.41	8.65	40.23
32	44.47	86.84	4.81	43.33	37.14	79.33	1.41	10.50	37.30	72.79	9.86	43.49
33	47.12	87.80	6.01	45.48	39.76	80.52	1.41	11.22	39.16	74.22	11.78	45.58
34	49.04	88.52	6.97	47.86	42.86	82.19	1.64	11.22	41.26	76.13	13.22	47.67
35	51.20	89.71	7.45	50.95	44.29	83.85	2.11	11.46	43.82	79.00	14.66	49.30
36	53.61	90.43	8.17	52.14	45.95	84.80	2.14	11.93	44.52	80.19	16.59	52.09
37	54.81	91.15	10.10	55.71	47.62	86.46	2.38	12.09	46.39	82.58	17.79	55.58
38	56.73	92.58	11.54	58.33	49.29	87.41	2.61	13.21	48.02	84.01	19.71	57.44
39	58.65	93.30	13.70	60.24	52.62	88.81	2.61	13.92	49.42	85.92	21.63	60.23
40	61.06	93.30	15.38	62.86	54.76	90.24	3.28	14.15	52.17	86.87	23.08	62.33
41	62.50	93.54	17.55	65.48	56.43	91.43	3.75	15.09	54.08	87.83	24.52	65.35
42	64.90	93.54	18.51	67.62	59.04	91.43	4.22	15.57	57.11	88.31	25.00	67.21
43	66.35	93.54	19.95	70.24	61.19	92.16	4.92	16.27	58.74	90.45	26.92	69.53
44	68.27	94.39	21.63	72.21	63.81	93.10	4.99	16.98	60.37	91.89	30.05	72.09
45	69.47	94.86	23.56	73.87	65.40	93.82	5.94	18.40	62.00	92.84	32.21	75.12
46	70.43	95.79	25.72	76.25	67.14	94.76	6.09	19.10	63.18	93.32	34.38	76.28
47	71.88	96.03	26.68	77.91	68.35	95.25	6.32	19.91	65.32	94.03	36.78	78.64
48	73.32	96.73	29.33	80.76	68.82	95.72	7.49	21.23	66.98	94.51	38.70	79.77
49	74.76	96.96	31.49	82.66	70.98	95.96	8.67	22.88	68.41	95.47	40.87	81.86
50	76.92	97.20	32.69	83.61	71.94	96.19	9.50	23.70	69.60	96.18	42.79	83.02
51	77.64	97.20	34.86	84.56	72.90	96.43	10.21	24.76	72.45	96.18	44.47	84.42
52	79.09	97.20	37.02	85.99	73.38	96.90	11.16	26.54	73.71	96.42	46.88	85.81
53	80.05	97.66	39.67	86.94	74.82	96.90	12.32	27.73	75.53	96.66	48.32	87.09
54	81.73	97.90	42.07	88.36	76.30	97.35	12.83	28.91	75.76	97.14	50.72	89.20
55	82.45	97.90	44.71	89.55	77.70	97.39	13.27	30.42	76.22	97.85	52.64	89.91
56	83.17	98.36	46.63	91.45	78.42	97.62	13.98	31.84	77.86	98.33	54.09	91.55
57	83.89	98.60	49.28	91.45	79.14	97.86	16.11	33.89	79.52	98.33	56.73	92.49
58	84.13	98.83	50.72	92.64	80.58	98.10	16.16	36.49	81.22	98.57	57.69	93.63
59	84.86	99.06	52.88	92.87	81.75	98.31	18.01	37.91	81.93	98.81	59.13	94.34
60	86.06	99.28	55.77	93.35	82.97	98.55	19.19	39.81	82.41	99.05	62.74	94.58
61	87.26	99.28	58.41	93.65	83.45	99.04	19.44	41.00	83.45	99.28	63.94	95.28
62	88.46	99.28	60.34	94.30	83.93	99.04	20.37	41.94	84.10	99.28	65.87	96.24
63	88.94	99.52	61.78	94.54	84.89	99.04	21.78	43.13	84.85	99.28	67.31	96.71
64	89.66	99.52	63.22	95.72	85.85	99.04	24.36	43.84	85.78	99.28	70.67	97.67
65	90.38	99.53	67.55	96.44	86.33	99.04	25.53	45.26	86.48	99.28	72.36	98.14
66	91.35	99.77	70.19	96.95	87.53	99.28	27.73	46.68	87.41	99.52	74.52	98.14
67	91.35	99.77	72.36	97.18	88.70	99.52	28.81	49.30	87.65	99.52	76.68	98.14
68	91.83	99.77	74.04	98.12	89.42	99.52	31.38	53.07	88.11	99.76	78.85	98.59
69	92.31	99.77	76.60	98.36	89.69	99.52	33.02	54.48	88.81	99.76	80.29	98.60
70	92.55	99.77	77.54	98.59	90.17	99.52	35.83	56.60	90.68	99.76	81.73	98.60

Appendix 4.3 Table I Continued

Cumulative percentage of variable range	Area		Perimeter		Displacement		Eccentricity		Nearest neighbour distance		Mean neighbour distance	
	Lower value	Upper value	Lower value	Upper value	Lower value	Upper value	Lower value	Upper value	Lower value	Upper value	Lower value	Upper value
71	92.79	99.77	79.20	98.59	90.65	99.52	37.85	58.49	91.51	99.76	83.41	99.07
72	93.27	99.77	80.38	98.59	91.35	99.53	40.65	60.61	91.92	99.76	84.62	99.07
73	93.99	99.77	81.09	98.83	91.35	99.53	41.47	62.03	92.16	99.76	86.78	99.30
74	94.23	99.77	82.03	98.83	92.55	99.53	44.31	63.44	92.64	99.76	87.26	99.30
75	94.47	99.77	82.74	99.06	93.05	99.53	46.68	64.08	93.59	99.76	88.63	99.53
76	95.43	99.77	84.40	99.06	93.05	99.76	48.58	66.28	93.63	99.77	88.70	99.53
77	95.67	99.77	85.58	99.53	93.29	99.77	50.71	69.69	93.63	99.77	89.42	99.53
78	96.15	99.77	87.23	99.53	94.01	99.77	52.13	72.08	94.58	99.77	90.52	99.53
79	96.39	99.77	89.36	99.77	94.25	99.77	56.40	73.95	95.01	99.77	91.00	99.53
80	96.45	99.77	90.63	99.77	94.50	99.77	59.00	77.44	95.72	99.77	92.07	99.53
81	96.63	99.77	91.02	99.77	94.96	99.77	61.61	80.00	96.20	99.77	92.31	99.77
82	96.63	99.77	92.91	99.77	95.20	99.77	65.40	81.40	96.20	99.77	92.31	99.77
83	96.92	99.77	93.03	99.77	95.20	99.77	68.01	83.95	96.63	99.77	94.23	99.77
84	97.39	99.77	93.27	99.77	95.68	99.77	71.80	84.96	97.10	99.77	94.71	99.77
85	97.41	99.77	93.51	99.77	95.68	99.77	74.47	86.63	97.10	99.77	95.19	99.77
86	97.84	99.77	94.23	99.77	96.16	99.77	75.41	89.26	97.58	99.77	95.97	99.77
87	97.84	99.77	95.19	99.77	96.88	99.77	77.99	90.69	97.60	99.77	96.21	99.77
88	97.84	99.77	95.67	99.77	96.88	99.77	80.71	91.98	97.60	99.77	96.45	99.77
89	98.08	99.77	96.39	99.77	97.12	99.77	82.67	93.16	98.10	99.77	96.68	99.77
90	98.10	99.77	96.88	99.77	97.12	99.77	85.25	94.74	98.34	99.77	96.88	99.77
91	98.10	99.77	97.63	99.77	97.36	99.77	87.59	95.65	98.56	99.77	97.36	99.77
92	98.36	99.77	97.87	99.77	97.60	99.77	88.99	97.17	98.57	99.77	97.60	99.77
93	98.36	99.77	98.08	99.77	98.08	99.77	90.82	98.10	98.57	99.77	97.84	99.77
94	98.36	99.77	98.36	99.77	98.32	99.77	91.33	99.05	98.80	99.77	98.56	99.77
95	98.83	99.77	98.80	99.77	98.32	99.77	92.97	99.29	98.82	99.77	98.80	99.77
96	99.05	99.77	98.83	99.77	98.56	99.77	95.32	99.76	98.82	99.77	99.04	99.77
97	99.28	99.77	98.83	99.77	98.80	99.77	97.19	99.77	98.82	99.77	99.04	99.77
98	99.29	99.77	99.52	99.77	99.28	99.77	98.35	99.77	99.52	99.77	99.28	99.77
99	99.76	100.00	99.76	100.00	99.76	100.00	99.52	100.00	99.76	100.00	99.52	100.00
100	100.00	100.00	100.00	100.00	100.00	100.00	100.00	100.00	100.00	100.00	100.00	100.00

Source: Reprinted, with permission, from Hutchings and Discombe (1986).

Further reading

- Bouxin, G. (1991) The measurement of horizontal patterns in vegetation: a review and proposals for models. In *Computer Assisted Vegetation Analysis*, E. Feoli and L. Orloci (eds). Kluwer Academic, Dordrecht, pp. 337–53.
- Burt, J.E. and Barber, G.M. (1996). *Elementary Statistics for Geographers*, 2nd edn. Guilford Press, New York.
- Diggle, P.J. (1983) *Statistical Analysis of Spatial Point Patterns*. Academic Press, New York.
- Krebs, J.C. (1999) *Ecological Methodology*, 2nd edn. Addison Wesley Longman, Menlo Park, CA.
- Ludwig, J.A. and Reynolds, J.F. (1988) *Statistical Ecology: A Primer on Methods and Computing*. John Wiley, New York.

Chapter Five

Biological and environmental indices

Summary

In environmental and ecological studies, large and often complex data sets are frequently collected. In order to interpret such data, methods are required that are able to simplify and summarise it effectively. One approach to this problem is the calculation of indices that characterise and highlight particular aspects of the data. Indices are sometimes developed by individual investigators to meet their particular needs. This chapter considers how such indices may be developed, how they behave and how they may be used. Section 5.2, examines how indices may be calculated and developed. Section 5.2.3 focuses on the use of the weighted average calculation as an effective means of summarising multivariate data sets, i.e. where more than one variable has been measured for each sample unit. Indices of niche breadth and overlap are described in Section 5.3; they are closely related to the indices of diversity considered in Chapter 2. Section 5.4 looks at population index numbers to identify trends in population size. The statistical properties of indices are considered in Section 5.5, along with methods for estimating the variance of an index. Section 5.6 considers the use of graphical methods to explore complex data sets.

5.1 *Introduction*

Ecological and environmental research frequently generate large data sets. Often they are multivariate, obtained by measuring more than one variable for each sample unit. Suppose the water chemistry at 20 lakes is investigated; the resulting data set might consist of the values for 6 chemical parameters (pH, conductivity, etc.) measured for each of 6 replicate samples, taken from 20 different lakes, giving a total of 720 ($6 \times 6 \times 20$) individual data values. By using mean values, this data set could be reduced to 120 values, 6 mean parameter values for each of the 20 lakes. Even when mean values are used, the interpretation of such large data sets is not straightforward. What is required is a series of methods that are able to summarise complex data sets and allow the relationships between variables to be explored. This chapter considers the use of indices to summarise data sets and highlight key features.

Several examples of widely used indices are given, but it is hoped that sufficient information is provided to allow readers to develop their own indices. The construction of indices and their properties are considered in Section 5.2. The use and calculation of weighted averages are also illustrated (Section 5.2.3). Weighted averages provide a very simple and effective method for describing the relationships between variables. The procedure has been used extensively and is easily generalised. Indices of species niche breadth and overlap are presented in Section 5.3 along with population index numbers in Section 5.4. The statistical properties of indices and procedures for estimating the variance of indices and other statistics are discussed in Section 5.5. Graphical approaches to the presentation of complex data sets are described briefly in Section 5.6. More complex, computer-based multivariate analyses are described in Chapters 8, 9 and 11.

5.2 *Indices*

An index may be constructed to provide a concise summary of the conditions that relate to a particular sample, individual or locality. To be useful, the index must allow valid inferences to be made from its values. For example, Amann's index of hygrothermy (H) provides a good quantitative summary of the environmental conditions at sites, and it can be used to infer the likelihood that a particular bryophyte assemblage will occur (Proctor, 1960):

$$H = \frac{PT}{t_h - t_c}$$

where P = annual precipitation (cm)

   T = mean annual temperature ($^\circ$C)

   $t_h - t_c$ = the difference between the mean hottest and mean coldest monthly temperatures ($^\circ$C)

The distribution of those bryophytes associated with the western seaboard of Europe (i.e. Atlantic species) tends to occur in the British Isles where H exceeds 60–70. The validity of an index of this type will depend on the factors it incorporates and the formula used to calculate it. There are no universal rules for either. In practice, deciding which factors or variables to include is probably easiest. A consideration of the ecology and biology of the system, along with the aims of the study, will usually allow a shortlist of potentially useful factors to be drawn up. The formula used to calculate the index is clearly crucial. Different mathematical operations (addition, subtraction, division, etc.) will determine the influence each variable has on the final index. Similarly, the units used to measure or express each factor will affect its relative influence on the final index value. When developing an index, there are three imperatives:

- Make sure you know how the index calculation is affected by including or excluding a factor.
- Make sure you know the relative influence (or weighting) of each factor, and whether or not it has a desirable effect on the index. Factors deemed to be most important have the strongest effects on the index.
- Set out the potential range of index values and make sure they can be easily interpreted.

And if possible, try to fulfil this fourth requirement:

- The index should be validated against an independent data set (i.e. data not directly used to develop the index). Sometimes it is possible to test an index by correlating index values against a relevant but independently measured variable. For example, a biotic index of pollution might be assessed by correlating index values against direct measures of pollutant concentration.

When developing an index, a trial and error approach is often required: different factors are included and excluded, or they are given different weightings; different mathematical formulae are tried.

5.2.1 *Additive indices*

The simplest indices are additive. A score is given for each factor incorporated in the index, then the factor scores are summed to give a final index value. For example, the national Red Data Book for British vascular plants (Perring and Farrel, 1977) lists endangered species and gives each a threat number which provides a measure or index of the vulnerability of the species. Each species is scored for six factors considered to contribute to the likelihood of extinction; individual scores are summed to give a threat number (Box 5.1). Several biological indices of freshwater quality have a similar general form. The Trent index, the Chandler index and the Biological Monitoring Working Party (BMWP) index all require the standardised sampling of bottom-dwelling, stream macro-invertebrate communities. Samples are sorted into predefined taxonomic units (identification to the species levels is not normally required). Each taxonomic group is given a score that reflects its known tolerance to pollution. The scores for each taxonomic group are then summed to give a final index value (Haslam, 1990; Mason, 1996). A similar approach has been used to develop numerous other indices; two books by Spellerberg (1991, 1992) cover many indices used in ecology, conservation and environmental impact assessment.

Oil pollution is a major environmental threat to seabird populations. Williams *et al.* (1995) have developed a quantitative oiling vulnerability index (OVI) for North Sea seabirds. The index is derived from published quantitative information on seabird ecology combined with data from several national seabird monitoring programmes. The index incorporates four factors for each species:

- *Factor a*: the proportion of dead or moribund birds found on shorelines which have been oiled and the proportion of time spent on the surface of the sea by each species. Both aspects are combined to give a score. The highest scores are given to species that spend much of their time on the sea surface and are frequently found to be oiled.
- *Factor b*: the estimated total population (pairs) of the species throughout its geographical range. Large populations are considered least vulnerable and score lowest.

Box 5.1 Threat numbers for British vascular plants

The distribution of vascular plants in Great Britain has been mapped on 10 km × 10 km squares; plants which occur in 15 or fewer 10 km squares are listed in the Red Data Book (approximately 18% of Britain's flora). For each plant included, a threat number is obtained by totalling the scores for the following factors. The threat number is obtained by summing the scores for all six factors. The maximum threat number is 15 and the minimum threat number is 0. Notice that the second factor, known localities, is given a larger weighting than the other factors.

1.	Past and present distribution. Assessed on the basis of the decline in the number of 10 km squares occupied by the species	0–33% decline 33–66% decline >66% decline	score 0 score 1 score 2
2.	Number of known localities in 10 km squares where species occurs	16 or more 10–15 localities 6–9 localities 3–5 localities 1–2 localities	score 0 score 1 score 2 score 3 score 4
3.	Attractiveness assessed subjectively. Attractiveness is included in the index because attractive plants are more likely to be collected, picked or suffer disturbance from the activities of naturalists and members of the public visiting sites	Not attractive Moderately attractive Highly attractive	score 0 score 1 score 2
4.	Extent of existing protection or conservation, measured as the proportion of known localities on nature reserves	>66% 66–33% <33%	score 0 score 1 score 2
5.	Remoteness of localities	Remote Moderately remote Not remote	score 0 score 1 score 2
6.	Accessibility of localities, judged subjectively. Included in the index as an indirect measure of the likelihood of the species suffering from human interference	Not easily reached Moderately easily reached Easily reached	score 0 score 1 score 2

● *Factor c*: the potential rate of recovery following a reduction in numbers. It is assessed on the basis of mean clutch size, maximum clutch size and age at first breeding. The lowest scores are given to species capable of rapid population growth, i.e. recovery.

● *Factor d*: reliance on the marine environment. It is based on an estimate of the proportion of the population which depends on the marine environment, calculated for for the whole year. Species that spend the majority of their time in the marine environment are scored highly compared with species that spend part of the year inland.

The scores given for each factor are derived directly from the available quantitative data. For each factor (*a* to *d*), the range of available values (e.g. population size) is divided into five classes, each of which is given a score between 1 and 5. The final OVI has a maximum value of 30 and is calculated from

$$OVI = 2a + 2b + c + d$$

The four factors are not weighted equally, factors a and b are considered to be most important and are weighted more heavily. The authors state that the weightings are arbitrary but explicit, and can therefore be easily modified in the light of experience. Similarly, the scaling used to convert the original quantitative data into scores is explicit and could be modified as more data becomes available. Besides allowing seabirds to be ranked by their susceptibility to oiling, the index can be used to assess and map the vulnerability of seashore areas to seabird oiling. Area vulnerability scores (AVS) are obtained by summing the OVI of each species multiplied by the natural logarithm of its population density in an area:

$$AVS = \sum_{i=1}^{s} \ln(p_i + 1)OVI_i$$

where s = the number of seabird species in the area
p_i = the density of the ith species
OVI_i = the oil vulnerability index for the ith species

Areas with high AVS contain large populations of seabirds vulnerable to oiling (i.e. species with high OVIs). Population densities were log transformed to smooth out variations in the number of birds recorded in the surveys contributing to the index while still highlighting large-scale variations between areas and species; one is added to avoid negative values. Area vulnerability scores were used by Williams *et al.* (1995) to produce a map of the North Sea showing the areas most vulnerable to seabird oiling.

5.2.2 Indices based on ratios

Ratios or percentage values often form the basis of indices. An example is the index of tolerance (I) used to assess the tolerance of plants to particular pollutants:

$$I = \frac{G_p}{G_c}$$

where I is the index of tolerance, G_p the growth of the plant in the presence of the pollutant, and G_c the growth of the plant under control conditions in the absence of the pollutant. The ratio is often multiplied by 100 and expressed as a percentage. In contrast to the additive indices described above, I is not based on discontinuous scores but is a continuous variable, more amenable to statistical analysis. Although frequently expressed as a percentage, its values are not constrained to the range 0–100%, so a logarithmic transformation is likely to be the most appropriate whenever transformation is required (Chapter 10).

A variation on I is often encountered in ecotoxicology. Microtox$^{™}$ and similar toxicity test systems have been widely used to assess the toxicity of chemicals and environmental samples. They are based on a comparison of the light output from the bioluminescent bacterium *Vibrio fisheri*, incubated under controlled conditions in the presence and the absence of the potential toxicant. The toxicity is measured by the percentage light inhibition:

$$\%IH = \left(1 - \frac{I_t/I_0}{C_t/C_0}\right) \times 100$$

where I_t = light output of bioluminescent bacteria after time t contact with sample toxicant
I_0 = light output of bioluminescent bacteria in contact with sample toxicant at $t = 0$

C_t = light output of bioluminescent bacteria in the absence of the toxicant, at time t
C_0 = light output of bioluminescent bacteria in the absence of the toxicant, at $t = 0$

The formula for %IH can also be written like this:

$$\%\text{IH} = \left(1 - \frac{I_t}{\text{KF} \times I_0}\right) \times 100 \qquad \text{KF} = \frac{C_t}{C_0}$$

The correction factor KF is needed because, even in the absence of a toxicant, light output from the bacteria will decline during the test. The quantity of interest is the additional loss in bioluminescence attributable to the toxicant. Where %IH values are determined for a range of toxicant concentrations the EC_{50} – the effective concentration which reduces light output to 50% of its level in the absence of the toxicant – can be obtained from a plot of %IH against toxicant concentration. The EC_{50} is a standard parameter routinely used to compare the toxicity of samples and chemicals (Hardman *et al.*, 1993). A related parameter, gamma (Γ), may be calculated from %IH values. Also called the light loss effect, Γ is the ratio of light lost during the test to the light output remaining at the end of the test:

$$\Gamma = \frac{\%\text{IH}}{100 - \%\text{IH}}$$

Γ can provide an insight into the possible kinetics of the inhibition mechanism. A plot of log Γ against log (toxicant concentration) should be linear if the mechanism of inhibition involves a reversible reaction of a single toxicant with a single target enzyme or substrate. If the reaction between the toxicant and the site of inhibition has reached equilibrium, reaction rate theory suggests that the slope of the log Γ versus log C plot is equal to the number of toxicant molecules that react reversibly with the target molecule or substrate. Even over shorter periods, i.e. before equilibrium has been reached, the slope of the plot can still be informative. Slopes of around 0.5, 1.0 and 2.0 are not uncommon and are consistent with a one-to-one, one-to-two or a two-to-one relationship between the toxicant and target enzyme or substrate (Beckman Instruments, 1982).

5.2.3 Weighted averages

Weighted averages have been used extensively to summarise community data sets. Greig-Smith (1983) provides a description of their early application, which in plant ecology dates back to the late 1940s. More recent work includes that of Atkinson *et al.* (1993), who used weighted averages to assess the development of wetland vegetation on created wetlands in Virginia (USA). Each plant species was given a weighting score (w_i) between 1 and 5. Following Reed (1988) species that occur on wetland sites with a frequency >99% were classed as obligate wetland plants and given a weighting of 1, whereas species that rarely occur on wetland sites, i.e. frequency <1%, were given a weighting of 5. Using a formula given by Jongman *et al.* (1987), a weighted average for each wetland plot was calculated:

$$\text{WA} = \tfrac{1}{100}(x_1 w_1 + x_2 w_2 + \cdots + x_s w_s)$$

where x_i is the relative percentage cover value for each species recorded in the sample plot and w_i is the weighting value (1 to 5) for the species. Dividing by 100 scales the WA values so that they range from 1 to 5. A plot dominated by obligate wetland species will have a WA close to 1, whereas a plot dominated by species associated with drier habitats will have a WA closer to 5. Using this approach, the entire vegetation of a plot is summarised by a single WA value. Here the species weighting values (w_i) are simply scores; although they are based on objective data (species frequency), they are essentially arbitrary. A different weighting system would give different results. If weighted averages are to be used, the weighting scheme (scores) must be chosen with care; it must be explicit, it must be consistent and it must be justified.

Weighting values need not be a sequence of discontinuous scores, they can be derived from continuous variables measured along with species abundance. Consider the normal form of a community data matrix. The data table is divided into two sections: the upper section contains information on the abundance of species at each of the k samples (e.g. quadrats, sites) and the lower section contains information on the physical and environmental factors measured at each site (e.g. altitude, soil pH). The relationship between each species and each environmental factor can be quantified by calculating a weighted average for each combination of species and environmental factor. Here is the general formula for calculating weighted averages:

w may be specific to the species as shown here with subscript j; or it may be specific to the site, with subscript i. n_{ij} is the abundance of species j in site i of k sites (sample units)

$$S_j = \sum_{i=1}^{k} n_{ij} w_j \Big/ \sum_{i=1}^{k} n_{ij} = \frac{1}{N} \sum_{i=1}^{k} n_{ij} w_j$$

Where the weighting values take the values of measured variables, e.g. altitude or soil pH, the calculated weighted average is also known as the centroid of distribution or niche centroid, and it provides a measure of the 'centre' of the species distribution along the environmental gradient measured by w_i. The standard deviation of the weighted average is given by

$$t_j = \sqrt{\sum_{i=1}^{k} \frac{n_i}{N} (w_i - S_j)}$$

The weighted standard deviation provides a measure of the niche breadth of the species; ter Braak and Verdonschot (1995) call it the tolerance of the species. Large values imply that the species is 'tolerant' or that its distribution is largely unaffected by the environmental factor measured by the weighting value (w_i). Small values indicate that the species is abundant only among a limited number of sites with a restricted range of weighting values. An alternative but related approach to quantifying niche width and breadth is outlined in Section 5.3.

By plotting the appropriate weighted averages, an ordination (i.e. an ordered plot) of either species or samples may be produced; a worked example is given in Box 5.2. Although their use in community ecology has largely been superseded by the more computer-intensive methods of ordination (Chapter 8), weighted averages can still prove useful. They can be particularly valuable for exploring relationships between variables in large data sets and for the construction of indices which highlight specific properties of the data set. Several pollution indices are based on weighted averages. Here the weighting values often relate to the tolerance of species to pollution and direct or indirect measures of environmental quality. For example, the lichen-based index of atmospheric purity (IAP) developed by Leblanc and De Sloover (1970) has been used in several studies to map regional variations in air quality (Showman, 1988); it is calculated for each site using the formula

frequency cover values of species j assessed on a scale of 1 to 5

$$IAP = \sum_{j=1}^{s} \frac{Q_j f_j}{10}$$

arbitrary scale factor to make final values more manageable

Box 5.2 **Weighted average ordination**

The density of ground plants was recorded at four woodland sites. Based on published data and habitat preferences, each species was ranked (1 to 5) in terms of its tolerance to shade and to waterlogging. Species associated with deep shade and tolerant of deep

Table 1 Original data

Species (j)	Sites (i)				Weightings	
	1	*2*	*3*	*4*	*Shade*	*Wetness*
1	0	0	50	280	5	5
2	0	0	180	225	5	2
3	0	50	200	60	4	2
4	20	80	100	0	4	4
5	30	300	40	15	3	5
6	55	34	30	10	3	3
7	75	56	0	0	2	3
8	85	15	0	0	2	2
9	100	0	0	0	1	1
10	200	0	0	0	1	1
Totals (N_i)	565	535	600	590		

Table 2 Weighted average calculation at site 1

wetness weighting values

Species (j)	C1 Site i = 1	C2 Shade	C3	C4 Wetness	
1	0	5	0	5	0
2	0	5	0	2	0
3	0	4	0	2	0
4	20	4	80	4	80
5	30	3	90	5	150
6	55	3	165	3	165
7	75	2	150	3	225
8	85	2	170	2	170
9	100	1	100	1	100
10	200	1	200	1	200
Totals (N_i)	565		955		1090

obtained by multiplying species abundance in C1 by wetness weightings in C4

$$WA_S = 1.69 \qquad WA_W = 1.93$$

divide by total of species abundance to give $WA_W = 1090/565 = 1.93$

obtained by multiplying C1 by C2

obtained by dividing the total of C3 by the total of C1

Table 3 Weighted averages at all four sites

Site	Shade	Wetness
1	1.69	1.93
2	3.11	4.15
3	4.27	2.83
4	4.81	3.52

shade were given a shade index value of 5; non-shade-tolerant species were given a value of 1. Similarly, species tolerant of waterlogging were given a wetness index value of 5, and species associated with dry sites were given a value of 1. These index values were used to weight species abundance values according to the shade and waterlogging tolerance of the species.

The original data is shown in Table 1; the weighted average calculation for shade and wetness values at site 1 is shown in Table 2. The calculations were performed using a spreadsheet. Once a calculation spreadsheet was established, values for the other sites were obtained by cutting and pasting appropriate data values into the site column (Table 3). Site weighted average values can be plotted to produce an ordination of the four sites (Figure 1).

From the ordination we can see that the sites can be ordered linearly from 1 to 4 in terms of the shade tolerance of their vegetation. There is a different ordering of the sites in terms of their vegetation's tolerance to waterlogging. Three broad types of woodland vegetation can be distinguished from the diagram. Vegetation associated with moderately wet and closed (shaded) woodlands (3, 4); wet woodlands but only moderately shaded (2), and open and dry woodlands (1). Although this is a relatively trivial example, the methods can be used to examine more complex data sets.

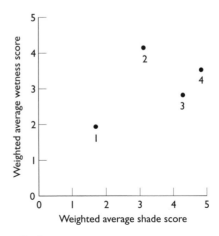

Figure 1 Weighted average ordination.

Known as the ecological index of species, Q_j is a measure of the diversity of the epiphyte communities in which species j occurs; it is effectively the average species richness of all sites where the species is present. High site IAP values will be obtained where the lichen species that occur are normally associated with species-rich lichen communities. As air quality deteriorates, lichen diversity decreases and IAP values will decline. The ecological assumption underlying the index is that community diversity decreases as a result of pollution. As pollution levels increase, species are lost from the community in accordance with their tolerance; non-tolerant species are rapidly excluded. As levels of contamination continue to increase, there remain fewer and fewer species capable of surviving.

5.3 *Niche breadth and niche overlap*

The niche of a species has been variously defined as the 'role or function' or the 'position' of the species in a community. The formulation of the concept by Hutchinson (1957) as essentially 'the complete set of environmental conditions necessary for the survival and reproduction of a species' stimulated efforts to measure the niche by attempting to determine the set of conditions or dimensions along which the niche of a species might be defined. The concept of niche is not without critics. Williamson (1972) provides an excellent critique, pointing out the practical and theoretical problems associated with niche description and measurement. Unfortunately the term 'niche' is frequently used loosely but it is too deeply ingrained to be ignored, particularly in work on competition and species diversity. Abrams (1983) provides a valuable review of the relationship between species niche, competition and diversity; Begon *et al.* (1996) and Stilings (1999) provide a modern synthesis of the subject.

Before considering how to measure it, we need to accept that niche is a property of a species not a habitat, and we need to recognise two forms:

- *Fundamental niche*: the niche space or set of conditions and resources occupied or exploited by the species in the absence of competitors or predators (or other community[1] species).
- *Realised niche*: the niche space or set of conditions and resources occupied or exploited by the species in the presence of competitors or predators (or other community species).

The realised (or post-competitive) niche is always smaller than the fundamental (or pre-competitive) niche. This highlights another important property of the species niche; not only is it a property of the species, but because species rarely if ever occur in isolation, it is also a property of the community in which the species exists.

In the context of field biology, the niche can most easily be visualised as the range and diversity of resources exploited by a species. Niche overlap, and therefore the potential for competition, depends on the extent to which two or more species attempt to exploit the same resource units. A species with a wide niche will exploit a wide range of resource units, whereas a species with a narrow niche will exploit a restricted range of resource units. In field or laboratory investigations the nature of the resource units is often defined pragmatically, based on the perception of the investigator. The type of prey item taken by a predator, the size of nesting hole, and the types of flower visited by a pollen-feeding insect, all might be considered as possible resource units or classes. Unfortunately, the organism's perception might not be the same as the investigator's.

With plants the situation can appear superficially simpler. Their sedentary nature means that competition among plants can often be interpreted as competition for space;

occupation of space ensures unhindered access to the resources present. Thus, if a hundred quadrats are randomly placed in the study area, each quadrat can be viewed as a separate resource unit (a unit of land) for which plants compete. A species that occurs in all quadrats could be considered to have a broad niche compared with a species that occurs in a only limited number of quadrats. The validity and usefulness of this interpretation depend on whether each quadrat has the same resource quality, i.e. whether it can provide the same amount and quality of light, nutrients, germination sites, etc. This is not easy to resolve.

One approach is to group quadrats on the basis of a measured environmental factor that is thought to be important in determining the performance and distribution of the species present. For example, in a study of the niche relationships among *Sphagnum* mosses, Greshon (1989) was able to assign quadrats into resource classes based on their height above the local water table. The study thus determined the niche breadth and overlap along a habitat dimension related to the local hydrology, considered to be an important environmental gradient affecting mire vegetation.

Numerous measures of niche breadth and overlap have been suggested (Ludwig and Reynolds, 1988; Krebs, 1989, 1999). Many of the diversity indices described in Chapter 2 have been used to assess species distribution among resources classes. High resource use diversity is equated with a wide or broad niche. For example, Simpson's index of diversity has been used to measure niche breadth along with a reciprocal form, known as Levins' index of niche width:

niche breadth of species j

$$\mathrm{NB}_j = 1 - \sum_{i=1}^{R} p_{ij}^2 \quad \text{or} \quad \mathrm{NB}_j = \frac{1}{\displaystyle\sum_{i=1}^{R} p_{ij}^2} \quad \text{and} \quad \sum_{j=1}^{s} p_j = 1.0$$

relative importance of species j out of s species, in resource unit i out of R resource classes

Levins' (1968) index of niche overlap has been widely used:

$$\mathrm{LO}_{12} = \frac{\displaystyle\sum_{i=1}^{R} p_{i1} p_{i2}}{\displaystyle\sum_{i=1}^{R} p_{i1}^2} \quad \text{and} \quad \mathrm{LO}_{21} = \frac{\displaystyle\sum_{i=1}^{R} p_{i1} p_{i2}}{\displaystyle\sum_{i=1}^{R} p_{i2}^2}$$

where LO_{12} = overlap between species 1 and 2
LO_{21} = overlap between species 2 and 1

These measures of niche overlap are not symmetrical. Notice that the equations differ only in terms of the denominator, which corresponds to Levins' niche breadth measure; that is, the degree of niche overlap measured by the numerator is standardised relative to the niche breadth of each species. Pianka (1973) proposed an alternative symmetrical form of Levins' index of niche overlap. In Pianka's index the denominator is replaced by the square root of the product of the niche breadth of both species:

$$O_{12} = \frac{\sum p_{i1} p_{i2}}{\sqrt{\sum p_{i1}^2 \sum p_{i2}^2}}$$

The Freeman–Tukey (FT) index of Smith (1982) and the percentage similarity[2] (PS) measure proposed by Feininger *et al.* (1981) are recommended here as indices of niche breadth:

$$FT_j = \sum_{i=1}^{R} p_{ij}q_i$$

absolute difference between p_{ij} and q_i

$$PS_j = \sum_{i=1}^{R} \min(p_{ij}, q_i) = 1 - \frac{1}{2}\sum_{i=1}^{R} |p_{ij} - q_i|$$

sum of minimum values; if $p_{ij} = 0.8$ and $q_i = 0.4$, the value summed is 0.4

As above, R is the number of resource classes, p_{ij} is the relative proportional abundance (use) made of resource class i by species j, and q_i is the proportional availability of resource class i. Note that $\sum_{i=1}^{R} q_i = 1.0$.

Unlike other indices of niche breadth, such as the commonly used index suggested by Levins (1968), both of these measures take into account the availability of resource classes. Smith (1982) provides formulae based on a Taylor series approximation which allow the variance of PS and FT to be estimated and 95% confidence limits to be calculated:

$$V(\widehat{FT}) = (1 - (FT)^2)/4N$$

$$V(\widehat{PS}) = \frac{1}{N}\left[1 - \left(\sum_{i=1}^{R} p_{ij}I_i\right)^2 - \sum_{i=1}^{R} p_{ij}J_i\right]$$

$$I_i = \begin{cases} -1 & \text{if } p_{ij} > q_i \\ 0 & \text{if } p_{ij} = q_i \\ 1 & \text{if } p_{ij} < q_i \end{cases}$$

The values of I_i and J_i depend on the relative sizes of p_{ij} and q_{ij}; N is the sample size.

$$J_i = \begin{cases} 1 & \text{if } p_{ij} = q_i \\ 0 & \text{otherwise} \end{cases}$$

The PS index effectively compares the distribution of resource class availability with species utilisation. The maximum value of 1.0 implies that the species distribution simply reflects resource class availability; lower values will occur if the distribution of species differs from the resource class distribution, i.e. the species is 'selectively utilising' the available resource classes. The FT index also has a maximum value of 1.0 when the species distribution does not differ from a random pattern of resource class occupation. The hypothesis that $FT = 1.0$ may be tested using the chi-squared goodness-of-fit statistic with $R - 1$ degrees of freedom:

$$\chi^2_{FT} = 8N(1 - \widehat{FT})$$

No equivalent method exists for the PS index (Smith, 1982). However, a tentative test of the hypothesis that $PS = 1.0$ may be made by considering the calculated confidence intervals about PS; if the intervals contain 1.0, the hypothesis may be accepted. The formulae used for estimating the variances of the indices represent the lower bounds of the actual variances and are strongly influenced by sample size. Be careful when using the test statistics, particularly with large sample sizes. And although both indices account for resource class availability, neither controls for the distinctiveness of resource classes. Be careful too when comparing the niche breadth measure of a species calculated from different resource data matrices (e.g. data from different sites), unless the data sets are equally heterogeneous (Colwell and Futuyama, 1971).

Box 5.3 Niche breadth and niche overlap

All of the values in the columns between C1 and C9 have been derived from the original data on resource class availability (C1, C2) and the abundance of species 1 in each resource class (C4). Column totals are used to calculate various indices of niche breadth. The frequency distribution of a second species (species 2) is presented in C10. Columns C11 to C13 make it possible to calculate measures of the niche overlap between species 1 and species 2.

C1 Resource class category (i)	C2 Number of sample units in each resource class	C3 Resource class frequency (q_i)	C4 Abundance of species 1 in each resource class	C5 Frequency of species 1 in each resource class (p_{i1})	C6 p_{i1}^2	C7 = C5 × C3 $p_{i1}q_i$	C8 $min(p_{i1}, q_i)$	C9 $p_{i1}\ln p_{i1}$	C10 Frequency of species 2 in each resource class (p_{i2})	C11 p_{i2}^2	C12 = C5 × C10 $p_{i1}p_{i2}$	C13 $min(p_{i1}, p_{i2})$
1	12	0.098361	29	0.06872	0.004722	0.006759	0.06872	−0.07992	0.032787	0.001075	0.002253	0.032787
2	15	0.122951	200	0.473934	0.224613	0.058271	0.122951	−0.15369	0.081967	0.006719	0.038847	0.081967
3	20	0.163934	23	0.054502	0.002971	0.008935	0.054502	−0.06887	0.327869	0.107498	0.017787	0.054502
4	9	0.07377	110	0.260664	0.067945	0.019229	0.07377	−0.15221	0	0	0	0
5	13	0.106557	11	0.026066	0.000679	0.002778	0.026066	−0.04129	0.333333	0.111111	0.008689	0.026066
6	23	0.188525	1	0.00237	5.62E−06	0.000447	0.00237	−0.00622	0.032787	0.001075	7.77E−05	0.00237
7	10	0.081967	28	0.066351	0.004402	0.005439	0.066351	−0.07817	0.027322	0.000747	0.001813	0.027322
8	20	0.163934	20	0.047393	0.002246	0.007769	0.047393	−0.06276	0.163934	0.026874	0.007769	0.047393
Totals	122	1	422	1	0.307585	0.109626	0.462124	−0.64312	1	0.255099	0.077319	0.272408

Levin's measures of niche breadth

Species 1
Using column total C6, the niche breadth for species 1:

$$NB_1 = 1 - \sum_{i=1}^{R} p_{i1}^2 = 1 - 0.3076 = 0.6924$$

Reciprocal form:

$$NB_1 = 1/\sum p_{i1}^2 = 1/0.3076 = 3.251$$

The maximum value for the reciprocal value is R, the number of resource classes

Species 2
Using the total from C10, the niche breadth for species 2:

$$NB_2 = 1 - \sum_{i=1}^{R} p_{i2}^2 = 1 - 0.25509 = 0.74491$$

Reciprocal form:

$$NB_1 = 1/\sum p_{i1}^2 = 1/0.25509 = 3.920$$

Freeman–Tukey (FT) index of niche breadth

Using the total of C7:

$$FT_1 = \sum \sqrt{p_{i1} q_i} = 0.109\,63 \qquad FT_2 \text{ is not calculated in the table, but it can be obtained by summing the result of C3} \times \text{C10.}$$

Percentage similarity: niche breadth.

$$PS_1 = \sum \min(p_{i1}, q_i) = 0.462\,124 \qquad PS_2 \text{ is not calculated in the table, but can be obtained from summing the minimum values C3 and C10}$$

This value is obtained from the sum of C8.

Shannon–Wiener diversity index as a measure of niche breadth

$$H_1' = -\sum p_{i1} \ln p_{i1} = -(-0.643\,12) = 0.643\,12 \qquad \longleftarrow \text{ required value obtained from the sum of C9}$$

A measure of the evenness of resource class use is given by

$$J_1 = H_1'/\ln R = 0.643\,12/\ln 8 = 0.3093 \qquad \longleftarrow R = 8, \text{ the number of resource classes}$$

Chapter 2 discusses H' and the related index of evenness J; the maximum value of J is 1.0, and the maximum value of H' is $\ln R$.

Levin's index of overlap

Overlap of species 1 with species 2

$$LO_{12} = \frac{\sum p_{i1} p_{i2}}{\sum p_{i1}^2} = \frac{0.077\,319}{0.307\,585} = 0.2514$$

Overlap of species 2 with species 1

$$LO_{21} = \frac{\sum p_{i1} p_{i2}}{\sum p_{i2}^2} = \frac{0.077\,319}{0.255\,099} = 0.3081 \qquad \swarrow \text{ total of C12}$$

$$\nwarrow \text{ total of C11}$$

Pianka's modified symmetrical version

$$O_{12} = \frac{\sum p_{i1} p_{i2}}{\sqrt{\sum p_{i1}^2 \sum p_{i2}^2}} = \frac{0.077\,319}{\sqrt{0.307\,585 \times 0.255\,099}} = 0.2760 \qquad \swarrow \text{ obtained from C6 and C11}$$

Percentage similarity: niche overlap

$$PS_{12} = \sum \min(p_{i1}, p_{i2}) = 0.272\,408 \qquad \longleftarrow \text{ obtained from the sum of C13}$$

The two indices differ in their sensitivity to species selectivity or occupation of rare resource classes; the FT index is more sensitive, whereas the PS measure gives more importance to dominant or more frequently used resource classes. Smith (1982) suggests that the PS index is more indicative of resource class avoidance than selectivity. Glime and Vitt (1987) found that the FT niche breadth measure was most reliable for narrow niche widths, where the species used a restricted range of resource classes. Feininger *et al.* (1981) have argued that the PS measure has the advantage of easy of interpretation. In addition it can also be used to provide a symmetrical measure of niche overlap. When using PS to measure niche overlap, p_{ij} retains its previous meaning, i.e. the proportional use of resource class *i* by species *j*; but q_i is replaced by p_{ik}, the proportional use of resource class *i* by species *k* (Colwell and Futuyama, 1971; Feininger *et al.*, 1981). Where niche overlap measures (PS) have been calculated for all possible species pairs, the values can be plotted using the polar ordination method described in Chapter 8 to produce a graphical representation of species niche relationships. Have a look at the example in Box 5.3.

5.3.1 Recommendations

Niche breadth
Resources classes or types identifiable   Where resources classes or types can be distinguished then FT and PS are recommended. Alternatively, if a limited number of distinct factors have been measured at each sample unit, weighted averages might prove useful (Section 5.2.3).

Resources not identifiable   If resource classes or types cannot be distinguished then a diversity index measure of niche breadth should be used, e.g. Levins' (1968) index or the Shannon–Wiener index of diversity (Chapter 2).

Niche overlap
PS is recommended for measuring niche overlap; it is versatile, readily interpretable and allows species ordinations to be produced.

5.4 Population index numbers

Population index numbers or indices have been used extensively to summarise wildlife monitoring data; this is especially true in ornithology. An index number for a year is defined as the ratio of the population size in that year to the population size in the base year. This ratio is normally multiplied by a 100, so the index number for the base year is 100. Imagine that, as part of a monitoring programme, the abundance of a species has been estimated at four sites over six years. In order to summarise the data and identify population trends, an index number can be calculated for each site and for the complete population. A reference base year must first be selected, often the first year for which reliable data exists; in each subsequent year the population is expressed as a percentage of the base year population. In this example the base year is year 1, the total estimated population is 272, and the index number is 100 (i.e. $272/272 \times 100$). For year 2 the index number is $342/272 \times 100 = 125.7$. If the population increases above the base year population the index will be greater than 100; if it declines below the base year population, the index will be less than 100. Using the same method, population index numbers may be calculated for each site and used to produce a composite index value (Table 5.1).

Table 5.1 Calculating population index numbers

| Year | Original species abundance values | | | | Totals | Overall index |
	Site 1	Site 2	Site 3	Site 4		
1	12	68	12	20	272	100
2	34	90	13	20	342	125.73
3	23	120	14	23	278	102.20
4	12	34	20	25	206	75.73
5	12	15	23	56	199	73.16
6	6	30	12	34	88	32.35

Year 1 values used as the base for the calculation of the overall index and the site indices shown below.

	Individual site population index values				Totals	Composite population index
1	100.00	100.00	100.00	100.00	400.00	100.00
2	283.33	132.35	108.33	100.00	624.02	156.00
3	191.67	176.47	116.67	115.00	599.80	149.95
4	100.00	50.00	166.67	125.00	441.67	110.42
5	100.00	22.06	191.67	280.00	593.73	148.43
6	50.00	44.12	100.00	170.00	364.12	91.03

Total of year 1 values used as the base reference

Totals of site population index values used to generate overall composite population index

Site-specific index numbers allow the behaviour of the population at the different sites to be compared. Notice that the composite and overall population index values are not the same. The reasons for this are quite simple. The value of the overall index will be strongly influenced by values for the most abundant populations. In comparison the influence of large population values on the composite index is reduced, but not entirely removed. Crawford (1991) suggests that calculating the index as the geometric mean may reduce the influence of large population values further:

$$\text{GM} = \left(\prod_{i=1}^{s} x_i \right)^{1/s} = (x_1 x_2 \ldots x_s)^{1/s} = (\log x_1 + \log x_2 + \cdots + \log x_s)/s$$

where x_i is the population size at site i and GM is the geometric mean of the population for all s sites. Values of GM for each year can then be used to generate a sequence of population index numbers.

Unfortunately, data sets are rarely complete; some site values may be missing for certain years and the investigator has to decide whether to remove these sites from the data or whether to find an alternative way of calculating the population index. One approach to this problem is known as the ratio method. To calculate the index for a particular year, only sites where values exist for both the current and previous year are summed to obtain a total for each year. Find the ratio of the current population total to the total for the previous year, then multiply by the previous year's index; this gives the new index value. The method is best illustrated by a simple example in which the population estimate for site 4 in year 3 is missing (Table 5.2).

Table 5.2 The ratio method calculates indices for incomplete data sets

					Totals based on sites		Missing value ratio (R)	Overall index value	Calculation
Year	Site 1	Site 2	Site 3	Site 4	1 to 3	1 to 4			
1	12	68	12	20		272		100	$(272/272) \times 100$
2	34	90	13	20	137	342		125.73	$(342/272) \times 100$
3	23	120	14	–	157	–	1.146[a]	144.09	$125.73 \times R$
4	12	34	20	25		206		75.73	$(206/272) \times 100$

[a] $R = 137/157$, i.e. total excluding site with missing value for year $n + 1$ divided by the corresponding total for year n.

Although this method is simple and has been widely used, simulation studies show that the short-term loss of values from an important site can have a persistent effect on the series of index numbers (Crawford, 1991; Underhill and Prys-Jones, 1994). An alternative approach is to model missing values. Underhill and Prys-Jones (1994) demonstrate how missing values may be modelled by assuming that site values depend on three factors: a site-specific factor (s), a year factor (y) and a monthly factor (m) for the date of recording. The expected value, $E(x)$, for the missing site is simply the product (sym) of these three factors. They present a method for estimating the site, year and monthly factors using the complete data set. They also show how a bootstrap procedure may be used to set confidence or consistency limits about index numbers (Section 5.5). In essence the bootstrap procedure involves drawing a random sample of constant size (with replacement) from the available site population values for each year and using them to calculate the index numbers. The process is repeated 1000 times. Each random sample will produce a slightly different index value distributed about an overall mean; the values are sorted and the lower and upper 5% are identified. Although the concept of index numbers is simple, it does provide a convenient way of summarising large data sets. The approach may be generalised to other situations. Crawford (1991) provides a detailed description of their calculation and use, and Prys-Jones *et al.* (1994) provide a good example on monitoring coastal bird populations in the United Kingdom.

5.5 *The statistical properties of indices*

In order to make tests of significance the statistical properties of an index need to be known, e.g. whether it is normally distributed. Unfortunately, the statistical properties of most indices are unknown. Without a reliable estimate of the variance, the index can only be used as a descriptive statistic. Four methods may be used to investigate the statistical properties of an index and provide an estimate of its variance, allowing statistical comparisons to be made.

Direct calculation of index variance
If the variances of the variables used to calculate an index are known, it is sometimes possible to estimate the variance of the index using the appropriate formula (Box 5.4). However, this approach is often cumbersome, particularly when the calculation of the index involves the multiplication and division of variables. When this is the case the covariances between variables and the variance of each variable need to be known or estimated. Once calculated, the estimate of variance is used to construct confidence intervals

---

Box 5.4 **Combined variance of random variables**

Variance of summed random variables

For independent variables

$$\text{var}(a_1 X_1 + \cdots + a_n X_n) \cong a_1 \sigma_1^2 + \cdots + a_n \sigma_n^2$$

Note the variance for the difference between two variables is the sum of the variable variances not the difference, i.e.

$$\text{var}(X_1 - X_2) \cong \sigma_1^2 + \sigma_2^2$$

For non-independent variables:

$$\text{var}(a_1 X_1 + \cdots + a_n X_n) \cong \sum_{i=1}^{n} \sum_{j=1}^{n} a_i a_j \, \text{cov}(X_i, X_j)$$

The sample covariance of two variables, X and Y, is given by:

$$\text{cov}(X, Y) = \frac{\sum (x - \bar{x}_1)(y - \bar{x}_2)}{n - 1}$$

$$\text{cov}(X, X) = \text{var}(X)$$

where n is the number of X and Y values. If X and Y are independent then the $\text{cov}(X, Y) = 0$.

Variance of a product of two random variables X and Y

$$\text{var}(XY) \cong \mu_X^2 \mu_Y^2 \left[\frac{\text{var}(X)}{\mu_X^2} + \frac{\text{var}(Y)}{\mu_Y^2} + \frac{2 \, \text{cov}(X, Y)}{\mu_X \mu_Y} \right]$$

Variance of a ratio of two random variables X and Y

$$\text{var}\left(\frac{X}{Y} \right) \cong \frac{\mu_X^2}{\mu_Y^2} \left[\frac{\text{var}(X)}{\mu_X^2} + \frac{\text{var}(Y)}{\mu_Y^2} - \frac{2 \, \text{cov}(X, Y)}{\mu_X \mu_Y} \right]$$

When using the product and ratio equations, the population means (μ) are replaced by the appropriate sample means ($\bar{x}, \bar{y}$).

---

or for hypothesis testing; the implicit assumption is that the index is normally distributed, but this may not be the case.

5.5.1 Simulation or Monte Carlo approach

Most general statistical packages such as MINITAB and SPSS can be used to generate random values. For a particular distribution, the user need only specify a limited number of key parameters. For the Poisson and exponential distributions, only the mean is required; the normal distribution requires the mean and standard deviation, and the binomial distribution requires the probability of success and the number of trials.[3] To simulate the distribution of the index, random values are generated for each of the variables involved in the calculation of the index. The index is then calculated using the randomly generated values. If 100 random values are generated for each variable, 100 simulated index values can be generated. The distribution of these simulated index values can then be investigated directly; once established, appropriate confidence intervals may be constructed as required. An example of this approach is presented in Section 4.5. Two practical problems can limit its usefulness:

- Knowledge about the distribution of the variables used to calculate the index is required. If uncertainty exists over the parameter values or distributions used to generate the random values, assess the sensitivity of the variance estimate to changes in these distribution parameters.

- The number of simulated values is normally large – 250, 500, perhaps 1000. In most cases the variance estimate and the index mean will stabilise rapidly as the number of values increases; if this does not happen then the method is clearly inappropriate for that index and it should be abandoned.

Note that a generalised form of this approach can be used to produce null model values. For example, under a null model, species might be assumed to be uniformly distributed among resource units. Based on this null model, the expected mean and variance of an index of resource use could be established from simulated random values. Experimental values may then be compared with the expected values, allowing statistical inferences to be made. A deeper insight into ecology or biology of a system may also be gained from a comparison of the expected values generated under different null models.

Jackknife estimates of variance

The jackknife provides a simple non-parametric method for estimating the variance about a parameter or statistic (e.g. an index) that has been derived from a sample of size n. Burt and Barber (1996) define the jackknife procedure as

a resampling procedure in which a sample of size n *is used to form* n *subsamples each containing* n − 1 *of the original observations. (A different observation is left out of each subsample.) Variation from subsample to subsample is used to estimate the standard error (or variance) of a statistic.*

Jackknifing thus requires three steps:

1. Generate the subsamples. Delete a single observation from the sample and calculate the parameter (θ) using the remaining $n - 1$ observations. Repeat until n estimates of θ are obtained, each time omitting a different value. These estimates are sometimes called pseudovalues.

2. Calculate the mean ($\bar{\theta}$) and standard deviation (S) of the n new estimates of θ, from which the standard error of the mean of θ may be calculated.

3. Calculate the jackknife standard error of the mean:

$$\text{SE} = \frac{S}{\sqrt{n}} = \sqrt{\frac{(n-1)}{n} \sum_{i=1}^{n} (\theta_i - \bar{\theta})^2}$$

parameter value obtained with observation *i* omitted

If 10 water samples (i.e. observations) are taken at each of two lakes and an index of pollution calculated for each lake, the jackknife procedure could be used to estimate the variance and standard error about the mean index value for each lake. For each lake the index would be calculated 10 times, each time omitting a different water sample; the variance and standard error of these pseudovalues are then calculated and used to make statistical inferences. The jackknife estimate of the standard error is simply the standard error of the pseudovalues.

Note that the method does not require the parameter being jackknifed to be normally distributed. But it does have limitations. Firstly, the values of θ must not depend on the order of observations in the sample. Secondly, if a function of a mean is to be jackknifed, the function must be continuous. Thirdly, jackknife estimates of standard errors may be biased. For non-linear variance functions (i.e. where the variance is not a linear function of the observations), the jackknife procedure can overestimate the error (variance).

An approximate measure of bias and its direction may be obtained by subtracting the jackknife estimate (i.e. the mean of the pseudovalues) from the estimate based on the original sample. If the bias is large, it may be subtracted from the jackknife estimate to give a more realistic value. Unlike the Monte Carlo approach the jackknife procedure cannot be extended to allow direct calculation of confidence intervals; this is because too few pseudovalues are generated for the lower and upper percentile (e.g. 2.5% and 97.5%) to be identified reliably (Efron, 1982; Dixon, 1993). However, confidence limits can be estimated by assuming a normal distribution and using the estimated standard error to calculate the interval in the usual way; $\theta \pm t_k \text{SE}_\theta$, where t_k is a critical value from the t-distribution with k degrees of freedom. Unfortunately, the appropriate number of degrees of freedom is not known, although the use of $n-1$, where n is the original sample size has been used successfully (Meyer *et al.*, 1986; Dixon, 1993).

The bootstrap estimate of variance

In the bootstrap procedure, the original sample of n values is used to generate a large number of new simulated samples (bootstrap samples) each of size n. The statistic (e.g. an index) is then calculated for each bootstrap sample. The unknown sampling distribution is approximated from the distribution of the bootstrap estimates. Bootstrap samples are obtained by repeated resampling of the original sample with replacement. Suppose that the original sample is represented by six uniform balls each with one of the numbers 2, 3, 3, 4, 4, 5 marked on it and placed in a bag. The sample contains two 3s and two 4s; 2 and 5 occur only once. To generate a random bootstrap sample, a ball would be drawn from the bag, the number recorded and the ball replaced before drawing another ball. To generate a single bootstrap sample, the process is repeated six times. Repeating the entire sampling process generates further bootstrap samples. Because the sampling is conducted with replacement, some values may be drawn more than once and others may not be selected at all. Manual bootstrap sampling is not practical, so a computer program is used to generate the samples. If a specialist bootstrapping program is not available using MINITAB[4] or a similar package, two approaches are possible:

- Number each of the n values in the original sample from 1 to n. Using a uniform random number generator, so that each number is equally likely to occur, generate a sequence of random numbers between 1 and n. Divide the random sequence into non-overlapping sets of n random numbers, and use these sets to identify the original sample values to be included in each bootstrap sample.

- Using an appropriate discrete distribution, generate a random sequence of values. Divide the sequence into non-overlapping sets of n values to form the bootstrap samples. To define the required discrete distribution, the original values and their associated probabilities need to be specified. For example, if the original values were 2, 3, 3, 4, 4, 5, they will need to be entered along with their associated probabilities. The values 2 and 5 each have a probability of 1/6 and the values 3 and 4 have a probability of $2/6 = 1/3$. The computer program uses these probabilities to generate the random sequence of values.

Once the bootstrap samples have been generated, the procedure is similar to the jackknife. The mean and standard error of the bootstrap samples are calculated, and the bias of the bootstrap estimate is obtained as before:

$$\text{bias} = \bar{\theta} - \theta$$

where $\bar{\theta}$ is the mean index or statistic calculated from the bootstrap samples and θ is the statistic calculated from the original sample. Using the normal formula, the standard deviation of the bootstrap estimate is given by:

$$S_\theta = \sqrt{\frac{1}{B-1} \sum_{i=1}^{B} (\theta_i - \bar{\theta})^2}$$

where B is the number of bootstrap samples. The larger the value of B, the greater the reliability of the bootstrap estimate. Typically 50 to 100 bootstrap samples are used to estimate the standard deviation and standard error (Efron, 1987). As with the jackknife procedure, if a normal distribution is assumed the estimated standard error may be used to set confidence

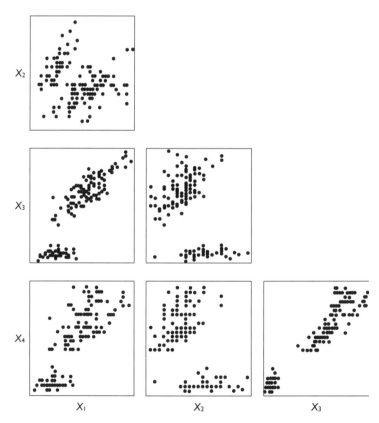

Figure 5.1 Triangular arrangement of all pairwise scatter plots for four variables. Variables describe the length and width of sepals and petals for 150 iris plants (50 plants in each of 3 species). Reprinted, with permission, from Tukey and Tukey, 1981, Graphical display of data sets in three or more dimensions, in *Interpreting Multivariate Data,* V. Barnet (ed.), John Wiley, Chichester, pp. 189–275.

limits about $\bar{\theta}$. Alternatively the confidence limits may be derived directly from the distribution of the bootstrap estimates. The simplest way is to sort the bootstrap estimates in numerical order and then produce a cumulative probability plot, from which the appropriate percentile levels may be read (Dixon, 1993). If confidence intervals are to be derived in this way, the number of bootstrap replicates should be as large as possible (1000 or more). But this may not be possible with small original sample sizes; for example, if the original sample size is 4 then there are only 256 (i.e. $4 \times 4 \times 4 \times 4$) possible different bootstrap samples. As with all statistical procedures, the reliability of any estimate improves with sample size. Both the bootstrap and jackknife procedures are non-parametric, but they require the original samples to be independent. Both procedures provide a convenient solution to a difficult problem. Bootstrapping is the more complex and computer intensive but it is often the more robust (Efron, 1987; Dixon, 1993).

5.6 *Graphing complex data sets*

Relationships between variables are often most easily identified when data is presented as a diagram or graph. Crothers (1981) provides an introduction to the use of different graphs and diagrams to display environmental data sets. The use of graphs and diagrams to present and analyse ecological data sets is discussed in depth by Tukey and Tukey (1981) and more recently by Ellison (1993). This section deals only with graphs that might be used to represent data sets that could also be summarised by the calculation of an appropriate index. The data will normally be of two forms. Either information will be available for many variables recorded at a large number of samples units (e.g. results of an ecological survey, species abundance recorded at a number of locations). Or information may be available for a limited

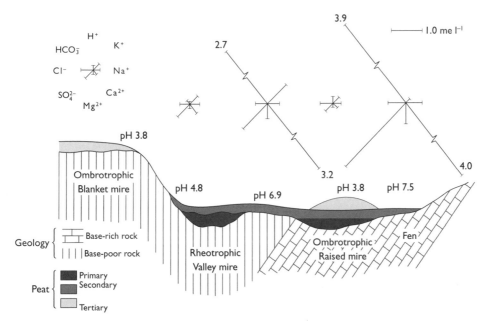

Figure 5.2 The interrelationship of primary, secondary and tertiary peat-forming environments. The rose diagrams show the relative concentrations (milliequivalents per litre) of important ions in the interstitial water of the surface peat. Reprinted, with permission, from J.R. Etherington, 1982, *Environment and Plant Ecology*, 2nd edn, John Wiley, Chichester, p. 77.

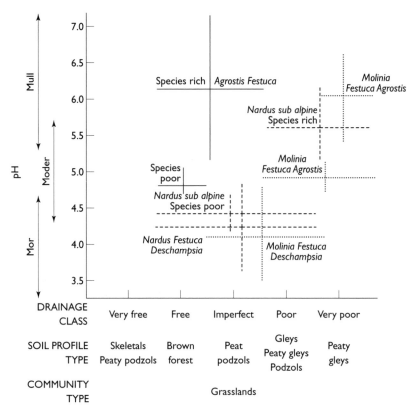

Figure 5.3 Two-dimensional direct ordination of grass-moorland community types in Scotland. Dominant species: (1) *Agrostis/Festuca*, (2) *Nardus stricta*, (3) *Molinia caerulea*. Adapted from J. Tivy, 1993, *Biogeography: A Study of Plants in the Ecosphere*, Addison-Wesley, Harlow, p. 105.

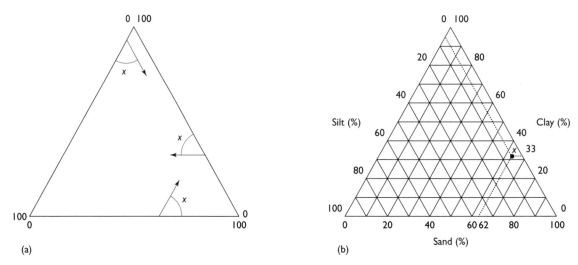

(a)　　　　　　　　　　　　　　　　　(b)

Figure 5.4 (a) How to carry values across a trilinear graph, $x = 60°$. (b) Soil composition x is 62% sand, 33% clay and 5% silt; notice that the percentages sum to 100.

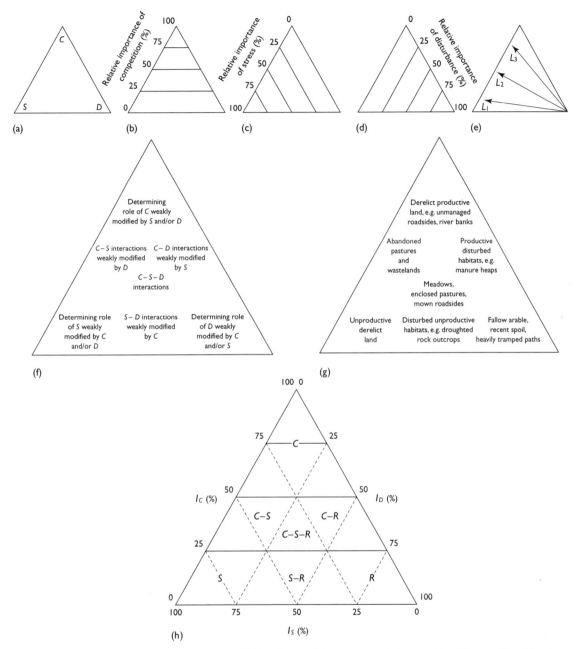

Figure 5.5 A triangular model of herbaceous vegetation. (a) Identification of the corners at which competition (*C*), stress (*S*) and disturbance (*D*) are exclusive determinants. (b, c, d) Contours in percentage contribution of competition, stress and disturbance, respectively. (e) Course of vegetation succession; the arrows represent lines of succession with low (*L*₁), moderate (*L*₂) and high (*L*₃) productivity. (f) Interaction of competition, stress and disturbance. (g) Location of selected habitat types. (h) Here *I*$_c$ is the relative importance of competition (—), *I*$_S$ is the relative importance of stress (– – –) and *I*$_D$ is the relative importance of stress disturbance (– · –). Parts (a) to (g) are reprinted, with permission, from Grime (1974) and part (h) is reprinted, with permission, from Grime (1977).

number of variables recorded at a large number of sample units that can be logically grouped (e.g. water quality parameters measured for replicated samples collected from a number of different lakes). In each case the number of individual data values is likely to be large, making the interpretation difficult. As we have seen, indices might be used to simplify and summarise the data, but valuable information can be lost and relationships obscured. A

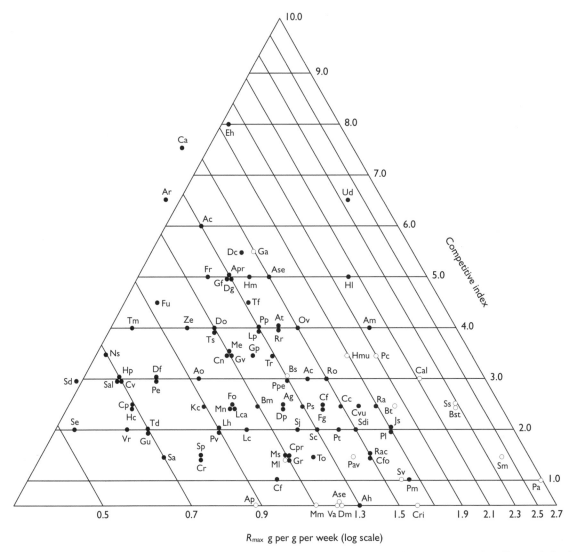

Figure 5.6 A triangular ordination of herbaceous species: (○) annuals, (●) perennials and biennials. The competitive index (CI) was calculated from the formula $CI = \frac{1}{2}(a + b + c)$ where a is estimated from the maximum height of the leaf canopy ($a = 1$ for height <12 cm, $a = 2$ for height 12–25 cm, $a = 3$ for height 25–37 cm, $a = 4$ for height 37–50 cm, $a = 5$ for height 50–62 cm, $a = 6$ for height 62–75 cm, $a = 7$ for height 75–87 cm, $a = 8$ for height 87–100 cm, $a = 9$ for height 100–112 cm, $a = 10$ for height >112 cm); b is the lateral spread ($b = 0$ for small therophytes; $b = 1$ for robust therophytes; $b = 2$ for perennials with compact, unbranched rhizome forming small (<10 cm diameter) tussock; $b = 3$ for perennials with rhizomatous system or tussock attaining diameter >100 cm; $b = 4$ for perennials attaining diameter 26–100 cm; $b = 5$ for perennials attaining diameter >100 cm); and c is estimated from the maximum accumulation of persistent litter ($c = 0$ for no cover, $c = 1$ for thin discontinuous cover, $c = 2$ for thin continuous cover, $c = 3$ for cover up to 1 cm deep, $c = 4$ for cover up to 5 cm deep, $c = 5$ for cover >5 cm deep). Letter codes identify the plotted species. Reprinted, with permission, from Grime (1974).

better alternative is to explore relationships within the data by graphical means before attempting to develop or calculate an index. But how should the data be plotted?

Two-dimensional scatter plots

Two-dimensional scatter plots are among the simplest type of graph. Values of one variable are plotted along the x-axis, values of a second variable along the y-axis. These graphs have two limitations: only two variables may be plotted at a time; and patterns can become obscured as the number of plotted points increases. The first problem may be partially overcome by plotting pairwise combinations of variables and arranging the plots in a triangular pattern (Figure 5.1). Alternatively, points may be plotted or represented as shapes. A simple example is given in Figure 5.2, where the arms radiating from each point are drawn to scale and represent a different variable. Plotting mean values can reduce the number of plotted points. Information on the extent of variation can be retained by plotting the range or standard deviation of values for both the x and y variables (Figure 5.3)

Three-dimensional graphs and trilinear graphs

Most spreadsheet programs can produce a three-dimensional plot of x, y and z variables, but they are not always easy to interpret and a simpler two-dimensional plot, a trilinear graph, may be more informative. Trilinear graphs can be easily produced, as shown in Figure 5.4. Each variable must be expressed as a proportion or a percentage; the axis values are arranged so they chase one another around the diagram. Grime (1974, 1977, 1979) has developed a triangular model of plant strategies. The model assumes that plant strategies have evolved in response to three distinct groups of selection pressures which relate to the intensity and frequency of competition, stress and disturbance. Grime suggests that these selective forces have resulted in the development of three primary plant strategies: competitive plants, stress tolerators and ruderals, i.e. plants able to succeed in sites subject to frequent disturbance. Conceptually, he envisages that plant species may be visualised as existing within a triangular ordination space, where the axes are scaled to measure the percentage importance of competition, stress and disturbance (Figure 5.5). In practice, Grime has produced an approximation to this model ordination by plotting only two variables. An index of competitive ability is plotted along the right-hand axis and log (maximum relative growth rate) along the bottom axis; the resulting pattern largely falls within the triangular model (Figure 5.6). Although not without its critics (Loehle, 1988; Grubb, 1998), Grime's triangular C-S-R strategy model has been extensively used and cited.[5] The model provides an interesting example of how complex concepts and data may be effectively summarised by a deceptively simple diagram.

Further reading

Dixon, P.M. (1993) The bootstrap and jackknife: describing the precision of ecological indices. In *Design and Analysis of Ecological Experiments*, S.M. Scheiner and J. Gurevitch (eds). Chapman & Hall, London, pp. 290–318.

Ellison, A.M. (1993) Exploratory data analysis and graphic display. In *Design and Analysis of Ecological Experiments*, S.M. Scheiner and J. Gurevitch (eds). Chapman & Hall, London, pp. 14–45.

Krebs, J.C. (1999) *Ecological Methodology*, 2nd edn. Addison Wesley Longman, Menlo Park, CA.

Spellerberg, I.F. (1992) *Evaluation and Assessment for Conservation*. Chapman & Hall, London.

PART TWO

Comparing
Data Sets

Chapter Six

Resemblance functions: distance and similarity

Summary

Methods that allow a quantitative assessment of the similarity (or dissimilarity) between two or more samples are described. Where the data collected from each sample or sample unit consists of records for the same or a similar range of traits, resemblance or distance measures may be used to compare the data sets. Typical data sets include community samples where species identity and abundance are recorded for a number of sites, and morphometric or taxonomic data sets obtained from scoring individual organisms for the same range of variables. In each case resemblance functions allow the similarity between samples or individual sample units to be assessed. If the data table is arranged in the normal way – rows to represent variables or traits and columns to represent sample units or samples – resemblance measures are typically used to compare columns. Different measures are appropriate for binary, qualitative, quantitative and mixed data sets. Suitable procedures are presented for each type and for combinations of data types. Resemblance measures are essentially descriptive statistics that place few restrictions on the nature of the data or the size of the samples. They do not require samples to be random.

6.1 *Introduction*

Ecologists and biologists frequently need to assess the degree of similarity or dissimilarity between two or more sets of data. The data sets might represent species abundance values in artificial samples (e.g. quadrats) taken from several distinct locations, or the results of sampling at one location over a period of time. Alternatively the samples may be 'natural', e.g. invertebrate communities associated with particular decomposing logs on a forest floor, or the range and abundance of ectoparasites found on different animals. In both cases the data may be presented as a simple two-way table, where the columns contain species abundance values obtained from a single sample unit or site. Values associated with a particular species are placed in a single row across the table. Similar data tables might be produced during morphological studies; then the columns would record values collected from individual plants or animals, and the rows would record values for particular morphological characteristics. In environmental studies the columns might represent sites and the rows soil characteristics or other specific physical parameters.

A large number of 'resemblance functions' have been developed to analyse data sets of this type (Legendre and Legendre, 1983; Wolda, 1981). But in practice, relatively few have proved to be both robust and informative (Ludwig and Reynolds, 1988; Digby and Kempton, 1987). This chapter describes some of the more common and more useful measures of similarity.

The most appropriate choice of resemblance function or index of similarity/dissimilarity will depend primarily on the purpose of the analysis and on the form of the data (i.e. binary, qualitative or quantitative). The following data set records the percentage abundance of nine species (a to i) at two sites (1, 2). The results can be represented in their original form or reduced to a presence/absence record for each species, where absence is scored 0 and presence 1 (Table 6.1).

This simple data set raises some interesting questions about the weighting or influence that particular matches and mismatches should have on our final assessment of the similarity between the sites. When only presence/absence data (i.e. binary data) is available, most measures of similarity place equal weighting on joint occurrences and mismatches where a species occurs in only one of the two samples. But what weighting should be given to the absence of a species from both sites, e.g. species i? This last point might appear rather trivial

Table 6.1 Abundance data for species a to i from two sample units, site 1 and site 2

Species	Abundance		Species presence/absence	
	Site 1	Site 2	Site 1	Site 2
a	44	39	1	1
b	20	18	1	1
c	0	14	0	1
d	15	1	1	1
e	6	2	1	1
f	2	1	1	1
g	1	0	1	0
h	1	1	1	1
i	0	0	0	0
Total summed abundance	89	75	–	–
Total no. of species	7	7	7	7

– common sense suggests that joint non-occurrences should be discounted. However, some measures of similarity give equal weighting to both joint occurrences and non-occurrences, effectively treating the absence of a species from both sites as a shared characteristic. This can be a desirable property. In numerical taxonomy, where the two columns of data might represent the occurrence of taxonomic traits possessed by two distinct specimens, the absence of particular traits from both specimens may be of equal interest as the joint presence of other traits. Similarly, if the columns of data being compared are part of a larger data table summarising the species composition of many sites, then the joint absence of a species (recorded elsewhere in the data set) from two sites may be an important common characteristic. Where quantitative data is available, analogous questions can be asked. Should equal amounts of rare and common species have an equal effect on the size of a calculated similarity index or distance measure? For example, should equal weighting be given to the amounts in common of species a, b, h despite the differences in the total abundance of each species? Are differences between the sites important in terms of the total number of species present or in terms of their summed abundance? The relative importance placed on these questions will largely depend on the objectives of the study and they should guide the choice of similarity or distance measure.

6.1.1 *Properties of similarity and distance measures*

Resemblance functions are descriptive coefficients; their values increase in a predictable way with either the degree of similarity or difference between data sets. The most commonly used measures of similarity do not have easily defined probability distributions, so it is rarely possible to set confidence limits on calculated similarity values or to perform statistical tests for significant differences between values. Similarity indices usually give values that range from 0 for samples which have no characteristics in common to 1.0 for samples that are identical. Where quantitative data is being analysed, note that the value obtained for a similarity or distance measure depends on the absolute values recorded for each characteristic in the data set. Correlation coefficients have been used and advocated as measures of similarity, but they do not have this property. Suppose the species abundances in the two sample units differ substantially, but the relative patterns (rankings) of individual species abundance values are similar, then the two samples will be highly correlated, implying a high degree of similarity. For this and other reasons (Chapter 7), correlation coefficients should not normally be used to assess sample similarity.

Three broad classes of resemblance functions can be recognised; similarity indices used to analyse binary data sets; similarity indices used to compare quantitative data sets; and distance measures which evaluate the distance or difference between data sets. There is a close relationship between measures of distance or dissimilarity (D) and measures of similarity (S); D and S are complements or opposites of each other, and conversion between them is easy using one of two relationships (Digby and Kempton, 1987):

$$D = 1 - S$$

$$D = -\log S$$

The relationship $D = 1 - S$ is more common and may be modified to $D = 100 - S$ where S is expressed as a percentage.

The resemblance functions described in this chapter are all symmetrical; that is, if the calculated similarity between sample 1 and sample 2 is 0.45 then the calculated similarity between sample 2 and sample 1 will also be 0.45. Additional properties of some resemblance functions can be important when they are used to produce graphs that represent the

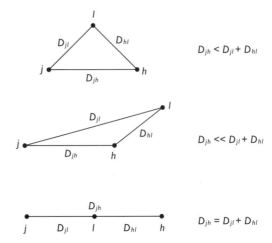

NON-EUCLIDEAN DISTANCES ARE NON-METRIC

Figure 6.1 Geometric representation of interpoint distances. Reprinted, with permission, from Fry (1993).

differences between sample units, i.e. ordination (Chapter 8), or to group and classify sample units (Chapter 9). Imagine a data set containing the results from a preliminary survey of three sites (1, 2, 3) where at each site the abundance of five species, common to all sites, was determined. In order to assess the differences between the sites, a dissimilarity value was calculated between each possible pair of sites, i.e. d_{12}, d_{13}, d_{23}, where d_{12} is the dissimilarity between sites 1 and 2, d_{13} is the dissimilarity between sites 1 and 3, and d_{23} is the dissimilarity between sites 2 and 3. The measure of dissimilarity is said to be metric if it is possible to represent the three sites as the points of a triangle whose side lengths correspond to d_{12}, d_{13}, d_{23} (Figure 6.1). For metric measures of dissimilarity, the triangle inequality $d_{ij} \leq d_{ik} + d_{ij}$ can be satisfied for any allocation of $1, 2, 3$ to i, j, k.

6.2 *Using resemblance functions*

6.2.1 *Binary similarity coefficients*

As with association analysis, binary presence/absence data can be summarised in the form of a 2×2 contingency table (Table 6.2). Using this notation the following commonly used similarity coefficients may be described.

Simple matching index

$$S_{sm} = \frac{\text{co-occurrences plus joint non-occurrences}}{\text{total number of occurrences and non-occurrences over the two samples}}$$

$$= \frac{a+d}{a+b+c+d} = \frac{6+1}{6+1+1+1} = \frac{7}{9} = 0.777$$

Table 6.2 Species presence and absence data from Table 6.1, presented as a 2 × 2 contingency table

Sample 2	*Sample 1*	
	Number of species present	*Number of species absent*
Number of species present	$a = 6$	$b = 1$
Number of species absent	$c = 1$	$d = 1$

Where a = number of species present in sample 1 and sample 2; b = number of species in sample 2 but absent from sample 1; c = number of species in sample 1 but absent from sample 2; d = numbers of species absent from both samples.

Jaccard index

$$S_j = \frac{\text{number of co-occurrences}}{\text{total occurrences over the two samples}}$$

$$= \frac{a}{a + b + c} = \frac{6}{6 + 1 + 1} = \frac{6}{8} = 0.75$$

Sorensen index

$$S_s = \frac{\text{twice the co-occurrences}}{\text{average of occurrences over the two samples}}$$

$$= \frac{2a}{2a + b + c} = \frac{2 \times 6}{(2 \times 6) + 1 + 1} = \frac{12}{14} = 0.857$$

The Sorensen index (Sorensen, 1948) is also known as the Dice index or the Czekanowski index. An alternative and closely related index, often called Sorensen's unweighted index, is

$$S_s = \frac{2a}{A + B} = \frac{2C}{A + B}$$

Here A and B are equal to the total number of species or traits recorded in the first and second samples, and C is the number of joint occurrences.

Ochiai index

$$S_o = \frac{\text{co-occurrences}}{\text{geometric mean of occurrences over the two samples}}$$

$$= \frac{a}{\sqrt{a + b} \sqrt{a + c}} = \frac{6}{\sqrt{7} \sqrt{7}} = 0.851 \qquad \text{(Ochiai, 1957)}$$

All these indices have performed well on real and simulated data sets. The simple matching index, S_{sm}, gives equal weight to co-occurrences and non-occurrences (values a and d in the contingency table). In most ecological studies this is not appropriate, so the index should only be used where it is deemed desirable, as is often the case in taxonomic studies (Dunn and Everitt, 1982). The values of Jaccard's S_j and Sorensen's S_s are not affected by joint non-occurrences (d is not included in the formula of either index). However, these indices differ in the weighting given to the number of joint occurrences. Sorensen's index (S_s) is most strongly influenced by the number of joint occurrences. Because of this, Krebs (1989) recommends that the Sorensen index should be used where it is thought that samples may not be complete or representative of the communities (sites) from which they were drawn; for example, where a substantial number of species are known to be present in the communities *but* have not been recorded in the sample. Thus, in practice it is probably safest to use the Sorensen index (S_s) unless the data has been obtained from (i) low diversity communities, or from (ii) samples known to be representative of the community as a whole, or (iii) where the sample units are characterised by a limited number of variables or traits that have been predetermined by the investigator, as might be the case in a study of site soil types. In these and analogous situations, Jaccard's index is favoured. Sorensen's index has been extensively used in molecular biology for studying ecology and evolution. It has been used to compare RNA and DNA nucleotide sequences; the similarity between sequences is calculated as $S_{AB} = 2N_{AB}/(N_A + N_B)$, where N_{AB} is the total number of identical oligo-nucleotide sequences common to organisms A and B, and N_A, N_B are the total number of oligonucleotide sequences identified in organism A and organism B. Since organisms with similar nucleotide sequences are assumed to be more closely related, patterns of organism nucleotide similarities can be used to establish phylogenetic trees or classifications (Altas and Bartha, 1998). The patterns of DNA banding produced on gels during DNA fingerprint-ing are typically compared using Sorensen's index. Here it is sometimes known as the *D*-value for unrelated individuals (Wetton *et al.*, 1987), the similarity index (Lynch, 1990), or the bandsharing value (Gullberg *et al.*, 1999). When used to compare gel bands, N_A and N_B represent the total number of bands scored for sample A and sample B, and N_{AB} equals the number of bands that are shared between the two samples.

Causton (1988) has illustrated the potential of the chi-squared statistic as a measure of similarity. Follow the normal procedure for chi-squared analysis of 2×2 contingency tables, and calculate the chi-squared test statistic (X^2) using the standard formula for a 2×2 contingency table:

$$X^2 = \frac{n(ad + bc)^2}{(a + b)(c + d)(a + c)(b + d)}$$

$$n = a + b + c + d$$

$$\text{d.f.} = 1$$

where a, b, c, d correspond to the values contained in the appropriately labelled cells of the table. The value of X^2 will depend on the number of species (or characters) in common, i.e. on the size of the values in cells a and d. If a is large in comparison to the other values in the table, a large positive value will be obtained, implying that the samples have a large proportion of their characteristics in common. The larger the value of X^2, the stronger the association. For the association to be significant at $p < 0.05$, it requires $X^2 > 3.84$. The value of X^2 may be converted into an index of similarity (S) whose values ranges from 0 to 1.0:

$$S_{X^2} = \frac{m + X^2}{2m}$$

where m is the total number of species present in the two samples.

Like other measures of similarity, this is purely a descriptive statistic, i.e. it cannot be used to test for significance. This particular measure of similarity does not perform well and has the disadvantage that its values depend not only on the species (or characters) that both samples have in common, but also on the number of species that neither sample contains, i.e. the values of d in the contingency table. The chi-squared procedure cannot be recommended as a measure of sample similarity, but it can be a useful measure of species association, i.e. a measure of the likelihood that two species will occur in the same sample unit. And it can form a basis for classifying sample units into distinct groups, each group being characterised by the presence or absence of a particular species (trait). This topic is discussed further in Chapters 7 and 9.

6.2.2 Qualitative data

Two approaches can readily be used to compare sets of qualitative data. The original data may be converted into a series of pseudobinary or pseudoquantitative variables, or the original data may be compared using an extension of the simple matching index (S_{sm}) described in Section 6.2.1. Suppose that, as part of an investigation into the distribution of hybrid forms of a particular species, individuals are recorded as having a range of qualitative characteristics. For example, if the study is concerned with the distribution and ecology of hybrids of the annual white-flowered white campion (*Silene alba*) and perennial red-flowered red campion (*Silene dioica*), the investigator might be interested in the presence of the following qualitative characters of each plant:

- *Flower colour*: white, pale pink, pink, red
- *Stems*: densely hairy, sparsely hairy
- *Calyx tooth length*: regular, irregular

These qualitative variables may be converted into a series of binary variables:

- Flower colour
    1   white: not white
    2   pale pink: not pale pink
    3   pink: not pink
    4   red: not red
- Stems
    5   densely hairy: not densely hairy
- Calyx tooth length
    6   regular: not regular

Once converted into six binary variables, individual plants may be scored for the occurrence or non-occurrence of each state and compared using the appropriate binary measures of similarity, e.g. Jaccard's index. It is also possible to convert qualitative variables into pseudoquantitative variables by giving 'weighting' values to particular qualitative states. For example, flower colours could be coded so that an individual plant is given a value of 6 for the pseudovariable flower colour if the flower is red, 4 if pale pink, 2 if pink, and 0 if white. Similar weighting values could be devised for the other qualitative variables. This approach is similar to using weighted averages for characterising sample units (Chapter 5). Once the data has been recoded in this way, similarities may be assessed using one of the standard measures of similarity outlined in Section 6.2.3.

Great care must be taken when converting qualitative variables to either pseudobinary or pseudoquantitative variables before calculating a similarity measure, otherwise distortion can easily be introduced into the data. In the flower example, one qualitative variable, flower colour, is replaced by four pseudobinary variables, each one representing a different colour state. As a result, flower colour will have a disproportionately large influence on the values of any binary index of similarity. In the same way, the quantitative weighting scores chosen for particular qualitative states can also distort the data set. In some cases this may be desirable. If certain characteristics are deemed to be of particular importance, they can be given a large range of weighting values, so that they have a strong influence on the calculated measure of similarity. However, great care must be taken. The investigator must be sure that each variable is given appropriate weighting and the relative influence of a particular variable on the analysis is fully appreciated and justified. Direct application of the simple matching coefficient (S_{sm}) on the original qualitative data avoids these problems. In this context S_{sm} is calculated as:

$$S_{sm} = \frac{\text{number of matching characteristics}}{\text{total number of characters}}$$

The use of the simple matching coefficient (S_{sm}) is therefore strongly recommended as the safest procedure, least likely to introduce distortion into the analysis of qualitative data. If it is decided to convert the original qualitative variables into pseudovariables, it is advisable to do a preliminary analysis using the simple matching coefficient. Comparisons between the preliminary analysis and any subsequent analyses will help the investigator to assess the degree, direction and desirability of any distortion introduced into the data.

6.2.3 Quantitative data

Measures of distance or dissimilarity are usually used to compare quantitative data sets. One group of measures, based on the Euclidean distance between samples has been used extensively. The difference or distance between two samples can easily be illustrated (Figure 6.2) for the simple case where each sample consists of the abundance values for two species only (X_1 and X_2). The distance between sample 1 and sample 2 is given by the length c, i.e. the hypotenuse of the right-angled triangle with sides a, b, c. From Pythagoras's theorem:

$$c^2 = a^2 + b^2 \quad \text{so} \quad c = \sqrt{a^2 + b^2}$$

where a = the absolute difference between the two samples in terms of the abundance of species X_1, i.e. $|x_{12} - x_{21}|$
           b = the absolute difference between the two samples in terms of the abundance of species X_2, i.e. $|x_{21} - x_{22}|$

The symbol $|\ldots|$ indicates absolute difference, i.e. all differences are treated as positive.

In the more general case, where the data is available for more than two variables, the total distance between the samples is obtained by summing the distances between the two samples

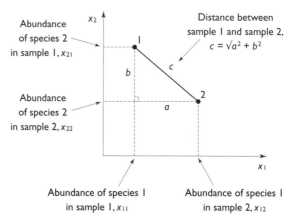

Figure 6.2 Calculation of Euclidean distance.

(calculated as above) for each variable:

$$ED_{jk} = \sqrt{\sum_{i=1}^{n}(x_{ij} - x_{ik})^2}$$

Squaring converts negative results of the subtraction into positive values, which add to the overall measure of distance.

where ED_{jk} = the complete or total Euclidean distance between sample j and sample k
   x_{ij} = the value of variable i in sample j
   x_{ik} = the value of variable i in sample k

The value of the complete Euclidean distance will depend on the number of terms (variables) contained within the summation. To overcome this, the summation can be divided by n, the number of variables; this gives the average or mean Euclidean distance (MED_{jk}):

$$MED_{jk} = \sqrt{\frac{1}{n}\sum_{i=1}^{n}(x_{ij} - x_{ik})^2}$$

More direct measures of distance, often favoured in taxonomic studies, are the simple absolute distance (AD) and the mean absolute distance (MAD), also known as the Manhattan metric. In both of these measures, corresponding values for all variables are subtracted and the absolute differences summed:

$$AD_{ik} = \sum_{i=1}^{n}|x_{ij} - x_{ik}| \qquad MAD_{ij} = \frac{1}{n}\sum_{i=1}^{n}|x_{ij} - x_{ik}|$$

The square root of the Euclidean distance is metric, as are measures based on absolute distance. Their values can range from 0 (both samples identical) to infinity. The maximum possible value is determined by the number of variables included in the summation, and the range between the lowest and highest values recorded for each variable in the data set. This means their values are strongly influenced by large variable differences, particularly the Euclidean distance measure, where variable differences are squared. To control for this, choose the scale of measurement carefully and the range of values for assessing each variable; avoid giving undue emphasis to particular traits. These effects may be reduced by calculating the relative Euclidean distance (RED) and the relative absolute distance (RAD). When calculating these relative measures of distance, the value of each character (x_i) is divided by the total of all character values for the sample (i.e. $\sum_{i=1}^{n} x_i$). For example, if the original data consists of 'absolute' species abundance values, replace them by relative abundance values (absolute abundance of species i divided by the sum of abundance values for all species):

$$RED_{jk} = \sqrt{\sum_{i=1}^{n}\left(\frac{x_{ij}}{\sum_{i=1}^{n}x_{ij}} - \frac{x_{ik}}{\sum_{i=1}^{n}x_{ik}}\right)^2} = \sqrt{\sum_{i=1}^{n}\left(\frac{x_{ij}}{X_j} - \frac{x_{ik}}{X_k}\right)^2} \qquad (\text{range 0 to } \sqrt{n})$$

$$RAD_{jk} = \sum_{i=1}^{n}\left|\frac{x_{ij}}{\sum_{i=1}^{n}x_{ij}} - \frac{x_{ik}}{\sum_{i=1}^{n}x_{ik}}\right| = \sum_{i=1}^{n}\left|\frac{x_{ij}}{X_j} - \frac{x_{ik}}{X_k}\right| \qquad (\text{range 0 to 2})$$

Calculation of relative values of x_{ij} and x_{ik}. The summation can be replaced by X_j and X_k, the sum of the x-values for samples j and k.

The absolute difference (AD) or Manhattan metric forms part of two other resemblance functions which have been extensively used in ecological studies, the Bray–Curtis measure and the Canberra metric (Lance and Williams, 1967). The Bray–Curtis measure (sometimes called the percentage similarity, the weighted Sorensen's similarity index and the Czeka-nowski index) was introduced into ecology by Bray and Curtis (1957) and is based on calculating the percentage similarity between the two samples being compared:

$$\mathrm{PS}_{ik} = \left(\frac{2W}{A+B} \right) \times 100$$

where A = the sum of species abundance (variables) values associated with sample j, i.e. $\sum_{i=1}^{n} x_{ij}$
B = the sum of species abundance (variables) values associated with sample k, i.e. $\sum_{i=1}^{n} x_{ik}$
W = the sum of the minimum abundance (variable) values which occur in both samples.

Another way to look at W is as the sum of the 'shared' abundances, abundances common to both samples:

$$W_{jk} = \sum_{i=1}^{n} \min(x_{ij}, x_{ik})$$

From the calculated percentage similarity, it is possible to obtain a distance measure called the percentage dissimilarity (PD):

$$\mathrm{PD} = 100 - \mathrm{PS}, \quad \text{or} \quad \mathrm{PD} = 1 - \left(\frac{2W}{A+B} \right) \qquad \text{(for a 0–1 scale)}$$

Alternatively the Bray–Curtis measure may be calculated directly from the formula given below. Notice that the numerator is the Manhattan metric and the denominator is the sum of all the variables.

$$\mathrm{PD}_{jk} = \frac{\displaystyle\sum_{i=1}^{n} |x_{ij} - x_{ik}|}{\displaystyle\sum_{i=1}^{n} (x_{ij} + x_{ik})}$$

If the absolute difference between samples for each species or variable is scaled relative to the combined abundance of the species, it produces a distance metric known as the Canberra metric:

$$D_{can} = \frac{1}{n} \left[\sum_{i=1}^{n} \frac{|x_{ij} - x_{ik}|}{x_{ij} + x_{ik}} \right]$$

Although D_{can} is a metric, unlike PD, its value is very sensitive to cases where a species occurs in one sample and is absent in all the others. To overcome this, a small value (e.g. 0.1) can be substituted for zero entries (Krebs, 1989). The Canberra metric is less sensitive to abundant species (i.e. large values) than the Bray–Curtis measure, which is hardly influenced by rare species with low abundance. Thus, where interest centres on rare species with low abundance within a community, it would be appropriate to choose the Canberra metric in preference to the Bray–Curtis measure (but see the later comments on standardisation of data sets). However, in practice the Bray–Curtis measure has been extensively and successfully used in ecological studies (Beals, 1984; Ludwig and Reynolds, 1988). It is easily interpreted and can be readily calculated from original data arranged in columns using a spreadsheet format. If the abundance or variable values associated with each sample sum to, or are scaled to sum to 100 or 1.0, then the Bray–Curtis measure reduces to:

$$PS_{jk} = \sum_{i=1}^{n} \min(x_{ij}, x_{ik})$$

$$PDS = 100 - PS$$

where PDS = percentage dissimilarity

        PS = percentage similarity (Renkonen index)

        x_{ij} = value of variable i in sample j

        x_{ik} = value of variable i in sample k

Note that variable values for each sample, j and k, must sum to 100 or 1.0 where values are expressed on a proportional basis when PDS $= 1 - PS$.

This form of the index is particularly useful when comparing community samples where relative species abundance values are used. Despite the simplicity of this resemblance measure, Wolda (1981) reports that it is one of the best and most reliable quantitative measures for similarity; it is less sensitive to sample size than many other measures, including the normal form of the Bray–Curtis measure.

6.2.4 Mixed data sets

Where data sets consist of a mixture of qualitative, binary and quantitative variables, comparisons may be made using Gower's index of similarity. In this index a similarity score, s_{jk}, is calculated for every variable; these scores are then summed to give an overall measure of similarity, which is then scaled to give a final value within the range 0 to 1.0. The scaling factors are chosen so that each variable, regardless of type (i.e. qualitative, binary or quantitative) contributes equally to the final value of the index. The formula for Gower's index is

$$G_{ijk} = \frac{\displaystyle\sum_{i=1}^{n} S_{ijk}}{\displaystyle\sum_{i=1}^{n} W_{ijk}}$$

sum of similarity values (scores) between sample j and sample K for all n variables i

sum of all weighting or scaling factors for all n variables i

To calculate Gower's index, the similarity scores associated with each variable type have to be calculated then summed. The method depends on the type of variable, as set out below.

For binary variables

When all the variables are in the form of Table 6.3, i.e. binary, Gower's index is equivalent to Jaccard's index of similarity.

Table 6.3 Similarity scores and weightings for binary data

Variable (k)	First sample (i)	Second sample (j)	Similarity score (s_{ijk})	Weighting (w_{ijk})
1	+	+	1	1
2	+	−	0	1
3	−	+	0	1
4	−	−	0	0

Note: + = presence, − = absence.

For qualitative variables

Qualitative variables with only two states are treated as above, i.e. as simple binary variables. Where the variable has more than two states, each matching state is given a similarity score (s_{ijk}) of 1.0, mismatches are scored 0. The similarity scores are totalled ($\sum s_{ijk}$), and then divided by the total of the weighting factors ($\sum w_{ijk}$), each variable state having been given a weighting value of 1.0. In this form the index is equivalent to the simple matching coefficient, with the number of matching variable states divided by the total number of variable states.

For quantitative variables

Similarity scores are calculated using the formula

$$S_{ijk} = 1 - D_{ijk}$$

$$D_{ijk} = \sum_{i=1}^{n} \frac{1}{r_i} |x_{ij} - x_{ik}| = \sum_{i=1}^{n} d_{ik}$$

D is a scaled or normalised form of the absolute distance measure (AD) considered in Section 6.2.3. For each variable the absolute difference $|x_{ij} - x_{ik}|$ is calculated. This value is divided by a 'normalising' or scaling factor (r_i) which is equal to the range of the variable, i.e. the difference between the largest and smallest values of that variable present in the *complete data set.*[1] For example, if $x_{ij} = 8$, $x_{ik} = 20$ and the variable i ranges from 6 to 24 then $r_i = 18$ and the dissimilarity score for variable i is $d_{ijk} = |8 - 20|/18 = 12/18 = 0.666$.

Scaling each dissimilarity score by the corresponding variable range ensures that all the scores lie between 0 and 1.0. Each variable is given a weighting value (w_{ijk}) of 1.0. This ensures that no variable has an undue influence on the final index. The index is obtained by summing the dissimilarity scores ($\sum d_{ijk}$) and dividing this by the sum of variable weighting values. The sum of these weightings ($\sum w_{ijk}$) will be equal to n, the number of variables involved in the summation of d_{ijk} values across all variable types. A D_{ij} value calculated for quantitative variable types corresponds to a normalised (or standardised) absolute distance measure. If Euclidean distances are used to obtain D_{ij} (in place of absolute distances), the normalising factor is r_i^2 and

$$D_{ijk} = \sum_{i=1}^{n} \frac{1}{r_i^2} (x_{ik} - x_{ij})^2$$

In this form D_{ij} is then equivalent to a normalised Euclidean distance measure. Gower's index has the desirable property that every variable, regardless of type, is given equal weighting and thus contributes equally to the final values of the index. Where variables of more than one type occur in a data set, the use of Gower's index is strongly recommended. The alternative of converting existing variable types (i.e. using pseudovariables) can easily introduce distortions and discrepancies into the analysis and should only be done with great care.

6.3 *Example calculations and evaluation*

The data set in Table 6.4 is an extension of the data in Table 6.1, used in Section 6.2.1 to illustrate the analysis of binary data. Columns 1 and 2 (C1 and C2) are taken directly from Table 6.1. The remaining columns are derived from the values in C1: C3 is obtained by adding 15 to each value in C1; C4 is obtained by multiplying each value in C1 by 1.2; and C5 is the reverse of C1, i.e. the species most abundant in C1 are given the lowest values in C5. Although this hypothetical data set is too simple for a full evaluation of the different distance measures, it does illustrate the effects of additive and multiplicative differences on

Table 6.4 Abundance data for species a to h from 5 sites

Species	(C1) Site 1	(C2) Site 2	(C3) Site 3	(C4) Site 4	(C5) Site 5
a	44	39	59	52.8	0
b	20	18	35	24	1
c	0	14	0	0	2
d	15	1	30	18	1
e	6	2	21	7.2	6
f	2	1	17	2.4	44
g	1	0	16	1.2	20
h	1	1	16	1.2	15
Total	89	76	194	106.8	89

the performance of distance measures. Besides that, the comparisons between C1, C2 and C5 reveal the sensitivity of the measures to minor (C1 versus C2) and major (C1 versus C5) changes in species abundance pattern.

The calculation of distance measures between C1 and C2 is illustrated in Table 6.5. The necessary calculation may be performed by following the procedures here. All of the entries in columns C3 to C10 are obtained by simple calculations from the original data values in C1 and C2. Individual distance measures may then be obtained from appropriate summation and division of column totals. The procedures set out in Table 6.5 can be easily accomplished using a spreadsheet program or MINITAB. Note that the zero values in C2 of Table 6.5 have been replaced by 0.001; although this introduces errors into the calculations, their effects are negligible and non-zero entries are needed for the Canberra metric to be calculated. The MINITAB commands given in Box 6.1 will calculate all the distance measures described in Section 6.2.2, and they were used to analyse the data in Table 6.5. The results of this analysis are presented in Table 6.6 (panel A). Also calculated were the correlation coefficients (Cor_{jk}) between the five samples (Chapter 7). Only positive values are presented since a negative correlation has no sensible interpretation. The poor performance of this statistic is readily apparent from the values in Table 6.6 (panel A); $Cor_{14} = 1.000$ implies that the samples are identical, despite the obvious differences in species abundance.

So it is possible to compare the performance of the difference measures, Table 6.6 gives a rank for each comparison and a relative percentage score. This percentage score has been calculated by dividing the distance values obtained for each comparison by the highest value recorded using that distance measure. Although the rankings do differ, there is a reasonable degree of consistency between the various measures; this can been seen from the correlation[2] of ranks and the percentage scores for the different resemblance functions.

Correlation of ranks

	AD_{jk}	ED_{jk}	RAD_{jk}	RED_{jk}	$D_{can,jk}$
ED_{jk}	1.00				
RAD_{jk}	0.777	0.777			
RED_{jk}	0.777	0.777	1.000		
PD_{jk}	0.842	0.842	0.938	0.938	
$D_{can,jk}$	0.806	0.806	0.876	0.876	0.867

Correlation of percentage scores

	AD_{jk}	ED_{jk}	RAD_{jk}	RED_{jk}	$D_{can,jk}$
ED_{jk}	0.979				
RAD_{jk}	0.868	0.920			
RED_{jk}	0.764	0.837	0.977		
PD_{jk}	0.861	0.902	0.993	0.974	
$D_{can,jk}$	0.864	0.845	0.849	0.750	0.870

Table 6.5 Calculation of resemblance functions between two samples $j = 1$ and $k = 2$ [a,b]

i	$C1$ x_{ij}	$C2$ x_{ik}	$C3 = C1 + C2$ $(x_{ij} + x_{ik})$	$C4 = \lvert C1 - C2 \rvert$ $\lvert x_{ij} - x_{ik} \rvert$	$C5 = (C4)^2$ $\lvert x_{ij} - x_{ik} \rvert^2$	$C6 = C1/\sum C1$ $x_{ij}/\sum x_{ij}$	$C7 = C2/\sum C2$ $x_{ik}/\sum x_{ik}$	$\lvert C6 - C7 \rvert$	$(C6 - C7)^2$	$C4/C3$
1	44	39	83	5	25	0.4944	0.5131	0.0188	0.000 352	0.060 241
2	20	18	38	2	4	0.2247	0.2368	0.0121	0.000 147	0.052 632
3	0.001	14	14.001	13.999	195.97	0.000 011	0.1842	0.1842	0.033 929	0.999 857
4	15	1	16	14	196.00	0.1686	0.0136	0.1554	0.024 143	0.875 000
5	6	2	8	4	16	0.0674	0.0263	0.0411	0.001 692	0.500 000
6	2	1	3	1	1	0.0225	0.0132	0.0093	0.000 087	0.333 333
7	1	0.001	1.001	0.999	0.998	0.0112	0.000 013	0.0112	0.000 126	0.998 002
8	1	1	2	0	0	0.0112	0.0132	0.0019	0.000 004	0.000 000
Totals	89.001	76.001	165.002	40.996	438.970	1.0	1.0	0.4340	0.060 476	3.819 060

[a] The variable values are placed in C1 and C2. Zero values have been replaced by 0.001 to allow calculation of the Canberra metric. If the Canberra metric is not going to be calculated, zero values should be retained.

[b] How to calculate the resemblance functions:

1. Relative species abundance values are calculated in C6 and C7.
2. The C4 total gives the absolute distance, $\text{AD}_{12} = 40.998$.
3. Dividing the C4 total by 8, the total number of species present in the data set, gives the mean absolute difference, $\text{MAD}_{12} = 40.998/8 = 5.125$.
4. The square root of the C5 total gives the total Euclidean distance, $\text{ED}_{12} = \sqrt{438.970} = 20.95$.
5. Dividing the square root of the C5 total by 8, the total number of species present in the data set, gives mean Euclidean distance, $\text{MED}_{12} = 20.95/8 = 2.619$.
6. The total of C8 give the relative absolute distance, $\text{RAD}_{12} = 0.4340$.
7. The total of C9 gives the relative Euclidean distance, $\text{RED}_{12} = 0.060\,476$.
8. Dividing the C4 total by the C3 total gives the Bray–Curtis distance measure, $\text{PD}_{12} = 40.998/165.002 = 0.2485$.
9. Dividing the C10 total by 8, the total number of species present in the data set, gives the Canberra metric, $D_{can,12} = 3.819/8 = 0.4774$.

Box 6.1   MINITAB commands for distance measures

MINITAB commands are printed as capital letters immediately to the left of >, the computer screen prompt. Comments and explanations are given in small type to the left of the MINITAB commands. Cn = column number n, Kn = constant n, which may be defined and stored within a MINITAB session. Before these commands can be used the data must be read, or inputted into C1 and C2, and the number of species must be stored in K1. All zero values in the data set are replaced with 0.001 so that the Canberra metric may be calculated.

`>LET C3 = C1 + C2`	Calculates sum of x_{ij} and x_{ik}
`>LET C4 = ABSOLUTE(C1-C2)`	Calculates absolute differences between x_{ij} and x_{ik}
`>LET C5 = C4**2`	Calculates $(x_{ij} - x_{ik})^2$
`>LET K2 = SUM(C3)`	Calculates column total of $(x_{ij} + x_{ik})$
`>LET K3 = SUM(C4)`	Calculates column total of absolute differences between x_{ij} and x_{ik}
`>LET K4 = SUM(C5)`	Calculates column total of $(x_{ij} - x_{ik})^2$
`>LET K5 = SQRT(K4)`	Calculates square root of K4
`>PRINT K3`	Gives absolute distance AD_{jk}
`>PRINT K5`	Gives total Euclidean distance ED_{jk}
`>LET K6 = K3/K1`	Divides AD_{jk} by number of species K1
`>LET K7 = K5/K1`	Divides ED_{jk} by number of species K1
`>PRINT K6`	Gives mean absolute distance MAD_{jk}
`>PRINT K7`	Gives mean Euclidean distance MED_{jk}
`>LET K8 = SUM(C1)`	Calculates column total of x_j values
`>LET K9 = SUM(C2)`	Calculates column total of x_k values
`>LET C6 = C1/K8`	Calculates relative values of x_j
`>LET C7 = C2/K9`	Calculates relative values of x_k
`>LET C8 = ABSOLUTE(C6-C7)`	Calculates absolute difference between relative values of x_j and x_k
`>LET C9 = C8**2`	Calculates squared differences between relative values of x_j and x_k
`>LET K10 = SUM(C8)`	Calculates total of values in column 8
`>LET K11 = SUM(C9)`	Calculates total of values in column 9
`>PRINT K10`	Gives relative absolute distance RAD_{jk}
`>PRINT K11`	Gives relative Euclidean distance RED_{jk}
`>LET K12 = K3/K2`	Calculates $AD_{jk} / \sum(x_{ij} + x_{ik})$
`>LET K13 = 1-K12`	
`>PRINT K12`	Gives Bray–Curtis distance measure PD_{jk}
`>PRINT K13`	Gives Bray–Curtis similarity measures PS_{jk}
`>LET C10 = C4/C3`	Calculates $(x_j - x_k)/(x_j + x_k)$
`>LET K14 = SUM(C10)`	Calculates total of C10
`>LET K15 = K14/K1`	Divides total of C10 by number of species K1
`>PRINT K15`	Gives Canberra metric $D_{can,jk}$
`>LET K16 = 1-K15`	
`>PRINT K16`	Gives Canberra metric similarity measure

The lowest distance value recorded by all of the measures was for comparison C1 versus C4 (where C4 equals $1.2 \times$ C1). However, two measures, RAD_{jk} and RED_{jk} gave a zero value, i.e. they failed to detect any difference between C1 and C4. These measures also estimated sample distances for several sets of comparisons to be equal, whereas all other measures gave unique estimates for each comparison. Measures differed in terms of which samples

Table 6.6 Distance measures calculated for data in Table 6.5 using MINITAB[a]

A. VALUES OBTAINED FOR EACH COMPARISON

Comparisons	(K3) AD_{jk}	(K5) ED_{jk}	(K6) MAD_{jk}	(K7) MED_{jk}	(K10) RAD_{jk}	(K11) RED_{jk}	(K12) PD_{jk}	(K15) $D_{can,jk}$	Cor_{jk}
C1 v C2	41.00	20.95	5.125	2.619	0.4340	0.0605	0.2485	0.4774	0.862
C1 v C3	105.00	39.69	13.13	4.960	0.4969	0.0544	0.3710	0.4827	0.957
C1 v C4	17.80	10.20	2.225	1.275	3.7E − 6	0.0000	0.0909	0.0795	1.000
C1 v C5	154.00	69.82	19.24	8.728	1.7303	0.6155	0.8651	0.8005	neg
C2 v C3	146.00	53.14	18.240	6.642	0.8993	0.1247	0.5407	0.7571	0.708
C2 v C4	58.80	27.24	7.350	3.405	0.4340	0.0605	0.3216	0.5318	0.862
C2 v C5	149.00	66.44	18.625	8.305	1.8048	0.6483	0.9030	0.7469	neg
C3 v C4	87.20	33.84	10.90	4.230	0.4969	0.0544	0.2899	0.4318	0.957
C3 v C5	172.99	80.69	21.625	10.086	1.3150	0.3403	0.6113	0.6343	neg
C4 v C5	170.20	77.17	21.275	9.646	1.7303	0.6155	0.8692	0.8078	neg

B. (RANKING) AND RELATIVE PERCENTAGE DISTANCE

Comparisons	(K3) AD_{jk}	(K5) ED_{jk}	(K10) RAD_{jk}	(K11) RED_{jk}	(K12) PD_{jk}	(K15) $D_{can,jk}$
C1 v C2	(9) 23.7	(9) 26.0	(6) 24.0	(6) 9.3	(9) 27.5	(8) 59.1
C1 v C3	(6) 60.7	(6) 49.2	(8) 27.5	(8) 8.4	(8) 31.6	(7) 59.6
C1 v C4	(10) 10.3	(10) 12.6	(10) 0.00	(10) 0.00	(10) 10.0	(10) 9.8
C1 v C5	(3) 89.0	(3) 86.5	(2) 95.9	(2) 94.9	(3) 95.8	(2) 99.1
C2 v C3	(5) 84.4	(5) 65.9	(5) 42.0	(5) 17.4	(5) 53.2	(3) 93.7
C2 v C4	(8) 33.5	(8) 33.8	(6) 24.0	(6) 9.3	(6) 35.6	(6) 65.8
C2 v C5	(4) 86.1	(4) 82.3	(1) 100	(1) 100	(1) 100	(4) 92.4
C3 v C4	(7) 50.4	(7) 41.9	(8) 27.5	(8) 8.4	(7) 32.1	(9) 53.4
C3 v C5	(1) 100	(1) 100	(4) 72.9	(4) 52.5	(4) 67.7	(5) 78.5
C4 v C5	(2) 98.4	(2) 95.6	(2) 95.9	(2) 94.9	(2) 96.3	(1) 100
Lowest value of index	17.80	10.20	0.00	0.00	0.0909	0.0795
Highest value of index	172.99	80.69	1.8048	0.6483	0.9030	0.8078

[a] The relative percentage distance score is calculated by dividing the distance values obtained for each comparison by the highest value recorded by that distance measure. See text for further details.

they assessed as the least similar samples, i.e. the most distinct samples units. The absolute distance (AD_{jk}) and the Euclidean distance (ED_{jk}) both performed well, along with their mean equivalents (MAD_{jk}, MED_{jk}). The absolute and Euclidean distances give the same rankings and similar relative percentage distances for all comparisons, placing C3 and C4 as the two most dissimilar samples. The percentage scores suggest that AD_{jk} is marginally more sensitive to additive effects than ED_{jk}. It appears there is little to be gained by the use of relative forms of either measure (RAD_{jk}, RED_{jk}). The Bray–Curtis distance measure (PD_{jk}) returned its highest values for C2 versus C5, and the highest values for the Canberra metric ($D_{can,jk}$) were obtained for C4 versus C5. This discrepancy is not as large as it might first appear, since both measures give similar ranks and/or percentage scores for other related comparisons, e.g. C1 versus C4, C2 versus C4, C2 versus C4 and C2 versus C5. The two measures do differ in the distribution of comparison percentage scores. $D_{can,jk}$ tends to bunch comparisons in the upper range, close to the extreme comparison (C4 versus C5) and away from the lowest value obtained for C1 versus C4. In contrast, PD_{jk} is more evenly distributed between 10 and 100%, providing better separation of the sample units and reflecting its sensitivity to changes in values for the abundant species. This simple data set is characterised by a high degree of species inequality which will affect the performance of the measures, highlighting differences in their performance. Although these differences will remain, they will be less marked where species abundances are more evenly distributed within and between sample units.

6.4 *Standardisation of data sets*

Since resemblance functions are sensitive to both the absolute magnitude and the relative magnitude of individual variables, their ability to estimate the distance between samples will be impaired where a few high magnitude variables dominate the data set, or where sample units contain large numbers of small values. This situation frequently occurs in ecological studies. For example, where samples are from the same community type (case 1), they will tend to contain high species abundance values associated with the community dominants. When samples are drawn from different communities or a diverse community (case 2), they will contain a large number of low abundance values associated with community rarities. In case 1 the differences between samples will be masked by the common occurrence of the high abundance community species; in case 2 the differences may be exaggerated by the occasional occurrence of community rarities. Rather than reflecting any fundamental differences between sample units, the occurrence of these low abundance species may be more related to the choice of sampling procedures.

One solution is to selectively remove from the data set any species which are present in all or the majority (>90%) of sample units at high levels of abundance and/or all species that occur rarely within the data set (<10% of sample units). The choice of threshold levels, hence the choice of species to exclude, is largely arbitrary; it should be guided by the aims of the investigation and the size and extent of the data set. The most appropriate course of action would be to analyse the data before excluding any species and to analyse it again after species have been excluded, using a range of threshold levels. In this way it should be possible to select the most appropriate threshold levels, i.e. those which allow clear patterns in the data to be observed but which exclude the minimum of the original data set. This problem is discussed by Greig-Smith (1983). An alternative approach to exclusion is to transform or standardise the data set. This is also suitable where the variables recorded for each sample unit are distinct and differ markedly in the range and scales of measurement; it often occurs in morphometric studies, where the choice of variables and units is frequently arbitrary. A logarithmic transformation of the data – each x_{ij} is replaced by $\log x_{ij}$ or $\log(x_{ij} + \text{constant})$ if some $x_{ij} = 0$ – compresses the upper scales of measurement and reduces the influence of large values relative to small values.

Standardisation converts individual x_{ij} values so they are all expressed on a common standard scale. This may be achieved in several ways. By subtracting from each x_{ij} value the corresponding row mean for trait i, i.e. x_{ij} is replaced by $x_{ij} - (\sum x_{ij}/n)$, where n is the number of sample units (columns) in the data table. This procedure is said to 'centre' the data set; x_i values now represent the difference between the value of a variable in the sample unit and its overall mean. Positive values will occur where x_i exceeds the row mean, and negative values where x_i is less than the row mean. Centring across the data set like this reduces the effects of uneven distributions between samples. Using the same approach, the data set may be centred within sites or sample units by subtracting the appropriate column mean (sample or sample unit mean) from individual x-values. This centres the data within sample units and reduces the effects of unevenness within samples. Both forms of centring may be performed on the data set, i.e. subtracting from each value in the data table the corresponding row mean and column mean. When this is done the data is said to be double centred. An alternative approach which further reduces the influence of scale differences and any large values, is to centre the data set through dividing the values by variable totals and/or sample unit totals. The data set will now be expressed on a common proportional basis. If the data set consists only of species abundance values, dividing by sample totals simply converts absolute abundance values to relative abundance values. Deciding whether to standardise or transform data sets is often difficult. Krebs (1999) suggests that two question are important:

- Are limited numbers of extreme values within sample units distorting the overall picture? If yes then transform the data. He suggests that, as a rule of thumb, the data should be transformed if a tenfold difference exists in terms of the absolute abundance between the most abundant species and the next most abundant species in the sample.

- Are differences in the absolute values of species abundance or variable values important within the context of the study? If no then standardise the data by replacing absolute values with proportional (relative) values.

Krebs (1989) also points out that by not standardising or transforming the data, the investigator is effectively making a decision that will affect the outcome of any subsequent analysis.

All resemblance measures are sensitive to sample size (Wolda, 1981; Krebs, 1999). Although some of this reported sensitivity may be an inherent property of some measures, in practice the effects of poor or inadequate sampling are likely to be more marked. To minimise the effects of sampling, every effort should be made to ensure the sample is representative and that reasonably precise estimates of variable or species abundance are obtained. The problems of sampling are discussed in Chapter 1. Comparisons between samples using resemblance measures should ideally be made where sampling effort or sample sizes do not differ substantially.

6.5 *Presenting the results*

In most studies the investigator will wish to compare all possible sample units. If the number of sample units in the data set is not excessive (≤ 25), the results may usefully be displayed as a half-matrix, allowing all comparisons to be easily inspected. Patterns of similarity may be highlighted by colour-coding or shading the elements in one half of the square matrix to indicate the strength of associations. When combined with reordering of sample units, so the high similarity values lie close to the principal diagonal, this can be very effective in identifying groups of closely related sample units (Figure 6.3). But even with a modest number of samples, further analysis and more advanced methods of display are required if relationships in the data are to be clearly revealed. Three general approaches exist: clustering (the construction of dendograms depicting the relationships between samples), ordination and the construction of constellation diagrams. Chapter 9 describes procedures for grouping and clustering of sample units. Chapter 8 covers the ordination of sample units, i.e. ordering of sample units and production of graphs which depict the similarities between them. Constellation diagrams are outlined in the next chapter.

Sometimes we are interested in only a limited number of the potential comparisons. For example, if the sample units are arranged along a transect, interest may centre on the similarity between successive sample units along the transect. In this situation successive similarity values may be plotted against distance along the transect. This approach can be an effective way of examining the effects of environmental gradients, establishing the

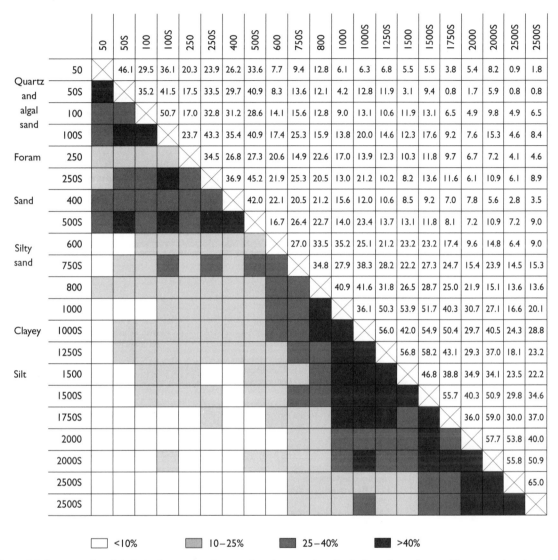

		50	50S	100	100S	250	250S	400	500S	600	750S	800	1000	1000S	1250S	1500	1500S	1750S	2000	2000S	2500S	2500S
Quartz and algal sand	50	✕	46.1	29.5	36.1	20.3	23.9	26.2	33.6	7.7	9.4	12.8	6.1	6.3	6.8	5.5	5.5	3.8	5.4	8.2	0.9	1.8
	50S		✕	35.2	41.5	17.5	33.5	29.7	40.9	8.3	13.6	12.1	4.2	12.8	11.9	3.1	9.4	0.8	1.7	5.9	0.8	0.8
	100			✕	50.7	17.0	32.8	31.2	28.6	14.1	15.6	12.8	9.0	13.1	10.6	11.9	13.1	6.5	4.9	9.8	4.9	6.5
	100S				✕	23.7	43.3	35.4	40.9	17.4	25.3	15.9	13.8	20.0	14.6	12.3	17.6	9.2	7.6	15.3	4.6	8.4
Foram	250					✕	34.5	26.8	27.3	20.6	14.9	22.6	17.0	13.9	12.3	10.3	11.8	9.7	6.7	7.2	4.1	4.6
	250S						✕	36.9	45.2	21.9	25.3	20.5	13.0	21.2	10.2	8.2	13.6	11.6	6.1	10.9	6.1	8.9
Sand	400							✕	42.0	22.1	20.5	21.2	15.6	12.0	10.6	8.5	9.2	7.0	7.8	5.6	2.8	3.5
	500S								✕	16.7	26.4	22.7	14.0	23.4	13.7	13.1	11.8	8.1	7.2	10.9	7.2	9.0
Silty sand	600									✕	27.0	33.5	35.2	25.1	21.2	23.2	23.2	17.4	9.6	14.8	6.4	9.0
	750S										✕	34.8	27.9	38.3	28.2	22.2	27.3	24.7	15.4	23.9	14.5	15.3
	800											✕	40.9	41.6	31.8	26.5	28.7	25.0	21.9	15.1	13.6	13.6
Clayey	1000												✕	36.1	50.3	53.9	51.7	40.3	30.7	27.1	16.6	20.1
	1000S													✕	56.0	42.0	54.9	50.4	29.7	40.5	24.3	28.8
	1250S														✕	56.8	58.2	43.1	29.3	37.0	18.1	23.2
Silt	1500															✕	46.8	38.8	34.9	34.1	23.5	22.2
	1500S																✕	55.7	40.3	50.9	29.8	34.6
	1750S																	✕	36.0	59.0	30.0	37.0
	2000																		✕	57.7	53.8	40.0
	2000S																			✕	55.8	50.9
	2500S																				✕	65.0
	2500S																					✕

☐ <10%   ☐ 10–25%   ☐ 25–40%   ☐ >40%

Figure 6.3 Percentage faunal similarity for samples of nematodes taken at various depths from the sea bottom. The upper triangular matrix gives the calculated similarities among pairs of samples, the lower triangular matrix gives their shaded representation. Reprinted, with permission, from Digby and Kempton (1987).

extent of 'edge' effects, and identifying the transition from one community to another across an ecotone. Comparison between samples in the same community type, i.e. within a 'uniform environment', will give high similarity values; similarity will decrease and then increase as you move from one community type, across the ecotone and into the second community. This approach has been used to good effect by Eilers *et al.* (1983), who delineate the landward limit of salt marshes that should be subject to US environmental protection regulations.

6.6 *Recommendations*

Resemblance or distance measures may be used where the aim of the analysis is to produce a quantitative assessment of the similarity (dissimilarity) between two or more sample units, for which the same traits (variables) have been recorded or scored. The form of the data largely governs the choice of measure. Different measures are appropriate for binary, qualitative, quantitative and mixed data sets. The choice of measure is illustrated in the flow diagram. Remember that resemblance measures are essentially descriptive statistics. It is not normally possible or appropriate to calculate the variance associated with a particular measure, or to place confidence limits on a value. Since they are not normally used for statistical hypothesis testing, there is no restriction on the nature or size of the samples. Data recorded from two quadrats or individual organisms can be compared. Resemblance measures do not require the

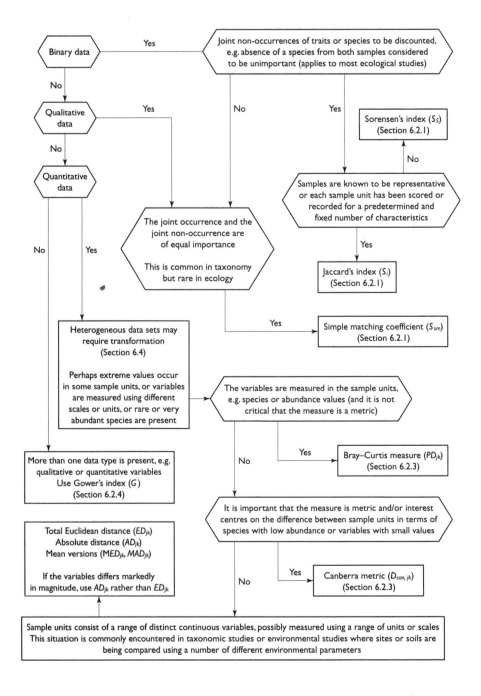

sample to be random. However, common sense and good practice dictate that, wherever possible, samples should be random and representative.

Further reading

Digby, P.G.N. and Kempton, R.A. (1987) *Multivariate Analysis of Ecological Communities*. Chapman & Hall, London.

Lynch, M. (1990) The similarity index and DNA fingerprinting. *Molecular Biology and Evolution* 7:478–84.

Orloci, L. (1978) *Multivariate Analysis in Vegetation Research*, 2nd. edn. W. Junk, The Hague. Although a little dated, it provides a very detailed treatment of similarity measures and related subjects.

Wolda, H. (1981) Similarity indices, sample size, and diversity. *Oecologia* **50**:296–302.

Chapter Seven

Association and correlation

Summary

The methods presented in this chapter are concerned with the detection, description and evaluation of association or correlation between paired variables (x, y). The variables x and y may both be binary (e.g. species presence or absence), continuous (e.g. species abundance or altitude) or mixed (one variable binary, the other continuous). For binary data sets, tests of association are typically based on the chi-squared procedure. Correlation analysis has been used to analyse continuous data sets. Both approaches are described, along with alternatives such as descriptive indices of association. Also presented are procedures for analysing data sets derived from discrete sample units (e.g. quadrats), transects and plotless sampling schemes (e.g. nearest-neighbour). The analysis of direct species–species contact data is also considered. Although emphasis is placed on the analysis of species–species and species–factor interactions, the methods described are easily generalised. Using these procedures it is possible to make multiple comparisons between pairs of variables (a versus b, a versus c, a versus d, etc.), but this approach is not recommended. The methods described in Chapters 8, 9 and 10 are more appropriate for multiple comparisons.

7.1 *Introduction*

Correlation and association are related concepts. Both describe the relationship between two or more variables. The techniques of association and correlation analysis are frequently used to investigate relationships between pairs of species, or between species and environmental factors. Association analysis is used to assess the degree of association between variables recorded from independent sample units and is applied to presence and absence data, i.e. to qualitative data sets that can be summarised as counts. When considering the occurrence and association of two species in a random set of sample units (e.g. quadrats), three outcomes are possible:

- *No association*: the two species occur independently of each other; the presence of one does not increase the probability of finding the other in a sample unit.
- *Positive association*: a positive association occurs when both species occur together in the same sample units more frequently than would be expected by chance.
- *Negative association*: a negative association implies that the two species occur less frequently together in the sample units than one would expect by chance. If one species occurs in the sample, it reduces the probability of the second species being present.

Correlation analysis may be used to test for similar relationships between variables which are continuous. For example, if random sediment cores are taken from an estuary and the total number of *Sabatieria punctata*, a common nematode of subtidal marine and estuarine sites in European waters, is determined for each core along with the sediment concentration of Zn^{2+}, the relations between the abundance of the nematode and the concentration of Zn^{2+} may be evaluated using correlation analysis. Here are the three possible outcomes:

- There is no significant correlation between the abundance of the nematode and the concentration of the Zn^{2+}. This implies that the abundance of the nematode is unaffected by the concentration of Zn^{2+}; high numbers of the nematode are equally likely to be found in sediment cores with high or low concentration of Zn^{2+}.
- Nematode abundance and Zn^{2+} concentration are positively correlated. This occurs when the abundance of *S. punctata* increases with sediment Zn^{2+} concentration. In this case the analysis suggests that high numbers of *S. punctata* are associated with contaminated sediments of high Zn^{2+} content.
- Nematode abundance is negatively correlated with sediment Zn^{2+} concentration. This suggests that the abundance of the nematode species declines as core Zn^{2+} concentrations increase.

Association and correlation analysis are extremely useful 'exploitative' methods of data analysis which often aid the development of hypotheses by suggesting possible patterns of variable interaction. These techniques, particularly correlation, are frequently useful in the interpretation of ordination diagrams (Chapter 8), and the method of community classification is based on simple species association analysis (Chapter 9). But note that a significant association or correlation between variables does not prove the existence of a causal relationship.

Associations and correlations may arise from many causes. For example, a negative correlation between two species may result from competitive interactions (one species competitively excluding or reducing the abundance of the other); from differing niche and habitat requirements; or from interactions with other species and/or environmental factors that were not measured in the study. Remember that the apparent relationship could be an artefact of poor sampling or the study design. Correlation and association analysis are of limited value for testing proposed explanations or theories. They can only show whether the results of a study are consistent with a particular hypothesis. A negative association or correlation between two species would be consistent with the explanation that species abundance is determined by competitive interaction. However, such a result is also consistent with the species having different microhabitat requirements. Further study, preferably involving manipulative experiments, would be required before the matter could be satisfactorily resolved.

7.1.1 Sampling constraints

Variable values are recorded as pairs (x, y), i.e. the occurrence or values of at least two variables are measured in each sample unit. The data thus consists of joint records (x, y) for each sample unit. The most frequently used tests of association and correlation require samples to be randomly collected. However, Greig-Smith (1983) points out that if the only aim of a study is to determine whether two variables are associated, the samples need not be random. In this case the null hypothesis is that the two variables are independent of one another, i.e. the occurrence of one species is statistically independent of the second. If true there is no advantage to be gained from the random placement or selection of samples; a systematic sampling scheme will be equally valid and often considerably easier to undertake. If a regular sampling scheme is to be used, the contiguous placement is favoured as it allows neighbouring samples to be combined and analysed independently. In this way the effects of scale on any association may be investigated. If a measure of the strength of the association or correlation is required then the samples must be *randomly* selected. Similar considerations apply to the analysis of spatial pattern (Chapter 4).

The sample units may be natural, e.g. decaying logs on a forest floor, rock pools, anthills, individual organisms, or artificial, e.g. uniform quadrats or blocks of artificial substrates placed in a river. Where natural sample units are used, they should be as uniform as possible. If this proves difficult, sample units should be classified into more homogeneous groups before analysis. If suitable groups of sufficient size cannot be formed, unusual samples should be noted and the effects of their inclusion and exclusion on the analysis carefully examined.

The ability of both procedures to detect relationships between variables is influenced by the number of sample units (n) and the size of individual sample units. Correlation analysis is generally the more powerful technique, capable of performing well even when applied to small sample sizes (<30). However, more stringent restrictions apply to correlation tests. Some tests of correlation require the variables to be linearly related and normally distributed.

The influence of sample unit size is readily appreciated by considering the effects of quadrat size on the detection of association between species A and B in Figure 7.1. If large quadrats are used, the majority of samples will contain both species, suggesting that the species are positively correlated or associated. If small quadrats are used, few sample units will contain both species A and B; most will contain only one species or neither species, suggesting that the species are negatively correlated or associated. If presence and absence data is all that is collected, the low frequency of observed and expected quadrats containing neither species (large quadrats) or both species (small quadrats) may prohibit the use of the normal procedures for testing association. Similarly it may be necessary to remove zero values from the data set before undertaking correlation analysis. The strength of the detected correlation and association will be greatest when the size of the quadrat corresponds most closely to the natural scale and pattern of aggregation between species A and B. Given the effects of sample size on the outcome of the analysis, it is important that the nature and

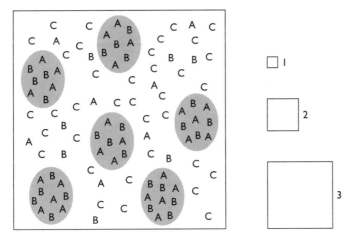

Figure 7.1 How quadrat size is related to the trend of association between species A, B, C. Reprinted, with permission, from Kershaw and Looney (1985).

size of the chosen sample unit are reported and considered carefully when interpreting the results of any study.

To avoid the effects of quadrat size, several 'plotless' sample methods have been developed. They involve one of three sampling approaches (Section 7.2.5):

- Record the presence or absence of species within the 'neighbourhood' of either randomly or systematically selected points or individual plants.
- Record the distribution of species along a transect.
- Record species actually in contact with either randomly or systematically selected individual plants.

7.2 *Qualitative binary data*

7.2.1 *Association between two species*

The traditional approach to the analysis of association between two species (or other binary variable) makes use of the chi-squared procedure. The test statistic X^2 follows a chi-squared distribution and is calculated using the formula

$$X^2 = \sum \frac{(O - E)^2}{E}$$

where $O =$ observed values
$E =$ expected values

Values of X^2 are compared with tabulated values of chi-squared (χ^2) values at an appropriate probability level (normally $p < 0.05$) and with the correct number of degrees of freedom (d.f.). Expected values are generated from the data set by assuming that the species are distributed among the sample units independently of each other.

For example, in a study of the association between two common pasture plants, the occurrence of *Trifolium repens* (white clover) and *Lolium perenne* (perennial ryegrass) was recorded in 200 randomly placed 25 cm × 25 cm square quadrats. The traditional method of association analysis is outlined below.

Table 7.1 The occurrence of T. *repens* and L. *perenne* in two hundred 25 cm square quadrats randomly placed in a lowland pasture

Quadrat group	Species A (T. repens)	Species B (L. perenne)	Observed number of quadrats (O)	Expected number of quadrats (E)	$(O-E)^2/E$
(a)	present (+)	present (+)	117	100.70	$(117-100.7)^2/100.7 = 2.6384$
(b)	present (+)	absent (−)	20	36.31	$(20-36.31)^2/36.31 = 7.3262$
(c)	absent (−)	present (+)	30	46.31	$(30-46.31)^2/46.31 = 5.7442$
(d)	absent (−)	absent (−)	33	16.68	$(33-16.68)^2/16.68 = 15.9678$
		Totals	200	200	$\sum(O-E)^2/E = 31.677$

Group the observations

The first stage of the analysis involves grouping observations into four classes: (a) the number of quadrats in which both species occur (++); (b) the numbers of quadrats in which *T. repens* alone occurs (+−); (c) the number of quadrats in which *L. perenne* only occurs (−+); and (d) the number of quadrats in which neither species occurs (−−). These values are entered in the first four rows of Table 7.1.

Calculate the species frequency

The frequency of each species in the sample is calculated from the tabulated data. The frequency of *T. repens* ($Freq_{Tr}$) is equal to the total number of quadrats in which it occurs divided by n, the sample size:

$$Freq_{Tr} = (a+b)/n = (117+20)/200 = 0.685$$

The frequency of *L. perenne* is

$$Freq_{Lp} = (a+c)/n = (117+30)/200 = 0.735$$

Calculate the expected values

The probability of a species occurring in a quadrat is equal to its frequency. Using species frequency values, it is easy to calculate the expected number of quadrats in each class under the null hypothesis of independence:

Expected number of quadrats containing both species

= Probability of a quadrat containing *T. repens*

× Probability of a quadrat containing *L. Perenne*

× Total number of quadrats

Expected number of quadrats containing *L. perenne* alone

= Probability of a quadrat containing *L. perenne*

× Probability of a quadrat not containing *T. repens*

× Total number of quadrats

Expected number of quadrats containing *T. repens* alone

= Probability of a quadrat containing *T. repens*

× Probability of a quadrat not containing *L. perenne*

× Total number of quadrats

Expressing these equations mathematically and substituting:

$E_a = \text{Freq}_{\text{Tr}} \times \text{Freq}_{\text{Lp}} \times n$

$= 0.685 \times 0.735 \times 200 = 100.70$

$E_b = \text{Freq}_{\text{Lp}} \times (1.0 - \text{Freq}_{\text{Tr}}) \times n$

$= 0.735 \times (1.0 - 0.685) \times 200 = 46.31$

$E_c = \text{Freq}_{\text{Tr}} \times (1.0 - \text{Freq}_{\text{Lp}}) \times n$

$= 0.685 \times (1.0 - 0.735) \times 200 = 36.31$

The expected number of quadrats containing neither species can be obtained from

$E_d = n - (E_a + E_b + E_c)$

$= 200 - (100.70 + 46.31 + 36.31) = 16.68$

Determine the degrees of freedom

The test statistic has one degree of freedom and is calculated as shown in Table 7.1. The degrees of freedom are derived as follows. From the original 4 terms in the summation, 1 degree of freedom is lost because the total number of quadrats must add up to 200 (once three values are known the fourth is fixed); a further 2 degrees of freedom are lost since the data is used to estimate two parameters (Freq_{Tr} and Freq_{Lp}). To obtain the degrees of freedom, take the number of terms in the summation, here 4, and subtract the number of degrees that are lost, here 3, which gives 1 (Fowler *et al.*, 1998).

The value $X^2 = 31.677$, greatly exceeds the tabulated values $\chi^2 = 3.841$ ($p < 0.05$), $\chi^2 = 6.635$ ($p < 0.01$) and $\chi^2 = 10.83$ ($p < 0.001$) with 1 d.f. The null hypothesis of independence may be confidently rejected. To distinguish between positive and negative association, the expected and observed values are compared:

- Positive if $O_a > E_a$: more sample units occur with both species present than would be expected if the species were independent.
- Negative if $O_a < E_a$: fewer samples units occur with both species present than would be expected if the species were independent.

In this case $O_a > E_a$ ($117 > 100.7$) so the association is positive and we conclude that *T. repens* and *L. perenne* are positively associated at the site studied and at the chosen scale of the quadrat.

If the data are arranged in a standard 2×2 contingency table, the test may be achieved in a single step using the formula

$$X^2 = \frac{n(ad - bc)^2}{(a + b)(c + d)(a + c)(b + d)}$$

where a, b, c, d, n have the same meanings as above and correspond to the values in the appropriate cell of the contingency table (Table 7.2). In order to decide whether any association

Table 7.2 The contingency table

First classification (*L. perenne*)	Second classification (*T. repens*)		Totals
	Presence of *B* (+)	Absence of *B* (−)	
Presence of *A* (+)	$a = 117$	$b = 30$	$a + b = 147$
Absence of *A* (−)	$c = 20$	$d = 33$	$c + d = 53$
Totals	$a + c = 137$	$b + d = 63$	200

This the sample size, $n = a + b + c + d$

is positive or negative, the expected number of quadrats containing both species (E_a) is compared with the observed number (O_a). The expected number of quadrats containing both species is given by

$$E_a = \frac{(a + b)(a + c)}{n} = \frac{147 \times 137}{200} = 100.695$$

Small sample size and Yates' correction for continuity

The chi-squared procedure performs poorly when sample sizes are small and should not be used if the expected value for any category is less than 5. The performance of the test can be improved by applying Yates' correction for continuity,[1] which involves subtracting 0.5 from each comparison of E and O in the summation. With Yates' correction the general formula for X^2 becomes

$$X^2 = \sum \frac{(|O - E| - 0.5)^2}{E}$$

where O = observed values
  E = expected values
  $|O - E|$ = the absolute difference of O and E

When applied to the chi-squared formula for data in a 2×2 contingency table, the formula becomes

$$X^2 = \frac{n(|ad - bc| - 0.5n)^2}{(a + b)(c + d)(a + c)(b + d)}$$

Yates' correction should be used routinely, especially where sample sizes are small ($n < 200$). However, even with Yates' correction, expected values must still exceed 5, else the procedure should not be used (Section 7.2.3). Although a little more time-consuming, the first procedure outlined above has the advantage of allowing small expected values to be spotted early as all expected values are estimated before calculating the test statistic. A worked example using MINITAB is given in Section 7.5.

7.2.2 Log-likelihood ratio or G-test

A better alternative to the standard chi-squared procedure is the log-likelihood ratio or *G*-test (Sokal and Rohlf, 1987; Fowler *et al.*, 1998). The *G*-test and chi-squared procedures are computationally similar. The same rules apply for calculating the number of degrees of freedom.

Both test statistics, G and X^2, follow a chi-squared distribution. G is calculated as follows:

$$G = 2 \sum O \ln(O/E)$$

$$\text{Williams' correction} = 1 + \frac{k^2 - 1}{6n\nu}$$

$$G_{adj} = \frac{G}{\text{Williams' correction}}$$

where n = sample size (the number of observed sample units)
   k = the number of categories or frequency classes
   ν = the degrees of freedom (often $k - 1$ but not always)

Before testing the significance of G, Williams' correction factor must be applied to give the adjusted G-test statistic (G_{adj}) which is then tested for significance. Williams' correction factor should be applied regardless of the sample size or the number of degrees of freedom. When applied directly as a test of independence to data summarised in a 2×2 contingency table, calculation of the G-test statistic involves three stages, in which the natural logarithms of cell frequencies, row total frequencies and column total frequencies ($\ln f$) are multiplied by themselves ($f \ln f$) and summed ($\sum f \ln f$). The general formula takes this form:

$$G = 2 \Big(\sum f \ln f \qquad \text{Calculated for all cell frequencies (a, b, c, d).}$$

$$- \sum f \ln f \qquad \text{Calculated for all row and column total frequencies (a + b, c + b, a + c, b + d).}$$

$$+ n \ln n \Big) \qquad \text{Calculated for the grand total frequency n.}$$

Note the negative sign of the second term and the multiplying factor of 2.

In this context, frequency refers to the counts associated with each class of quadrat, a, b, c, d. Summarising the data for the association between *T. repens* and *L. perenne* (Table 7.1) as a 2×2 contingency table and applying the G-test procedure, we obtain the results in Table 7.3.

- Calculate $\sum f \ln f$ for all cell frequencies:

$$\sum f \ln f = a \ln a + b \ln b + c \ln c + d \ln d$$

$$= 117 \ln 117 + 30 \ln 30 + 20 \ln 20 + 33 \ln 33$$

$$= 557.17 + 102.04 + 59.91 + 115.38$$

$$= 834.50$$

Table 7.3 The contingency table

First classification (L. perenne)	Second classification (T. repens)		
	Presence of B (+)	Absence of B (−)	Totals
Presence of A (+)	a = 117	b = 30	a + b = 147
Absence of A (−)	c = 20	d = 33	c + d = 53
Totals	a + c = 137	b + d = 63	200 (n = a + b + c + d)

● Calculate $-\sum f \ln f$ for all row and column total frequencies:

$$-\sum f \ln f = \left((a+b)\ln(a+b) + (c+d)\ln(c+d) + (a+c)\ln(a+c)\right.$$
$$\left. + (b+d)\ln(b+d)\right)$$
$$= -\left(147\ln 147 + 53\ln 53 + 137\ln 137 + 63\ln 63\right)$$
$$= -\left(733.59 + 210.43 + 674.04 + 261.02\right)$$
$$= -1879.08$$

● Calculate $\sum n \ln n$:

$$n \ln n = 200 \ln 200$$
$$= 1059.66$$

● Sum the results and multiply by 2 to obtain G:

$$G = (834.50 - 1879.08 + 1059.04) \times 2$$
$$= 14.46 \times 2$$
$$= 28.92$$

This value is much greater than the tabulated critical values of 3.841 at $p < 0.05$ (d.f. $= 1$), so the null hypothesis may be rejected. As with the chi-squared procedure, a continuity correction factor should be applied when the sample size is small. The correction factor reduces the value of G making the test more conservative and reducing the likelihood of rejecting the null hypothesis that the observed and expected values do not differ significantly. In this case the Williams continuity correction factor (q) for data in a 2×2 contingency table is given by

$$q = 1 + \frac{1}{6n}\left[\left(\frac{n}{a+b}\right) + \left(\frac{n}{c+d}\right) - 1\right]\left[\left(\frac{n}{a+c}\right)\left(\frac{n}{b+d}\right) - 1\right]$$

$$G_{adj} = G/q$$

Notice that all the denominators in the parentheses are row totals or column totals from the contingency table. A worked example using MINITAB is given in Section 7.5.

7.2.3 Small sample size

Where samples sizes are small ($n < 20$) or if individual cell totals are small (<5), an alternative to the G-test and the chi-squared test is to perform an exact test of independence; this calculates the probability of obtaining a particular contingency table by chance. Using the standard contingency cell labelling (a for $++$, b for $+-$, c for $-+$, d for $--$), the probability of observing a sample units where both species are present, given the marginal totals $a + b$, $a + c$ and a sample size n, is

! means factorial

$6! = 6 \times 5 \times 4 \times 3 \times 2 \times 1 = 720$

$$P(a|n, a+b, a+c) = \frac{(a+b)!\,(c+d)!\,(a+c)!\,(b+d)!}{a!\,b!\,c!\,d!\,n!}$$

This is the standard way of writing a conditional probability. In this case the probability of interest is that of obtaining *a* given all of the conditions to the left of the line and enclosed in the bracket.

The probability obtained from this calculation tells you how probable is the number of joint occurrences observed (a) if the species are distributed independently. Low values of Pr_a (<0.05) would suggest that the species are associated and the null hypothesis of independence should be rejected. A worked example showing this calculation is given in Section 7.5.

If, because of prior evidence, it is reasonable to assume that the species are either positively or negatively associated with one another, a one-tailed test[2] may be used to test these two alternatives. In each case determine the probability of the difference between the observed and expected numbers of joint occurrences ($E(a) - a$)) occurring by chance. The probability of obtaining the number of observed joint occurrences (a), is obtained by summing the probabilities (calculated as above) for all values of a consistent with each hypothesis.

For negative association

$$\text{Pr (a negative association, } E(a) > a) = \sum_{i=a_{\min}}^{a} P(i|n, a+b, a+c)$$

The probabilities of obtaining different numbers of joint occurrences (i) are summed from $i = a_{\min}$, the minimum possible value of a ($a_{\min} = 0$) to $i = a$, the actual observed number of joint occurrences.

For positive association

$$\text{Pr (a positive association, } E(a) < a) = \sum_{i=a}^{a_{\max}} P(i|n, a+b, a+c)$$

The probabilities of obtaining different numbers of joint occurrences (i) are summed from $i = a$, the observed number of joint occurrences, to $i = a_{\max}$, the maximum number of possible joint occurrences; the maximum equals ($a+b$), the total observed frequency for species A in the table.

The calculation of the necessary conditional probabilities to test for positive or negative association can be extremely time-consuming. For small samples where the total number of observations is less than 26, tables for performing Fisher's 2×2 exact test are provided in Appendix 7.1. Where column and row totals are <50, calculations can be avoided by using the tables produced by Finney *et al* (1963) and Beyer (1968). Outside the range of these tables, the fact that distribution of a (joint occurrences) tends to normality (Pielou, 1977) can be exploited to calculate a test statistic that may be treated as a standardised normal variable (z). The mean[3] and variance of a are needed to calculate this test statistic X:

$$E(a) = \frac{(a+c)(a+b)}{n} \qquad \text{var}(a) = \frac{(a+b)(a+c)(b+c)(b+d)}{n^2(n-1)}$$

$$X = \frac{a - E(a)}{\sqrt{\text{var}(a)}}$$

If a two-tailed test is applied at the 5% probability level, i.e. no distinction is made between a being greater than or less than $E(a)$, X must exceed 1.96. If a one-tailed test is applied, i.e. testing either $a > E(a)$ or $a < E(a)$, the critical value of X at the 5% probability level is 1.65.

In these calculations and those associated with the G-test and the chi-squared test, the marginal totals $a+b$, $a+c$, $c+d$ and $b+d$ are assumed to be fixed. By using these procedures we are actually testing whether the species *in the sample* are distributed independently. The assumption of fixed marginal totals is only true if the data set contains the complete population of all possible sample units. If a series of random samples are taken from a population of the two species, then not only will the individual cell counts vary, but marginal totals which give the frequency of each species will also vary. The generalisation of these tests from samples to populations is justified largely on intuition (Poole, 1974). Greig-Smith (1983) points out that the chi-squared procedure provides a statistically conservative test, and that the problem may be partly overcome by using large and representative samples. The distinction between samples and populations becomes particularly important when the sample size is small (Meagher and Burdick, 1980).

7.2.4 *Descriptive measures of association*

Indices of association
Although the G-test and the chi-squared test provide evidence for a positive or negative association, they do not provide a measure of its strength. Hence a great many descriptive measures of association have been developed. Of these measures, several are similar to the indices of sample similarity (Chapter 6) and provide a qualitative measure of the strength of association.

Using the standard contingency cell labelling, here are two of the more commonly used indices shown by Goodall (1973) to function well:

Dice index $\quad D = 2a/(2a + b + c)$

Jaccard index $\quad J = a/(a + b + c)$

Both vary from 0 (no association between the species) to 1.0 (maximum association); at maximum association the species only occur together in the sample units, never separately. Of the two, Jaccard's index is least affected by small sample size, functioning well when $n > 10$. Pielou (1977) distinguishes between 'complete association' and 'absolute association'. Absolute association between two species or traits occurs when neither is present in the absence of the other, they only ever occur together. In terms of the normal 2×2 contingency table, absolute association occurs when $b = 0$ and $c = 0$, this may be viewed as 'maximum associated' and both the Dice and Jaccard indices will give values of 1.0. Complete association occurs when one species A only ever occurs in the presence of B, but the second species B does occur in the absence of A; in this case $c > 0$ and the Dice and Jaccard indices will be less than 1.0. The Yule index of association (Q) has been extensively applied as a descriptive measure of association, but it fails to distinguish between absolute and complete association, so it cannot be recommended as a general measure of ecological association.

$$Q = \frac{ad - bc}{ad + bc} \qquad \text{var}(Q) = \frac{1 - Q^2}{4}\left(\frac{1}{a} + \frac{1}{b} + \frac{1}{c} + \frac{1}{d}\right)$$

The difference between absolute and complete association is illustrated in Table 7.4. The two data sets are presented in the form of standard contingency tables and the three indices are applied to both of them.

Binary correlation as a measure of association
For any contingency table it is possible to calculate a coefficient of contingency (C); this provides a measure of the degree of relationship between the table classes. Although C distinguishes between absolute and complete association, it can only give a value of $+1.0$ when $c, b = 0$ (the condition for complete association) and $a = d$. This last condition limits its use as an effective descriptive measure of association. Related to the coefficient of contingency is the correlation coefficient r_b for binary variables. Where the variables x and y can only take

Table 7.4 The difference between absolute and complete association[a]

	Absolute association			Complete association		
	Species B occurs only with A but A occurs in the absence of B			*Species B occurs only with A, and A occurs in the presence of B*		
	B (+)	*B* (−)		*B* (+)	*B* (−)	
A (+)	$a = 50$	$b = 40$	$a + b = 90$	$a = 50$	$b = 0$	$a + b = 50$
A (−)	$c = 0$	$d = 20$	$c + d = 20$	$c = 0$	$d = 20$	$c + d = 20$
	$a + c = 50$	$b + d = 60$	$n = 110$	$a + c = 50$	$b + d = 20$	$n = 70$

Yule
$$Q = \frac{ad - bc}{ad + bc} = \frac{50 \times 20 - 40 \times 0}{50 \times 20 + 40 \times 0} = 1.0 \qquad\qquad Q = \frac{50 \times 20 - 0 \times 0}{50 \times 20 + 0 \times 0} = 1.0$$

Dice
$$D = \frac{2a}{2a + b + c} = \frac{2 \times 50}{(2 \times 50) + 40 + 0} = 0.7143 \qquad\qquad D = \frac{2 \times 50}{2 \times 50 + 0 + 0} = 1.0$$

Jaccard
$$\mathcal{J} = \frac{a}{a + b + c} = \frac{50}{50 + 40 + 0} = 0.5 \qquad\qquad \mathcal{J} = \frac{50}{50 + 0 + 0} = 1.0$$

[a] In comparison to the Jaccard index, the Dice index places greater emphasis on the joint occurrences of both species, i.e. the number of sample units belonging to cell *a* in the contingency table.

the values 1 or 0, the correlation between x and y is given as follows:

$$C = \sqrt{\frac{X^2}{X^2 + n}}$$

$X^2 = \sum (O - E)^2 / E$ and $n =$ **total number of sample units** (Section 7.2.1).

$$r_b = \sqrt{\frac{X^2}{n(k - 1)}}$$

General form of correlation coefficient for a $k \times k$ table.

$$r_b = \sqrt{\frac{X^2}{n}}$$

Equation for a 2×2 contingency table where $k = 2$.

$$r_b = \frac{ad - bc}{\sqrt{(a + b)(c + d)(a + c)(b + d)}}$$

Formula for calculating r_b directly from a contingency table.

The correlation coefficient r_b has the desirable properties of distinguishing between absolute and complete association (Pielou, 1977) and of varying from +1 for perfect positive association through 0 for no correlation to −1 for perfect negative correlation. Although the variance of r_b can be calculated (Pielou, 1977), the significance of r_b is not normally tested. The significance of any relationship should be assessed using the chi-squared statistic and r_b used to assess the degree and direction of any association (Causton, 1988).

7.2.5 *Plotless alternatives to quadrat methods*

When quadrats are used to collect data on species association, the choice of quadrat size implicitly and largely arbitrarily imposes spatial restrictions or definitions of species association. For a particular quadrat size, positive association is detected when the probability of a quadrat containing both species is significantly greater than would be expected by chance, given the abundance for each species. If the average distance between individuals is larger, fewer quadrats will contain both species; if the distance between plants is reduced, more quadrats will contain both species. As quadrat size is reduced to the size of the individual,[4]

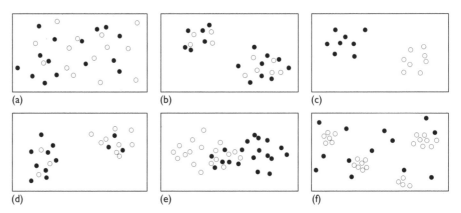

Figure 7.2 Six possible patterns for two-species populations: (a, b) unsegregated, (c) fully segregated, (d, e, f) partly segregated. Reprinted, with permission, from Pielou (1961).

the association between two species tends to become negative simply because the presence of one individual spatially precludes the presence of a second. Thus, the likelihood of detecting a positive or negative association will depend on the size of the quadrat used. This problem arises because a discrete sampling unit, i.e. a quadrat, is used to sample a continuous quantity, i.e. the spatial distribution of individuals. The effects of quadrat size on the detection of species association have caused people to develop several 'plotless' methods. Three of these methods are described here: the nearest-neighbour approach, the use of transects and the leaf contacts method.

Nearest-neighbour approach

Pielou (1961) introduced the concept of species 'segregation'. The degree of species segregation may be viewed as a measure of the species intermingling (Figure 7.2). Species which are completely segregated occur independently of one another and show no degree of association. In contrast, species which are not segregated are spatially associated with each other (Figure 7.2). The procedure suggested by Pielou (1961) is based on the analysis of nearest-neighbour relationships. Consider only two species A and B; if individuals of each species are selected and the identity of the nearest neighbour recorded, four distinct nearest-neighbour classes are possible (Table 7.5).

The results may be summarised in a 2×2 contingency table (Table 7.6) and analysed in the normal way, as if testing for species association (Sections 7.2.1 and 7.2.2). In this case the null hypothesis is that if the two species are segregated (i.e. occur independently of one another), the likelihood of recording any of the four nearest-neighbour classes depends

Table 7.5 The four nearest-neighbour classes

Identity of selected individual (base species)	Identity of nearest neighbour	Notation for observed number of occurrences
A	A	O_{AA}
A	B	O_{AB}
B	B	O_{BB}
B	A	O_{BA}

Table 7.6 How to summarise the results in a contingency table

	Base plant (i.e. selected plant)		
Nearest neighbour	*Species A*	*Species B*	*Totals*
Species A'	$O_{AA'}$ (a)	$O_{BA'}$ (b)	$(a + b)$
Species B'	$O_{AB'}$ (c)	$O_{BB'}$ (d)	$(c + d)$
Totals	$(a + c)$	$(b + d)$	$n = (a + b + c + d)$

Where n = the total number of nearest-neighbour pairs recorded; Freq_A = proportion of base plants of species $A = (a + c)/n$; Freq_B = proportion of base plants of species $B = (b + d)/n$; $\text{Freq}_{A'}$ = proportion of nearest neighbours recorded as being species $A = (a + b)/n$; $\text{Freq}_{B'}$ = proportion of nearest neighbours recorded as being species $B = (c + d)/n$.

only on the relative abundances of the four species. Expected value are generated from these frequencies:

$$E_{AA} = n \times \text{Freq}_A \times \text{Freq}_{A'}$$

$$E_{AB} = n \times \text{Freq}_A \times \text{Freq}_{B'}$$

$$E_{BA} = n \times \text{Freq}_B \times \text{Freq}_{A'}$$

$$E_{BB} = n \times \text{Freq}_B \times \text{Freq}_{B'}$$

The normal chi-squared or *G*-test procedure is used to test for significant differences between the observed and expected values. A worked example is given in Box 7.1. This method is independent of scale, since it records the identity of only the nearest relevant species; the distance from the selected base plant is not recorded. If the X^2 or G values are significant, the nature of the relationship between species A and B is determined by comparing the O_{AB} and O_{BA} with their expected values. If $O_{AB} < E_{AB}$, $O_{BA} < E_{BA}$ and $O_{AA} > E_{AA}$, $O_{BB} > E_{BB}$ then the two species are segregated. The degree of segregation is given by Pielou's coefficient of segregation (S):

$$S = 1 - \frac{\text{observed number of } AB \text{ and } BA \text{ relationships}}{\text{expected number of } AB \text{ and } BA \text{ relationships}}$$

$$S = 1 - \frac{O_{AB} + O_{BA}}{n(\text{Freq}_{A'} \times \text{Freq}_B) + n(\text{Freq}_A \times \text{Freq}_{B'})}$$

S is equal to 1.0 when the two species are completely segregated. Negative values occur when the species are closely intermingled, i.e. when they tend to occur together.

Although this method appears to deal effectively with the problem of scale inherent in quadrat-based approaches, it is not without drawbacks. Species segregation and association are not one and the same thing. The degree to which species are segregated largely reflects patterns of spatial distribution, not species association. This can be clearly seen from the cases in Figure 7.2. In Figure 7.2b, the species are unsegregated but they clearly have a positive association at one scale; yet at larger scales (quadrat sizes) the strength of this association would become less apparent or it would disappear completely. Thus, when interpreting the results of this analysis the relationship between segregation and association needs to be

Box 7.1 **Pielou's nearest-neighbour method**

Observed data arranged as a contingency table

Nearest neighbour	Base plant (i.e. selected plant)		
	Species A	Species B	Totals
Species A'	25 (O_{AA} or a)	26 (O_{BA} or b)	51 ($a + b$)
Species B'	38 (O_{AB} or c)	14 (O_{BB} or d)	52 ($c + d$)
Totals	3 ($a + c$)	40 ($b + d$)	103 ($n = a + b + c + d$)

Calculating of proportional frequencies

Freq_A = proportion of base plants of species $A = (a + c)/n = 63/103 = 0.612$

Freq_B = proportion of base plants of species $B = (b + d)/n = 40/103 = 0.388$

$\text{Freq}_{A'}$ = proportion of nearest neighbours recorded as being species A

$\qquad = (a + b)/n = 51/103 = 0.495$

$\text{Freq}_{B'}$ = proportion of nearest neighbours recorded as being species B

$\qquad = (c + d)/n = 52/103 = 0.505$

Using frequencies to calculate expected values

Nearest-neighbour class	Observed values	Expected values	$(O - E)^2/E$
Base species A			
AA'	25	$103 \times 0.612 \times 0.495 = 31.203$	1.233
AB'	38	31.797	1.210
Base species B			
BA'	26	19.782	1.954
BB'	14	20.218	1.912
Totals	103	103	$6.309 = X^2$

Calculating the coefficient of segregation (S)

$$S = 1 - \frac{O_{AB} + O_{BA}}{n(E_{AB} + E_{BA})}$$

$$= 1 - \frac{O_{AB} + O_{BA}}{n((\text{Freq}_{A'} \times \text{Freq}_B) + (\text{Freq}_A \times \text{Freq}_{B'}))}$$

$$= 1 - \frac{38 + 26}{103((0.495 \times 0.388) + (0.621 \times 0.505))}$$

$$= 1 - \frac{38 + 26}{19.782 + 32.30} = 1 - \frac{64}{52.082} = 1 - 1.228 = -0.228$$

$S = 0$ for an unsegregated population.

$S = 1.0$ for a fully segregated population where no member of an A-clump has a member of a B-clump as a neighbour.

Negative values imply that AB pairs occur more frequently than expected. The minimum value of -1.0 occurs when the numbers of A and B are equal and they occur as isolated pairs AB.

Since $X^2 = 6.309$ exceeds the critical value of $\chi^2 = 3.84$ at $p < 0.05$ with d.f. $= 1$, the null hypothesis of independence is rejected. Since observed species pairings of AB' and BA' exceed the expected values, the species are not segregated but appear to be associated; they are nearest neighbours more often than one would expect by chance. The lack of segregation is reflected in the low values of S.

considered carefully. The use of a procedure based on a 2×2 contingency table can also be criticised. Meagher and Burdick (1980) point out that, among other problems (e.g. the fixed marginal totals of Section 7.2.3), the assumption of independence may not hold. This gives rise to a non-symmetrical contingency table, i.e. unequal frequencies of reciprocal nearest-neighbour pairs AB (O_{AB}) and BA (O_{BA}). A non-symmetrical table will generate large X^2 and G values, increasing the likelihood of the null hypothesis being wrongly rejected. If O_{AB} and O_{BA} differ substantially, the table is not symmetrical and the nearest-neighbour procedure is not valid for analysing the data set. Pielou (1961) suggests that any difference between the two frequencies may be easily tested by calculating X^2 (d.f. $= 1$) using Yates' correction:

$$X^2 = \frac{(|O_{AB} - O_{BA}| - 1)^2}{O_{AB} + O_{BA}}$$

Transect approaches
Several methods have been developed to analyse data collected from transects running through plant communities. More than one transect may be used and the transects may be oriented randomly or arranged in a systematic way. The width of the transect and whether sampling is continuous or at regular fixed points varies from one method to another.

Test of species segregation along a transect
The method suggested by Pielou (1962) requires that the occurrence of *individuals* of the two species (A and B) are recorded as they are successively encountered along the transect. The belt transect must be sufficiently narrow so that no two individuals (of either species) can occur side by side at the same point on the transect. The data collected in this way may be represented as a sequence of letters: A represents occurrence of one species and B represents occurrence of the other. The distance between occurrences and the length of transect are not relevant to the analysis. Here is a possible data set:

AAAABBBBABAAABBBBAABABBB . . .

The null hypothesis assumes that the two species are distributed independently of each other along the transect. If this is the case then the probability of obtaining a run of s successive records of species A (i.e. a run length of s) is equal to $a^{s-1}b$, where a and b are the overall probabilities of encountering species A and B along the transect. If the species are distributed independently along the transect, probabilities a and b should sum to 1. The calculations assume that run lengths follow a geometric distribution and they proceed as follows.

Step 1   For each species calculate the mean run length, m_A and m_B. Run length is the number of consecutive letters of the same type. For example, ignoring the first and last letters, since these may be either the end or the start of runs having unknown length, the sequence BAAAABAABA contains a run of 4 A's, a run of 2 A's, and two runs of a single B.

Step 2   Estimate the overall probability of encountering each species (this is essentially the probability that any randomly selected record from the sequence will be either A or B). These probabilities are estimated from the mean run lengths obtained in step 1, but notice m_B is used to estimate a and m_A to estimate b.

$$a = 1/m_B \qquad b = 1/m_A$$

Step 3   The variance for each of these probabilities is estimated using the formulae:

$$\text{Variance of } a \quad S_a^2 = \frac{1}{n_B}\left(\frac{m_B - 1}{m_B^3}\right)$$

$$\text{Variance of } b \quad S_b^2 = \frac{1}{n_A}\left(\frac{m_A - 1}{m_A^3}\right)$$

where n_A is the total number of recorded encounters of species A and n_B is the total number of recorded encounters of species B.

Step 4   A 95% probability confidence interval is obtained for the sum of probabilities a and b, and then used to test whether $a + b = 1$. If the calculated interval does not contain 1 then $a + b \neq 1.0$ and the null hypothesis of independence is rejected.

$$\text{Confidence interval} = a + b \pm 1.96\sqrt{S_a^2 + S_b^2}$$

- If $a + b > 1.0$ the two species are unsegregated, run lengths are shorter than expected, and the species tend to be mingled or intermixed. This is consistent with the two species being positively associated.

- If $a + b < 1.0$ the two species are segregated and run lengths are longer than expected; there is little mingling of species and they tend to be isolated from each other. This is consistent with a negative species association.

- If $a + b = 1.0$ the two species are distributed independently along the transect, consistent with no species association.

A runs type test statistic

Knight (1974) presents a closely related method which can easily be applied to data presented as a letter sequence. In this procedure the identities of species encountered along a line transect are recorded as a letter sequence. If A and B are the target species then what is of interest is whether the number of adjacent occurrences of letters A and B (K_{ab}) are more frequent than would be expected by chance. The expected number of adjacent occurrences is calculated and confidence limits are placed around it. The observed number of adjacent occurrences are recorded and compared with the calculated expected number. No distinction is made between the adjacent occurrences BA and AB, thus $K_{ab} = 3$ for A$\underline{B}\overline{B}\underline{A}$B and $K_{ab} = 2$ for C$\underline{A}$BBCC$\underline{A}$BCADDB.

For large samples the normal approximation of K_{ab} and its variance are given by

$$\hat{K}_{ab} = \frac{2n_a n_b}{n} \qquad \text{var}(\hat{K}_{ab}) = \frac{2n_a n_b}{n}\left(\frac{(n - n_a)(n - n_b) + (n_a n_b - n)}{n(n - 1)}\right)$$

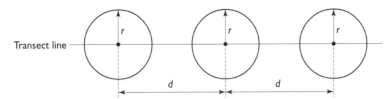

Transect line

Figure 7.3 The 'species region' method of Stowe and Wade.

where n equals the total number of letters in the letter sequence, n_a is the total number of A's and n_b is the total number B's. This procedure is only applicable when $n > n_a + n_b$, i.e. the sequence contains letters coding for species other than A and B. Knight (1974) provided a recursive method for the analysis of small samples and the special case of $n = n_a + n_b$.

The 'species region' method
Stowe and Wade (1979) present the 'species region' method, a transect-based procedure for detecting small-scale spatial patterns in vegetation. Sharing many features with the transect methods of Pielou, it is based on examining the likelihood of a species occurring in a region centred on one of two species. Data is collected along a line transect or series of transects running through the site. At regular points, distance d along the transect, record the occurrence of the nearest plant species to a point, within a radius r. If no species of interest occurs within this radius, record a blank. To avoid overlap between the data collected at each point, the maximum values of the search radius r must be less than or equal to half the distance d between consecutive sample points, i.e. $r \leq d/2$ (Figure 7.3). As r decreases from this maximum, the search area around each point becomes smaller and the number of blank records will increase. If r is too small, few plants will be recorded, the sampling will be inefficient and the large number of blank records generated will make the analysis unreliable. Stowe and Wade (1979) suggest r and d values should be chosen by trial and error so that r is sufficiently large to ensure that only 5–10% of sample points are recorded as blank.

As before, the collected results are summarised as a sequence of letters, where each letter represents a single species occurring nearest to each sample point and − represents a blank record.

AACCCA−BBB−NNCAAB−D . . .

The sequence is then collapsed, replacing runs of a species by a single letter and the primary and secondary species of interest are chosen (here A and B):

ACA−B−NCAB−D . . .

Once the primary and secondary species are selected, regions associated with the primary species are identified. A region is simply a portion of the letter chain enclosed by the primary species (e.g. ACA) or a portion enclosing the primary species (e.g. CAB); that is, regions are defined by considering species immediately adjacent to the primary and secondary species. Where regions overlap, species occurrences should not be recorded twice. With species A as the primary species and species B as the secondary species, there are four possibilities for distributing B relative to A along the letter sequence. These frequencies are recorded as follows:

a = number of occurrences of B in the regions of A (e.g. ABA)

b = number of occurrences of letters other than B or A
   in the regions of A (e.g. ACA or A−A)

c = number of occurrences of B outside the regions of A (e.g. −B− or CBC)

d = number of occurrences of letters other than B outside the regions of A

Blank records (−) are treated as if they are letters other that A or B.

Where the sample size is greater than 30, significant association between species A and B may be tested using the standard chi-squared or G-test approach.[5] Note that this procedure is 'directional' and for any two species (A and B) the analysis may be performed in two ways: with A as the primary species and with B as the primary species.

Consider the sequence of 29 collapsed occurrences:

$$--ABA-B---B---ABA---A-B--ABA-$$

For A as the primary species and B as the secondary species, we have $a = 3, b = 8, c = 3, d = 8$. To see how these numbers were obtained, consider a series of circles each of 3 letters diameter and drawn about each A in the sequence:

Then a is obtained by counting the number of B's that are enclosed in the circles centred on the A's present in the sequence; b is the number of non-(A or B) letters (i.e. blanks) enclosed by the circles, c is the number of B's not enclosed by the circles and d is the number of letters other than B (i.e. blanks) outside of the circles.

Taking B as the primary species and A as the secondary species gives a different set of values: $a = 6, b = 6, c = 1, d = 10$.

Using Jarrard's index as a measure of association:

For A primary and B secondary $\quad \mathcal{J}_A = \dfrac{a}{a+b+c} = \dfrac{3}{3+8+3} = 0.214$

$(a = 3, b = 8, c = 3, d = 8)$

For B primary and A secondary $\quad \mathcal{J}_B = \dfrac{a}{a+b+c} = \dfrac{6}{6+6+1} = 0.462$

$(a = 6, b = 6, c = 1, d = 10)$

The low $\mathcal{J}_A$ of 0.21 implies that the distribution of species B along the transect is largely independent of species A, and the higher $\mathcal{J}_B$ of 0.46 suggests that species A tends to be associated with regions of species B. If this pattern association were significant, biologically it could mean that species A is commensal with species B. The significance of any relationship is assessed using the standard chi-squared or G-test procedures.

One advantage of this sampling scheme is that, by changing d and r, it is possible to investigate the influence of scale on the pattern of species associations. Stowe and Wade (1979) discuss further refinements of this approach and they present an alternative method that allows the association between all possible species pairs to be assessed. However, the calculation of expected values requires complex numerical routines that are not readily available and this limits its ease of application.

Species contact method

A novel plotless approach, originally suggested by Yarranton (1966) for the analysis of plant species associations, involves using the plant as the sample unit. Sample plants are selected, either randomly or at regular intervals in the study area, and the species identity of the sample plant and all plants actually in contact with it (contact neighbours) are recorded. The process is repeated until the community has been adequately sampled. This approach has the advantage of providing a 'plant-centred' view of community structure for each species. Unfortunately, in practice this sampling method is not without problems and the application of a standard chi-squared procedure, as suggested by Yarranton (1966), is not always valid (De Jong *et al.*, 1983). The method has subsequently been modified by several workers (Turkington and Harper, 1979a,b; De Jong *et al.*, 1980, 1983; Aarssen and Turkington, 1985). The modified procedure described here does not record all contacts; it only records the identity of the *nearest* neighbouring plant (*j*) actually *in contact* with the initially selected sample plant (*i*). By repeated sampling in this way, it is possible to build up a picture of the overall pattern of species associations.

The investigator must make certain sampling decisions before collecting the data. Having selected a sample plant of species *i*, there are three possibilities when recording the identity of species *j* in contact with this plant:

- The contact mate is a different species, $j \neq i$.
- The contact mate is the same species, $j = i$.
- There is no contact mate; the plant of species *i* is isolated.

Any study is likely to encounter these three situations; how they are treated and recorded by the investigator will determine which method of analysis is appropriate (De Jong *et al.*, 1983). The sampling and recording options are outlined in Table 7.7.

Recording non-contacts (option 2b) does provide information on the degree to which a species occurs as an isolated individual. However, since no-contact species cannot be selected as a sample plant, their inclusion will cause the table of results to be biased. Thus, no-contact species should be removed from the final table of results before any statistical analysis. The data may be tabulated in several ways. The traditional approach is to produce a folded triangular array, with no distinction between the order in which species were encountered,

Table 7.7 Options for sampling and recording

Identity of initial sampling plant (first species, i)	Identity of nearest neighbouring plant, 'contact mate' (second species, j)	Tabulate result, i.e. record contact	Sampling options
Species *A*	Species *B*	yes	Continue sampling, selecting new sampling plants
Species *A*	No contact	no	*Option 2a*: reject sampling point and resample; select a new sampling plant
		yes	*Option 2b*: record non-contact as a no-contact species; continue sampling, selecting a new sampling plant
Species *A*	Species *A*	yes	*Option 3a*: continue sampling without rejection, selecting a new sampling plant
		no	*Option 3b*: reject sampling point and resample; select a new sampling plant
		no	*Option 3c*: retain initial sampling plant but record next-nearest neighbour until no intraspecific contact is recorded

Table 7.8 The unfolded table has two distinct advantages

A. DATA TYPES FROM CONTACT SAMPLING

Original data

		Sample									
		1	2	3	4	5	6	7	8	9	10
Species	a	×	×	×					×		
	b	×		×			×			×	×
	c		×		×	×	×	×		×	×
	d				×	×		×	×		

Contingency matrix

		Species			
		a	b	c	d
Species	a	4	2	1	1
	b	2	5	3	0
	c	1	3	7	3
	d	1	0	3	4

$N = 10$

B. CONTACT SAMPLING COUNT MATRIX[a]

	First selected species (i)	Second species (j)											Total (f_i)
		(1)	(2)	(3)	(4)	(5)	(6)	(7)	(8)	(9)	(10)	(11)	
(1)	*Agropyron repens*	–	0	1	5	0	7	12	23	1	1	5	55
(2)	*Agrostis alba*	0	–	0	3	11	4	13	17	0	0	4	52
(3)	*Dactylis glomerata*	5	0	–	1	3	2	8	32	2	1	6	60
(4)	*Festuca rubra*	1	0	2	–	10	4	4	15	0	0	3	39
(5)	*Holcus lanatus*	3	1	0	7	–	17	65	85	3	7	13	201
(6)	*Lolium perenne*	5	6	4	3	18	–	17	70	1	8	3	135
(7)	*Poa compressa*	8	10	18	3	70	19	–	214	4	10	44	400
(8)	*Trifolium repens*	12	13	15	14	71	43	149	–	6	5	21	349
(9)	*Cirsium arvense*	0	1	1	1	3	3	10	3	–	0	3	25
(10)	*Ranunculus acris*	0	1	0	1	4	3	14	10	1	–	4	38
(11)	*Taraxacum officinale*	2	2	1	0	5	2	19	20	0	1	–	52
	Total (s_j)	36	34	42	38	195	104	311	489	18	33	106	1406

C. COUNT MATRIX GENERATED BY CONTACT SAMPLING

First selected species	Second selected species					Total
	(1)	(2)	(3)	$...$	(k)	
(1)	n_{11}	n_{12}	n_{13}	$...$	n_{1k}	f_1
(2)	n_{21}	n_{22}	n_{23}	$...$	n_{2k}	f_2
(3)	n_{31}	n_{32}	n_{33}	$...$	n_{3k}	f_3
$\vdots$	$\vdots$	$\vdots$	$\vdots$	$...$	$\vdots$	$\vdots$
(k)	n_{k1}	n_{k2}	n_{k3}	$...$	n_{kk}	f_4
Total	s_1	s_2	s_3	$...$	s_k	N

[a] For data collected from a 40 year old pasture community in British Columbia. *Sources*: Yarranton (1966) and De Jong *et al.* (1983)

i.e. whether a particular record or contact between i and j was the result of species i being the selected sampling plant and j a recorded contact, or vice versa. The alternative approach is to produce an unfolded square table where the order of i and j is clearly distinguished. The unfolded table has two distinct advantages: it does not assume that the contacts and thus associations between species i and j are symmetrical, and it clearly shows the frequency of each species (Table 7.8).

The unfolded results table may be either symmetrical or asymmetrical. Where species have a similar morphology and the vegetation is not multilayered, contacts between species may fit the proportionality hypothesis, i.e. the probability of a species being a contact neighbour is proportional to the frequency with which the species occurs as the initial sample plant (De Jong *et al.*, 1983). Symmetrical tables are obtained when the proportionality hypothesis is found to hold. In the majority of cases the results table will be asymmetrical; the probability of a species being selected as the initial sampling plant does not equal the probability of its occurrence as the contact species. Asymmetrical tables largely result from the different ways in which the initial sample plants and contact species are selected, and this is partly a function of plant size, morphology and the canopy structure of the community being sampled. Where there is minimal vertical structure, such as in lichen or bryophyte vegetation, the degree of asymmetry may be negligible. For most communities this will not be the case and information on differently ordered pairs of contacts should be retained, the results being recorded as an unfolded table (De Jong *et al.*, 1983).

The relative merits of these different approaches are discussed in detail by De Jong *et al.* (1983). Their recommended approach to analysing these sampling schemes and the resulting tables is to begin by testing the complete table of species pairs for departures from a random pattern of association and then, if appropriate, to test individual species pairs in turn. For option 3a only, where within-species contacts are allowed and no-contacts are removed from the table, it is possible to calculate the expected values directly from the tabulated results without using a complex iterative approach. This procedure is outlined below.

Step 1 Departure of the whole table from a random pattern of species associations is tested using the standard chi-squared or G-test procedures for large tables:

$$X^2 = \sum_i \sum_j (n_{ij} - e_{ij})^2 / e_{ij}$$

$$G = 2 \sum_i \sum_j n_{ij} \ln \left(\frac{n_{ij}}{e_{ij}} \right)$$

where n_{ij} = observed number of occurrences of species i as the first (sampling) species and species j as the second (contact) species

           e_{ij} = expected number of occurrences of species i as the first (sampling) species and species j as the second (contact) species

Two methods can be used to calculate e_{ij} values:

- If the proportionality hypothesis is not applied, then

$$e_{ij} = f_i s_j / N \qquad \text{d.f.} = (K - 1)^2$$

- If the proportionality hypothesis is applied, then

$$e_{ij} = (f_i + s_i)(f_j + s_j) / 4N \qquad \text{d.f.} = K(K - 1)$$

where f_i = sum of the occurrences of species i as the first species (i.e. the row total corresponding to species i)

s_j = sum of occurrences of species j as the second species (i.e. the column total corresponding to species i)

N = the grand total of contacts

K = the total number of species present

Where the table is folded, G and X^2 have $K(K-1)/2$ degrees of freedom. Substituting the appropriate f and s values allows all the required expected counts to be calculated. A large and significant test statistic allows the null hypothesis of independent random species associations to be rejected.

Step 2   Where sample sizes are large, the contribution of individual species pairs to the overall test statistic may be assessed by examining the standardised residuals, which approximately follow the standard normal distribution. The species pair standard residuals are $\mathrm{Sr}_{ij} = (n_{ij} - e_{ij})/\sqrt{e_{ij}}$ for X^2 and $\mathrm{Sr}_{ij} = 2n_{ij}\ln(n_{ij}/e_{ij})$ for G. High standardised residual values imply that the species pairs are associated in some way and contribute to the significant departure of the table from the null hypothesis of random or independent association between species. The significance of individual standardised residual values can be assessed by comparing them with standard normal probability tables. For the unfolded table, De Jong *et al.* (1983) present a method under this sampling scheme (option 3a) for the exact analysis of species contact pairs.

Where the proportionality hypothesis is *not* applied for any two species, two types of 2×2 contingency tables may be produced and independence tested using the standard chi-squared test or the G-test (Sections 7.2.1 and 7.2.2).

- *Type 1 table (single species)*: This table tests whether species A demonstrates greater or fewer within-species (intraspecies) contacts than expected under the null hypothesis of random association. Four observed frequencies can be identified:

  Q_{AA} = number of times species A occurs as both first and second species, i.e. intraspecies contacts (n_{ii})

  Q_{AB} = number of times species A occurs as the first species and the second species is other than $A, A \neq B, (f_i - n_{ii})$

  Q_{BA} = number of times species A occurs as the second species when $B, B \neq A$, is the first species $(s_i - n_{ii})$

  Q_{BB} = number of times that species A does not occur as either the first or second species $(N - s_i - f_i + n_{ii})$

- *Type 2 table (species pairs)*: Frequency values for the four categories of contact pairs $(i,i), (i,j), (j,i), (j,j)$ are arranged in a 2×2 contingency table. For any selected pair of species (A and B) four observed frequency values may be extracted from the results table:

  Q_{AA} = number of times species A occurs as both first and second species, i.e. intraspecies contacts (n_{ii})

  Q_{AB} = number of times species A occurs as the first species and species B occurs as the second species (n_{ij})

  Q_{BA} = number of times species B occurs as the first species and species A occurs as the second species (n_{ji})

Q_{BB} = number of times species B occurs as both the first
and second species, i.e. intraspecific contacts (n_{jj})

If the proportionality hypothesis is invoked and the same four categories of contact pairs are considered, the probability of species i and j contacts, p_i and p_j, are estimated from $p_i = (n_{ii} + \frac{1}{2}n_{ij} + \frac{1}{2}n_{ji})/M$ and $p_j = (n_{jj} + \frac{1}{2}n_{ij} + \frac{1}{2}n_{ji})/M$ with $M = n_{ii} + n_{jj} + n_{ij} + n_{ji}$. These probabilities are then used to generate the expected cell counts $e_{ii} = Mp_i^2$, $e_{jj} = Mp_j^2$, $e_{ij} = e_{ji} = Mp_ip_j$. Once the expected values have been generated, a chi-squared test or G-test is performed. There are three points to note:

- The inclusion of within-species contacts may cause practical problems in the field, where distinguishing within-plant contacts from contacts between different plants of the same species may prove difficult, particularly among grass species.

- The data is ordered, i.e. the occurrence of species i followed by species j (n_{ij}) is distinguished from the opposite ordered pair (n_{ji}), where the occurrence of species j is followed by the occurrence of species i.

- The method assumes that all species encountered in the field are recorded. In diverse communities this can prove to be extremely time-consuming. The method can be modified by recording only contacts among a limited number of target species of particular interest.

Although only one sampling scheme can be easily analysed using the contingency table approach suggested by Yarranton (1966), the plant-centred contact recording has much to recommend it. It seems logical to assume that a greater ecological insight is to be gained from considering contacts between actual plants, than from the usual procedure of describing plant communities in terms of the abundance of species that touch randomly located steel pins descending from above. Rather than pursuing statistical methods which allow the significant species associations to be tested, the interpretation and analysis of plant–plant contact data may be better served by using the descriptive methods of ordination and cluster analysis (Chapters 8 and 9).

7.3 *Continuous data*

Where quantitative measures of species abundance or values of appropriate environmental factors have been recorded, correlation analysis may be used to assess the nature and strength of covariation between species or factors. Although the concepts of covariation and association are similar, they are not the same (Ludwig and Reynolds, 1988). For example, it is possible for two species with similar habitat requirements to be positively associated, i.e. the species tend to occur together in the same sample units, but for their abundance to be negatively correlated, so high abundance values of one species tend to occur in sample units where the second species is not abundant.

Two correlation coefficients are commonly used, the Pearson product-moment correlation coefficient and the Spearman rank correlation. In both cases, if the strength of correlation is to be assessed then the data must be collected from randomly placed quadrats or selected natural sample units. The presence of many zero values will distort the analysis. Paired zeros (i.e. where $x = 0$ and $y = 0$) are best removed, especially if the overall sample size is small. Where a number of variables have been recorded for each sample unit, with the intention of undertaking multiple correlations, those variables with large numbers of zeros (e.g. a low frequency species) should be removed entirely from the data set. If the aim of the study is to investigate the possible occurrence of competition between two species, then quadrats containing neither species should be removed. Worked examples of both correlation tests using MINTAB are given in Section 7.5.

7.3.1 Pearson's product-moment correlation

The Pearson product-moment correlation coefficient is the more powerful procedure but requires that the variables are normally distributed and linearly related. The Pearson product-moment correlation coefficient (r) is calculated from the formula

$$r = C_{xy}/S_x S_y$$

where x_i, y_i are the value pairs for the two species or variables recorded in the ith sample unit; $C_{xy} = \sum (x_i - \bar{x})(y_i - \bar{y})$ is the covariance of variables x and y; S_x, S_y are the standard deviations of x and y; and x, y are the corresponding sample means. The number of degrees of freedom is $n - 2$, where n is the number of sample units.

High covariance (C_{xy}) values will be obtained when $(x_i - \bar{x})$ and $(y_i - \bar{y})$ are large (i.e. when extreme values of x and y tend to occur in the same sample unit). Covariance is thus a direct measure of correlation. But C_{xy} is strongly influenced by the absolute values of x and y (i.e. the scale of measurement used) and because of this it is difficult to interpret as a measure of correlation. Dividing C_{xy} by the product of $S_x S_y$ will standardise (scale) the covariance, giving a correlation coefficient ranging from -1.0 to 1.0. The significance of r is assessed by consulting appropriate statistical tables; if tables are not available then the significance may be assessed by testing whether $r = 0$ using Student's t-test:

$$t = \frac{1}{r} \sqrt{\frac{1 - r^2}{n - 2}} \qquad (\text{d.f.} = n - 2)$$

The analysis should proceed as follows.

Check that values are normally distributed
Test the data for normality and, if necessary, transforms the data (Chapter 10). If values are expressed as percentages or proportions, particularly if values fall outside of the range 30–70%, the data should be arcsine transformed. The arcsine transformation reduces the effects of the truncating values to a scale from 0 to 1.0 (the normally distributed values may range from $-\infty$ to $+\infty$. The arcsine transformation can only be applied to proportions, so percentage values must be divided by 100. The arcsine of the square root of the proportion is taken; that is, the transformed values are $p^* = \arcsin \sqrt{p}$. Arcsin is the inverse sine or $\sin^{-1}$ on most calculators! So if $p = 0.81$, $p^* = \arcsin \sqrt{0.81} = \arcsin 0.91 = 64.158$.

Check that variables are linearly related
Plot the two variables against one another to ensure they are linearly related. If the variables are not linearly related, it may be necessary to transform one or both variables (Section 10.2.4). Most plots will show a lot of scatter, but the important thing is that there should be no obvious or pronounced non-linear trends.

Calculate r and assess its significance
Box 7.2 shows how to calculate r by hand and using a spreadsheet. Most basic hand calculators are able to calculate r and the associated linear regression equation directly from the input of paired x and y values.

Correlation is often undertaken as part of regression analysis. Regression can be seen as involving two stages. The correlation between the variables is determined and then used

Box 7.2   **Pearson's correlation coefficient**

Calculation of correlation coefficient

Data		Deviations		Squared deviations		
x	y	$(x - \bar{x})$	$(y - \bar{y})$	$(x - \bar{x})(y - \bar{y})$	$(x - \bar{x})^2$	$(y - \bar{y})^2$
6.6	86	−1.6700	−69.4000	115.8980	2.7889	4816.3600
6.9	92	−1.3700	−63.4000	86.8580	1.8769	4019.5600
7.3	71	−0.9700	−84.4000	81.8680	0.9409	7123.3600
7.5	74	−0.7700	−81.4000	62.6780	0.5929	6625.9600
8.2	185	−0.0700	29.6000	−2.0720	0.0049	876.1600
8.3	85	0.0300	−70.4000	−2.1120	0.0009	4956.1600
9.1	201	0.8300	45.6000	37.8480	0.6889	2079.3600
9.2	283	0.9300	127.6000	118.6680	0.8649	16281.7600
9.4	255	1.1300	99.6000	112.5480	1.2769	9920.1600
10.2	222	1.9300	66.6000	128.5380	3.7249	4435.5600

Mean 8.27   155.4   Total =   740.7200   12.7610   61134.4000

d.f. = 9   Variances   82.3022   1.4179   6792.7111

                       St. dev.   1.1908   82.4179

$$r = \qquad 0.83863 \qquad\qquad S_x \text{ and } S_y$$
$$\text{d.f.} = n - 2 \qquad 8$$

$$r = \frac{\text{cov}(x, y)}{S_x S_y} \qquad\qquad \text{cov}(x, y) = \frac{\sum(x - \bar{x})(y - \bar{y})}{n - 1} \qquad$$

significance at 1% level (0.765 from tables for $p < 0.01$ and d.f. = 8)

$r = 1.0$ when $\text{cov}(x, y) = $ product of variance in sample variables

Method normally used for calculation by hand

x	y	x^2	y^2	xy
6.6	86	43.56	7396	567.6
6.9	92	47.61	8464	634.8
7.3	71	53.29	5041	518.3
7.5	74	56.25	5476	555
8.2	185	67.24	34225	1517
8.3	85	68.89	7225	705.5
9.1	201	82.81	40401	1829.1
9.2	283	84.64	80089	2602.6
9.4	255	88.36	65025	2397
10.2	222	104.04	49284	2264.4

Regression line is
$$y = a + bx$$
$$a = \bar{y} - b\bar{x}$$
$$b = \frac{\text{cov}(x, y)}{S_x^2} = r\frac{S_y}{S_x}$$
$$r = \frac{n\sum xy - \sum x \sum y}{([n\sum x^2 - (\sum x)^2][n\sum y^2 - (\sum y)^2])^{1/2}}$$

$\sum x$

Totals   82.7   1554   696.69   302626   13592.3 ← $\sum xy$

Squared totals   6839.29   2414916 $(n = 10)$

$$(\sum x)^2 \quad (\sum y)^2 \quad \sum y \qquad \sum x^2 \quad \sum y^2$$

to calculate the position of the best-fit regression line. This line provides a model or representation of the relationship between the variables in the form of a straight-line equation. For linear regression this equation is simply $y = c + mx$ where c and m are constants: m is the slope of the plotted line and c is its intercept on the y-axis. From the equation, values of y can be calculated or predicted from values of x. Both x and y should be normally distributed and linearly related, but these requirements are more important for linear regression than for correlation. Greater detail is given in Chapter 10.

7.3.2 Spearman's rank correlation

The Spearman rank correlation test is an example of a non-parametric test, i.e. it does not require the data to be normally distributed or to follow any particularly distribution. And compared with the parametric Pearson product-moment correlation, it is also less sensitive to departures from a linear relationship between the variables. Two procedures may be used, and both require the values to be ranked. Each variable is ranked with reference to itself only; the ranks of the variables are then compared and the null hypothesis is that the ranks are uncorrelated. Note that the variable values are ranked *not* sorted. Individual values are replaced by a number which gives the ranked position of that value; the pairing of values from the same original sample unit is retained. Spearman's rank correlation coefficient (r_S) may be calculated by performing a Pearson correlation (as described above) on the ranked data or by using the formula

$$r_S = 1 - \frac{6 \sum_{i=1}^{n} d_i^2}{n^3 - n}$$

where d = the difference between the ranked x and y values
n = the number of paired values, i.e. sample units

Here is an example that examines the relationship between lead concentrations in estuary sediment and the species richness of the nematode community present in the cores (Table 7.9). The very large range of the Pb concentration (12.5 to 9580 ppm) suggests that the values are not normally distributed. Spearman's coefficient is thus the most appropriate correlation with which to begin an analysis. If it proves possible to transform the data so it conforms to a normal distribution, a Pearson correlation could then be applied:

$$r_S = 1 - \frac{6 \sum_{i=1}^{n} d_i^2}{n^3 - n} = 1 - \frac{6 \times 788}{15^3 - 15} = 1 - \frac{4728}{3360} = 1 - 1.4071 = -0.407$$

The r_S of -0.407 suggests that the species richness of the nematode fauna is negatively correlated with Pb concentration, i.e. species richness decreases with increasing sediment Pb concentration. The significance of r_S may be found from tabulated critical values. If a table of critical r_S values is not available,[6] for $n > 10$ a table of critical values for Pearson's r may be used. The critical value for r_S ($n = 15$) at $p < 0.05$ is 0.5214. Although -0.407 is close to the required critical value, it is not large enough to reject the null hypothesis of no correlation between Pb concentration and the ranked values of species richness in the nematode community. Although the data requirements for Spearman's correlation are less restrictive than for Pearson's correlation, the test is less powerful. Therefore, the Pearson correlation test should be used even if it requires the data to be transformed.

Table 7.9 Examining the relationship between lead concentration and nematode species richness in estuary sediment

(C1) Sample unit	(C2) Unranked x-values[a]	(C3) Ranked x-values	(C4) Unranked y-values[b]	(C5) Ranked y-values	(C6 = C3 − C5) d	(C7) d²
1	28.8	3	13	8	−5	25
2	50	7	10	5	2	4
3	12.5	1	11	6	−5	25
4	401	11	7	1	10	100
5	186	10	8	2.5	7.5	56.25
6	154	9	20	12.5	−3.5	12.25
7	28.1	2	20	12.5	−10.5	110.25
8	46.1	5	21	14	−9	81
9	44	4	24	15	−11	121
10	55.9	6	17	11	−5	25
11	3230	13	16	10	3	9
12	9580	15	12	7	8	64
13	5060	14	8	2.5	11.5	132.25
14	429	12	14	9	3	9
15	102	8	9	4	4	14

$$\sum d_i^2 = 788$$

[a] Concentration of Pb (ppm) in estuary sediment cores.
[b] Number of nematode species in estuarine sediment cores.

7.4 *Mixed data sets*

Sometimes a data set may contain both continuous and binary variables. Although it is possible to calculate a correlation between a binary variable and a continuous variable (Chapter 11), very often this is not warranted. Imagine that the levels of mercury have been determined in soil samples from 20 sites. And on collection, the presence or absence of soil springtails was recorded. Springtails are small invertebrates of the order Collembola; they are found in leaf litter and soil and they are frequently used to monitor soil contamination. In this case the data set would consist of a continuous x-variable, Hg concentration, and a binary y-variable, the presence (1) or absence (0) of springtails. The easiest and most direct way to test whether springtail occurrence is associated with high or low concentrations of soil Hg, is to divide the data set into two groups: samples that contain springtails and samples that don't. The sample mean and variance of soil Hg concentration is then calculated. If there is no association between Hg concentration and the occurrence of springtails, the means should be the same. If there is a negative association, as one might expect, the mean Hg concentration for samples that contain springtails should be lower than the mean for samples that don't contain springtails. If the sampling was *random*, the significance of any association between soil Hg and the presence or absence of springtails may be assessed by testing the significance of any differences between the means using the *t*-test or the *d*-test, depending on the sample size:

$n_1, n_2 > 30$

$$d = \frac{\bar{x}_1 - \bar{x}_2}{\sqrt{S_1^2/n_1 + S_2^2/n_2}}$$

Large-sample test: at $p < 0.05$ the absolute values of d must be greater than 1.96 for the means to differ significantly.

$$n_1, n_2 < 30$$

$$t = \frac{\bar{x}_1 - \bar{x}_2}{\sqrt{S_p^2/n_1 + S_p^2/n_2}}$$

Small-sample test: t-values are compared with tabulated values at $p = 0.05$ and d.f. $= n_1 + n_2 - 2$. This version of the t-test assumes that the sample variances are equal but unknown. If the variances differ, the Welch t-test should be used (Chapter 10).

$$S_p = \frac{n_1 S_1^2 + n_2 S_2^2}{(n_1 - 1) + (n_1 - 1)}$$

where $\bar{x}_1, \bar{x}_2 = $ the sample means for group 1 and group 2
$S_1^2, S_2^2 = $ the sample variances for group 1 and group 2
$n_1, n_2 = $ the sample sizes for group 1 and group 2
$S_p = $ a pooled estimate of variance based on all the data values used in the calculation

7.5 *Multiple variables*

All the methods described, except for the species contact method (Section 7.2.5), are designed to assess the relationship (if any) between two variables. If data has been collected on all species present in each sample unit, then all possible species combinations may be tested for the occurrence of significant associations or correlation. The results of such a study may be presented as a species-by-species half-matrix in which the entries indicate the strength and nature of the relationship between each species pair. The results may also be presented graphically by producing a plexus or constellation diagram. This is essentially a scatter diagram. The distance between plotted points on the page represents the strength of the relationship between species (distances are based on the size of the appropriate test statistic, e.g. a correlation coefficient). Positive relationships may be shown by solid lines and negative relationships by dashed lines. In practice it is difficult, often impossible, to produce plexus diagrams in which all significant relationships between the plotted points are accurately reflected in the relative position of the points. Diagrams are often more easily produced if a limited number of fixed scaled distances are used to depict various grouped levels of significance. Alternatively the distances between points may be arbitrary. The strength of the relationship between points is then indicated by the colour or thickness of the line used to link the points (Figure 7.4).

This approach has obvious attractions; it allows the pattern of species relationships to be easily viewed. But it is not without problems and cannot be recommended. Some of the problems are common to any situation where multiple comparisons are made using statistical tests developed to assess the relationship between only two variables (e.g. Student's *t*-test). The number of possible comparisons increases dramatically as the number of variables increases. With S species, the number of possible comparisons is $S(S - 1)/2$. Thus if 6 species are recorded, the total number of possible pairwise comparisons is $6(6 - 1)/2 = 15$; with 12 species the number of comparisons more than doubles to $12(12 - 1)/2 = 66$. Thus, with even modest numbers of variables, producing a plexus diagram is likely to prove difficult.

A more fundamental problem arises when we consider the significance of any particular relationship. By convention the minimum level of significance adopted in scientific studies is 5% ($p < 0.05$). By adopting this level of significance, we are effectively saying we are happy to accept that two variables differ or are related significantly only when the test statistics we obtain could only occur by chance less than 5% of time. Imagine you take

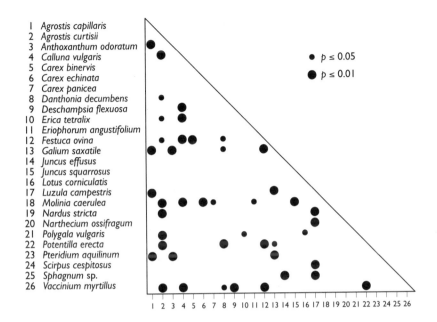

1. *Agrostis capillaris*
2. *Agrostis curtisii*
3. *Anthoxanthum odoratum*
4. *Calluna vulgaris*
5. *Carex binervis*
6. *Carex echinata*
7. *Carex panicea*
8. *Danthonia decumbens*
9. *Deschampsia flexuosa*
10. *Erica tetralix*
11. *Eriophorum angustifolium*
12. *Festuca ovina*
13. *Galium saxatile*
14. *Juncus effusus*
15. *Juncus squarrosus*
16. *Lotus corniculatus*
17. *Luzula campestris*
18. *Molinia caerulea*
19. *Nardus stricta*
20. *Narthecium ossifragum*
21. *Polygala vulgaris*
22. *Potentilla erecta*
23. *Pteridium aquilinum*
24. *Scirpus cespitosus*
25. *Sphagnum* sp.
26. *Vaccinium myrtillus*

$p \leq 0.05$
$p \leq 0.01$

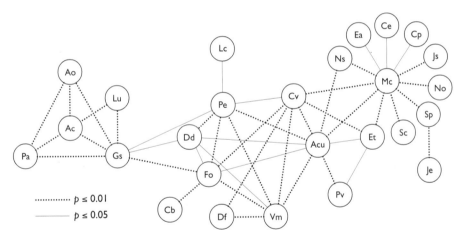

$p \leq 0.01$
$p \leq 0.05$

Figure 7.4 Chi-squared matrix of positive associations between 26 species in a catchment (top). Constellation diagram derived from the chi-squared matrix (bottom). Reprinted, with permission, from Kent and Coker (1992).

two populations which are known not to differ and you compare their means 100 times using the *t*-test. Each time you take two random samples, one from each population, and you calculate and compare the means. Even though the means do not differ, we would expect the test to find a significant difference on at least five occasions, purely due to sampling errors. Thus, 1 in 20 (i.e. 1 in 100/5) significant results may occur purely by chance. In a table summarising the 66 possible pairwise relationships among 12 species, we might expect to find at least 3 significant relationships by chance alone. How do we distinguish them from the real significant relationships?

There is no easy answer to this problem. One approach is to set more stringent critical values to the test, reducing the likelihood that significant results occur by chance. This can be achieved by using the Bonferroni procedure. The initial choice of significance level

Box 7.3 Correlation analysis using MINITAB

Chi-squared procedure

The 2×2 contingency values are stored in two columns: C1 contains the values for cells a and c, C2 the values for cells b and d.

	C1	C2
1	23	58
2	47	22

Larger tables are entered in the same way; each combination of row and column represents a cell of the data table.

```
MTB > ChiSquare C1 C2.
```

MINITAB command, may be typed in directly at the prompt or entered via Stat on the main menu bar. Select Tables then Chi-Square Test.

Chi-Square Test   **Output**

```
Expected counts are printed below observed counts
          C1      C2     Total
    1     23      58       81
        37.51   43.49
```

The calculated expected values are 43.49 and 36.51.

```
    2     46      22       68
        31.49   36.51
Total    69      80      149
```

Individual cell contributions to the overall χ^2 value of 22.907, which is highly significant.

```
Chi-Sq = 5.613 + 4.841 +
         6.686 + 5.767 = 22.907
DF = 1, P-Value = 0.000
MTB >
```

MINITAB does not print out more than 3 significant decimal places (some routines display results to more than 3 places). We can take 0.000 as showing that $p < 0.001$.

Pearson moment correlation analysis

Testing for normality

The data is 25 paired values x, y stored in columns C1 and C2; the variables are continuous. MINITAB provides three tests of normality:

- The Anderson–Darling test (the default) is an ECDF (empirical cumulative distribution function) test.
- The Ryan–Joiner test (similar to the Shapiro–Wilk test) is a correlation-based test.
- The Kolmogorov–Smirnov test is an ECDF test.

The Anderson–Darling and Ryan–Joiner tests have similar power for detecting non-normality. The Kolmogorov–Smirnov test is less powerful but more widely known. The common null hypothesis for these three tests is H_0: data follow a normal distribution.

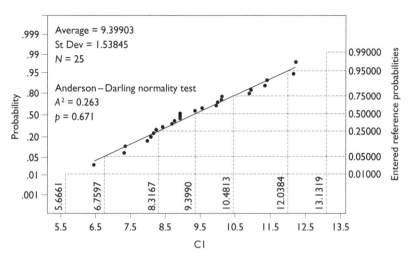

Figure 1 Testing C1 for normality.

If the p-value of the test is *less* than the chosen α-level ($p = 0.05$) then reject H_0; the data is not normally distributed and transformation is required (Chapter 10).

Since these tests involve producing a probability plot, they are not appropriate for small sample sizes. With sample sizes of 10 and lower, it is not possible to be sure that a distribution is really normal. Inspection of the relative sizes of the standard deviation, median, mode and mean may help in reaching a decision (Chapter 1). As discussed in Chapter 1, unless the departures from normality are large, parametric statistics are still likely to prove more useful than their non-parametric alternatives.

To perform these tests using MINITAB, a set of reference probabilities must be stored. These reference probabilities must be between 0 and 1.0 and are used simply to establish the marks and scales on the right-hand y-axis of the probability plot. The test is performed by selecting **Stat** then **Basic Statistics** then **Normality Test**. Applying this procedure to the data stored in column C1 produces Figure 1. And since the calculated p-value of 0.671 exceeds $p = 0.05$, the null hypothesis of normality may be accepted. An alternative method is to produce a standard probability plot using **Graph** then **Probability Plot** with **Normal Distribution** selected in the dialogue box. If the data is normally distributed, the probability plot should be linear. Applying this approach to the variable stored in C2 yields Figure 2. Again we can safely assume that C2 is normally distributed.

Testing for a linear relationship between x and y

The easiest way to assess whether the data values stored in C1 and C2 are linearly related is to plot them against each other. This can be achieved by selecting **Plot** from the **Graph** option on the main menu bar. Once the **Plot** dialogue box is displayed, the columns associated with the x and y variables are declared. When applied to C1 and C2, Figure 3 is produced. From Figure 3, it is clear that the two variables are linearly related.

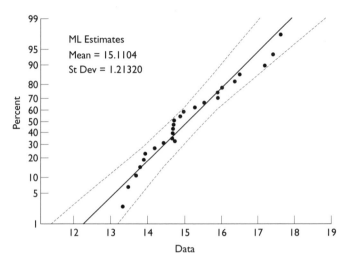

Figure 2 Normal probability plot for C2.

Pearson moment correlation

The correlation between C1 and C2 may be undertaken by entering the command as shown, or selecting **Correlation** from the options under **Basic Statistics**, which is entered from the **Stat** option on the main menu.

```
MTB > Correlation C1 C2.
```
Where more than two columns are specified, MINITAB will calculate the correlation coefficient for all possible pairs.

```
Correlations (Pearson)
Correlation of C1 and C2 = 0.973, P-Value = 0.000
MTB >
```

It is clear that the C1 and C2 are positively correlated at a probability of $p < 0.001$.

Spearman Rank Correlation

MINITAB does not support the Spearman rank correlation. To perform a Spearman rank correlation, both variables must be ranked and then correlated using the Pearson moment

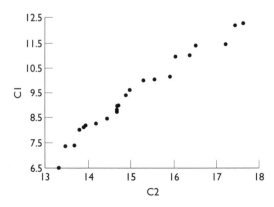

Figure 3 C1 and C2 are linearly related.

correlation. This can be accomplished using the following commands:

```
MTB > Rank C1 C3.          Calculates ranks of values in Cl and stores the results in C3.
MTB > Rank C2 C4.
MTB > Correlation C3 C4     Performs correlation on ranks stored in C3 and C4.

Correlations (Pearson)
Correlation of C3 and C4 = 0.994, P-Value = 0.000
MTB >
```

Not surprisingly, this also indicates that C1 and C2 are strongly correlated.

Using the *t*-test for association

Besides the two continuous variables stored in C1 and C2, suppose that C3 stores a binary variable which codes each sample unit for the presence or absence of a factor; this variable may be used to split the data stored in C1 or C2 into two distinct classes. The mean associated with those sample units for which C3 = 0 can be compared with the mean of those sample units for which C3 = 1.

For example, C2 might contain values of the dissolved oxygen content of river water, and C3 might code for the presence (1) or absence (0) of a particular species of fish. The investigator might be interested in whether the mean oxygen content differs for samples where the species occurs and where it is absent. The means may be compared in this way using the following commands.

The *t*-test with the data stored in one column is selected using the sequence **Stat** then **Basic Statistic** then **2-Sample t**. Now choose these options: sample in one column, alternative 'not equal'. Declare sample values in C2 and subscripts in C3. The following output will be obtained:

```
MTB > TwoT 95.0 C2 C3;     Summary of commands entered via menu options.
SUBC> Alternative 0.

Two Sample T-Test and Confidence Interval
Two sample T for C2

C3    N    Mean    StDev    SE Mean
0     11   8.453   0.833    0.25
1     14   10.97   1.01     0.27

95% CI for mu (0) - mu (1): ( -3.29, -1.76)
T-Test mu (0) = mu (1) (vs not =): T = -6.84 P = 0.0000 DF = 22

MTB >
```

We have $t = -6.84$ and $p < 0.0001$ so we can conclude that the means of the two groups differ significantly.

(*a*) is divided by the number of comparisons (*k*) being made. So if $a = 0.05$ and $k = 45$ (this corresponds to 9 species) the new apparent significance level is $0.05/45 = 0.0011$, so the critical test statistic for the 5% significance level would now be the statistic usually associated with the 0.1% ($p < 0.001$) significance level. In pairwise association testing, 3.84 is the usual critical value for the chi-squared statistic with d.f. $= 1$ at $p < 0.05$; but using the Bonferroni procedure, the value required when 45 comparisons are being made is 10.83. Thus for any significance to be attributed to one particular pairwise comparison at $p < 0.05$ the test statistic, either X^2 or G^2, must exceed 10.83 (not the usual value of 3.84). By setting lower apparent significance levels (a/k), the Bonferroni procedure reduces the likelihood of wrongly attributing significance to individual comparisons but it also reduces the overall sensitivity of the approach, i.e. some real relationships may no longer be significant.

Ludwig and Reynolds (1988) present an alternative approach developed by Schluter (1984). For a table of presence and absence data, i.e. an unfolded table, a test statistic W is calculated from a variance ratio. The null hypothesis is that there are no associations among the S species. This may be true under two conditions: (1) the species are all independent or (2) the positive and negative association exactly cancel each other out. Although the test can distinguish between cases where overall there are more positive or negative associations between species, it does not allow particular associations between pairs of species to be identified or evaluated. If the primary aim of the study is to examine relationships between many variables, it is better to use the appropriate multivariate procedures (Chapters, 8, 9 and 10).

7.6 *Recommendations*

The methods described in this chapter aim to detect and/or quantify the strength of association or correlation between paired variables (x, y). For example, they might investigate the relationship between two species whose presence/absence or abundance has been recorded for a series of sample units. Multiple comparisons between pairs of variables (a versus b,

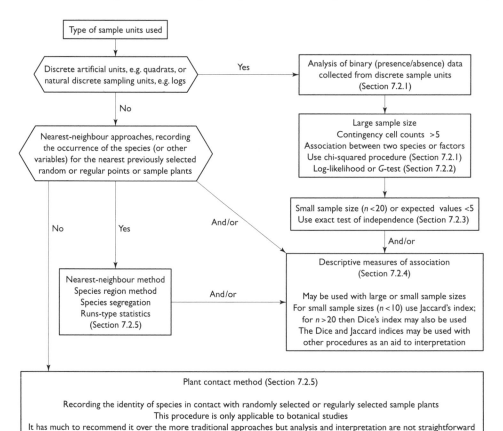

a versus *c*, *a* versus *d*, etc.) can be made using the procedures in this chapter, but this is not recommended. The methods described in Chapters 8, 9 and 10 are more appropriate. Samples may be non-random if the aim of the study is only to test whether the variables are associated or correlated. The samples must be random if the strength of any relationship is to be assessed or if different studies are to be compared. If the data set is mixed, i.e. one variable is continuous and the other binary, then the *t*-test may be used on random samples to assess the strength of any relationship between the two variables (Section 7.4).

The choice of method is largely governed by the nature of the data set. A guide to the procedures for binary data sets is given in the flow diagram. Where continuous variables are recorded for each sample unit, correlation is the most appropriate method. Two procedures are presented. Where the data is normality distributed, and variables linearly related (perhaps after data transformation) the Pearson product-moment correlation (Section 7.3.1) is the most appropriate procedure, otherwise use the less powerful, non-parametric Spearman rank correlation (Section 7.3.2).

Appendix 7.1

Fisher's 2 × 2 exact test

Where data may be summarised as a 2 × 2 contingency table, Fisher's 2 × 2 exact test may be used as a test of association. Summarise the data as a 2 × 2 contingency table (see below). Category I might represent the presence (X) or absence (Y) of a particular species, category II the presence (W) or absence (Z) of a second species or two classes of soil or habitat type. The values A, B, C and D are the observed numbers (frequencies) of sample units in each cell of the contingency table.

The following pages give critical values of C. Find the appropriate row of the table for your values of N, $A + B$, A and B. The rest of the row gives critical values of C at different probability levels. Compare your observed value of C with those tabulated. For your value of C to be significant, it must be *less than or equal to* the tabulated value.

The test makes two assumptions:

1. Samples classed as W or Z will contain the same relative frequencies of X and Y scores. If category I and category II are concerned with the presence or absence of two species in each sample unit, the null hypothesis assumes that the distribution of the two species among sample units is independent.

2. The two samples are independent and random.

One-tailed and two-tailed tests may be conducted.

Summarise the data as a 2 × 2 contingency table

| | *Category I* | | |
Category II	X	Y	Totals
W	A	B	$A + B$
Z	C	D	$C + D$
Totals	$A + C$	$B + D$	N

Appendix 7.1 Table I

N	A + B	A	B	2-Tail 10% 1-Tail 5%	5% 2.5%	2% 1%	0.2% 0.1%
8	4	4	0	C ≤ 0	0		
8	5	5	5	0	0		
8	6	6	0	0			
9	5	4	1	0			
9	5	5	0	0	0	0	
9	6	5	1	0			
9	6	6	0	0	0		
9	7	7	0	0			
10	5	4	1	0	0		
10	5	5	0	1	0	0	
10	6	5	1	0	0		
10	6	6	0	1	0	0	
10	7	6	1	0			
10	7	7	0	0	0	0	
10	8	8	0	0	0		
11	6	4	2	0			
11	6	5	1	0	0		
11	6	6	0	1	1	0	
11	7	5	2	0			
11	7	6	1	0	0		
11	7	7	0	1	0	0	
11	8	7	1	0	0		
11	8	8	0	0	0	0	
11	9	9	0	0	0		
12	6	4	2	0			
12	6	5	1	1	0	0	
12	6	6	0	2	1	1	
12	7	5	2	0			
12	7	6	1	0	0	0	
12	7	7	0	1	1	0	
12	8	6	2	0			
12	8	7	1	0	0		
12	8	8	0	1	1	0	
12	9	7	2	0			
12	9	8	1	0	0		
12	9	9	0	1	0	0	
12	10	9	1	0			
12	10	10	0	0	0		
13	7	4	3	0			
13	7	5	2	0	0		
13	7	6	1	1	0	0	
13	7	7	0	2	1	1	0
13	8	5	3	0			
13	8	6	2	0	0		
13	8	7	1	1	0	0	

Appendix Table I Continued

N	A + B	A	B	2-Tail 10% / 1-Tail 5%	5% / 2.5%	2% / 1%	0.2% / 0.1%
13	8	8	0	$C \leq 2$	1	1	0
13	9	6	3	0			
13	9	7	2	0	0		
13	9	8	1	0	0	0	
13	9	9	0	1	1	0	
13	10	8	2	0			
13	10	9	1	0	0		
13	10	10	0	1	0	0	
13	11	10	1	0			
13	11	11	0	0	0		
14	7	4	3	0			
14	7	5	2	0	0		
14	7	6	1	1	1	0	
14	7	7	0	3	2	1	0
14	8	5	3	0			
14	8	6	2	0	0	0	
14	8	7	1	1	1	0	
14	8	8	0	2	2	1	0
14	9	6	3	0			
14	9	7	2	0	0		
14	9	8	1	1	0	0	
14	9	9	0	2	1	1	0
14	10	7	3	0			
14	10	8	2	0	0		
14	10	9	1	1	0	0	
14	10	10	0	1	1	0	0
14	11	9	2	0			
14	11	10	1	0	0		
14	11	11	0	1	0	0	
14	12	11	1	0			
14	12	12	0	0	0		
15	8	5	3	0	0		
15	8	6	2	1	0	0	
15	8	7	1	2	1	1	
15	8	8	0	3	2	2	0
15	9	5	4	0			
15	9	6	3	0	0		
15	9	7	2	1	0	0	
15	9	8	1	1	1	0	
15	9	9	0	2	2	1	0
15	10	6	4	0			
15	10	7	3	0	0		
15	10	8	2	0	0	0	
15	10	9	1	1	1	0	
15	10	10	0	2	1	1	0
15	11	8	3	0			

Appendix Table I Continued

N	A + B	A	B	2-Tail 10% 1-Tail 5%	5% 2.5%	2% 1%	0.2% 0.1%
15	11	9	2	$c \leq 0$	0		
15	11	10	1	1	0	0	
15	11	11	0	1	1	1	0
15	12	9	3	0			
15	12	10	2	0	0		
15	12	11	1	0	0	0	
15	12	12	0	1	0	0	
15	13	12	1	0			
15	13	13	0	0	0	0	
16	8	4	4	0			
16	8	5	3	0	0		
16	8	6	2	1	1	0	
16	8	7	1	2	1	1	0
16	8	8	0	3	3	2	1
16	9	5	4	0			
16	9	6	3	0	0		
16	9	7	2	1	1	0	
16	9	8	1	2	1	1	0
16	9	9	0	3	2	2	1
16	10	6	4	0			
16	10	7	3	0	0		
16	10	8	2	1	0	0	
16	10	9	1	2	1	1	0
16	10	10	0	3	2	2	0
16	11	7	4	0			
16	11	8	3	0	0		
16	11	9	2	1	0	0	
16	11	10	1	1	1	0	
16	11	11	0	2	2	1	0
16	12	8	4	0			
16	12	9	3	0	0		
16	12	10	2	0	0	0	
16	12	11	1	1	0	0	
16	12	12	0	1	1	1	0
16	13	10	3	0			
16	13	11	2	0	0		
16	13	12	1	0	0	0	
16	13	13	0	1	0	0	
16	14	13	1	0	0		
16	14	14	0	0	0	0	
17	9	5	4	0	0		
17	9	6	3	1	0	0	
17	9	7	2	1	1	0	
17	9	8	1	2	2	1	0
17	9	9	0	4	3	2	1
17	10	5	5	0			

Appendix Table I Continued

N	A + B	A	B	2-Tail 10% 1-Tail 5%	5% 2.5%	2% 1%	0.2% 0.1%
17	10	6	4	C ≤ 0	0		
17	10	7	3	1	0	0	
17	10	8	2	1	1	0	
17	10	9	1	2	2	1	0
17	10	10	0	3	3	2	1
17	11	6	5	0			
17	11	7	4	0	0		
17	11	8	3	1	0	0	
17	11	9	2	1	1	0	
17	11	10	1	2	1	1	0
17	11	11	0	3	2	2	0
17	12	7	5	0			
17	12	8	4	0	0		
17	12	9	3	0	0	0	
17	12	10	2	1	0	0	
17	12	11	1	1	1	0	0
17	12	12	0	2	2	1	0
17	13	9	4	0			
17	13	10	3	0	0		
17	13	11	2	0	0	0	
17	13	12	1	1	1	0	
17	13	13	0	1	1	1	0
17	14	11	3	0			
17	14	12	2	0	0		
17	14	13	1	0	0	0	
17	14	14	0	1	1	0	
17	15	13	2	0			
17	15	14	1	0	0		
17	15	15	0	0	0	0	
18	9	5	4	0	0		
18	9	6	3	1	0	0	
18	9	7	2	2	1	1	
18	9	8	1	3	2	2	0
18	9	9	0	4	4	3	1
18	10	5	5	0			
18	10	6	4	0	0		
18	10	7	3	1	0	0	
18	10	8	2	2	1	1	
18	10	9	1	3	2	2	0
18	10	10	0	4	3	3	1
18	11	6	5	0	0		
18	11	7	4	0	0		
18	11	8	3	1	0	0	
18	11	9	2	2	1	1	
18	11	10	1	2	2	1	0
18	11	11	0	3	3	2	1
18	12	6	6	0			

Appendix Table I Continued

N	A + B	A	B	2-Tail 10% 1-Tail 5%	5% 2.5%	2% 1%	0.2% 0.1%
18	12	7	5	$C \leq 0$	0		
18	12	8	4	0	0		
18	12	9	3	1	0	0	
18	12	10	2	1	1	0	
18	12	11	1	2	1	1	0
18	12	12	0	3	2	2	1
18	13	8	5	0			
18	13	9	4	0	0		
18	13	10	3	0	0	0	
18	13	11	2	1	1	0	
18	13	12	1	1	1	1	0
18	13	13	0	2	2	1	0
18	14	9	5	0			
18	14	10	4	0	0		
18	14	11	3	0	0		
18	14	12	2	1	0	0	
18	14	13	1	1	1	0	
18	14	14	0	2	1	1	0
18	15	11	4	0			
18	15	12	3	0	0		
18	15	13	2	0	0		
18	15	14	1	0	0	0	
18	15	15	0	1	1	0	
18	16	14	2	0			
18	16	15	1	0	0		
18	16	16	0	0	0	0	
19	10	5	5	0	0		
19	10	6	4	1	0	0	
19	10	7	3	1	1	0	
19	10	8	2	2	2	1	0
19	10	9	1	3	3	2	0
19	10	10	0	5	4	3	2
19	11	6	5	0	0		
19	11	7	4	1	0	0	
19	11	8	3	1	1	0	
19	11	9	2	2	1	1	0
19	11	10	1	3	2	2	0
19	11	11	0	4	4	3	1
19	12	6	6	0			
19	12	7	5	0	0		
19	12	8	4	1	0	0	
19	12	9	3	1	1	0	
19	12	10	2	2	1	1	0
19	12	11	1	3	2	1	0
19	12	12	0	4	3	2	1
19	13	7	6	0			
19	13	8	5	0	0		

Appendix Table I Continued

N	A + B	A	B	2-Tail 10% / 1-Tail 5%	5% / 2.5%	2% / 1%	0.2% / 0.1%
19	13	9	4	C ≤ 0	0	0	
19	13	10	3	1	0	0	
19	13	11	2	1	1	0	
19	13	12	1	2	2	1	0
19	13	13	0	3	2	2	1
19	14	8	6	0			
19	14	9	5	0	0		
19	14	10	4	0	0		
19	14	11	3	1	0	0	
19	14	12	2	1	1	0	
19	14	13	1	2	1	1	0
19	14	14	0	2	2	1	0
19	15	10	5	0			
19	15	11	4	0	0		
19	15	12	3	0	0	0	
19	15	13	2	1	0	0	
19	15	14	1	1	1	0	
19	15	15	0	2	1	1	0
19	16	12	4	0			
19	16	13	3	0	0		
19	16	14	2	0	0		
19	16	15	1	0	0	0	
19	16	15	1	1	1	0	
19	17	15	2	0			
19	17	16	1	0	0		
19	17	17	0	0	0	0	
20	10	5	5	0	0		
20	10	6	4	1	0	0	
20	10	7	3	2	1	0	
20	10	8	2	3	2	1	0
20	10	9	1	4	3	2	1
20	10	10	0	5	5	4	2
20	11	6	5	0	0		
20	11	7	4	1	0	0	
20	11	8	3	2	1	0	
20	11	9	2	2	2	1	0
20	11	10	1	3	3	2	1
20	11	11	0	5	4	3	2
20	12	6	6	0	0		
20	12	7	5	0	0		
20	12	8	4	1	0	0	
20	12	9	3	2	1	0	
20	12	10	2	2	2	1	0
20	12	11	1	3	3	2	1
20	12	12	0	4	4	3	2
20	13	7	6	0	0		
20	13	8	5	0	0		
20	13	9	4	1	0	0	

Appendix Table I Continued

N	A + B	A	B	2-Tail 10% 1-Tail 5%	5% 2.5%	2% 1%	0.2% 0.1%
20	13	10	3	C ≤ 1	1	0	
20	13	11	2	2	1	1	0
20	13	12	1	3	2	2	0
20	13	13	0	4	3	3	1
20	14	7	7	0			
20	14	8	6	0	0		
20	14	9	5	0	0		
20	14	10	4	1	0	0	
20	14	11	3	1	1	0	
20	14	12	2	2	1	1	0
20	14	13	1	2	2	1	0
20	14	14	0	3	3	2	1
20	15	9	6	0			
20	15	10	5	0	0		
20	15	11	4	0	0	0	
20	15	12	3	1	0	0	
20	15	13	2	1	1	0	
20	15	14	1	2	1	1	0
20	15	15	0	2	2	2	0
20	16	10	6	0			
20	16	11	5	0			
20	16	12	4	0	0		
20	16	13	3	0	0	0	
20	16	14	2	1	0	0	
20	16	15	1	1	1	0	
20	16	16	0	2	1	1	0
20	17	12	5	0			
20	17	13	4	0			
20	17	14	3	0	0		
20	17	15	2	0	0	0	
20	17	16	1	1	0	0	
20	17	17	0	1	1	0	0
20	18	16	2	0			
20	18	17	1	0	0		
20	18	18	0	0	0	0	
20	19	19	0	0			
21	11	6	5	1	0	0	
21	11	7	4	1	1	0	
21	11	8	3	2	1	1	0
21	11	9	2	3	2	2	0
21	11	10	1	4	3	3	1
21	11	11	0	5	5	4	2
21	12	6	6	0	0		
21	12	7	5	1	0	0	
21	12	8	4	1	1	0	
21	12	9	3	2	1	1	0
21	12	10	2	3	2	2	0

Appendix Table I Continued

N	A + B	A	B	2-Tail 10% 1-Tail 5%	5% 2.5%	2% 1%	0.2% 0.1%
21	12	11	1	C ≤ 4	3	2	1
21	12	12	0	5	4	4	2
21	13	7	6	0	0		
21	13	8	5	1	0	0	
21	13	9	4	1	1	0	
21	13	10	3	2	1	1	0
21	13	11	2	2	2	1	0
21	13	12	1	3	3	2	1
21	13	13	0	4	4	3	2
21	14	7	7	0			
21	14	8	6	0	0		
21	14	9	5	1	0	0	
21	14	10	4	1	1	0	
21	14	11	3	2	1	1	
21	14	12	2	2	2	1	0
21	14	13	1	3	2	2	1
21	14	14	0	4	3	3	1
21	15	8	7	0			
21	15	9	6	0	0		
21	15	10	5	0	0	0	
21	15	11	4	1	0	0	
21	15	12	3	1	1	0	
21	15	13	2	2	1	1	0
21	15	14	1	2	2	1	0
21	15	15	0	3	3	2	1
21	16	9	7	0			
21	16	10	6	0	0		
21	16	11	5	0	0		
21	16	12	4	0	0	0	
21	16	13	3	1	0	0	
21	16	14	2	1	1	0	
21	16	15	1	2	1	1	0
21	16	16	0	2	2	2	1
21	17	11	6	0			
21	17	12	5	0	0		
21	17	13	4	0	0		
21	17	14	3	0	0	0	
21	17	15	2	1	0	0	
21	17	16	1	1	1	0	0
21	17	17	0	2	1	1	0
21	18	13	5	0			
21	18	14	4	0			
21	18	15	3	0	0		
21	18	16	2	0	0	0	
21	18	17	1	1	0	0	
21	18	18	0	1	1	0	0
21	19	16	3	0			

Appendix Table I Continued

N	A + B	A	B	2-Tail 10% / 1-Tail 5%	5% / 2.5%	2% / 1%	0.2% / 0.1%
21	19	17	2	$C \leq 0$			
21	19	18	1	0	0		
21	19	19	0	0	0	0	
21	20	20	0	0			
22	11	6	5	1	0	0	
22	11	7	4	2	1	0	
22	11	8	3	2	2	1	0
22	11	9	2	3	3	2	0
22	11	10	1	5	4	3	1
22	11	11	0	6	5	5	3
22	12	6	6	0	0		
22	12	7	5	1	0	0	
22	12	8	4	2	1	0	
22	12	9	3	2	2	1	0
22	12	10	2	3	3	2	0
22	12	11	1	4	4	3	1
22	12	12	0	6	5	4	3
22	13	7	6	0	0		
22	13	8	5	1	0	0	
22	13	9	4	2	1	0	
22	13	10	3	2	2	1	0
22	13	11	2	3	2	2	0
22	13	12	1	4	3	3	1
22	13	13	0	5	5	4	2
22	14	7	7	0	0		
22	14	8	6	0	0	0	
22	14	9	5	1	0	0	
22	14	10	4	1	1	0	
22	14	11	3	2	1	1	0
22	14	12	2	3	2	2	0
22	14	13	1	3	3	2	1
22	14	14	0	5	4	3	2
22	15	8	7	0	0		
22	15	9	6	0	0		
22	15	10	5	1	0	0	
22	15	11	4	1	1	0	
22	15	12	3	2	1	1	0
22	15	13	2	2	2	1	0
22	15	14	1	3	3	2	1
22	15	15	0	4	3	3	2
22	16	8	8	0			
22	16	9	7	0	0		
22	16	10	6	0	0		
22	16	11	5	1	0	0	
22	16	12	4	1	1	0	
22	16	13	3	1	1	0	
22	16	14	2	2	1	1	0

Appendix Table I Continued

N	A + B	A	B	2-Tail 10% 1-Tail 5%	5% 2.5%	2% 1%	0.2% 0.1%
22	16	15	1	C ≤ 2	2	1	0
22	16	16	0	3	3	2	1
22	17	9	8	0			
22	17	10	7	0			
22	17	11	6	0	0		
22	17	12	5	0	0	0	
22	17	13	4	1	0	0	
22	17	14	3	1	1	0	
22	17	15	2	1	1	1	0
22	17	16	1	2	1	1	0
22	17	17	0	2	2	2	1
22	18	11	7	0			
22	18	12	6	0			
22	18	13	5	0	0		
22	18	14	4	0	0	0	
22	18	15	3	1	0	0	
22	18	16	2	1	0	0	
22	18	17	1	1	1	0	0
22	18	18	0	2	1	1	0
22	19	14	5	0			
22	19	15	4	0	0		
22	19	16	3	0	0		
22	19	17	2	0	0	0	
22	19	18	1	1	0	0	
22	19	19	0	1	1	0	0
22	20	17	3	0			
22	20	18	2	0			
22	20	19	1	0	0		
22	20	20	0	0	0	0	
22	21	21	0	0			
23	12	6	6	0	0	0	
23	12	7	5	1	1	0	
23	12	8	4	2	1	1	
23	12	9	3	3	2	1	0
23	12	10	2	4	3	2	1
23	12	11	1	5	4	3	2
23	12	12	0	6	6	5	3
23	13	7	6	1	0	0	
23	13	8	5	1	1	0	
23	13	9	4	2	1	1	0
23	13	10	3	3	2	1	0
23	13	11	2	4	3	2	1
23	13	12	1	5	4	3	2
23	13	13	0	6	5	4	3
23	14	7	7	0	0		
23	14	8	6	1	0	0	
23	14	9	5	1	1	0	

Appendix Table I Continued

N	A + B	A	B	2-Tail 10% 1-Tail 5%	5% 2.5%	2% 1%	0.2% 0.1%
23	14	10	4	C ≤ 2	1	1	0
23	14	11	3	2	2	1	0
23	14	12	2	3	3	2	1
23	14	13	1	4	4	3	1
23	14	14	0	5	5	4	3
23	15	8	7	0	0		
23	15	9	6	1	0	0	
23	15	10	5	1	1	0	
23	15	11	4	2	1	1	
23	15	12	3	2	2	1	0
23	15	13	2	3	2	2	0
23	15	14	1	4	3	2	1
23	15	15	0	5	4	4	2
23	16	8	8	0			
23	16	9	7	0	0		
23	16	10	6	1	0	0	
23	16	11	5	1	0	0	
23	16	12	4	1	1	0	
23	16	13	3	2	1	1	0
23	16	14	2	2	2	1	0
23	16	15	1	3	3	2	1
23	16	16	0	4	4	3	2
23	17	9	8	0			
23	17	10	7	0	0		
23	17	11	6	0	0	0	
23	17	12	5	1	0	0	
23	17	13	4	1	1	0	
23	17	14	3	1	1	1	0
23	17	15	2	2	2	1	0
23	17	16	1	3	2	2	0
23	17	17	0	3	3	2	1
23	18	10	8	0			
23	18	11	7	0	0		
23	18	12	6	0	0		
23	18	13	5	0	0	0	
23	18	14	4	1	0	0	
23	18	15	3	1	1	0	
23	18	16	2	1	1	1	0
23	18	17	1	2	2	1	0
23	18	18	0	3	2	2	1
23	19	12	7	0			
23	19	13	6	0	0		
23	19	14	5	0	0		
23	19	15	4	0	0	0	
23	19	16	3	1	0	0	
23	19	17	2	1	1	0	
23	19	18	1	1	1	1	0

Appendix Table I Continued

N	A + B	A	B	2-Tail 10% 1-Tail 5%	5% 2.5%	2% 1%	0.2% 0.1%
23	19	19	0	C ≤ 2	1	1	0
23	20	14	6	0			
23	20	15	5	0			
23	20	16	4	0	0		
23	20	17	3	0	0		
23	20	18	2	0	0	0	
23	20	19	1	1	0	0	
23	20	20	0	1	1	0	0
23	21	18	3	0			
23	21	19	2	0	0		
23	21	20	1	0	0		
23	21	21	0	0	0	0	
23	22	22	0	0			
24	12	6	6	1	0	0	
24	12	7	5	1	1	0	
24	12	8	4	2	2	1	0
24	12	9	3	3	2	2	0
24	12	10	2	4	4	3	1
24	12	11	1	5	5	4	2
24	12	12	0	7	6	5	4
24	13	7	6	1	0	0	
24	13	8	5	2	1	0	
24	13	9	4	2	2	1	0
24	13	10	3	3	2	2	0
24	13	11	2	4	3	3	1
24	13	12	1	5	4	4	2
24	13	13	0	7	6	5	3
24	14	7	7	0	0	0	
24	14	8	6	1	0	0	
24	14	9	5	2	1	0	
24	14	10	4	2	2	1	0
24	14	11	3	3	2	2	0
24	14	12	2	4	3	2	1
24	14	13	1	5	4	3	2
24	14	14	0	6	5	5	3
24	15	8	7	0	0	0	
24	15	9	6	1	0	0	
24	15	10	5	1	1	0	
24	15	11	4	2	2	1	0
24	15	12	3	3	2	1	0
24	15	13	2	3	3	2	1
24	15	14	1	4	4	3	2
24	15	15	0	5	5	4	3
24	16	8	8	0	0		
24	16	9	7	0	0	0	
24	16	10	6	1	0	0	
24	16	11	5	1	1	0	

Appendix Table I Continued

N	A + B	A	B	2-Tail 10% 1-Tail 5%	5% 2.5%	2% 1%	0.2% 0.1%
24	16	12	4	$C \leq 2$	1	1	0
24	16	13	3	2	2	1	0
24	16	14	2	3	3	2	1
24	16	15	1	4	3	3	1
24	16	16	0	5	4	4	2
24	17	9	8	0	0		
24	17	10	7	0	0	0	
24	17	11	6	1	0	0	
24	17	12	5	1	1	0	
24	17	13	4	2	1	1	0
24	17	14	3	2	2	1	0
24	17	15	2	3	2	2	0
24	17	16	1	3	3	2	1
24	17	17	0	4	4	3	2
24	18	9	9	0			
24	18	10	8	0	0		
24	18	11	7	0	0		
24	18	12	6	0	0	0	
24	18	13	5	1	0	0	
24	18	14	4	1	1	0	
24	18	15	3	2	1	1	0
24	18	16	2	2	2	1	0
24	18	17	1	3	2	2	1
24	18	18	0	3	3	2	1
24	19	10	9	0			
24	19	11	8	0			
24	19	12	7	0	0		
24	19	13	6	0	0		
24	19	14	5	0	0	0	
24	19	15	4	1	0	0	
24	19	16	3	1	1	0	
24	19	17	2	2	1	1	0
24	19	18	1	2	2	1	0
24	19	19	0	3	2	2	1
24	20	12	8	0			
24	20	13	7	0			
24	20	14	6	0	0		
24	20	15	5	0	0		
24	20	16	4	0	0	0	
24	20	17	3	1	0	0	
24	20	18	2	1	1	0	
24	20	19	1	1	1	1	0
24	20	20	0	2	2	1	0
24	21	15	6	0			
24	21	16	5	0			
24	21	17	4	0	0		
24	21	18	3	0	0	0	

Appendix Table I Continued

N	A + B	A	B	2-Tail 10% 1-Tail 5%	5% 2.5%	2% 1%	0.2% 0.1%
24	21	19	2	$C \leq 0$	0	0	
24	21	20	1	1	0	0	
24	21	21	0	1	1	0	0
24	22	19	3	0			
24	22	20	2	0	0		
24	22	21	1	0	0		
24	22	22	0	0	0	0	
24	23	23	0	0			
25	13	7	6	1	1	0	
25	13	8	5	2	1	1	
25	13	9	4	3	2	1	0
25	13	10	3	4	3	2	1
25	13	11	2	5	4	3	1
25	13	12	1	6	5	4	2
25	13	13	0	7	7	6	4
25	14	7	7	1	0	0	
25	14	8	6	1	1	0	
25	14	9	5	2	1	1	0
25	14	10	4	3	2	1	0
25	14	11	3	3	3	2	1
25	14	12	2	4	4	3	1
25	14	13	1	5	5	4	2
25	14	14	0	7	6	5	4
25	15	8	7	1	0	0	
25	15	9	6	1	1	0	
25	15	10	5	2	1	1	0
25	15	11	4	2	2	1	0
25	15	12	3	3	3	2	1
25	15	13	2	4	3	3	1
25	15	14	1	5	4	4	2
25	15	15	0	6	6	5	3
25	16	8	8	0	0		
25	16	9	7	1	0	0	
25	16	10	6	1	1	0	
25	16	11	5	2	1	1	0
25	16	12	4	2	2	1	0
25	16	13	3	3	2	2	0
25	16	14	2	4	3	2	1
25	16	15	1	4	4	3	2
25	16	16	0	6	5	4	3
25	17	9	8	0	0		
25	17	10	7	1	0	0	
25	17	11	6	1	1	0	
25	17	12	5	2	1	0	
25	17	13	4	2	1	1	0
25	17	14	3	3	2	1	0
25	17	15	2	3	3	2	1

Appendix Table I Continued

N	A + B	A	B	2-Tail 10% 1-Tail 5%	5% 2.5%	2% 1%	0.2% 0.1%
25	17	16	1	$C \leq 4$	3	3	1
25	17	17	0	5	4	4	2
25	18	9	9	0	0		
25	18	10	8	0	0		
25	18	11	7	1	0	0	
25	18	12	6	1	0	0	
25	18	13	5	1	1	0	
25	18	14	4	2	1	1	0
25	18	15	3	2	2	1	0
25	18	16	2	3	2	2	0
25	18	17	1	3	3	2	1
25	18	18	0	4	4	3	2
25	19	10	9	0			
25	19	11	8	0	0		
25	19	12	7	0	0	0	
25	19	13	6	1	0	0	
25	19	14	5	1	1	0	
25	19	15	4	1	1	0	
25	19	16	3	2	1	1	0
25	19	17	2	2	2	1	0
25	19	18	1	3	2	2	1
25	19	19	0	3	3	3	1
25	20	11	9	0			
25	20	12	8	0	0		
25	20	13	7	0	0		
25	20	14	6	0	0	0	
25	20	15	5	1	0	0	
25	20	16	4	1	1	0	
25	20	17	3	1	1	0	
25	20	18	2	2	1	1	0
25	20	19	1	2	2	1	0
25	20	20	0	3	2	2	1
25	21	13	8	0			
25	21	14	7	0			
25	21	15	6	0	0		
25	21	16	5	0	0	0	
25	21	17	4	0	0	0	
25	21	18	3	1	0	0	
25	21	19	2	1	1	0	
25	21	20	1	1	1	1	0
25	21	21	0	2	2	1	0
25	22	16	6	0			
25	22	17	5	0	0		
25	22	18	4	0	0		
25	22	19	3	0	0	0	
25	22	20	2	0	0	0	
25	22	21	1	1	0	0	

Appendix Table I Continued

N	A + B	A	B	2-Tail 10% / 1-Tail 5%	5% / 2.5%	2% / 1%	0.2% / 0.1%
25	22	22	0	C ≤ 1	1	0	0
25	23	19	4	0			
25	23	20	3	0			
25	23	21	2	0	0		
25	23	22	1	0	0	0	
25	23	23	0	0	0	0	
25	24	24	0	0			
26	13	7	6	1	1	0	
26	13	8	5	2	1	1	0
26	13	9	4	3	2	2	0
26	13	10	3	4	3	2	1
26	13	11	2	5	4	3	2
26	13	12	1	6	6	5	3
26	13	13	0	8	7	6	4
26	14	7	7	1	0	0	
26	14	8	6	1	1	0	
26	14	9	5	2	2	1	0
26	14	10	4	3	2	2	0
26	14	11	3	4	3	2	1
26	14	12	2	5	4	3	2
26	14	13	1	6	5	4	3
26	14	14	0	7	7	6	4
26	15	8	7	1	0	0	
26	15	9	6	2	1	0	
26	15	10	5	2	2	1	0
26	15	11	4	3	2	2	0
26	15	12	3	4	3	2	1
26	15	13	2	5	4	3,	2
26	15	14	1	6	5	4	3
26	15	15	0	7	6	6	4
26	16	8	8	1	0	0	
26	16	9	7	1	0	0	
26	16	10	6	2	1	0	
26	16	11	5	2	2	1	0
26	16	12	4	3	2	1	0
26	16	13	3	3	3	2	1
26	16	14	2	4	4	3	1
26	16	15	1	5	5	4	2
26	16	16	0	6	6	5	3
26	17	9	8	1	0	0	
26	17	10	7	1	0	0	
26	17	11	6	1	1	0	
26	17	12	5	2	1	1	0
26	17	13	4	2	2	1	0
26	17	14	3	3	3	2	1
26	17	15	2	4	3	3	1
26	17	16	1	5	4	3	2

Appendix Table I Continued

N	A + B	A	B	2-Tail 10% 1-Tail 5%	5% 2.5%	2% 1%	0.2% 0.1%
26	17	17	0	$C \leq 6$	5	4	3
26	18	9	9	0	0		
26	18	10	8	0	0	0	
26	18	11	7	1	0	0	
26	18	12	6	1	1	0	
26	18	13	5	2	1	1	0
26	18	14	4	2	2	1	0
26	18	15	3	3	2	2	0
26	18	16	2	3	3	2	1
26	18	17	1	4	4	3	2
26	18	18	0	5	4	4	3
26	19	10	9	0	0		
26	19	11	8	0	0	0	
26	19	12	7	1	0	0	
26	19	13	6	1	1	0	
26	19	14	5	1	1	0	
26	19	15	4	2	1	1	0
26	19	16	3	2	2	1	0
26	19	17	2	3	2	2	1
26	19	18	1	3	3	2	1
26	19	19	0	4	4	3	2
26	20	10	10	0			
26	20	11	9	0	0		
26	20	12	8	0	0		
26	20	13	7	0	0	0	
26	20	14	6	1	0	0	
26	20	15	5	1	1	0	
26	20	16	4	1	1	0	0
26	20	17	3	2	1	1	0
26	20	18	2	2	2	1	0
26	20	19	1	3	2	2	1
26	20	20	0	3	3	3	1
26	21	11	10	0			
26	21	12	9	0			
26	21	13	8	0	0		
26	21	14	7	0	0		
26	21	15	6	0	0	0	
26	21	16	5	1	0	0	
26	21	17	4	1	1	0	
26	21	18	3	1	1	0	0
26	21	19	2	2	1	1	0
26	21	20	1	2	2	1	0
26	21	21	0	3	2	2	1
26	22	13	9	0			
26	22	14	8	0			
26	22	15	7	0	0		
26	22	16	6	0	0		

Appendix Table I Continued

N	A + B	A	B	2-Tail 10% 1-Tail 5%	5% 2.5%	2% 1%	0.2% 0.1%
26	22	17	5	C ≤ 0	0	0	
26	22	18	4	1	0	0	
26	22	19	3	1	0	0	
26	22	20	2	1	1	0	
26	22	21	1	1	1	1	0
26	22	22	0	2	2	1	0
26	23	16	7	0			
26	23	17	6	0			
26	23	18	5	0	0		
26	23	19	4	0	0		
26	23	20	3	0	0	0	
26	23	21	2	0	0	0	
26	23	22	1	1	0	0	
26	23	23	0	1	1	1	0
26	24	20	4	0			
26	24	21	3	0			
26	24	22	2	0	0		
26	24	23	1	0	0	0	
26	24	24	0	0	0	0	
26	25	25	0	0			

Source: Reprinted, with permission, from Meddis (1975).

Further reading

There are few textbooks or papers which cover association analysis and correlation and place an emphasis on their application to ecology and environmental sciences. Most of the introductory statistical texts, such as Fowler *et al.* (1998), will provide a basic treatment of correlation and the chi-squared procedures described in this chapter. Any number of advanced statistical texts, such as Sokal and Rohlf (1995), Spent (1993) and Zar (1996), will provide details of other alternative correlation measures and procedures for analysing data in a contingency table.

Sokal, R.R. and Rohlf, F.J. (1995) *Biometry*, 3rd edn. W.H. Freeman, New York.

Sprent, P. (1993) *Applied Nonparametric Statistical Methods*, 2nd edn. Chapman & Hall, London.

Zar, J.H. (1996) *Biostatistical Analysis*, 3rd edn. Prentice Hall, London.

Chapter Eight

Ordination: patterns and gradients among samples

Summary

The methods described in this chapter are concerned with the analysis of multivariate data sets. Many environmental studies measure several variables at a number of sites; the resulting data set is multivariate, each site or sample unit being characterised by more than one variable. The methods described include polar ordination (PO), principal component analysis (PCA) and correspondence analysis (CA). These procedures allow joint relationships between variables and sample units to be described and quantified. They can also produce ordination diagrams, in which sample units or variables are plotted as points in a two- or three-dimensional graph. The plotted points depict the relationships between sample units or variables. Ordination is an efficient way to summarise large and complex data sets; it is often used to explore the relationship between species distribution and environmental factors.

8.1 *Introduction*

The methods described in this and the remaining chapters are concerned with the analysis of multivariate data sets. Many environmental studies measure several variables at a number of sites; the resulting data set is multivariate, each site being characterised by more than one variable. The term 'multivariate statistics' encompasses a wide range of methods (Manly, 1994). These methods allow the *joint relationships* of variables in data sets that contain inter-correlations to be described and quantified. Since multivariate methods are able to consider several variables simultaneously, interpretations can be made that are not possible with the more common univariate statistics (James and McCulloch, 1990). Coupled with their ability to produce succinct summaries of large and complex data sets this makes multivariate statistics so valuable, and widely used in ecology and environmental sciences.

Consider a data set consisting of 10 columns and 20 rows, where the columns represent stands of vegetation and the rows represent species recorded at each stand. It is impossible to plot all this information on a single graph. One might choose two rows (species), one to form the *x*-axis and the other to form the *y*-axis of a graph. Each stand could then be plotted on this graph. The resulting diagram would summarise the relationship between stands, but only with regard to two variables. What about the information contained in the other 18 rows of the data matrix? One solution might be to plot more scattergrams using a different pair of species as the axes for each diagram, but it is not a viable option. As the number of variables increases, the number of graphs will escalate rapidly, making them impractical to produce or interpret. What is required is a procedure that reduces the number of graphs and axes needed to summarise the relationships (structure) present in the original multivariate data set. Polar ordination (PO), principal component analysis (PCA) and correspondence analysis (CA) provide ways of achieving this. Each of these methods can be used to produce a single diagram capable of summarising the complete data set. To produce the diagram, three conditions have to be satisfied:

- The measured variables must be combined to produce a limited number of new *component variables* capable of summarising the original variable relationships without distortion. This is often called data reduction or variable reduction.

- Using component variables, it must be possible to calculate unique sample scores (values) which summarise the relationships between samples (i.e. order them). Similar samples have similar component scores.

- By taking sample scores for the two components that account for the maximum amount of variation and using them as the *x* and *y* coordinates, a two-dimensional ordination diagram can be plotted. To be useful, the diagram must be such that the relative positions of the plotted points depict their similarity. Similar points are close together; more different points are farther apart.

This approach – combining the original variables or representing them as a single axis that summarises the relationship between samples – is sometimes known as indirect gradient analysis. The spread of samples along the constructed axes is considered to indicate the operation of a complex environmental gradient. The alternative approach of plotting species abundance values against a single measured variable is called direct gradient analysis (Chapter 11). The weighted average approach for calculating environmental indices (Chapter 5) may also be used to ordinate samples.

8.1.1 *Guide to the chapter*

The chapter contains a detailed description of polar ordination (Section 8.2) and principal component analysis (Section 8.3). Both methods may be applied to binary data and continuous quantitative data, although some methods may require continuous variables to be scaled. Polar ordination (PO) is the simplest and least mathematically demanding technique. It may be executed by hand, and although somewhat eclipsed by more recent methods, it generally performs well and is perfectly acceptable and valid.

Principal component analysis (PCA) is mathematically much more demanding and cannot be executed by hand. The method is described in detail, but with the mathematics kept to a minimum. Explanations at different levels of mathematical sophistication are presented separately in Boxes 8.1, 8.2 and 8.3. Even if your mathematical confidence is low, you should still be able to grasp the concepts behind the methods. PCA is important not only because it is a valid method in its own right, but also because other commonly used methods of ordination (Sections 8.4 and 8.5) can be seen as variants or developments of PCA. For this reason alone, I would strongly urge you to read the whole chapter. However, those who wish to conduct only a polar ordination can do so by reading Sections 8.1.3 and 8.2.

The rest of this introduction covers the possible forms of the data matrix (Section 8.1.2), sampling (Section 8.1.3) and data transformation (Section 8.1.4). Section 8.5 presents an overview of the methods and considers possible solutions to some of the problems that may be encountered.

8.1.2 The data matrix: Q and R modes

The results of an environmental investigation might be summarised as a data matrix or table consisting of s rows and n columns. For example, each column might contain results from one of n different sites, each row containing the values recorded for each of the s measured variables. In this case the data matrix consists of variables (rows) at sites (columns); other examples might be attributes (rows) shown by individuals (columns) or species (rows) recorded in different samples (quadrats) or at different sites (columns). Many other possibilities exist. The data matrix may also be partitioned; for example, the abundance of s species at n sites in the first s rows, plus a further f rows containing information on f environmental factors (soil pH, slope, etc.) measured at each of the n sites. The data set (Table 8.1) would then consist of $s + f$ rows (species plus factors) by n columns (sites).

Different analyses may have different objectives; here are some of them:

- To identify and describe relationships between the n sites (columns) in terms of the s species or attributes (rows) recorded. Comparisons are made across the tables, between columns.
- To identify and describe the relationships between the s species or attributes (rows) in terms of the n sites or sample units (columns) in which they were recorded. Comparisons are made down the table, between rows.
- To identify and quantify the relationships which exist between patterns observed in the top part of the table ($s \times n$) and those identified in the bottom part of the table (rows n to $n + f$). Comparisons are made between the top and bottom portions of the table.

Note that the two halves of the table may be analysed separately, i.e. each data matrix may be analysed independently. The procedures described here and in Chapter 9 are primarily concerned with the direct analysis of either the top or bottom parts of the data table (tables of $s \times n$, or $f \times n$), allowing the first two objectives to be achieved. Chapters 10 and 11 describe methods for achieving the third objective: linking the analysis and interpretation of both parts of the matrix.

Where rows correspond to species and columns to sites, the first objective is concerned with the production of a site or sample ordination. In a sample ordination the distribution of n sites plotted in the resulting two- or three-dimensional diagram reflects the similarities

Table 8.1 A partitioned data matrix

	Columns $j = 1$ to $j = n$									
	1	2	3	.	.				.	n
Rows $i = 1$ to $i = s$										
1										
2										
3										
.										
.										
.										
s										
Rows $n + 1$ to $s + f$										
$s + 1$										
$s + 2$										
$s + 3$										
.										
.										
.										
$s + f$										

For example, n sites, samples or individuals

For example, s species abundances or variable values

For example, f environmental factors used to characterise the sites, samples or individuals

between sites in terms of the abundance of species present at each site. The second objective can be fulfilled by producing a species ordination in which the relative positions of s points in the ordination diagram depict the similarities between species in terms of their relative distribution among the n sites. The third objective attempts to relate patterns in these ordinations with the measured environmental factors.

Many texts refer to two modes of analysis, R and Q (e.g. Ludwig and Reynolds, 1988; Kent and Coker, 1992). R-mode studies focus on the similarities between species; they use resemblance functions (Chapters 6 and 7) to calculate the similarities between species (rows) before producing a species ordination. The more commonly used Q-mode is concerned with the production of a site or sample ordination and involves the initial calculation of a matrix of similarities between all sites (columns). Q and R mode analyses may be carried out on the same data set. Correspondence analysis (Section 8.4) is able to perform Q and R mode analyses simultaneously. To complete a Q and R mode study, using the other procedures described in this chapter, a two-stage process is required: (1) the initial data matrix is analysed; (2) the data matrix is transposed by exchanging rows and columns then the transposed matrix is analysed.

8.1.3 Sampling

Both random and regular samples may be ordinated, but generalisations based on non-random samples must be treated with caution. It is not safe to assume that the observed patterns are general and applicable to other samples. A regular sampling scheme, e.g. a grid of 20 quadrats, represents a single observation not 20 distinct samples. For this reason it is generally best to employ either a random or stratified random sampling scheme (Chapter 1).

All ordination methods are sensitive to the effects of outliers, i.e. unusual or deviant samples. Although they may be removed from the data set before analysis, unusual samples can only be reliably identified if the sample is adequate and representative. Mohler (1981) has shown that the tendency under certain circumstances for the ordination methods to produce distorted ordinations of community data sets (species by sites) is reduced if extreme and unusual environments in the study area are favoured during sampling. Mohler suggests that a simple random or haphazard location of samples is likely to produce ordinations of low interpretability.

8.1.4 Data transformation

It may be desirable to transform the data before analysis, where each data value is modified in a similar way. Transformation is normally undertaken for three reasons: (i) to ensure the data conforms to particular statistical requirements, e.g. transforming non-normally distributed data; (ii) to reduce effects of extreme values (high and low values) on the outcome of the analysis; and (iii) to highlight characteristics of the data which are of primary interest (Noy-Meir, 1973). Transformation is not always necessary. Often the transformation of data is embedded in the chosen method of analysis; by adopting a particular method, the data is implicitly transformed. Here are the most commonly used transformations associated with the ordination and classification (Chapter 9) of samples, along with their effects and the reasons for choosing them.

Removing extreme values from a data set
Rare species may be removed, i.e. those with either a low mean abundance or those which occur in only a small proportion of the sites. The criteria used to select species for removal vary between studies, but typically for large data sets species which occur in less than 5% or 10% of sample units are routinely removed.

Scaling to reduce the effects of extreme values
Gauch (1982) advocates the use of an octave scale (essentially a logarithmic scale to base 2); others are the Braun–Blanquet scale and the Domin scale (Table 8.2). An alternative to single-digit scales is to estimate species abundance (cover) by 1% units up to 5%; 2% or 5% units up to 20% then 10% units up to 100%. If the data is scaled, the effects of the scaling must be considered carefully; different scales weight rare and abundant species differently. The use of scales can help to reduce the effects of recording errors and variation due to differences between investigators. Scales that score species abundance within the range from 0 to 10 have frequently been used and perform well. They can allow quantitative and qualitative information to be combined without either having undue influence.

Transforming the data using logarithms

$$x'_{ij} = \log_e(x_{ij} + C)$$

where i = the row number
j = the column number

Table 8.2 Commonly used systems for scale data values

Octave scale[a]		Scaling to units of 1%, 5% and 10%[a]		Braun–Blanquet cover scale		Domin cover scale	
Species abundance (0–100%)	Scale value	For species abundance of	Record or scale values as	Species abundance (0–100%)	Record or scale values as	Species abundance (0–100%)	Record or scale values as
0	0	<1	0	<1	+(0)	a single individual no measurable cover	+(0)
$0 \leq x < 0.5$	1	$1 \leq x < 5$	1, 2, 3, 4	1–5%	1	1–2 individuals no measurable cover	1
$0.5 \leq x < 1$	2	$5 \leq x < 20$	5, 10, 15	6–25%	2	several individuals cover less than 1%	2
$1 \leq x < 2$	3	$20 \leq x < 100$	20, 30, 40, 50, 60, 70, 100	26–50%	3	1–4%	3
$2 \leq x < 4$	4			51–75%	4	4–10%	4
$4 \leq x < 8$	5			76–100%	5	11–25%	5
$8 \leq x < 16$	6					26–33%	6
$16 \leq x < 32$	7					34–50%	7
$32 \leq x < 64$	8					51–75%	8
$64 \leq x < 100$	9					76–90%	9
						91–100%	10

[a] These schemes may be extended to scale data values which extend beyond range 0–100.

The constant C, a small arbitrary value, is needed to deal with zero values which have no logarithm. If the data consists of species abundance values with a range of 0 to 100, C is frequently set at 1.0 or 0.5. The logarithmic transformation has been extensively used in ecological studies. It has the effect of compressing the range of values, reducing the influence of large values relative to small. Since many species appear to demonstrate a lognormal distribution in relation to environmental gradients, rather than a normal distribution, it has been suggested that logarithms of species abundance values should be taken as a matter of routine. Natural logarithms are normally used.

Centring the data

Differences between row or column means need not be of ecological importance; they may reflect the arbitrary choice of scale used to record values and/or differences in the sampling efficiency (Digby and Kempton, 1987). The effects of differences in the magnitude of row and column means can be removed by centring data sets. After centring, rows or columns will have a mean of 0:

- Centring by row (e.g. centring by species or variable) is achieved by subtracting the row mean from each individual row value:

  mean of row i
  $$x'_{ij} = x_{ij} - \bar{x}_i$$

- Centring by column (e.g. centring by sample or site) is achieved by subtracting the column mean from each individual value in the column:

  mean of column j
  $$x'_{ij} = x_{ij} - \bar{x}_j$$

Data values may be centred by both row and column:

$$x''_{ij} = x_{ij} - \bar{x}_i - \bar{x}_j + (T/N)$$

where T = grand total of all values
N = total number of values

Standardising the data

After centring, the data may be standardised to unit standard deviation by dividing centred values by the row or column standard deviation:

- Standardisation by row (e.g. standardisation by species or variable):

  standard deviation of row i
  $$x'_{ij} = (x_{ij} - \bar{x}_i)/\sigma_i$$

- Standardisation by column (e.g. standardisation by site or sample):

  standard deviation of column j
  $$x'_{ij} = (x_{ij} - \bar{x}_j)/\sigma_j$$

As a result of standardisation, a row or column will have a mean of 0 and a standard deviation of 1.0. Standardisation of environmental and morphological variables is often desirable, since they may be gauged using a range of measures and scales; but the case for standardising species abundance values obtained using the same sampling method is less clear. Digby and Kempton (1987) argue that the removal of differences in the variance of species abundance will reduce the amount of ecologically relevant information present in the data set.

Species with high between-sample variance are likely to prove more useful for discriminating between samples than those with low between-sample variance. Low sample variance suggests that a species does not discriminate between samples and tends to be evenly distributed among the samples. It is also possible to standardise using column totals and row totals:

- Standardisation by column totals (e.g. by site or sample totals):

$$x'_{ij} = \frac{x_{ij}}{\sum_{i=1}^{n} x_{ij}} \longleftarrow \text{column total}$$

- Standardisation by row totals (e.g. by species or variable totals):

$$x'_{ij} = \frac{x_{ij}}{\sum_{j=1}^{m} x_{ij}} \longleftarrow \text{row total}$$

Standardisation by column totals means that each column element is divided by the column total. This transformation removes the effects of having different column totals; different column totals often result from differences in the sampling efficiency and sample size. After standardisation by column totals, each column will sum to 1.0 (100 if expressed as percentages). In the case of community data matrices, this equates to replacing species abundance values with *relative species importance* values (p_i), which may be use to calculate species diversity (Chapter 3). Unless differences in sample size or sampling efficiency are negligible, or the variation in column totals is considered to be a valid characteristic of the data set, standardisation to column total is recommended, especially for community data sets.

Standardisation by row totals means that row elements are divided by row totals, so each row sums to 1.0 (or 100 if expressed as percentages). This removes the effects of differences in the row totals. Where rows represent the abundance of species at different sites (columns) this is rarely justified. Standardisation by row totals may be appropriate if rows represent variables or species abundance values that have been measured using different scales.

8.2 *Polar ordination*

Polar ordination (PO) was originally developed by Bray and Curtis (1957) and, although superseded by more recent computer-based methods, it is still a useful technique that has much to recommend it. The ordination diagram is based on sample distance measures (Chapter 6). The usual measure is the Bray–Curtis percentage dissimilarity, but other distance measures can be used. The diagram may be constructed using a pair of compasses or from calculations based on simple geometric relationships. In each case the starting point is a matrix containing dissimilarity distances for all possible pairs of samples.

8.2.1 *Procedure and presentation of results*

Selecting the first axis endpoints　Starting with the matrix of sample dissimilarity values, select the two most dissimilar sample units (i.e. those with highest dissimilarity value) as the left and right endpoints or reference points for the first axis (L_{ep} and R_{ep}). The first axis is then drawn to scale (e.g. 1 cm = 10% dissimilarity) as a straight line at the base of the diagram with the reference sample units marked at each end (Figure 8.1). Now plot the remaining samples along this axis. All the remaining samples will vary in terms of their

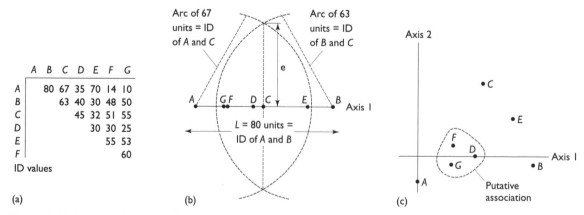

Figure 8.1 (a) Community dissimilarity matrix for the seven stands, showing indices of difference (ID). (b) After the endpoint stands, A and B, have been located on axis 1, all other stands are located between them by swinging arcs that correspond to their ID values with A and B. Stand C has an ID of 63 with B and an ID of 67 with A. The crossing arcs define a line perpendicular to the axis; where that line crosses the axis is the location of stand C. The poorness of fit is the distance e, measured from the crossing arcs to the axis. (c) Creation of a second axis pulls the stands apart much better than the first axis alone. Stands F, G and D (within the dashed line) appear to cluster together; they represent an approximately homogeneous unit, perhaps an association. Reprinted, with permission, from Barbour et al. (1987).

similarity to both endpoints. For each sample unit it is assumed that a point exists on the axis which uniquely summarises its relationship to both reference points. Notice two things:

- No dissimilarity value should be greater than those used to construct the first axis, so the first axis should depict the maximum 'variation' present in the data set.

- The choice of axis is determined by the size of the dissimilarity values alone; it is not a subjective choice by the investigator.

Plotting sample units onto the first axis   Centred on L_{ep}, draw an arc with a radius scaled to equal the dissimilarity between the sample and the left-hand reference point (L_{ep}). Now, centred on R_{ep}, draw a second arc with a radius scaled to equal the dissimilarity between the sample and the right-hand reference stand (R_{ep}). Where the two arcs cross, drop a perpendicular line to cut the axis. Plot the sample at this point on the line connecting the two reference points. This procedure is repeated until all the samples have been plotted. At this stage a single-axis ordination has been produced, all samples having been arranged (ordered) along the axis in terms of their relative similarity to the two reference points.

Poorness of fit: the error value
If the axes selected during a polar ordination provide a good description (model) of the data set, the arcs drawn should actually meet on the axis or intercept very close to it. The distance e, i.e. the distance from the axis to the point where the arcs cross, is a measure of the variation that remains to be explained. Because of this, e is often known as the error value or the poorness of fit value. High e-values imply that a substantial amount of variation cannot be adequately described in terms of the differences between the samples and the two reference points. Two, three or more axes may be required to adequately describe the complex pattern relationships among the samples.

Selecting endpoints and drawing the second axis   Numerous methods have been used to select the endpoints or reference points for the second axis (Orloci, 1978). The simplest approach is to select two samples which occur near the centre of the first axis but which are dissimilar from each other, i.e. have a high dissimilarity value. These samples are then used as the reference points for the second axis. But in practice this can be a cumbersome procedure, especially when many samples occur in the central portion of the first axis. The recommended procedure is to select L_{ep} as the point which has the highest e on the first axis, i.e. the point where the arcs crossed farthest from first axis. Now take R_{ep} as the point most dissimilar to L_{ep}. Once the endpoints have been selected, all the remaining samples (including the two samples used as endpoints for the first axis) are plotted along the second axis, as described above. A third axis and further axes can be constructed in the same way. The second axis will be shorter than the first axis, as less variation remains to be described; the same goes for the third and fourth axes, and so on.

Producing the final diagram   A two-dimensional diagram is produced by arranging the axes at right angles to each other and plotting the position of each sample in the normal way. Sample positions on the first axis provide the x-coordinates, sample positions of the shorter second axis give the corresponding y-coordinates. Where a third axis is produced, this may also be plotted to produce a three-dimensional graph with three axes x, y, z arranged at 90° to each other.

Calculating the sample positions directly   Based on Pythagoras's theorem, the position of samples on an axis may be calculated directly using the formula

$$x_i = (L^2 + d_{i1}^2 - d_{i2}^2)/2L \quad \text{with} \quad e_i = \sqrt{d_{i1}^2 - x_i^2}$$

where L = the length of the axis, i.e. the dissimilarity between the two reference points
d_{i1} = the dissimilarity between the first reference point (L_{ep}) and sample point i
d_{i2} = the dissimilarity between the second reference point (R_{ep}) and sample point i
x_i = the position of sample point i along the x-axis
e_i = the error value associated with sample point i on the x-axis

The reference samples for the first axis are selected from the matrix of dissimilarity values by inspection. A second axis may be produced by selecting a second set of reference points (as described above) and then applying the formula to calculated sample positions along the second axis (the y-axis).

8.2.2 *Problems and how to solve them*

Heterogeneous data sets and the choice of reference samples
When applied to homogeneous data sets, the procedure outlined above generally performs well, yielding ordination diagrams with good separation of points. However, there can be problems with heterogeneous data sets obtained from samples taken along a large or steep environmental gradient. These data sets frequently contain several pairs of samples with dissimilarity values of 100%. Since each of these samples pairs could be selected as axis endpoints, the construction of the first axis becomes ambiguous and more than one ordination diagram can be produced. Heterogeneous data sets are also likely to include particularly unusual (outlier) samples which may distort the ordination. Polar ordination is strongly influenced by the presence of outliers. The method of constructing the polar ordination diagram means that outliers will cause points to cluster at the centre of the axes, producing a final ordination diagram with poor separation of points. These problems can be solved in several ways.

Subjective choice of reference samples based on a priori *knowledge*   This approach allows the investigator to accentuate and explore the effects of known differences between samples. It has the computational advantage of not requiring the entire matrix of sample dissimilarity

values to be calculated. Only dissimilarities between each sample and the endpoints are required to draw the diagram. Gauch (1982) and Ludwig and Reynolds (1988) suggest that this approach allows a rapid and flexible analysis of data sets and it can yield a very useful ordination.

Objective choice of endpoints based on summed dissimilarity values   Sum the dissimilarity values associated with each of the possible endpoints. To choose the endpoints, select the sample points with the highest summed dissimilarity values.

Removal of outliers and/or subdivision of the data set   Where the data set is clearly heterogeneous (indicated by a large number of high dissimilarity values distributed through-out the dissimilarity matrix), it should be divided into more homogeneous subsets. The clustering methods in Chapter 9 could be used to achieve this in an objective way. This approach can also be used to deal with the presence of non-linear data structures (Section 8.5). Where isolated outliers exist (indicated by the concentration of high dissimilarity values among a limited number of samples), the only effective solution is to remove suspected outliers from the data set then examine how this affects the ordination.

Failure of arcs to intersect

Occasionally it is not possible to construct a polar ordination because the arcs drawn from each end of the axis fail to intersect. This happens when the chosen index of dissimilarity is not metric. A metric distance measure is one that satisfies the triangle equality, $D_{13} < D_{12} + D_{23}$ where D_{ij} is the value of the distance between the ith and jth sample. If this equality is satisfied then the differences between any three sites (1, 2, 3) may be plotted in two dimensions:

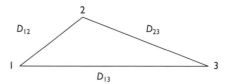

The Bray–Curtis percentage dissimilarity measure (based on the percentage similarity of Chapter 6) is normally used in polar ordination but it is not a metric. Here are two possible solutions.

Select different endpoints   The problem may be avoided by choosing alternative endpoints. Although choosing different axis endpoints will produce apparently different ordinations, the relationship between the samples will conserved (Kent and Coker, 1992).

Use metric dissimilarity measures   Orloci (1978) advocates the use of metric measures such as Euclidean distances. However, the percentage similarity and its complement, the dis-similarity, are metric if the data is first standardised by column totals before analysis (Beals, 1984). This is equivalent to performing the analysis on a matrix of relative species abundance values, each column summing to 1.

Non-perpendicular axis

The axes of a polar ordination diagram are normally drawn as orthogonal, i.e. at right angles to each other. This implies that the two axes are independent of each other. But in practice the second axes will be oblique to the first. The assumption of independence will introduce a degree of distortion. This distortion can be removed by drawing the axes at the correct oblique angle to each other. To achieve this, one endpoint of the second axis is located above the first axis at the intersection of the drawn arcs, and the other endpoint is located below the first axis (again where the arcs intersect). Individual samples are plotted perpendicular to their positions on each axis (Causton, 1988). Alternatively, Orloci (1978) provides procedures which will correct for non-perpendicular ordination axes. However, since the degree of correction is usually minor, it is acceptable to assume the axes are perpendicular (Kent and Coker, 1992).

8.2.3 Recommendations

Despite the problems outlined above, polar ordination has much to recommend it. It provides a flexible and robust approach to multivariate analysis. The method is easily understood and axis lengths are readily interpreted in terms of the relative dissimilarity between samples. For ecological work, the Bray–Curtis percentage dissimilarity generally yields the most readily interpretable ordinations (Beals, 1984). The recommended procedure for polar ordination is as follows:

- Standardise the data set by column totals before analysis.
- Use the Bray–Curtis percentage dissimilarity measure.

For homogeneous data sets:

- Apply the objective procedure for the selecting the endpoints and assume the axes are orthogonal.

For heterogeneous data sets:

- Either divide the data sets into subsets that are more homogeneous and assume the axes are orthogonal.
- Or select the endpoints subjectively and assume the axes are orthogonal.

8.3 *Principal component analysis*

Principal component analysis (PCA) is one of several ordination methods that depend on the mathematical extraction of eigenvectors and eigenvalues from a matrix of sample resemblance values. In the case of PCA, the resemblance function is normally the Pearson moment correlation coefficient (Chapter 7). Using matrix algebra, PCA extracts from the matrix of correlation coefficients a series of equations (components) which summarise the relationships between variables and account for the variation present in the matrix. These equations, or principal components, are then used to calculate unique sample scores, which can be plotted to produce an ordination diagram. Box 8.1 provides a geometrical interpretation of P.C.A. Boxes 8.2 and 8.3 provide an outline of the necessary matrix algebra.

Initially the relationships between samples are summarised by calculating the correlation coefficients between all the different pairs. For a matrix of 10 columns and 20 rows, this would produce a symmetrical 10×10 matrix of correlation values. PCA then extracts from this matrix a series of equations (components) which summarise the relationships between variables and allows the calculation of sample scores. Each variable contributes to the value of this score. The component equations take the general form

$$z = a_1 V_1 + a_2 V_2 + a_3 V_3 + \cdots + a_n V_n$$

where z is the component score and a_1 to a_n give the loadings of each variable V_1 to V_n on the component. Coefficients a_1 to a_n are the elements of the eigenvector corresponding to that

Box 8.1   **Geometrical interpretation of PCA**

A geometrical interpretation of PCA is possible. A variable may be symbolised by a vector – a straight line in a particular direction. The length of the vector represents the magnitude of the variable. The correlation between two variables is given by the cosine of the angle α between their vectors. Thus, two variables A and B may be represented by the vectors $\overrightarrow{OA}$ and $\overrightarrow{OB}$, the correlation between them by the angle α.

If $\overrightarrow{OA}$ and $\overrightarrow{OB}$ have the same length, the variables are of equal size. If $\alpha = 0°$, i.e. they act in the same direction, the corresponding correlation coefficient between A and B is equal to 1.0. If $\alpha = 180°$ they operate in completely opposite directions and the correlation coefficient is equal to -1.0. Where $\alpha = 90°$ the variables are completely independent of each of other, and the correlation coefficient is 0 (Figure 1).

The correlation between the two variables is given by the cosine of α. Consider the line $\overrightarrow{OA}$ of unit length 1.0, and the triangle formed by the perpendicular AB which drops down from the tip of $\overrightarrow{OA}$. As $\overrightarrow{OA}$ sweeps about the point O, the cosine of the angle α varies from 1.0 (when $\alpha = 0$) through 0 (when $\alpha = 90°$) to -1.0 (when $\alpha = 180°$); this is illustrated in Figure 2.

The important point is that the cosine relationship allows correlation coefficients to be expressed in geometric terms. Thus, if the correlation between A and B is 0.8, this may be represented by two vectors with an angle of 37° between them. In the case of PCA, vector length is related to the variance of each variable, and after the data has been standardised, the vector for each variable will have length 1. Thus, a correlation matrix for six variables (A to F) might be represented by Figure 3.

Formation of the principal axis

Remember the aim of PCA is to represent the complexity of relationships between variables in the minimum number of dimensions. From Figure 3 it is clear that the dominant pattern of correlation could be summarised by a vector in the general direction of A, D, C

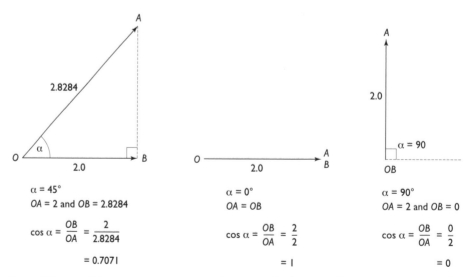

Figure 1 The correlation between two vectors can be measured by the cosine of the angle between them. The length of the line OB is determined by dropping a perpendicular down from point A

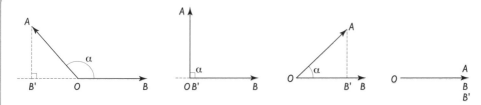

Figure 2 As $\overrightarrow{OA}$ sweeps around O, the value of $\cos \alpha$ changes.

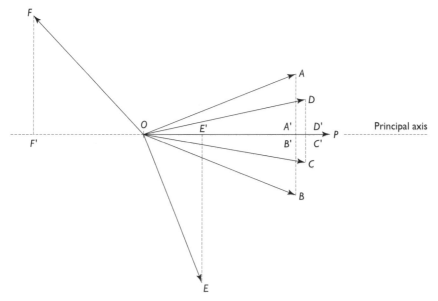

Figure 3 A correlation diagram for six variables, A to F.

and B. This vector, $\overrightarrow{OP}$, forms the first primary axis or component. By drawing perpendicular lines from the tip of each vector on to the principal axis, each variable can be uniquely represented by a point on $\overrightarrow{OP}$ defined by the distances O to A', O to B', etc. Notice that if $\overrightarrow{OP}$ is allowed to sweep around O, it changes the distance from O to the points where the variable perpendiculars cross $\overrightarrow{OP}$. As the direction of $\overrightarrow{OP}$ approaches the direction of a variable, e.g. D, the distance OD' approaches distance OP. When both coincide completely, $OD' = OP = 1.0$.

These distances (OA' to OF') give the correlation between variables and the axis; they are known as loading coefficients or weighting coefficients. In matrix terms they correspond to the eigenvector for that component (obtained from the correlation matrix). The exact position of the axis is chosen to maximise the sum of the squared loading values. This sum equals the eigenvalue for that component. The procedure for selecting the direction of $\overrightarrow{OP}$ ensures that the 'correlation' between the principal axis and all the variables is as high as possible and that $\overrightarrow{OP}$ provides a good description or summary of the relationships between the variables. The size of the eigenvalue provides a measure of the amount of variation accounted for by the component. The higher the eigenvalue, the greater the explanatory power of that component.

Second and higher axes

The second principal axis is drawn at $90°$ (orthogonal) to the first. As for the first axis, loading coefficients are obtained by the perpendicular projection of vector ends onto the new axis. The explanatory power of the new axis is given by the sum of the squared loading coefficients, which is also equal to the second component eigenvalue. Because the two axes are orthogonal, they are independent and variable scores will be completely uncorrelated. Higher sets of axes may be constructed in the same way. But successive axes have less and less explanatory power as the eigenvalues progressively decrease.

principal component (PC). They provide a measure of the correlation between each variable and the axis represented by the component. Sample scores can be obtained by substituting the appropriate values V_n into the equation for z. Variables with high coefficients will influence the scores more strongly than variables with low coefficients.

For any $n \times n$ matrix there are n possible principal components (i.e. eigenvectors). Not all of them are valuable for summarising the variation in the data. The amount of variation explained by each component is indicated by its associated eigenvalue (λ). The proportion of variation explained by a component is approximately equal to its eigenvalue divided by the sum of all the component eigenvalues. Typically the majority of variation is accounted for by the first two or three PCs, which will have the highest eigenvalues. The scores for these PCs allow samples to be plotted. The scores associated with the first PC are used to plot samples along the x-axis, i.e. they provide the x-coordinates. The scores for the second PC provide the y-coordinates.

Effectively, PCA can be seen as a variable-reducing technique. The number of variables required to describe the data set is reduced by constructing a set of dummy variables (the z-values of the PCs), and only a small number of the dummy variables are required to describe most of the variation in the data set. Boxes 8.1, 8.2 and 8.3 provide geometric and matrix interpretations of PCA. Do consult them; they will give you a conceptual understanding of PCA and the eigenanalysis of matrices, techniques which underpin all widely used multivariate methods.

8.3.1 Procedures and presentation of results

Procedures

PCA cannot realistically be performed by hand; it must be done using a statistics package, the majority of which support PCA. The use of MINITAB to perform PCA is shown in Box 8.4. Most packages offer two methods of PCA: one utilises a resemblance matrix of Pearson moment correlation coefficients, the other uses a matrix of variance–covariance values. Depending on which is selected, different implicit data transformations are adopted. By using the correlation coefficient, the data is centred and standardised. In a community data ordination this weights each species equally. In contrast, the covariance matrix centres the data only, and species are weighted according to their frequency and abundance (Gauch, 1982; Causton, 1988).

R and Q mode PCA ordinations may be conducted. In R-mode, similarity coefficients are calculated between rows (variables, species) and component scores are calculated for columns (objects, individuals, samples). When they carry out an R-mode PCA ordination, many computer packages scale component loadings to unity, so the sum of squares of an eigenvector equals 1.0, and the component scores are scaled so that the sum of squares equals the

Box 8.2   **Matrix interpretation of PCA**

Basic guide to matrices

A matrix is a rectangular array of numbers. By convention a matrix is normally denoted by a single bold capital letter, e.g. $\mathbf{A}$. Individual elements of a matrix are denoted by a lower case letter, a_{ij}, with two subscripts (ij) that identify the row and column of the element.

$$\mathbf{A} = \begin{bmatrix} a_{11} & a_{12} & a_{13} \\ a_{21} & a_{22} & a_{23} \\ a_{31} & a_{32} & a_{33} \end{bmatrix} = \begin{bmatrix} 1 & 2 & 3 \\ 4 & 5 & 6 \\ 7 & 8 & 9 \end{bmatrix}$$

Suppose then $a_{23} = 6$, the element in the second row $(i = 2)$ and the third column $(j = 3)$. Matrix $\mathbf{A}$ is an example of a square matrix – the number of rows is equal to the number of columns. Now consider matrices $\mathbf{X}$ and $\mathbf{I}$.

$$\mathbf{X} = \begin{bmatrix} x_1 \\ x_2 \\ x_3 \end{bmatrix} \qquad \mathbf{I} = \begin{bmatrix} 1 & 0 & 0 \\ 0 & 1 & 0 \\ 0 & 0 & 1 \end{bmatrix}$$

Matrix $\mathbf{X}$ is an example of a column matrix or column vector.[4] Where the elements relate to important variables which describe the state of a system, a column vector is called a state vector. Matrix $\mathbf{I}$ is a particular type of square matrix known as an identity matrix. In an identity matrix all the elements apart from the diagonal elements are equal to 0; the diagonal elements all equal 1. A symmetric matrix is a matrix where the diagonal elements may take any values, but the elements above and below the diagonal are identical, i.e. $a_{ij} = a_{ji}$.

Matrices of the same size may be easily added and subtracted from each other by adding and subtracting corresponding elements. Multiplication by a single value (a scalar) is also straightforward – each element in the matrix is multiplied by the scalar:

$$\mathbf{B} = \begin{bmatrix} b_{11} & b_{12} \\ b_{21} & b_{22} \end{bmatrix} \qquad k\mathbf{B} = \begin{bmatrix} kb_{11} & kb_{12} \\ kb_{21} & kb_{22} \end{bmatrix}$$

Multiplication of one matrix by another is a little more complex, involving the multiplication of rows by columns followed by summation. The matrix equation $\mathbf{AX} = \mathbf{Y}$ may be set out like this:

$$\begin{bmatrix} a_{11} & a_{12} & a_{13} \\ a_{21} & a_{22} & a_{23} \\ a_{31} & a_{32} & a_{33} \end{bmatrix} \begin{bmatrix} x_1 \\ x_2 \\ x_3 \end{bmatrix} = \begin{bmatrix} a_{11}x_1 + & a_{12}x_2 + & a_{13}x_3 \\ a_{21}x_1 + & a_{22}x_2 + & a_{23}x_3 \\ a_{31}x_1 + & a_{32}x_2 + & a_{33}x_3 \end{bmatrix} = \begin{bmatrix} y_1 \\ y_2 \\ y_3 \end{bmatrix}$$

To be able to multiply two matrices together, the number of columns in the first matrix $(\mathbf{A})$ must be equal to the number of rows in the second matrix $(\mathbf{X})$. As well as addition, subtraction and multiplication, a matrix may be transposed by interchanging the rows and columns. The transpose of $\mathbf{A}$, written $\mathbf{A}^T$, is given by

$$\mathbf{A} = \begin{bmatrix} a_{11} & a_{12} & a_{13} \\ a_{21} & a_{22} & a_{23} \\ a_{31} & a_{32} & a_{33} \end{bmatrix} = \begin{bmatrix} 1 & 2 & 3 \\ 4 & 5 & 6 \\ 7 & 8 & 9 \end{bmatrix}$$

$$\mathbf{A}^T = \begin{bmatrix} a_{11} & a_{21} & a_{31} \\ a_{12} & a_{22} & a_{32} \\ a_{13} & a_{23} & a_{33} \end{bmatrix} = \begin{bmatrix} 1 & 4 & 7 \\ 2 & 5 & 8 \\ 3 & 6 & 9 \end{bmatrix}$$

Notice that the diagonal elements of $\mathbf{A}$ are unchanged in the transposed matrix. The element subscripts from $\mathbf{A}$ have been retained in the transpose matrix, so that their origin is identified. In practice they would be replaced by new subscripts which identify the position of each element in $\mathbf{A}^T$; the first subscript identifies the row, and the second subscript identifies the column.

Interpretation of PCA by analogy to population growth

The growth of an age-structured population can easily be modelled using matrices. Consider a population of American bison. If the females are divided into three age classes (calves, yearlings and adults aged ≥ 2 years), the age structure of the population may be represented by the column matrix $\mathbf{X}$, where the elements x_1, x_2, x_3 correspond to the number of calves, yearlings and adult females present in the population. The total size of the population is equal to the sum of the elements of $\mathbf{X}$. The dynamics of the population may be modelled by constructing a Leslie matrix, the off-diagonal elements of which represent the probability of individuals surviving from one age class to the next, and the elements of row 1 the birth rate of female bison in each age class. In the example given by Cullen (1983) the probability of calves surviving to become yearlings is set at 0.6, the probability of yearlings reaching adulthood is 0.75, and the probability of an adult surviving from one year to the next is 0.95. The average birth rate of adult female bison is 0.42. This demographic information can be summarised as a Leslie transition matrix $\mathbf{A}$ and a column matrix $\mathbf{X}$:

$$\mathbf{A} = \begin{bmatrix} a_{11} & a_{12} & a_{13} \\ a_{21} & a_{22} & a_{23} \\ a_{31} & a_{32} & a_{33} \end{bmatrix} = \begin{bmatrix} 0 & 0 & 0.42 \\ 0.60 & 0 & 0 \\ 0 & 0.75 & 0.95 \end{bmatrix}$$

In this matrix, elements a_{11}, a_{12}, a_{13} represent the average number of female offspring produced by calves ($a_{11} = 0$), yearlings ($a_{12} = 0$) and adults ($a_{13} = 0.42$). The probability of calves surviving to become yearlings, i.e. moving from age class x_1 to age class x_2, is given by $a_{21} = 0.60$; the probability of yearlings reaching adulthood, i.e. moving from age class x_2 to age class x_3, is given by $a_{32} = 0.75$. The probability of an adult surviving from one year to the next, i.e. remaining in the same age class, is given by $a_{33} = 0.95$. If the initial population consists of 100 adults, the size and structure of the population the next year can be calculated as follows:

- Number of new calves produced:

$$a_{11}x_1 + a_{12}x_2 + a_{13}x_3 = (0 \times 0) + (0 \times 0) + (0.42 \times 100) = 42$$

Table I Projected growth of the bison population

Year (t)	Calves (x_1)	Yearlings (x_2)	Adults (x_3)	Total population size (N)	Rate of population increase N_{t+1}/N_t	Calves in the population (%)	Yearlings in the population (%)	Adults in the population (%)
0	0	0	100	100	1.370	0	0	100
1	42	0	95	137	1.131	30.7	0	69.3
2	40	25	90	155	1.070	25.8	16.1	58.1
3	38	24	104	166	1.108	22.9	14.5	62.6
4	44	23	117	184	1.103	23.9	12.5	63.6
5	49	26	128	203	1.103	24.1	12.8	63.1
6	54	29	141	224	–	24.1	12.9	63.0

- Number of yearlings:

$$a_{21}x_1 + a_{22}x_2 + a_{23}x_3 = (0.6 \times 0) + (0 \times 0) + (0 \times 100) = 0$$

- Number of adults:

$$a_{31}x_1 + a_{32}x_2 + a_{33}x_3 = (0 \times 0) + (0.75 \times 0) + (0.95 \times 100) = 95$$

Thus the population after one year consists of 42 calves and 95 surviving adults.

Notice that these three equations are exactly the same as doing the matrix multiplication **AX**. Thus the same result would have been obtained by the matrix multiplication **AX = Y**, where **Y** is a column vector describing the population after one year of growth. If **Y** is then multiplied by the transition matrix **A**, the population in the next year will be given by the resulting column vector. Repeated multiplications will give the growth and structure of the population in subsequent years. These calculations are tedious by hand but very easy on a computer. Table 1 shows the projected growth of the bison population over six years, obtained by successive matrix multiplications. And there are two key points:

- After some initial instability, the population growth rate becomes constant at 1.103.

- The relative abundances of the three age classes become constant after 4 years of population growth.

The constant rate of population growth corresponds to the dominant (i.e. the largest) eigenvalue of transition matrix **A** and the proportional abundances of the age classes are the elements of its eigenvector. The dominant eigenvalue λ for the transition matrix **A** is therefore 1.103 and the three elements of the eigenvector expressed on a proportional basis are 0.240, 0.129, 0.630. The eigenvalue and eigenvector are characteristic of the matrix **A**, and they are independent of the initial values used in the column vector **X**. If all three elements of **X** had been set at 1.0, the outcome would eventually have been the same, but the number of multiplications required before the growth rate became constant would have been greater. However, any change to the values in the transition matrix will produce a different eigenvalue and associated eigenvector.

Suppose the matrix **A** had contained the correlation coefficients between three sites, suppose arbitrary values had been given to initial elements of the column matrix **X**, and suppose the matrix **X** had been repeatedly multiplied by **A**, as in the bison example. The rate of change of the sum of the elements of **X** would eventuallly have stabilised as would their relative values. The resulting eigenvalue (stable rate of change) and the eigenvector (relative values of the elements of **X**) is then equivalent to the first component generated by PCA. The eigenvalue is a measure of the variation present in the matrix of correlation coefficients described by the first component, the eigenvector corresponding to the loading of factors on the component. The relationships between sites (variables) will be reflected in the pattern of correlation contained in the matrix; any change in this pattern will produce a different matrix with different eigenvalues and eigenvectors.

The approach outlined above only allows the first axis of a PCA to be obtained; to obtain higher components one must resort to matrix algebra and computer packages. However, it does illustrate the basis of several multivariate methods of ordination. There are analogies between this approach and correspondence analysis (Section 8.5), where sample and variable ordination scores are obtained directly from the data matrix.

eigenvalues. Q-mode PCA generally has the opposite scaling. Not all packages operate in this way. Some will perform a Q-mode scaling on the entered data matrix, and the eigenvectors will be scaled to the eigenvalue rather than unity. Details of different approaches to scaling are given by Pielou (1984), Jolliffe (1986) and Manly (1994).

Presentation of results: three diagrams
An x,y plot of component loading coefficients The loadings associated with the first extracted component are plotted on the x-axis, those associated with the second component on the y-axis. The axes may be centred so that they cross at the centre $(0,0)$ of the diagram. If the normal mode of analysis has been conducted on a species (variable) by site matrix, the resulting diagram will provide an ordination of the species (variables). This diagram may be used to aid interpretation of the extracted principal axes. The diagram depicts the pattern of correlations between the variables. High loading values on the x-axis indicate variables which are strongly correlated with the first component and influence the size of component site scores. A component with large negative and large positive loading coefficients may be described as contrasting the two groups of variables; this pattern of loadings will tend to separate sites or samples that have high values for either group of variables. The second and further components are interpreted in a similar way.

An ordination plot of component scores The first component scores are plotted on the x-axis, those associated with the second component on the y-axis. The axes may be centred so they cross at the centre $(0,0)$ of the diagram. If the normal mode of analysis has been conducted on a species by site matrix, the resulting diagram provides an ordination of sites. The spatial arrangements of the plotted site scores reflects the similarity between sites or samples.

A combined plot of the ordination component scores and the variable loading coefficients
Biplots are produced by plotting component scores and loading coefficients on the same graph. The axes must be scaled differently for loading coefficients and component scores.

Box 8.3　　**Eigenvalues and eigenvectors**

The set of n simultaneous linear equations in n unknowns x_1 to x_n:

$$a_{11}x_1 + a_{12}x_2 + \cdots + a_{1n}x_n = b_1$$

$$a_{21}x_2 + a_{22}x_2 + \cdots + a_{2n}x_n = b_2$$

$$\vdots$$

$$a_{n1}x_2 + a_{n2}x_2 + \cdots + a_{nn}x_n = b_n$$

can be represented in matrix form as

$$\mathbf{AX} = \mathbf{B}$$

where matrix $\mathbf{A}$ is an $n \times n$ matrix, the elements of which correspond to the n coefficients of x_i in the set of equations; $\mathbf{X}$ is a column matrix containing the n unknowns x_1 to x_n; and $\mathbf{B}$ is a column matrix containing the n values b_i. Solutions for the unknowns can be obtained using matrix algebra to solve:

$$\mathbf{AX} = \lambda\mathbf{X} \quad \text{or} \quad (\mathbf{A} - \lambda\mathbf{I})\mathbf{X} = \mathbf{0}$$

where $\mathbf{I}$ is an $n \times n$ identity matrix. For the majority of matrices these equations can be solved. In fact n possible solutions exist. In each case λ is a scalar known as the latent root or eigenvalue. The largest eigenvalue and the corresponding column vector $\mathbf{X}$ (which contains one set of possible x_i that satisfy the set of equations) are called the dominant eigenvalue (latent root) and dominant eigenvector. For any given λ the equations can be solved by arbitrarily setting $x_1 = 1.0$. A set of unique eigenvalues and eigenvectors exist for virtually every matrix. For simple matrices it is possible to extract the eigenvalues and eigenvectors by hand, but most are solved by computer. The methods of solving matrix equations are too complicated to be described here; the interested reader is referred to Namboodri (1984) and Gillman and Hails (1997).

　　PCA can be accomplished by extracting the eigenvalues and eigenvectors from a matrix of correlation coefficients (or covariance values). The first step is to correlate all n samples with one another; this will produce an $n \times n$ symmetric matrix of correlation coefficients. The eigenvalues and associated eigenvectors are then extracted. The elements of the eigenvector associated with the largest eigenvalue correspond to the loading coefficients for the first component. Sample scores are obtained by multiplying the eigenvector elements by the appropriate variable values, obtained from the data matrix, and summing the results. Final sample scores will depend on whether a covariance or correlation matrix has been used and on whether the data has been standardised before analysis. Except for polar ordination, all of the more common multivariate methods of ordination are related; they require eigenanalysis of a symmetric matrix of sample resemblance values or eigenanalysis of a data matrix.

Arrows are drawn from the origin of the graph $(0, 0)$ to represent each variable (Figure 8.2). The angle of the arrow reflects the extent of correlation between the variable and the two principal components. The direction of the arrow is important. The arrow points in the direction of the maximum variation in the variable values (e.g. species abundance). The length of the arrow is proportional to the maximum rate of change. Thus variables with long arrows, i.e. ending at the edges of the diagram, are most useful in indicating differences between the ordinated sites (ter Braak and Prentice, 1988; Kent and Coker, 1992).

Box 8.4 Principal components using MINITAB

Original data placed in columns C1 to C6. Note that the 'variables' (here species abundance) are placed in columns and the sites are represented by rows.

```
MTB > Print C1-C6
```

Data Display

Row	Sp1	Sp2	Sp3	Sp4	Sp5	Sp6
1	85	65	45	25	5	0
2	0	85	65	45	25	5
3	5	0	85	65	45	25
4	25	5	0	85	64	45
5	45	65	85	0	5	25

Command to carry out **PCA** followed by three subcommands. Coefficients (i.e. eigenvectors) are stored in columns C10 to C15. Scores are stored in columns C16 to C20. The maximum number of components is equal to 6, corresponding to the number of variables (columns); the maximum number of scores is equal to 5, corresponding to the number of sites/samples (rows). GScore produces a plot of scores for samples (Figure 1).

```
MTB > PCA 'Sp1'-'Sp6';
SUBC> Coefficients C10-C15;
SUBC> Scores C16-C20;
SUBC> GScore.
```

Principal Component Analysis

Eigenanalysis of the Correlation Matrix

Eigenvalue	3.8247	1.1847	0.6523	0.3382	0.0000	-0.0000
Proportion	0.637	0.197	0.109	0.056	0.000	-0.000
Cumulative	0.637	0.835	**0.944**	1.000	1.000	1.000

This means that 94.4% of the variation is explained by PC1, PC2 and PC3.

Variable	PC1	PC2	PC3	PC4	PC5	PC6
Sp1	0.271	-0.722	0.324	-0.312	0.249	-0.376
Sp2	0.438	0.006	-0.490	0.565	0.197	-0.458
Sp3	0.284	0.689	0.392	-0.289	0.191	-0.413
Sp4	-0.474	-0.002	-0.388	-0.347	-0.350	-0.617
Sp5	-0.508	0.047	-0.136	-0.018	0.849	0.004
Sp6	-0.413	-0.048	0.575	0.616	-0.138	-0.312

Notice that 94.4% of variation present in the data set is explained by these three components.

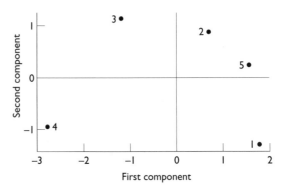

Figure 1 Score plot of Sp1 to Sp6.

```
MTB > Print C10-C15

Data Display
Row    C10         C11         C12         C13         C14         C15
1       0.271358   -0.721588    0.324123   -0.312142    0.248773   -0.375899
2       0.438416    0.006492   -0.490420    0.564880    0.197005   -0.457533
3       0.284159    0.689036    0.392436   -0.288872    0.190620   -0.413152
4      -0.474463   -0.001918   -0.388237   -0.346756   -0.350250   -0.617445
5      -0.507535    0.046609   -0.136145   -0.017977    0.849331    0.003773
6      -0.413162   -0.048195    0.575468    0.616010   -0.137578   -0.312114

MTB > Print C16-C19
```

Since the last two components have eigenvalues of zero, their score values are not printed out.

```
Data Display

Row    C16         C17         C18         C19
1       1.76179    -1.30509    -0.18161    -0.551752
2       0.69169     0.88277    -1.18826     0.292330
3      -1.20231     1.13430     0.45513    -0.692593
4      -2.80370    -0.95446    -0.06173     0.353717
5       1.55253     0.24248     0.97646     0.598298

MTB >
```

Component scores C16 and C17 correspond to sample scores for the first and second principal components. They are plotted to produce the final ordination diagram.

Notes

1. This analysis may be achieved by selecting the **Stat** option from the top menu bar, followed by **Multivariate** and then **Principal Components**. Once in the **Principal Components** dialogue box, the correlation matrix is selected and details specified as required: location of variables, storage of coefficients and scores, etc.

2. The correlation coefficients between variables may be saved and printed out during the PCA or they may be obtained by using the **Correlation** command:

```
MTB > Correlation C1-C6

Correlations (Pearson)
         Sp1         Sp2         Sp3         Sp4         Sp5
Sp2      0.286
Sp3     -0.181       0.301
Sp4     -0.536      -0.738      -0.583
Sp5     -0.593      -0.811      -0.547       0.958
Sp6     -0.331      -0.760      -0.401       0.532       0.745
```

Heavy metals in mussels and sediments

A more detailed and quantitative account of the interpretation of PCA ordination diagrams is given by ter Braak (1983), and Zitko (1994) illustrates the use PCA for the analysis of environmental data. In most cases a data set will be adequately described by the first two

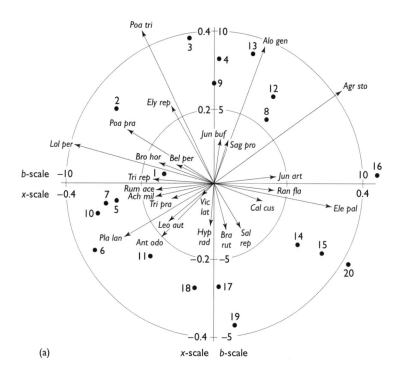

(a)

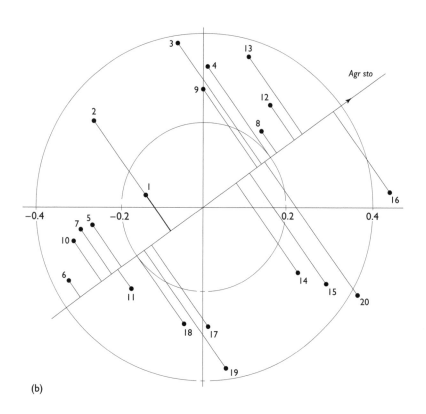

(b)

components. Occasionally a third or fourth might need to be considered, then the results can be presented as a three-dimensional graph or as a series of two-dimensional graphs with different combinations of components serving as the x and y axes. As a guide, components with eigenvalues less than 1.0 can be safely ignored. A component with an eigenvalue less than 1.0 contributes no more to explaining the variability in the data than any one of the original variables (Kent and Coker, 1992).

Berrow (1991) provides an interesting example of PCA applied to environmental research. Berrow measured the concentration of 6 heavy metals in 13 samples of sediments and 11 samples of mussels (*Mytilus edulis* L.) collected from different coastal locations around Cork Harbour, Ireland. The data matrix consisted of 6 variables (metal concentrations) and 24 samples. This example is particularly interesting because the data set contains two distinct types of samples. The first three principal components accounted for 55%, 22% and 10% of the variation respectively. Thus 77% of the variation can be depicted by a two-axis ordination diagram. The plot of component loadings suggests that the first component scores are strongly influenced by high values of Cu, Zn and Hg, which are clustered together and have high positive loadings on the first axis. In contrast, Ni shows a high but negative loading on this axis.

The high loadings of Cr and Pd on the second component suggest that the second component scores reflect the concentrations of these two metals in the samples (Fig 8.3a). The ordination of samples, based on components scores, is shown in Figure 8.3b. Sediment and mussel samples are clearly segregated along the first axis into two distinct groups. Both groups, sediments and mussels, demonstrate a gradient from the top of the diagram to the bottom, i.e. they are spread along the second axis. Given the pattern of metal loadings, we might conclude that in comparison with other samples, mussels from samples 9, 10 and 12 accumulate high levels of Pd and Cr.

The relationship between the concentration of metals present in the sediments and mussels, as indicated by the lines connecting samples from the same locations, is complicated. The bio-availability of the metals clearly differs between sites and is not directly related to their concentration in the sediments. For example, on the basis of the measured metal concentrations, sediments 1 and 3 are very similar. However, the mussels obtained from these sites appear to bio-accumulate metals to very different degrees, M1 and M3 being clearly separated in the ordination diagram. These two diagrams summarise a considerable amount of interesting information, which reflects differences in the bio-availability, environmental chemistry and possibly the distribution of the metals in Cork Harbour.

The production of ordination diagrams is frequently the endpoint of PCA but, depending on the nature of the data set, there are other possibilities. For example, if the data matrix consists of variables measured on a single object or site at a number of different times, temporal patterns can be investigated by plotting component scores against time. This approach allows the monitoring of complex changes in community structure. Fromentin *et al.* (1997) used this approach to examine changes through time in the composition of macrobenthic assemblages. When PCA is used primarily as a tool for variable reduction, the component scores may be treated as separate variables, each measuring a distinct sample attribute. The scores will be normally distributed and can be used to test for differences between groups of samples (Manly, 1994).

Figure 8.2 PCA biplot for some dune meadow data. (a) The species are represented by arrows, the quadrats by dots; the *b*-scale applies to species and the *x*-scale to quadrats or sites; species close to the origin are not plotted. (b) Interpretation of part (a) for *Agr sto (Agrostis stolonifera)*. Part (a) uses data from Jongman *et al.* (1987) and part (b) was devised by ter Braak (1987); the figures are reprinted, with permission, from Kent and Coker (1992) and with the permission of Agralin (formerly PUDOC), Wageningen.

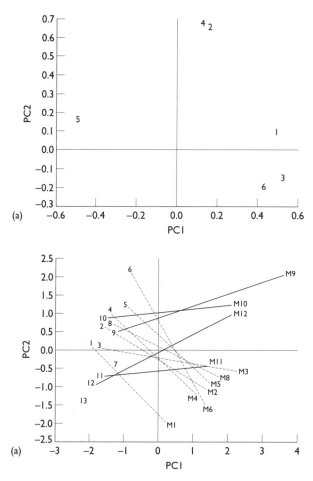

Figure 8.3 Heavy metals in sediments and mussels from Cork Harbour, Ireland. (a) Loadings on the first two principal components, PCI and PC2. Numbers indicate variables: 1 is Cu, 2 is Pb, 3 is Zn, 4 is Cr, 5 is Ni and 6 is Hg. The variables form three groups; this grouping may indicate different sources. (b) Plot of scores in the coordinates of the first two principal components, PCI (55% of variance) and PC2 (22% of variance). Sediment samples are indicated by 1 to 13 and mussel samples by M1 to M12. Corresponding sediment and mussel samples are indicated by connecting lines; note the two slopes of the relationships. Reprinted, with permission, from Berrow (1991).

8.3.2 *Problems and how to solve them*

For the analysis of environmental variables, PCA is one of the most effective and widely used methods (James and McCulloch, 1990; Kent and Coker, 1992). Many of the problems associated with the use of PCA in ecology and environmental science centre around its application to the analysis of community data sets. Essentially, when applied to community data sets, PCA can introduce an attenuation of the length of the first axis and a curvilinear (arched) distortion into the ordination (Gauch, 1982). Because of these problems, PCA is not normally recommended for community analysis (Gauch, 1982; Kent and Coker, 1992). However, with appropriate data transformation and careful application, recent studies suggest that PCA may function as well as, if not better than, some of the recommended alternatives. This topic is considered in more detail in Section 8.5, which considers the ordination of community data sets.

Interpretation of loading values PCA ordination is particularly sensitive to outliers, and the loading coefficients are sensitive to sampling variability. Because of this, one should not overemphasise the importance of particular values when attempting to interpret a component.

Nature of the data Although PCA performs satisfactorily when applied to count or presence/absence (1/0) data (Jolliffe, 1986), it does assume continuous data. PCA assumes that variables are normally distributed and are linearly related to the extracted components; it does not function well with non-linear data patterns. Because of this, when applied to community data sets, PCA is best applied to relatively narrow ranges of environmental and compositional variation within which a linear model may be assumed to apply (Ludwig and Reynolds, 1988; Kent and Coker, 1992).

Replicated samples values Contrary to some recommendations, James and McCulloch (1990) advise against applying PCA to data sets containing multiple replicated samples. Such data sets contain a large amount of redundancy which compounds the effects of within-sample and between-sample variance. Because of this it can be more efficient to perform PCA on group means. The amount of redundancy in the data set may be reduced by clustering before analysis (Chapter 9).

8.3.3 Recommendations

The recommended procedure for PCA ordination is as follows:

- Transform the variable values to obtain a normal distribution.
- Identify outliers, deviant sample unit values or deviant samples and remove them from the data set.
- Use correlation-based PCA, unless differences in the magnitudes of the row means are considered particularly important.

The results of the ordination should be plotted as three plots:

- A plot of loading coefficients
- A plot of site or sample scores
- A biplot

Heterogeneous data sets should be divided into subsets that are homogeneous.

8.3.4 Extension and related methods

Principal coordinate analysis

PCA can be considered as a specific example of principal coordinate analysis (PCO) involving the eigenanalysis of a matrix containing correlation values or variance–covariance values.[1] This general approach may be applied to matrices of other resemblance functions, although it is not always possible to interpret the resulting ordination in terms of a reduced dimensional plot within a space of *n* species by *m* samples. Gower (1966) showed that the PCA procedure could legitimately be applied to a matrix of between-sample Euclidean distances (Chapter 6). Euclidean distances between all *n* samples are calculated and then squared. The matrix of resulting values is then multiplied by 0.5 to give an *n* × *n* matrix **A**. Squaring the Euclidean distances and dividing by 2 transforms them into measures of association or similarity. An ordination is obtained by extracting the eigenvalues and eigenvectors from this matrix. This method may be generalised to any symmetric matrix of association or similarity measures.

Digby and Kempton (1987) illustrate the use of PCO by applying it to a matrix of plant-to-plant contacts obtained by Yarranton (1966; see Chapter 7). In this case the measure of association is the number of actual leaf contacts recorded between species pairs. Distance measures may used if transformed beforehand as $a'_{ij} = -0.5d^2_{ij}$. Where PCO is conducted on a matrix of similarity values only, it will not be possible to ordinate samples since the original data matrix is needed to calculate sample scores. Because the method may generate negative eigenvalues which have no sensible meaning in the context of ordination, care must be taken when using eigenvalues as measures of the variation explained by a component. Gower (1966) shows that a matrix of similarity functions can only be represented in Euclidean space[2] if the matrix has no negative eigenvalues. Small negative eigenvalues may be safely ignored, but large negative eigenvalues indicate that the ordination is flawed (Dunn and Everitt, 1982; Digby and Kempton, 1987). Legendre and Legendre (1983) provide a good review of the method.

Factor analysis

Factor analysis (FA) is computationally similar to PCA and is well supported by most statistical packages. The only substantive difference is that in FA the axes are rotated to maximise the correlation between the extracted factors (components) and the original variables. Thus the axes (factors) obtained using FA are not orthogonal as in PCA, but may instead be correlated. FA and PCA have different objectives. PCA is primarily a descriptive technique used for data summarisation and variable reduction, whereas FA attempts to explain the extracted components (factors) in terms of the original variables, the underlying assumption being that the factors represent real factors or realistic combinations of variables that occur in nature.

In contrast to PCA, factor analysis is a subjective procedure: the number of factors to be included in the final model and the method of rotation are determined by the investigator (Manly, 1994). This has led some to doubt its value (James and McCulloch, 1990). However, it has proved to be a very powerful and useful technique in some areas of study, particularly psychometrics (Kline, 1994). There may be advantages to be gained from allowing component axes to be correlated. To explain this, consider the geometric interpretation of PCA given in Box 8.1. The first principal axis will almost always have some explanatory power. However, once the first axis has been selected, the positions of the second and higher axes are fixed; the second axis is orthogonal to the first. And although the first axis may represent a valid and interpretable gradient, it is possible that the second and higher axes may represent trivial relationships between variables. There is no a priori reason to suppose that the variables should correlate strongly with a second axis constrained to be orthogonal with the first. In fact, it would not be surprising if complex multivariate environmental gradients were correlated. Kent and Coker (1992) raise this as a potential problem within the context of PCA ordinations, but it applies equally to correspondence analysis (Section 8.4) and the methods developed from it (Section 8.5).

8.4 *Correspondence analysis*

The application of correspondence analysis (CA) to ordination in ecology was first advocated by Hill (1973), who presented the method as reciprocal averaging. Correspondence analysis can be seen as an extension of the weighted average ordination procedure in Chapter 5. It has the distinct advantage over polar ordination and PCA of producing both species (variable) and site (sample) scores simultaneously. The basis of the method is best explained by example. In its simplest form it involves a two-way iterative averaging processes (hence the alternative name of reciprocal averaging). Consider a matrix of n rows and m columns obtained by recording the abundance of n species in m quadrats. Initially a set of arbitrary weighting values, scaled to range from 0 to 100, are assigned to each species. These weighting values are then used to calculate initial quadrat scores for each quadrat, which are 'averaged' by dividing each one by its column total c_j. Quadrat scores (QS_j) are obtained by rescaling initial quadrat scores (IQS) to range from 0 to 100 with the largest IQS_j value set to 100 and the lowest to 0. Once a complete set of scaled quadrat scores have been calculated, they are used to calculate a new set of species scores (S). The process is repeated until both species and quadrat scores no longer change. These final scores give the positions of quadrats and species on the first axis of the quadrat ordination and the associated species ordination:

$$IQS_j = \frac{1}{C_j} \sum_{i=1}^{n} a_{ij} S_i \qquad IS_j = \frac{1}{r_j} \sum_{j=1}^{m} a_{ij} QS_j$$

where a_{ij} = the abundance of species i in the jth quadrat
          S_i = the current species score for species i (scaled IS_i), used to calculate new quadrat scores (QS_j)
          QS_j = the current quadrat score for quadrat j (scaled IQS_j), used to calculate new species scores (S_i)
          IQS_j = initial quadrat score
          IS_j = initial species score
          C_j = total of column j
          r_i = total of row i

This procedure is illustrated below using a trivial example:

		Quadrats			Totals (r_i)	$S0_i$	$S1_i$	$S2_i$
		1	2	3				
Species	a	1	2	3	6	0	57.01	57.49
	b	0	4	1	5	50	0	0
	c	2	0	4	6	100	100	100
Totals (c_j)		3	6	8				
	$QS1_j$	100	0	68.91				
	$QS2_j$	100	0	78.57				
	$QS3_j$	100	0	78.59				

1. The arbitrary initial species scores ($S0_i$), ranging from 0 to 100%, are assigned to the three species. They are then used to calculate the first set of quadrat scores ($QS1_j$). The initial quadrat score for column 1 is obtained from

$$IQS1_1 = ((a_{11} \times S0_1) + (a_{21} \times S0_2) + (a_{31} \times S0_3))/c_1$$

$$IQS1_1 = ((1 \times 0) + (0 \times 50) + (2 \times 100))/3 = 66.6$$

The remaining two initial quadrat scores are calculated similarly:

$$IQS1_2 = ((2 \times 0) + (4 \times 50) + (0 \times 100))/6 = 33.3$$

$$IQS1_3 = ((3 \times 0) + (1 \times 50) + (4 \times 100))/8 = 56.25$$

2. These initial scores are then rescaled. Zero is assigned to the lowest value and 100 to the highest, the remaining values are then rescaled within this range:

$$IQS1_2 = 33.3 \quad \rightarrow \quad QS1_2 = 0$$
$$IQS1_1 = 66.6 \quad \rightarrow \quad QS1_1 = 100$$
$$QS1_3 = \frac{56.25 - 33.3}{66.6 - 33.3} = 68.91$$

3. The process is then reversed. The newly calculated quadrat scores (QS1's) are used to calculate the next set of species scores, i.e. $S1_1 = 57.01$, $S1_2 = 0$, $S1_3 = 100$. The process is continued until both sets of scores become stable. If the scores are not rescaled at every iteration, they become progressively larger or smaller, making the calculation increasingly cumbersome and identification of the endpoint more difficult.

4. A second axis (and higher axes) may be extracted by selecting new species scores which are used to initiate the process. Hill (1973) recommends that they should be close to the final species scores of the first axis. The reciprocal pattern of calculation is then repeated, but at each iteration the first axis species scores are multiplied by an integer and subtracted from the newly calculated scores. If this is not done, the scores associated with the lower axis will gradually re-establish themselves.

8.4.1 Procedure and presentation of results

Although the procedure outlined above can be easily understood and clearly illustrates the relationship between CA and the weighted average ordination, it is not a practical method of analysis for anything other than very small data sets. In practice CA is best performed using matrix algebra. Ludwig and Reynolds (1988) present the calculation scheme given in Figure 8.4. These calculations can be completed in stages using any computer package that supports basic matrix algebra. MINITAB could be used to perform them, but this is no longer necessary now that recent versions of MINITAB support correspondence analysis. To complete a CA ordination using MINITAB, select **Simple Correspondence Analysis** from the **Tables** option, entered from the **Stat** on the main menu bar. The data is most easily entered using the columns of a contingency table; the columns containing the data are specified along with columns containing the row and column labels. MINITAB readily generates separate and combined ordination graphs (Figure 8.5). From inspection of these diagrams, it is clear that both CA and PCA yield very similar ordination diagrams. Compared with the PCA ordinations (Box 8.4), the CA version produced by MINITAB is reflected about the first axis but the configuration of points is conserved.

8.5 *An overview of methods*

When applied to certain community data sets, the commonly used methods of ordination (PO, PCA and CA) can produce flawed ordinations. When applied to artificial data sets in which samples are drawn from a hypothetical gradient along which species optima are evenly spaced, the resulting two-dimensional ordinations are often distorted. Two problems are recognised: arch effects and edge effects. Instead of a linear arrangement of evenly spaced samples, a curved ordination is produced; samples are arched into a horseshoe pattern of points, with samples at each end of the axes closely clumped together (Gauch *et al.* 1977, 1982; Jongman *et al.*, 1987). Although all the methods described in this chapter are prone to these problems, PCA is considered to be particularly sensitive (Kent and Coker, 1992; but see below). Because of its mode of construction, with the two most dissimilar samples forming the ends of successive axes, PO is least likely to demonstrate the arch affect where samples clump at axes ends.

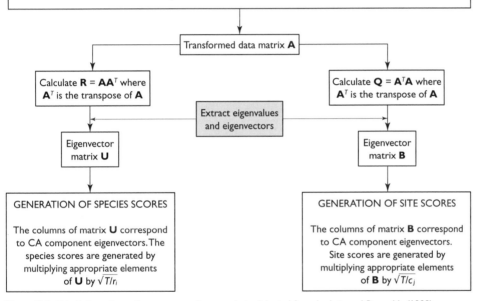

Figure 8.4 Calculation scheme for correspondence analysis. Adapted from Ludwig and Reynolds (1988).

These distortions, particularly the arch affect, are frequently evident in community ordinations and are generally considered to be an artefact of the data reduction (but see below) and the presence of a mathematical relationship between axes that should be independent. Non-linear patterns of species abundance are thought to be one cause of these problems. Ordination methods generally assume a linear relationship between species abundance and environmental gradients (Ludwig and Reynolds, 1988; ter Braak and Prentice, 1988). Depending on the length of the gradient, species will show both linear and non-linear patterns of abundance (Figure 8.6). Over short gradients the relationship might be expected to be linear, the abundance of the different species either increasing or decreasing along the short section of the gradient. But if the gradient is longer, some species may pass through their entire distribution or tolerance range, entering samples at one point on the gradient, increasing in abundance along the gradient and then decreasing before being lost from the gradient altogether. The spacing of species along the gradient also affects the performance of ordination methods. The underlying model assumes that species optima are equally spaced along the gradient; marked departures from this hypothetical model can reduce the

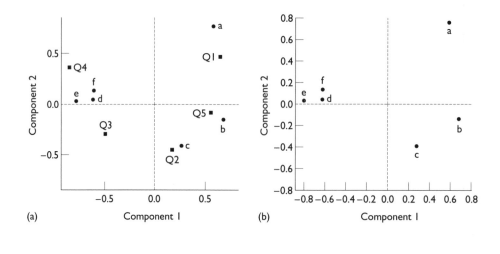

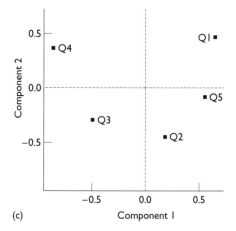

Figure 8.5 MINITAB plots: (a) combined, (b) row, (c) column. Q1 to Q5 are the quadrats, a to f are the species. The combined plot can be turned into a biplot by taking points a to f and joining each one to the origin with a straight line.

ability of ordination to reliably depict community (data) structure (ter Braak and Prentice, 1988).

8.5.1 Possible solutions to the arch effect and axis compression

Detrending

The most commonly adopted solution to the perceived arch and edge effects has been the widespread (almost universal in plant ecology) application of a modified form of CA known as detrended correspondence analysis (DCA). DCA was developed by Hill and Gauch (1980) as a modification of the reciprocal averaging method of CA (Section 8.4). They assume a random distribution of species optima along the gradient, each species having a similar range (tolerance). As a result of the edge effect, species range curves will be narrower (constricted) at the ends of axes, tending to reduce the within-site (within-sample) variance in species abundance compared to the within-site variance at the centre. The method divides the axis into small segments, and depending on their within-site variance, these segments are scaled so that all points along the axis have equal within-site variance. Sample scores are calculated as weighted averages of the species scores and

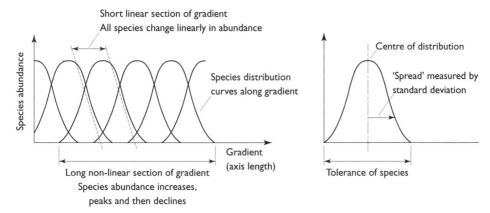

Figure 8.6 Species abundance patterns over long and short gradients. Short gradients tend to show linear patterns, long gradients may show non-linear patterns.

standardised so the within-site variance is equal to 1.0. The arch effect is removed by dividing the first axis into a number of segments, adjusting the site scores of points on the second axis so the mean scores within the segments are the same.

One result of the procedure is that the scores are effectively scaled to the standard deviation of the species abundance along a gradient that is represented by the axes. Hill and Gauch (1980) define the length of the ordination axes to be the range of site scores. The length is expressed in standard deviation (SD) units. If it is assumed that species distributions along a gradient (axis) are normal, the species should appear, rise to its maximum abundance, decrease and disappear within approximately 4 standard deviation units.[3] Thus, if the axis is relatively short, less than 3–4 SD units, species turnover along the gradient will be low, whereas a long axis (say 12 SD units) will probably have completely different sets of species at either end (Figure 8.6). The algorithm required to perform a DCA ordination is extremely complicated and cannot be reproduced here. ter Braak and Prentice (1988) provide an outline to the general computational procedures involved, and Kent and Coker (1992) give a good general account of the method.

DCA has been extensively used and appears to work remarkably well (Hill and Gauch, 1980; Gauch *et al.*, 1981; ter Braak, 1985). But it is an ad hoc solution (James and McCulloch, 1990) which sometimes fails and introduces distortion of its own (Pielou, 1984; Kenkel and Orloci, 1986; Minchin, 1987). In a comparative study of ordination methods, Jackson (1993) found that DCA did not perform as well as CA when applied to real benthic invertebrate community data sets. In the same study, correlation-based PCA was found to perform well. Interestingly, non-metric multidimensional scaling (NMDS) – a complex method based on ranking the distance measures between pairs of sites (Ludwig and Reynolds, 1988) and advocated as being able to deal with non-linear relationships – failed to perform particularly well. Jackson (1993) concluded that there was no advantage to be gained by adopting non-metric multidimensional scaling over its metric counterparts.

Other detrending methods have been suggested. Ludwig and Reynolds (1988) describe a method for detrending PCA ordinations based on work by Phillips (1978). The method may be applied to the results of any ordination. A two-axis ordination is first performed. Using a polynomial regression the second-axis site scores (y) are regressed onto the first-axis scores (x):

$$y = b_0 + b_1 x + b_2 x^2$$

where b_0, b_1, b_2 are regression constants. A single combined axis is then constructed by projecting site positions perpendicularly on to the fitted parabolic curve. The parabolic curve is then unfolded to produce a new straight-line axis on which the relative distances between sites are conserved. For small data sets, the projection of points onto the curved line and subsequent unfolding may be done by eye, alternatively Phillips (1978) provides a more precise algebraic method. This approach has a number of advantages, not least of which is its ready availability; DCA requires access to specialist programs. Polynomial regression analysis is supported by even the most basic statistical and graphics packages that will also give the associated *F*-value and significance of the fitted line. There is no need to detrend an ordination if the polynomial line does not provide a good, i.e. significant, description of the pattern of points. However, with large data sets the arch effect may be masked by the scattering of points along both axes, making it difficult to adequately describe the distribution of points by a polynomial curve.

To detrend or not to detrend?

The desirability of detrending ordinations to remove the arch effect has been questioned. Remember that the gradient depicted on the *x*-axis in Figure 8.6 is derived from the original data set. We assume that differences in presence/absence data or species abundance data reflect the operation of environmental differences between sites, and we assume they can be summarised by arranging sites along a hypothetical gradient represented by components extracted from a matrix of site similarity coefficients. Unfortunately, unless information is available on the nature of the actual gradient or the extent of environmental differences between sites then, prior to analysis, there is no reliable way of judging the length or nature of species distribution along an ordination gradient.

Several authors have argued strongly that the arch and compression of axis length should not be dismissed as mathematical artefacts, but considered as reflecting valid ecological properties of the data set (Allen and Starr, 1982; Wartenberg *et al.*, 1987). The fundamental problem revolves around the adequacy of the model used to describe the distribution of species along gradients, and their use to evaluate and interpret ordinations. Although the graphical model shown in Figure 8.6 provides a useful conceptual framework in which to consider community ordination, it is an abstraction. Some data sets may conform to the model, others may approach it after appropriate transformation. However, in some cases, species may be both non-linear and non-monotonic (e.g. bimodal) in their distribution. Such a pattern of species relationships cannot be represented by a monotonic model.

These issues have led James and McCulloch (1990) to state that 'previous criticisms of PCA as an indirect ordination technique (e.g. Gauch, 1982) should be reconsidered in the light of these arguments'. This assertion is supported by Brando and Ranka (1994), who have shown that by applying the general standardisation procedure (GSP) to data before using PCA, it is possible to correct the effects of curvilinear distortion and attenuation of the ordination axes:

$$ x'_{ij} = \frac{x_{ij}}{\left[\sum_{i=1}^{n} (x_{ij}^q) \right]^{1/q}} $$

where x'_{ij} = the transformed value

         x_{ij} = the original value

         q = a constant that determines the effect of the transformation

Brando and Ranka (1994) found that PCA performed well when GSP is applied to both species and sites, with $q = 1$ for species and $q = 0.5$ or 0.6 for sites. With these settings,

PCA performed better than CA, correcting the compression of sites at the extremes of the axes and the arch effect, both of which were evident in the CA ordinations. But if the routine and unquestioned application of DCA is not always warranted or desirable, where does this leave the investigator? How should we approach the ordination of community data sets?

8.5.2 Suggested approach

The key is to apply more than one cycle of analysis combined with careful visual comparison of the resulting ordination diagrams. Consistent features are assumed to depict real characteristics; inconsistent features should be viewed as possible artefacts of the chosen method (Ludwig and Reynolds, 1988). Here are the four steps:

1. Ensure that rare species, outliers or deviant sites are removed from the data sets.

2. Repeat the ordination using several transformations and standardisation; compare the results. If non-linear species relationships are suspected, try ranking the species abundances. Jackson (1993) reports that this form of standardisation performs well

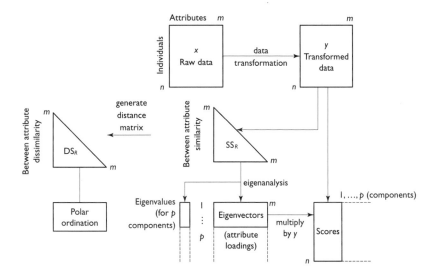

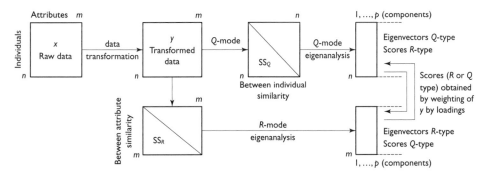

Figure 8.7 Steps in PCA and PO using the *R*-mode approach (top); data transformation may be implicit within the chosen index of resemblance, such as a correlation coefficient. The dual nature of the *Q* and *R* mode PCA solutions (bottom). Adapted from Randerson (1993).

and will linearise relationships between species exhibiting monotonic patterns in abundance. If using PCA, consider using the general standardisation procedure suggested by Brandko and Popovic (1994); this appears to be capable of correcting both edge effects and arch distortion.

3. If possible, compare the results of detrended and standard ordinations (PCA or CA) on the same data set. This should help to assess whether detrending is required and what its effects might be.

4. If unable to perform a detrended ordination, examine the ordinations carefully for arch distortion or edge effects. If they are evident or suspected, divide the data set into smaller, more homogeneous subsets. Repeat the ordinations on each subset of data. The data may be divided using cluster routines described in Chapter 9. Alternatively, the position of samples or sample units along the first axis may be used to divide the data set into groups of sites occurring together in the same segment of the axis. The ordination of overlapping groups, and the subsequent search for consistent patterns, should make it possible to recover the structure in the original data so it can be explored.

The relationships between the procedures are shown in Figure 8.7. Multivariate ordination methods should be viewed as exploratory or descriptive statistical procedures; if they do not help with ecological interpretation, they are of little value. As with any statistical procedure, they should not be applied blindly.

Methods to aid the interpretation of ordination diagrams and axes are described in Chapter 11.

Further reading

Ludwig, J.A. and Reynolds, J.F. (1988) *Statistical Ecology: A Primer on Methods and Computing*. John Wiley, New York. Provides a concise account of ordination.

Manly, B.F.J. (1994) *Multivariate Statistical Methods: A Primer*. Chapman & Hall, London. Although it emphasises the statistical and mathematical basis of PCA and related methods, the material is presented and written in a very accessible way.

Kent, M, and Coker, P. (1992). *Vegetation Description and Analysis: A Practical Approach*. Belhaven Press, London. Provides a thorough account of the development and application of ordination methods in ecology.

Kline, P. (1994) *An Easy Guide to Factor Analysis*. Routledge, London. An excellent non-mathematical introduction to the subject.

Randerson, P.F. (1993) Ordination. In *Biological Data Analysis: A Practical Approach*. J.C. Fry (ed.). Oirl Press at Oxford University Press, Oxford, pp. 173–209. This chapter and the book as a whole provide a very readable account of a range of important statistical methods; a good balance is maintained between theory and application.

Chapter Nine

Classification: comparing and grouping samples

Summary

The methods described in this chapter accentuate the discontinuous nature of data, assuming that the sample units may be placed or classified into meaningful groups which reflect real and interpretable characteristics. They assume that sample units may all be uniquely allocated to a number of distinct groups. The primary aim is to group like with like, so that the members of a group have more in common with each other than with any sample or sample unit outside the group or belonging to any other groups. The data sets must be multivariate, i.e. more than one variable or trait is recorded for each sample unit. Methods are presented for the grouping of binary and continuous data sets. Two general approaches are presented. A divisive classification method takes the data set and divides it into smaller and smaller groups; a cluster-based procedure starts by treating each individual sample unit as a group then forms them into larger and larger groups.

9.1 *Introduction*

The ordination methods described in Chapter 8 assume that samples may be ordered along a series of continuous gradients represented by the axes of an ordination diagram. In contrast, the methods described in this chapter accentuate the discontinuous nature of data, assuming that the sample units may be placed or classified into meaningful groups which reflect real and interpretable characteristics of the data. They assume that samples may all be uniquely allocated to a number of distinct groups. The primary aim is to group like with like, so that the members of a group have more in common with each other than with any sample outside the group or belonging to any other groups. Put more precisely, in the final arrangement of samples, within-group similarity should be greater than between-group similarity.

Although classification and ordination accentuate contrasting properties, they should be viewed as complementary procedures. Classification can be viewed as a procedure that partitions the ordination spaces into regions of high point density (i.e. discrete clusters of points), separated by regions of low point density (Figure 9.1). Numerous procedures have been developed for the grouping of samples:

- *Division methods* treat the complete data set as the initial group, which is then divided into smaller groups (normally two) that in turn are divided into smaller groups. The process continues until the groups formed are considered to be homogeneous or contain only one member and cannot be divided further.

- *Agglomeration methods* operate in the opposite direction. Each sample (member) of the original data set is initially treated as a separate group; similar samples are then joined to form groups, which in turn are fused to form new larger groups. The process continues until all the groups have been fused to produce one group containing all the samples.

The division or agglomeration may be either monothetic or polythetic. At each stage of the classification process, monothetic procedures consider only one variable when assigning samples to groups. For example, when classifying stands of vegetation, a divisive classification strategy might allocate stands to groups on the basis of whether a particular species is present or absent. Because of their reliance on a single variable at each level of group formation, monothetic classifications are particularly sensitive to sampling errors; failure to detect the presence of a species can have a marked effect on the final classification of samples. Polythetic procedures take account of all sample attributes, joining or separating groups

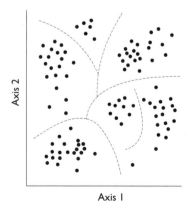

Figure 9.1 Subjective partitioning of a two-axis ordination plot. Reprinted, with permission, from Kent and Coker (1992).

on the basis of their overall similarity, which is normally assessed using one of the resemblance functions described in Chapter 6. Because polythetic methods use more of the available information, the resulting classifications are normally more reliable. The exact arrangement of samples in a classification produced using a given polythetic procedure will depend on the resemblance function used to assess group similarities. Different resemblance functions emphasise different data characteristics (Chapter 6).

It is not possible to give unambiguous advice on which of the methods in this chapter are likely to be most appropriate for a particular data set. All may be used to classify binary or continuous quantitative data sets, although the association analysis algorithm (Section 9.2.1) cannot be applied to quantitative data sets without substantial modification. In general, polythetic procedures should be used whenever possible, e.g. cluster analysis (Section 9.3). For large data sets, the final choice of method is likely to be governed by the availability of appropriate computer packages. The availability of computer programs, the ease of hand calculations when computers are unavailable, and the flexibility of the method, all three advantages make cluster analysis a most useful and versatile technique. But do read the whole of this chapter before adopting a particular approach.

9.2 *Divisive classification methods*

9.2.1 *Association analysis*

Association analysis is a divisive, monothetic procedure developed by Williams and Lambert (1959a) for the classification of community data sets (e.g. s species recorded in n quadrats). The method uses the χ^2-statistic to select 'divisor species' which are used to separate the data into two groups, only one of which contains samples in which the divisor species occurs. At each level of the division the χ^2-test of association (Chapter 7) is performed on all possible species pairs. If no significant associations are found, the analysis is considered complete and the grouped quadrats are assumed to form a single homogeneous group. If significant species associations are present, the group is divided in two and the process repeated on each group until all groups contain no further significant associations. Because the method relies on the χ^2-test, association analysis is used to classify binary data sets, i.e. presence and absence data only. Start with the complete data set of n samples (quadrats) and carry out the following procedure:

1. Using species presence and absence data, calculate the χ^2 measure of association for all possible species pairs.

2. Compare all calculated χ^2-values with the critical value of 3.84 ($p = 0.05$, d.f. $= 1$) normally used to test the significance of single paired species comparisons.

   - If no χ^2-values exceed 3.84 then the analysis is completed for that set of samples; no further division of the group is required.

   - If some χ^2-values exceed 3.84 then separately sum for each species all values of χ^2 greater than 3.84 (values below 3.84 are ignored or given a value of 0). Of the species present, the species with the highest summed χ^2 will account for the largest amount of within-group variation that remains.

3. Select the species with the highest summed χ^2 as the divisor species.

4. Based on the presence or absence of the divisor species, divide the sample units (quadrats) into two groups. All sample units containing the divisor species are allocated to one group; the remaining sample units, which lack the divisor species, are placed in the second group.

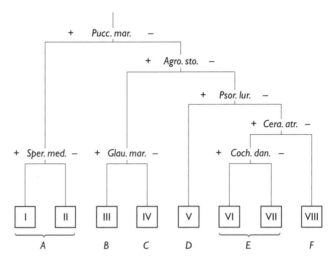

Figure 9.2 A binary key for identifying types of salt-marsh habitat. Division into eight groups is based on the presence or absence of the species shown. Also marked is an additional grouping into six groups (A to F). The data is from Ivimey-Cook and Proctor (1966) and the figure is reprinted, with permission, from Digby and Kempton (1987).

5. Repeat steps 1 to 5 on the two newly formed groups.

The results are normally presented as a dendrogram where the vertical axis plots the summed χ^2-values for divisor species or χ^2_{max}, the highest χ^2 present in the group prior to division. An example of association analysis is given in Figure 9.2.

9.2.2 Problems and how to solve them

Association analysis suffers from two major problems. Firstly, it can involve a considerable amount of computation. The number of pairwise comparisons, $\frac{1}{2}s(s-1)$, increases rapidly with the number of species (s) present in the data set. In addition the process has to be repeated on each newly formed group. Without access to specialist computer programs, association analysis cannot easily be undertaken. A more fundamental problem concerns the operation of 'stopping rules' to decide when a group is homogeneous and requires no further division.

Objective stopping rules
In the procedure outlined above a χ^2-value of 3.84 is used to decide whether to divide or stop the division of a group. The use of this value can be criticised on both statistical and practical grounds. The χ^2-value of 3.84 indicates a significant association for a *single pairwise comparison* only; it is not valid to apply it as a critical level of significance when multiple comparisons are made. Thus no inference of significance should be drawn from individual χ^2-values or summed χ^2-values. The true significant critical value of χ^2 for multiple comparisons will be considerably greater than 3.84. By using a lower value (i.e. 3.84) the original data set may become excessively divided, producing a fragmented classification containing many small groups.

One solution suggested by Goodall (1954) is to pool the end groups and then test each of the newly formed groups for homogeneity. However, this is not a very satisfactory approach, as the investigator is faced with finding a valid criterion for the selection and pooling of end groups and for assessing the homogeneity of the newly formed group. The alternative is to set a higher χ^2-value as the threshold for divisions. Williams and Lambert (1959a,b) and Madgwick and Desrochers (1972) present several mathematical criteria which may be used to select a more appropriate threshold value. In practice, a threshold level of χ^2 equal to $\sqrt{n}$, where n is the total number of samples in the data set (Causton, 1988), coupled with a rule of thumb that end groups should contain a minimum of 6 samples (Madgwick and Desrochers, 1972), will generally perform reasonably well. Strauss (1982) and Wildi and Orloci (1990) provide more detailed consideration of these issues.

Subjective stopping rules
The 'trial and error' approach advocated by Ludwig and Reynolds (1988) is recommended here. The threshold $\chi^2 = 3.84$ is applied but viewed only as a convenient index of species association and not as a test of significance. The resulting classification and levels of division are reviewed by the investigator after the analysis has been completed. The numbers of divisions and end groups presented in the final classification are selected to avoid small groups and to produce the most ecologically meaningful classifications of samples. Although the later criteria may seem difficult to achieve, it is important to realise that methods such as association analysis are of little value if they generate results which cannot be interpreted. Multivariate methods of classification and ordination should be viewed primarily as aids to the interpretation of complex data sets, capable of summarising data and hopefully without distortion. If the methods available were based on realistic models, relevant to the ecological processes and data characteristics, the results would have value in their own right, allowing the investigator to assess whether the underlying model provided an adequate explanation of the apparent structure present in the data. Unfortunately the available methods have yet to reach this level of sophistication.

In common with other monothetic procedures, the results of association analysis are very sensitive to the effects of chance species occurrences. Use of binary data further reduces the robustness of the classification produced by association analysis. For this reason it is wise to remove rare species – low frequency species which occur in only a small number of samples – before attempting an association analysis (Madgwick and Desrochers, 1972). However, removal of rare species can substantially reduce the amount of useful information present in the data. Some species may be rare because they have very specific environmental requirements. The distribution of such species can provide a valuable indicator of the environmental conditions associated with particular samples.

Association is rarely used today, being largely replaced by polythetic, divisive methods, particularly TWINSPAN (Section 9.2.3). But although it is not generally recommended, association analysis can provide a flexible classification with the advantage of producing a dichotomous key – each group defined by the presence and absence of the divisor species – allowing new samples to be 'keyed out' and related to an existing classification.

Extensions of the method
Association analysis is most frequently used to classify samples (quadrats) on the basis of the species they contain, known as normal association analysis (a Q-mode analysis). But by transposing the data matrix, it is possible to perform an inverse association analysis, which classifies species using the samples in which they occur (an R-mode analysis). The results of normal and inverse analyses may be combined by cross-tabulation, and the subsequent search for nodes, coincident groups of samples and species is known as nodal analysis (Lambert and Williams, 1962; Boesch, 1977).

Wratten and Fry (1980) describe an alternative procedure which does not depend on the χ^2 measure of association. In this procedure the between-group sum of squares (ΔSS) is used to select a divisor species that will form two groups which differ most. For each species in turn, the data set is divided into two subgroups: a subgroup that contains the species (a) and a subgroup that doesn't (b). The difference between the two subgroups is then assessed by calculating ΔSS using the formula

$$\Delta SS = \frac{n_a n_b}{n_a + n_b} \left(\sum_{j=1}^{S} (p_{aj} - p_{bj})^2 \right)$$

where n_a, n_b are the numbers of sample units in subgroup a and subgroup b; S is the total number of species; and p_{aj}, p_{bj} are the proportions of samples in each subgroup containing the species j. The species which, when used to form subgroups a and b, gives rise to the highest ΔSS is selected to make the final division of the group. The analysis is then repeated by dividing subgroup a into two subgroups and dividing subgroup b into two subgroups. The procedure is continued until a satisfactory classification has been achieved, or the largest ΔSS value is less that 10. Wratten and Fry (1980) suggest that this procedure, which they have called MONO classification, is rapid, easily programmed and can be relatively easily executed by hand for small data sets.

Several authors have shown that the association analysis algorithm can be applied to quantitative data if an alternative to the χ^2 measure of association is used. Covariance (Kershaw, 1961) and correlation (Poole, 1974) matrices have been suggested as suitable substitutes for measuring species association (Kent and Coker, 1992). But any measure of species association or similarity could be used. Alternatively, row (variable) sum of squares or variance could be used to select species which contribute most to group heterogeneity. Although the use of quantitative measures may produce more robust classifications, the lack of an objective stopping rule still remains a problem.

9.2.3 Polythetic methods

Association analysis has largely been succeeded by more reliable polythetic methods involving the ordination of samples. In these procedures the samples are ordinated before group division. Sample positions relative to the centre of the first ordination axis are used as the criteria for group division. All samples occurring to the left of the centre are placed in one group, those occurring to the right are placed in the other group. The process of ordination followed by the division of samples about the centre of the first axis is then repeated on each newly formed group until a satisfactory classification has been achieved (Digby and Kempton, 1987). This approach is likely to be a successful classification strategy since a key feature of ordination is that the first axis coincides with the direction of the maximum variation in the data (Causton, 1988). However, samples occurring close to the centre of the axis can be prone to misclassification. The characterisation of end-group species composition is also not straightforward; unlike association analysis, it does not produce a key to the classification. These problems have largely been overcome by the method of TWINSPAN developed by Hill (1979a). Currently TWINSPAN is probably the most frequently used procedure for the classification of community data sets (Kent and Ballard, 1988; Kent and Coker, 1992).

One reason why TWINSPAN is popular is because it is based on correspondence analysis (CA), which produces an ordination of both samples (e.g. quadrats) and species (Section 8.4). Thus TWINSPAN is able to produce a classification of sample units along with a complementary classification of species (Hill, 1979a,b). That is, TWINSPAN is able to perform a normal (Q-mode) and inverse (R-mode) classification of a data set. Unfortunately, although TWINSPAN has proved to be an extremely valuable and extensively applied classification procedure, it cannot realistically be performed using the commonly available versions of most standard statistical packages. However, because of its importance, the procedure is explained below in some detail, particularly the concept of indicator species (Box 9.1),

Box 9.1   Indicator species analysis

Identification of indicator species

Indicator species are those that occur predominantly among the samples at one end of an ordination axis. Their distribution should reflect, i.e. indicate, the environmental characteristic of the samples at either end of the gradient depicted by the ordination axis.

Procedure

Samples along the ordination axis are divided into two groups about the centre of the axis. Those to the right of the centre are placed in one group, called the positive group (+); those to the left are placed in a different group, called the negative group (−). Based on the distribution between these groups, an indicator value is calculated for each species using the formula

$$I_j = \frac{n_j^+}{N^+} - \frac{n_j^-}{N^-}$$

where I_j = the indicator value for species j

n_j^+ = the number of samples in the positive (right-hand) group containing species j

n_j^- = the number of samples in the negative (left-hand) group containing species j

N^+, N^- = the numbers of samples in the positive group and the negative group

$I_j = -1$ when the species occurs in all of the quadrats in the negative group only

$I_j = +1$ when the species occurs in all of the quadrats in the positive group only

$I_j = 0$ when the species occurs equally among the sample of both groups

If $I_j = 0$ the species shows no discriminatory power and it has no value as an indicator. Within the context of TWINSPAN:

- Species with the five highest indicator values (I), whether positive or negative, are selected as indicator species.
- For a single species, only one pseudospecies may be used as an indicator species. (Concept otapseudospecies is explained in the text).
- Indicator species are only selected if they are at least three times more frequent in one group.

This procedure is capable of considerable modification. Any species that are not uniformly distributed along an ordination axis are potential indicator species. It is assumed that the distribution of species is partly a reflection of the prevailing environmental conditions. Sample units containing similar assemblages of species are likely to have environmental conditions in common. The identification of such species may considerably aid the interpretation of ordination diagrams. When viewed as a descriptive tool, the calculation of species indicator values can be modified to consider any portion of the ordination axis. For example, the axis might be divided into four equal sections and the discrimination of species between these sections assessed by considering their frequency within each section. Assigning indicator status to species along an ordination axis and plotting their abundance or frequency, this provides a link between direct gradient analysis and indirect ordination (Chapter 8).

Table 9.1 TWINSPAN uses the concept of pseudospecies

Species percentage cover value	Pseudospecies
0–2%	1
3–5%	2
6–10%	3
11–20%	4
>20%	5

which can be applied to any ordination as an aid to their interpretation. Both Causton (1988) and Kent and Coker (1992) provide more detailed accounts. Fundamental to TWINSPAN is the concept of pseudospecies. Each species abundance is coded into a number of pseudospecies according to the Table 9.1. Suppose the maximum recorded percentage cover for the plant species *Plantago coronopus* is 15%, then the abundance of *P. coronopus* in each sample will be scored by the presence or absence of four pseudospecies: *P. coronopus* 1, *P. coronopus* 2, *P. coronopus* 3, and *P. coronopus* 4. If a sample contains 1% *P. coronopus*, it will be coded using one pseudospecies, *P. coronopus* 1. If a sample contains 8%, it will be coded using three pseudospecies: *P. coronopus* 1, *P. coronopus* 2, and *P. coronopus* 3. This technique converts quantitative data into presence/absence data about pseudospecies. Although information on the abundance of species is retained, the pseudospecies scaling will reduce the influence of large abundance values on the ordination of samples. The major advantage of recording species abundance as pseudospecies is that it allows the occurrence and abundance of a species to be treated as essentially separate variables, recognising that both can be important characteristics of an association (Kershaw and Looney, 1985).

Following the conversion of the data into a table of pseudospecies, the samples are ordinated using correspondence analysis (CA). Then instead of simply using sample position on the primary ordination axis to produce the final division of the data, TWINSPAN introduces an intermediate stage in which five 'indicator' species are selected and used to refine the ordination of samples. Indicator species are chosen on the basis of two properties. Firstly, that they show a clear preferential distribution between the two groups formed from the initial division of samples along the primary ordination, i.e. they occur only or predominantly in one or other of the groups. Secondly, when samples are scored for their presence, they are able to reproduce the structure (ordering) of samples along the primary ordination axis (Box 9.1).

Based on the scoring of samples for the presence and absence of the selected indicator species, a second ordering of samples is produced, called a refined ordination. The refined ordination is then used to divide the samples into two groups reflecting their indicator species score. The number of indicator species is essentially arbitrary; five represents a compromise between using one species or all of the species, and it has been shown to perform well. A useful key to the classification can be obtained by listing the frequency of the indicator species used to form the groups at each level of division. Although TWINSPAN is normally considered a polythetic procedure, since the final division is made on the basis of a limited number of species, the method is not truly polythetic. The distribution of samples along the primary CA axis or the associated eigenvalue at each level of division could be enlisted to provide objective stopping rules. In practice Hill's (1979b) recommendations that division should be limited to six successive levels and that end groups should not contain less than four samples, are widely adopted and appear to perform well on most ecological data. However, the final decision should be based on whether the groupings are capable of meaningful interpretation.

9.3 *Cluster analysis*

Cluster analysis and similarity analysis are general terms used to describe a group of polythetic, agglomerative classification procedures. Initially, all samples are considered to represent separate entities or groups with only one member. A hierarchical classification is derived from a matrix of sample similarity or distance measures. Based on the values in the matrix, samples are joined to form groups, which in turn are joined to produce larger groups. At each level of fusion, groups are joined on the basis of their similarity to other groups, in essence like is fused with like. The process is continued until all the samples are agglomerated (fused) into a single group.

9.3.1 *Procedures*

Cluster analysis is not a single procedure. The exact method, and hence the resulting classification, depends on the choice of data transformation or standardisation, the resemblance function and the rule for fusing samples or groups.

Transformation and standardisation of data sets
The results of cluster analysis, as with any other form of multivariate analysis, may be unduly influenced by variables with large ranges or values. To minimise the effects of these variables, it is normally a good idea to standardise the data set. The effects of data standardisation are discussed at length in Section 8.1.4, which should be consulted. The decision whether or not to standardise the data, should be made in the light of the resemblance function chosen and the aims of the analysis.

Choice of resemblance functions
In theory it is possible to use any measures of sample distance or similarity. But each measure emphasises particular data characteristics. The final choice should be governed by the nature of the data and the aims of the study. Taxonomic and systematic studies on continuous data frequently use the Euclidean and Manhattan metrics, whereas studies on binary data sets use simple matching or the Jaccard coefficient (Dunn and Everitt, 1982). Generally these measures do not perform well when applied to ecological data, particularly community data sets. For most ecological studies the metric form of the simple percentage similarity measure (Section 6.2.2) performs well, and Sorensen's index may be used for binary data sets (Chapter 6).

Group fusion rules (clustering strategy)
The first fusion – the joining of two samples to form the first group – is achieved in the same way for all clustering procedures. The matrix of similarity (distance) measures is searched and the two samples with the highest similarity are joined. If tied similarity values occur, more than one group will be formed at this level. However, once the first group has been formed, several different strategies may be used to form subsequent groups. The most commonly used fusion rules, which do not require the complete recalculation of the similarity matrix, are outlined below and illustrated in Figure 9.3.

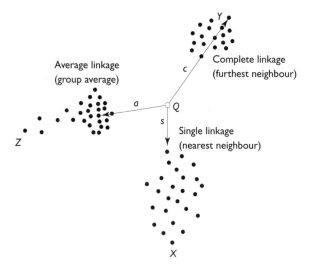

Figure 9.3 Three different sorting strategies or clustering methods. Q represents a quadrat to be assigned to one of three groups X, Y, Z; s = the shortest distance from Q to the nearest neighbour (single linkage), c = the shortest distance from Q to the farthest neighbour (complete linkage), a = the average linkage (group average). Reprinted, with permission, from Kent and Coker (1992).

Single-linkage (nearest-neighbour or minimum method)

1. A sample is joined to a group if the similarity value between the sample and the most similar member (nearest neighbour) of that group is higher than its similarity to any other sample.

2. Two groups are fused when the similarity value of a group member to the most similar member (nearest neighbour) of another group is greater than with any other group.

Complete-linkage (farthest-neighbour or maximum single linkage method)

1. A sample is joined to a group if the similarity value between the sample and the most dissimilar (remote) member (farthest neighbour) of that group is higher than its similarity to any other sample.

2. Two groups are fused when the similarity value of a group member to the most dissimilar (remote) member (farthest neighbour) of another group is greater than with any other group.

Complete group average (unweighted group average linkage)

1. A sample is joined to a group if the average similarity values between it and all members of the group is higher than its similarity to any other sample.

2. Two groups are fused if the average similarity between all members of each group is higher than with any other group.

The application of these clustering strategies to a simple data set is illustrated in Box 9.2. Many other clustering procedures have been suggested (Everitt, 1980; Wildi and Orloci, 1990). However, Dunn and Everitt (1982) conclude that no single method is best in all situations, but that the group average clustering methods generally perform best. Although it is possible to cluster small data sets by hand, this process is tedious and prone to error. Luckily, many statistical packages support a wide range of clustering procedures. For example,

Box 9.2   **Comparing linkage methods**

Consider a simple community data set of 5 samples by 6 species. To cluster the samples, draw up a 5×5 sample similarity matrix:

	1	2	3	4	5
1	100				
2	83.3	100			
3	50.0	58.3	100		
4	16.7	25.0	66.7	100	
5	25.0	33.3	58.3	75	100

the similarity between samples 4 and 3 (S_{34}) is 66.7%

Here are three different methods for clustering the samples. They all produce the same classification but they lead to different similarity levels for group fusion.

Single-linkage method

The highest entry is 83.3 for S_{12}, so samples 1 and 2 are joined to form group 1 (12). The similarities between group 1 (12) and the remaining samples are calculated as follows:

$$S_{(12)3} = \max\{S_{13}, S_{23}\} = \max\{50.0, 58.3\} = S_{23} = 58.3$$

$\uparrow$

Select the maximum, i.e. highest, value from within the curly brackets

$$S_{(12)4} = \max\{S_{14}, S_{24}\} = S_{24} = 25.0$$

$$S_{(12)5} = \max\{S_{15}, S_{25}\} = S_{23} = 33.3$$

Form a second similarity matrix with the values for the new group (12) and the remaining samples:

	(12)	3	4	5
(12)	100			
3	58.3	100		
4	25.0	66.7	100	
5	33.3	58.3	75	100

search for the highest value, $S_{45} = 75$

Form group 2 (45) and calculate the similarity values between (45) and (12) and between (45) and sample 3:

$$S_{(12)(45)} = \max\{S_{14}, S_{15}, S_{24}, S_{25}\} = \max\{16.7, 25.0, 25.0, 33.3\} = S_{25} = 33.3$$

$$S_{(45)3} = \max\{S_{34}, S_{35}\} = S_{34} = 66.7$$

Produce a third matrix:

	(12)	3	(45)
(12)	100		
3	58.3	100	
(45)	33.3	66.7	100

search for the highest value, $S_{(45)3} = 66.7$

▶

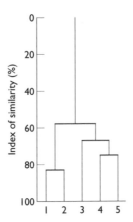

Figure 1 Single-linkage dendrogram.

Having formed group 3 (453), the process is almost complete; the last step is to calculate the similarity between (12) and (345):

$$S_{(12)(345)} = \max\{S_{13}, S_{14}, S_{15}, S_{23}, S_{24}, S_{25}\} = S_{23} = 58.3$$

The results may be presented as a dendrogram (Figure 1) or a table showing the composition of groups and the level at which they were joined.

Level	%	Groups
0	100	(1) (2) (3) (4) (5)
1	83.3	(12) (3) (4) (5)
2	75	(12) (3) (45)
4	66.7	(12) (345)
5	58.3	(12345)

Complete-linkage method

The highest entry is 83.3 for S_{12}, so samples 1 and 2 are joined to form group 1 (12). The similarities between group 1 (12) and the remaining samples are now calculated in essentially the same way as above, but the lowest relevant values are selected:

$$S_{(12)3} = \min\{S_{13}, S_{23}\} = \min\{50.0, 58.3\} = S_{13} = 50.0$$

select the minimum, i.e. lowest, value from within the curly brackets

$$S_{(12)4} = \min\{S_{14}, S_{24}\} = S_{24} = 16.7$$
$$S_{(12)5} = \min\{S_{15}, S_{25}\} = S_{25} = 25.0$$

Produce a second matrix:

	(12)	3	4	5
(12)	100			
3	50.0	100		
4	16.7	66.7	100	
5	25.0	58.3	75	100

search for the highest value, $S_{45} = 75$

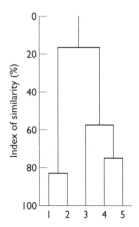

Figure 2 Complete-linkage dendrogram.

Form group 2 (45) and calculate the similarity values between (45) and (12) and between (45) and sample 3.

$$S_{(12)(45)} = \min\{S_{14}, S_{15}, S_{24}, S_{25}\} = \min\{16.7, 25.0, 25.0, 33.3\} = S_{14} = 16.7$$

$$S_{(45)3} = \min\{S_{34}, S_{35}\} = S_{35} = 58.3$$

Produce a third matrix:

	(12)	3	(45)
(12)	100		
3	50.0	100	
(45)	16.7	58.3	100

search for the highest value, $S_{(45)3} = 58.3$

Having formed group 3 (453), all that remains is to calculate the similarity between (12) and (345):

$$S_{(12)(345)} = \min\{S_{13}, S_{14}, S_{15}, S_{23}, S_{24}, S_{25}\} = S_{14} = 16.7$$

The results may be tabulated or plotted as a dendrogram (Figure 2).

Level	%	Groups
0	100	(1) (2) (3) (4) (5)
1	83.3	(12) (3) (4) (5)
2	75	(12) (3) (45)
4	58.3	(12) (345)
5	16.7	(12345)

Unweighted group average method

Initially this method proceeds as before, with samples 1 and 2 being fused at the 83.3% similarity level. The new similarity values, between the groups and the remaining samples, are then calculated as the average of each set of relevant similarity values:

$$S_{(12)3} = (S_{13} + S_{23})/2 = (50.0 + 58.3)/2 = 54.2$$

$$S_{(12)4} = (S_{14} + S_{24})/2 = 20.9$$

$$S_{(12)5} = (S_{15} + S_{25})/2 = 29.2$$

Produce a second matrix:

	(12)	3	4	5
(12)	100			
3	54.2	100		
4	20.9	66.7	100	
5	29.2	58.3	75	100

search for the highest value, $S_{45} = 75$

Form group 2 (45) and calculate the similarity values between (45) and (12) and between (45) and sample 3:

$$S_{(12)(45)} = (S_{14} + S_{15} + S_{24} + S_{25})/4 = 25$$

$$S_{(45)3} = (S_{34} + S_{35})/2 = 62.5$$

Produce a third matrix:

	(12)	3	(45)
(12)	100		
3	50.0	100	
(45)	25.0	62.5	100

search for the highest value, $S_{(45)3} = 62.5$

Sample 3 is joined to (45) to produce group 3 (453) at the 62.5% level. The joining level for the two groups (12) and (453) is then calculated:

$$S_{(12)(345)} = (S_{13} + S_{14} + S_{15} + S_{23} + S_{24} + S_{25})/6 = 34.7$$

The results may be tabulated or plotted as a dendrogram (Figure 3).

Level	%	Groups
0	100	(1) (2) (3) (4) (5)
1	83.3	(12) (3) (4) (5)
2	75	(12) (3) (45)
4	62.5	(12) (345)
5	34.7	(12345)

An alternative method of calculating $S_{(12)(45)}$ is to average the previously calculated values for $S_{(12)4}$ and $S_{(12)5}$:

$$S_{(12)(45)} = (S_{(12)4} + S_{(12)5})/2 = (20.9 + 29.2)/2 = 25.02$$

Applying this method to $S_{(12)(345)}$ gives

$$S_{(12)(345)} = (S_{(12)3} + S_{(12)(45)})/2 = (50.0 + 25.05)/2 = 37.53$$

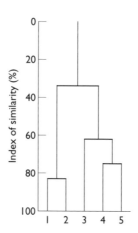

Figure 3 Group average dendrogram.

This method, sometimes called McQuitty's method, produces very similar results but is more easily applied when attempting to cluster a data set by hand (Figure 4). Instead of producing a new matrix, the original matrix may be altered after each fusion and then searched for the highest remaining similarity values. Values associated with samples in the original matrix, or groups in the extended matrix, are crossed out once they form part of a group. An additional row is added to the base of the matrix, into which are entered the similarities between the newly formed groups and the ungrouped samples. These additional rows are extended to the right to form a secondary matrix for the similarities between groups. This approach allows quite large samples to be clustered by hand, although it can be tedious.

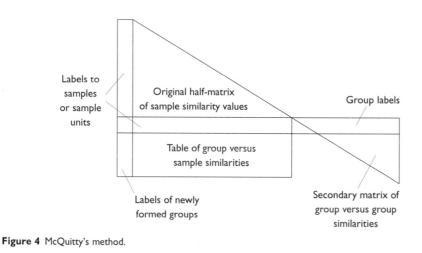

Figure 4 McQuitty's method.

MINITAB under the **Multivariate** option offers a number of clustering procedures which allow Q and R mode analyses to be performed on either the original data matrix (e.g. variables by samples matrix) or a sample distance matrix. The use of MINITAB to cluster the same data set ordinated in Chapter 8 is illustrated in Box 9.3, which also gives the

Box 9.3 Cluster analysis using MINITAB

Data table entered in the MINITAB spreadsheet. Entered in this way MINITAB's Cluster Observations **command clusters the rows into groups based on the relative values of the six variables Sp1 to Sp6.**

	C1	C2	C3	C4	C5	C6
	Sp1	Sp2	Sp3	Sp4	Sp5	Sp6
1	85	65	45	25	5	0
2	0	85	65	45	25	5
3	5	0	85	65	54	25
4	25	5	0	85	65	45
5	45	65	85	0	5	25

```
MTB > Cluo 'Sp1'-'Sp6';
SUBC> Average;
SUBC> Manhattan;
SUBC> Standardize;
SUBC> Dendrogram.
```

Commands may be typed in at the command prompt, but they are most easily entered from the menu bar: Stat **then** Multivariate **then** Cluster Observations.

In the dialogue box specify Location of Data **as** C1-C6, Linkage Method **as Average (there are other options) and** Distance Measure **as Manhattan. In this case the options to standardise the data and to produce a dendrogram were also selected. The option** Number of Clusters **is left on the default setting of 1; this means all observations will be grouped.**

Output
```
Hierarchical Cluster Analysis of Observations

Standardized Variables, Manhattan Distance, Average Linkage

Amalgamation Steps
```

Step	Number of clusters	Similarity level	Distance level	Clusters joined		New cluster	Number of obs. in new cluster
1	4	59.84	4.425	1	5	1	2
2	3	52.64	5.215	3	4	3	2
3	2	51.42	5.353	1	2	1	3
4	1	20.51	8.758	1	3	1	5

MINITAB calculates the distance between clusters *i* and *j* as $s_{ij} = (1 - d_{ij}/d_{max}) \times 100$, where d_{max} is the maximum value in the matrix of dissimilarity values D **that MINITAB calculates from the entered data. Note** D **may be stored and printed out.**

```
MTB >
```

MINITAB will also print out summary information on the groups formed (Figure 1). A complete printout for each group and a printout of group distances can be obtained by setting **Number of Clusters** in the dialogue box to 4, i.e. the number of groups produced by the clustering. Once entered, the analysis is rerun to obtain information on all groups formed during the analysis.

Transposing the data table

In order to cluster the species by the sites (i.e. rows), the original data table must be transposed so that the rows will now represent Sp1 to Sp6 and columns represent sites 1 to 5. This may be done in MINITAB by copying the columns holding the data into a matrix

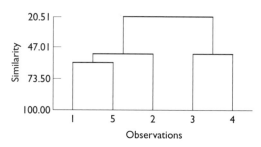

Figure 1 Dendrogram for the original data: observations correspond to the five sites.

which is given a name by the user, e.g. M1. This matrix is then transposed and its columns are copied into the spreadsheet.

```
MTB >
MTB > Copy 'Sp1'-'Sp6' M1.
MTB >
```
Commands to copy columns labelled Sp1 to Sp6 into a matrix named M1. This can be done from the menu by selecting Calc then Matrices then Copy.

To transpose the matrix and copy the resulting matrix into the spreadsheet, use the following commands:

```
MTB > Transpose M1 M2.
MTB > Copy M2 C10-C14.
MTB >
```
This too may be achieved using the options available under Matrices.

The species may now be clustered using the **Cluster Observations** commands but specifying that the data is stored in columns C10 to C14. When this is done the following results are produced along with the dendrogram in Figure 2.

Hierarchical Cluster Analysis of Observations

Standardized Variables, Manhattan Distance, Average Linkage

Amalgamation Steps

Step	Number of clusters	Similarity level	Distance level	Clusters joined	New cluster	Number of obs. in new cluster
1	5	74.13	2.248	4 5	4	2
2	4	55.16	3.896	4 6	4	3
3	3	49.32	4.404	2 3	2	2
4	2	32.01	5.908	1 2	1	3
5	1	15.17	7.371	1 4	1	6

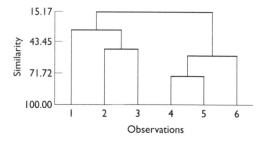

Figure 2 Dendrogram for the transposed data: observations correspond to the six species.

commands necessary to transpose the data table. This can be very useful, as it removes the need to re-enter the data where both Q and R modes are to be undertaken.

9.3.2 Problems and possible solutions

As with the divisive methods of classification (Section 9.2), the choice of a cut-off or stopping level can present problems. The central question is how many of the formed groups should be considered to represent real groupings of similar sample units capable of interpretation. If an index of similarity (or dissimilarity) is adopted as the resemblance measure, an objective cut-off level can be used. For example, the use of percentage similarity allows a reasonable, if somewhat arbitrary, level of 60% to be selected as a cut-off level. At this level, valid groups are defined as those in which all members of the group are at least 60% similar, i.e. they have more characteristics in common with each other than with non-group members. Groups fulfilling this criterion can readily be identified from the dendrogram by drawing a line across the diagram at appropriate similarity levels. Other threshold levels may be drawn on the same diagram, clearly illustrating how the cut-off level affects the final classification (Figure 9.4).

If the original samples are random, differences between the means or variances of selected end groups may be tested for significance. Alternatively the classification may be tested against the original sample similarity or distance matrix by the calculation of the cophenetic correlation. To do this, the classification of samples is used to assign similarity (distance) values to sample pairs. For example, if sample 1 is fused with a group containing samples 3, 4, 5 at a level of 50% similarity, then based on the classification, the similarities between these samples are $cS_{13} = cS_{14} = cS_{15} = 50$. In this way a classification can be summarised as an ordered sequence of similarity or distance values (cS_{ij} or cD_{ij}). Using the Pearson product-moment correlation, this sequence is compared with the same sequence of values obtained from the original similarity (distance) matrix. The higher the correlation, the better the dendrogram summarises the relationships among samples. However, the significance of the correlation cannot easily be assessed, and Rohlf (1970) warns that even cophenetic correlations close to 0.9 do not necessarily mean that the dendrogram represents a good summary of the phenetic relationships. It is probably best to view the cophenetic correlation as a

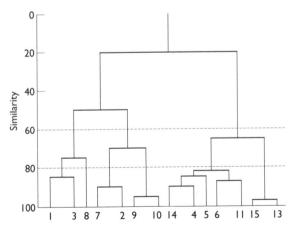

Figure 9.4 Threshold level affects the size and number of end groups. A threshold of 60% similarity leads to three groups: (1, 3, 8), (7, 2, 9, 10) and (14, 4, 5, 6, 11, 15, 13). A threshold of 80% similarity leads to six groups: (1, 3), (8), (7, 2), (2, 9), (14, 4, 5, 6, 11) and (15, 13).

descriptive statistic that allows the effectiveness of different classification procedures to be compared.

9.4 *Recommendations*

Monothetic or polythetic? Polythetic methods should be selected whenever possible; they are generally more robust and less prone to the misclassification of samples. Monothetic classification procedures, i.e. association analyses (Section 9.2.1), can only be recommended as the method of choice when a major objective of the study is to produce a dichotomous key to the classified samples.

Divisive or agglomerative? In ecology, divisive methods are generally recommended over agglomerative procedures, particularly for the classification of community data sets. It is assumed that the classification of samples into broad categories is usually of more interest than the relationships between particular pairs of samples (Hill *et al.*, 1975; Gauch, 1982; Digby and Kempton, 1987). Of the divisive procedures, TWINSPAN (Section 9.2.3) is most strongly advocated (Kent and Coker, 1992). TWINSPAN is the established method for classifying community data sets, but cluster analysis (Section 9.3) should be considered if TWINSPAN is not available.

Sokal *et al.* (1984) have shown that TWINSPAN can be a robust method, capable of reconstructing hierarchical phylogenetic relationships as effectively as cladistic methods. However, James and McCulloch (1990) point out that in both systematics and ecological studies the results are prone to overinterpretation. If the primary aim of the analysis is to reduce the number of samples by grouping replicated samples before further analysis, then cluster analysis should be the method of choice. Without a community data set, there appears to be no obvious reason why TWINSPAN should perform more reliably than an appropriate cluster analysis. If cluster analysis is undertaken, the resemblance function should meet the recommendations of Chapter 6, and the complete group average linkage clustering strategy should initially be adopted.

Methods for the comparison and interpretation of end groups are described in Chapter 11.

Further reading

Bridge, P.D. (1993) Classification. In *Biological Data Analysis: A Practical Approach*. J.C. Fry (ed.). Oirl Press at Oxford University Press, Oxford, pp. 219–41. This chapter and the book as whole provide a very readable account of a range of important statistical methods; a good balance is maintained between theory and application.

Digby, P.G.N. and Kempton, R.A. (1987). *Multivariate Analysis of Ecology Communities*. Chapman & Hall, London. A thorough treatment of classification, it looks at methods to compare and assess the efficiency of different classifications.

Kent, M. and Coker, P. (1992). *Vegetation Description and Analysis: A Practical Approach*. Belhaven Press, London. Provides a clear account of TWINSPAN.

Ludwig, J.A. and Reynolds, J.F. (1988) *Statistical Ecology: A Primer on Methods and Computing*. John Wiley, New York. Provides a concise account of classification.

Manly, B.F.J. (1994) *Multivariate Statistical Methods: A Primer*. Chapman & Hall, London. Although it emphasises the statistical and mathematical basis of PCA and related methods, the material is presented and written in a very accessible way.

PART THREE

Relating Data Sets to Environmental Factors

Chapter Ten

Data for a single species or variable: ANOVA and regression

Summary

This chapter introduces two major statistical procedures: analysis of variance (ANOVA), which allows sample means to be compared, and regression analysis, which determines the strength and nature of the relations between variables. Regression analysis may be viewed as an extension of correlation analysis (Chapter 7), providing a measure of correlation between two or more variables, and a summary of this relation in the form of a simple linear equation. Both are widely used and have extensive applications in the analysis of ecological and environmental data.

10.1 *Introduction*

This chapter introduces two major statistical procedures: analysis of variance (ANOVA), which allows sample means to be compared, and regression analysis, which determines the strength and nature of the relations between variables. Regression analysis may be viewed as an extension of correlation analysis (Chapter 7), providing a measure of correlation between two or more variables, and a summary of this relation in the form of a simple linear equation. Both are widely used and have extensive applications in the analysis of ecological and environmental data. The chapter has two major sections:

- If the primary aim of the data analysis is to test for the occurrence of significant differences between sample means, consult Section 10.2 on ANOVA.
- If the primary aim of the data analysis is to describe and test for the occurrence of significant relationships between variables (normally linear, but not always), consult Section 10.3 on regression analysis.

Each section may be read independently, but since both methods are closely related, a greater understanding will be obtained by reading the whole chapter.

10.2 *Analysis of variance*

Introduction and theory

Consider a simple experiment designed to investigate the effects of salinity on the growth of a salt-marsh plant species. Seeds are randomly collected from a salt marsh and germinated under uniform conditions. After 4 days of growth, similar-sized seedlings are potted up, one per pot. The pots are then randomly allocated to one of four salinity treatments. Each treatment is replicated five times, i.e. five randomly chosen pots are allocated to each treatment. The plants are grown under uniform conditions and harvested after 6 months of growth, when the total above-ground biomass of each plant is measured. The results of the experiment are given in Table 10.1.

One aim of the data analysis might be to determine whether the different strengths of saline solution used to water the plants significantly affected plant growth. This could be approached by calculating the mean and standard deviation of plant biomass for each

Table 10.1 Table of dry plant biomass after 6 months' growth[a]

Replicates	Treatments			
	1	*2*	*3*	*4*
1	25.2861	25.8615	19.8047	10.9658
2	25.2784	25.2293	16.4905	8.8345
3	32.2894	27.3122	19.1865	7.2738
4	26.5976	24.5835	20.0697	13.5813
5	27.8517	24.4672	19.6210	10.4386
Means	27.46	25.491	19.034	10.22

[a] Treatment levels are solution salinities. Treatment 1 is the control treatment, where plants were watered with distilled water; treatments 2, 3 and 4 are increasing levels of salinity.

treatment and then testing for significant differences between means for all possible pairs of treatment means using Student's *t*-test (Box 10.1). Apart from being inefficient and cumbersome, this approach suffers from the statistical problems associated with multiple comparisons. With 4 treatments, there are 6 possible pairwise comparisons. Thus, if a significance level of 5% ($p = 0.05$) is adopted, there is a 30% chance (6×0.05) that at least one of the comparisons will be significant by chance alone. This is known as a type I error – falsely rejecting the null hypothesis (H_0). Equally important are type II errors, accepting the null hypothesis when it should be rejected. In this case a type II error will occur if it is falsely concluded that the means did not differ significantly.

This problem is avoided by analysis of variance (ANOVA), which provides an efficient method for testing whether group or sample means are equal. The underlying model of ANOVA is quite straightforward. If we represent individual plant biomass values by x_{ij}, where the subscript i identifies the particular replicate and j the treatment level, each value may be considered as the sum of three components:

$$x_{ij} = G + a_j + e_{ij}$$

where G = the overall or grand mean, calculated from all the recorded values

e_{ij} = the error associated with the observation

a_j = the effect of treatment j on the values of x

if $a_j = 0$ then the treatment has no effect

if $a_j > 0$ then the treatment tends to increase the values of x

if $a_j < 0$ then the treatment tends to decrease the values of x

Under the null hypothesis, treatment effects are assumed to be zero; values of x differ randomly as a result of the errors of measurement about the overall mean (G). That is, under H_0, $a_1 = a_2 = a_3 = a_4 = 0$ or in terms of treatment means, $\mu_1 = \mu_2 = \mu_3 = \mu_4$. Analysis of variance partitions the total variance or variability (V_{total}) of the data set into different components. In a one-way ANOVA, where there is only one treatment factor, e.g. salinity, there are only two sources of variability:

- *Within-treatment* variation (V_{within}) is the variability that results from the random scatter of sample values about each treatment mean. It is a measure of the residual variation or sample error.

- *Between-treatment* variation ($V_{between}$) is the variability between samples due to differences between treatment means. It is a measure of the treatment effects.

These two sources of variation are additive:

$$V_{total} = V_{between} + V_{within}$$

If the null hypothesis is true, all the values of x are effectively drawn from a single normal distribution centred on G, so allowing for sample errors, treatment means should be equal and have the same variance. If this is the case then both between ($V_{between}$) and within (V_{within}) variability should contribute equally to the total variability (V_{total}), i.e. $V_{between} = V_{within}$. This can be tested for by using the F-test for equal variance. If the variance associated with treatment effects is significantly greater than the within-sample variance, the null hypothesis is rejected. The F_{max} test provides a very useful test for *homogeneity of variance*, i.e. equality of variances. The F-statistic is calculated by dividing the *larger* sample variance by the *smaller* sample variance. If the variances are equal then $F = 1.0$. Since the larger variance is always divided by the smaller, if the variances differ, then $F > 1.0$. The significance of the departure of F from 1.0 is assessed by comparing the calculated value with tabulated critical values of F for degrees of freedom v_1 and v_2, where v_1 and v_2 are the degrees of freedom for the samples with the larger and smaller variance respectively

Box 10.1 **Tests for comparing two means**

The *t*-test and the *z*-test (or *d*-test) may be used in the appropriate circumstances. The *t*-test requires the data to be normally distributed, the *z*-test doesn't. The large sample sizes required for the *z*-test make it possible to apply the central limit theorem, which states that the means of a series of samples drawn from a single population (regardless of the actual distribution) will be normally distributed. However, $n > 30$ will not be adequate if the populations are badly skewed; badly skewed populations require $n > 50$ in order to apply the *z*-test.

Small sample sizes ($n < 30$)

- *t*-test to compare means of two samples with unknown variances but assumed to be equal

$$t = \frac{\bar{x}_1 - \bar{x}_2}{s\sqrt{\dfrac{1}{n_1} + \dfrac{1}{n_2}}}$$

where s is the sample standard deviation based on combined samples. Where n_1 and n_2 are the size of samples 1 and 2. Alternatively the pooled estimate of sample standard deviation may be used obtained from:

$$S = \sqrt{\frac{(n_1 - 1)s_1^2 + (n_2 - 1)s_2^2}{(n_1 + n_2 - 2)}}$$

Where s_1^2 and s_2^2 are the sample variances for samples 1 and 2. t has $n_1 + n_2 - 2$ degrees of freedom. Critical values may be found from Appendix 10.1.

- *t*-test to compare means of two samples with unknown variances assumed not to be equal

Test for equal sample variance using the *F*-test:

$$F = \frac{S_1^2}{S_2^2} \quad \text{where} \quad S_1^2 > S_2^2$$

Use the two-tailed table of *F*-values (Appendix 10.2) to assess the significance. If the sample variances differ significantly, calculate t from

$$t = \frac{\bar{x}_1 - \bar{x}_2}{\sqrt{\dfrac{S_1^2}{n_1} + \dfrac{S_2^2}{n_2}}}$$

Welch's t-test is used for small sample sizes (n_1, $n_2 < 30$) when the sample variances are not equal.

$$\text{d.f.} = \frac{\left(\dfrac{S_1^2}{n_1} + \dfrac{S_2^2}{n_2}\right)^2}{\left(\dfrac{S_1^2}{n_1}\right)^2\left(\dfrac{1}{n_1 - 1}\right) + \left(\dfrac{S_2^2}{n_2}\right)^2\left(\dfrac{1}{n_2 - 1}\right)}$$

Use this formula and round d.f. to the nearest whole number.

● Confidence interval

$$\bar{x} \pm t_{p,(n-1)}(S/\sqrt{n})$$

Large sample sizes ($n > 30$)

Use $z = \dfrac{(\bar{x}_1 - \bar{x}_2)}{\sqrt{\dfrac{S_1^2}{n_1} + \dfrac{S_2^2}{n_2}}}$

● Critical values of z

$z = 1.96 \quad (p = 0.05)$

$z = 2.58 \quad (p = 0.01)$

$z = 3.89 \quad (p = 0.001)$

● Confidence interval

$$\bar{x} \pm z(S/\sqrt{n}) \qquad \text{for a 95\% confidence limit } z = 1.96$$

(Appendix 10.3). Notice that different tables of critical F values are used when comparing sample variance and when assessing the significance of the F statistic generated during ANOVA. When comparing sample variance a two tailed test should be applied and the critical F values in Appendix 10.2 used. A one tailed F test is used in AVONA and the critical values in Appendix 10.3 are used.

In practice, the ANOVA calculations are performed using the sum of squares (SS) in place of the variance. The sum of squares provides an easily calculated, additive measure of sample variance; dividing it by the appropriate degrees of freedom gives the required variance values, i.e. the mean of the squares (MS), usually called the mean square; see Box 10.2. During ANOVA the total sum of squares is partitioned among treatment and error effects:

$$\text{SS}_{total} = \text{SS}_{between} + \text{SS}_{within}$$

The calculations associated with ANOVA are usually presented as in Table 10.2, where a is the number of groups or treatment levels; N is the the total number of observations; and MS is the mean square, which provides an estimate of the variance associated with each source. The test statistic F will have degrees of freedom $(a - 1)$ and $(N - a)$. If F exceeds the tabulated values for $p = 0.05$ and degrees of freedom $(a - 1)$ and $(N - a)$, the null hypothesis is rejected and the alternative hypothesis that the means differ is accepted. In many textbooks the within-group MS(MS_{within}) is known as the error of residual MS. Box 10.3 gives a worked example showing procedures for performing an ANOVA by hand and Box 10.4 shows how to do it using MINITAB.

10.2.2 Comparing means

A completed ANOVA table may allow the null hypothesis to be rejected, but it provides no information on whether particular treatment means or a group of means differ significantly. In order to assess the significance of differences between treatment means, a further series of tests must be applied to the data. The choice of test is governed by whether the test can be described as *a priori* or *a posteriori*. This is an important distinction and should be considered when planning the experiment and before analysing any data.

Box 10.2 **Sample variance and sum of squares**

Sample variance (S^2) measures the dispersion of values about the sample mean ($\bar{x}$):

$$S^2 = \frac{1}{n-1} \sum (x - \bar{x})^2$$

where n = the number of values used to calculate $\bar{x}$ (d.f. = $n - 1$)
$(x - \bar{x})$ = the deviation from the mean (the residual)
$\sum (x - \bar{x})^2$ = the sum of squares of the deviation, more often called the sum of squares (SS)

The sample variance of variable x is equal to the sum of squares of x (SS_x) divided by $n - 1$, the degrees of freedom. When calculating SS_x by hand, the easiest way is to use this formula:

called the correction term

$$SS_x = \sum x^2 - \frac{1}{n} \left(\sum x \right)^2$$

The mean squares (MS) estimates the variance of x; it is obtained by dividing SS by the number of degrees of freedom, here $n - 1$.

- A priori tests are planned comparisons that could sensibly be conducted before the ANOVA. For example, suppose that the treatment groups consist of replicated samples of stream invertebrates collected at five stations along a river which is joined by a tributary between stations 3 and 4. It would be logical to compare the mean density of stream invertebrates above and below the tributary; this comparison could be described as a planned a priori comparison. In contrast, there is no a priori reason for comparing two apparently similar stations next to each other on the same uniform stretch of river. Other a priori comparisons may also be justified, perhaps between sites associated with high and low water velocities. However, it is not valid to claim that all possible pairs are bona fide planned comparisons!

- A posteriori tests are described as unplanned comparisons. For example, in the plant growth experiment described above, there is no logical reason, before the experiment, why any two particular means should be compared. All of the possible comparisons could equally be chosen. However, once the experiment has been

Table 10.2 How to present ANOVA calculations

Source of variance	d.f.	SS	MS	F
Between groups (i.e. treatment effects)	$a - 1$	$SS_{between}$	$(SS_{between})/(a - 1) = MS_{between}$	$MS_{between}/MS_{within}$
Within groups (i.e. residual or error effects)	$N - a$	SS_{within}	$(SS_{within})/(N - a) = MS_{within}$	
Total	$N - 1$	SS_{total}		

Box 10.3 **One-way ANOVA: a worked example**

Table 1 contains the yields in kilograms per plot for four varieties of wheat. ANOVA is used to test for significant difference in the mean yields obtained from the four varieties. Using the values in the table, we can find the correction term (CT) and the total sum of squares (SS_{total}).

$$CT = \frac{(GT)^2}{N} = \frac{(697.7)^2}{19} = 25\,620.28$$

$$SS_{total} = A - CT = 25\,830.49 - 25\,620.28 = 210.21$$

The sum of squares between samples ($SS_{between}$) is calculated by summing T_j/n_j for all four varieties ($j = 1, 2, 3, 4$) and then subtracting the correction term:

$$SS_{between} = \left(\frac{T_1^2}{n_1} + \frac{T_2^2}{n_2} + \frac{T_3^2}{n_3} + \frac{T_4^2}{n_4} \right) CT$$

$$= \left(\frac{31\,648.41}{5} + \frac{57\,408.16}{6} + \frac{17\,450.41}{4} + \frac{21\,933.61}{4} \right) - 25\,620.28$$

$$= 123.44$$

Finally SS_{within} is obtained by subtraction:

$$SS_{within} = SS_{total} - SS_{between} = 210.21 - 123.44 = 86.77$$

These results may be entered into the standard ANOVA table for calculating MS, where *a* is the number of groups or treatment levels.

Table 1 Yield per plot for four varieties of wheat

Row or replicate number (plots)	Column or treatment numbers (wheat varieties)				
	$j = 1$	$j = 2$	$j = 3$	$j = 4$	
$i = 1$	34.3	40.4	30.5	33.1	
$i = 2$	35.7	38	32	38.4	
$i = 3$	37.8	38.3	33.4	35.7	
$i = 4$	36.9	40.6	36.2	40.9	
$i = 5$	33.2	38.8	–	–	
$i = 6$	–	43.5	–	–	
$\bar{x}_j =$	35.58	39.93	33.02	37.02	
$n_j =$	5	6	4	4	$N = \sum n_j = 19$
$T_j = \sum x_{ij} =$	177.9	239.6	132.1	148.1	Grand total GT = 697.7
$T_j^2 =$	31\,648.41	57\,408.16	17\,450.41	21\,933.61	
$\sum x_{ij}^2 =$	6\,343.67	9\,589.1	4\,380.25	5\,517.47	Total of all x^2 values $A = 25\,830.49$

Source of variance	d.f.	SS	MS	F
$SS_{between}$	$a-1=4-1=3$	123.44	$123.44/3 = 41.15$	$41.15/5.79 = 7.11$
SS_{within}	$N-a=19-4=15$	86.77	$86.77/15 = 5.79$	
SS_{total}	$N-1=19-1=18$	210.21		

The critical F-values with d.f. $= 3, 15$ (in this order) are 3.29 ($p = 0.05$) and 5.42 ($p = 0.01$). Since the calculated value of 7.11 exceeds these values, we can safely conclude that the means differ significantly and the null hypothesis can be rejected. We can conclude that although within-group variability is high, the yields differ significantly between the varieties of wheat sown.

Comparing group means

Since the group sizes differ, the means are compared using Scheffé's procedure. Consider the means for groups 1 and 3 ($j = 1$ and $j = 3$). Obtain the confidence interval for the difference between the two means:

$$\bar{x}_1 - \bar{x}_3 \pm \sqrt{\frac{1}{r_1} + \frac{1}{r_3}} \times \sqrt{MS_{within} \times F_{p=0.05,1,18}}$$

$$35.58 - 33.02 \pm \sqrt{\frac{1}{5} + \frac{1}{4}} \times \sqrt{41.15 \times 4.41}$$

$$2.56 \pm 9.037$$

$$LCL = -6.477$$

$$UCL = 11.59$$

The calculated confidence interval from -6.477 to 11.49 contains zero, so we conclude that the means for treatment levels 1 and 3 do not differ significantly. Other pairwise comparisons may be made (Section 10.2.2).

conducted, if ANOVA results indicate that salinity has a significant effect on plant growth, the significance of several particular comparisons may be of interest to the investigator.

Planned tests of comparison
Planned or a priori tests of comparison are valid regardless of the significance of the ANOVA, but only $a - 1$ comparisons are permitted (where a is the total number of treatment means). The least significant difference (LSD) procedure is one of several methods that are only valid as an a priori test. The calculated LSD, as the name suggests, is the smallest difference required between the two means for them to differ significantly. If the difference between the means exceeds the calculated LSD, then the means are considered to differ significantly. The LSD is easily calculated:

$$LSD_{ij} = t_{p(MS_{within})} \sqrt{\left(\frac{1}{r_i} + \frac{1}{r_j}\right) MS_{within}}$$

Box 10.4   One-way ANOVA using MINITAB

MINITAB can be used to perform a one-way analysis of variance on the salinity data in Table 10.1. The output shows that the probability of obtaining an F-value of 68.93 is less than $p = 0.001$, so we can conclude that the means are not equal and the null hypothesis can be rejected with confidence. It is clear that the plant growth is significantly affected by salinity. From inspection of the simple graph produced by MINITAB, it appears that the lowest salinity, level 2, has no significant effect on plant growth, but above this level the plant growth is inhibited by salinity.

MTB > AOVOneway C1-C4.   **Data stored in columns C1 to C4. Command executed by selecting** Stat **then ANOVA then** One-way (Unstacked). **A stacked option,** One-way, **is also available. This option will perform a one-way ANOVA on data stored in two columns, one containing the response variable, the other the factor levels.**

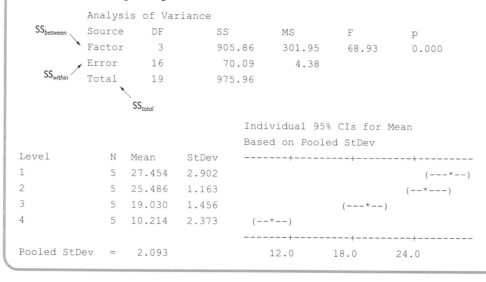

where LSD_{ij} is the least significant difference between the ith and jth treatment means; MS_{within} is the within-group or error mean of the squares (MS_{error}); r_i and r_j are the number of observations associated with the ith and jth treatment means; $t_{p(\text{MS}_{within})}$ is Student's t-statistic with degrees of freedom equal to that of the MS_{within} or MS_{error} (i.e. $N - a$), and probability $p = 0.05$. Where multiple comparisons are made, the level of p should be adjusted to reduce the probability of making a type I error. If an overall significance level of $\alpha = 0.05$ is required, the value of p is calculated as $p = \alpha/l$, where l is the number of comparisons (Kleinbaum *et al.*, 1998). Thus if 5 comparisons are made, $t_{p=0.01\,(df=N-a)}$ should be selected in place of $t_{p=0.05\,(df=N-a)}$. Tables of t-values are given in Appendix 10.1.

Unplanned tests of comparison
Unplanned, a posteriori tests of comparison should only be conducted if the original ANOVA is significant. There is no practical restriction on the number of comparisons that can be made; if required, all possible pairs of means may be tested. One of the simplest and most

robust procedures is the Tukey–Kramer method; it calculates the minimum significant difference (MSD), which is analogous to the LSD:

$$\text{MSD} = Q_{p(a,\text{df}_{within})} \sqrt{\frac{1}{2}\left(\frac{1}{r_i} + \frac{1}{r_j}\right) \text{MS}_{within}}$$

Values of Q, the studentised range statistic, may be obtained from Appendix 10.4. The subscript p refers to the required probability level, normally $p = 0.05$; the required number of degrees of freedom is a, the total number of treatments or group means and the number of degrees of freedom associated with the MS_{within} or MS_{error} term from the original ANOVA table.

Mean comparison tests for unequal samples sizes

Both the LSD and Tukey–Kramer method perform best if the sample sizes are equal, i.e. the same number of observations are used to calculate each treatment mean. If sample sizes are unequal, Scheffé's method may be used. This procedure also allows confidence limits to be set around groups of means. Suppose the investigator is interested in assessing whether the treatment mean $\bar{x}_1$ differs significantly from the average of the treatment means $\bar{x}_2$ and $\bar{x}_3$. This is equivalent to asking whether $\bar{x}_1 - \frac{1}{2}(\bar{x}_2 + \bar{x}_3) = 0$. Scheffé's procedure allows a confidence interval about this difference to be calculated; if 0 is contained in the interval then $\bar{x}_1$ does not differ significantly from the average of the other two treatment means. The comparison or contrast, $\bar{x}_1 - \frac{1}{2}(\bar{x}_2 + \bar{x}_3)$, may be described in more general terms as

$$c_1\bar{x}_1 + (c_2\bar{x}_2 + c_3\bar{x}_3)$$

where $c_1 = 1$, $c_2 = c_3 = -1/2$. Note that because c_2 and c_3 are negative, the two terms in the expression are added. Any contrast, including the comparison between two means (when $c_1 = 1$ and $c_2 = -1$), can be represented in this way; note that c-values must sum to zero. Expressing contrasts in this way, the general form of Scheffé's procedure is given by

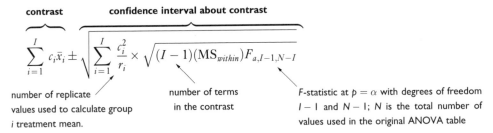

If only two means are being compared, the formula reduces to

$$\bar{x}_1 - \bar{x}_2 \pm \sqrt{\frac{1}{r_1} + \frac{1}{r_2}} \times \sqrt{\text{MS}_{within} \times F_{a,1,N-1}}$$

number of replicates in samples 1 and 2

10.2.3 Assumptions of ANOVA

Samples should be randomly selected and normally distributed   As with any statistical test, reliable inferences can only be made if the samples are representative, i.e. random. Data values should be normally distributed; in the majority of cases this may be achieved by appropriate data transformation (Section 10.2.4). However, ANOVA is considerably more tolerant of departures from normality than commonly supposed. Green (1979) argues that non-normally distributed data is often best analysed using ANOVA rather than the alternative non-parametric procedures, which are considerably less sensitive.

Errors are independent and normally distributed   The error associated with data values should not vary systematically between samples and should be normally distributed. The distribution of errors is most easily assessed by the inspection of residuals. The residuals, the differences between data values and the treatment or group mean $(x - \bar{x})$, are a measure of the error or goodness of fit of the model. If the errors are normally distributed, the residuals will be normally distributed. Most computer programs allow residuals to be stored and plotted to test for a normal distribution. Plotting residual values against data values or an ordered sequence allows systematic variations in errors to be identified. If either problem is identified, it can often be solved by appropriate data transformation (Section 10.2.4).

Homogeneity (equality) of group or treatment variance   Homogeneity of variance is the most important assumption and should always be tested. The simplest test for homogeneity of variances is Hartley's F_{max} test:

$$F_{max} = \frac{S^2_{max}}{S^2_{min}}$$

highest treatment group sample variance

lowest treatment group sample variance

In this case F_{max} has degrees of freedom equal to a, the number of treatment means, and $r - 1$, the degrees of freedom associated with each sample. If the sample sizes (i.e. r-values) are unequal, the degrees of freedom associated with the smallest samples should be used. Critical values are given in Appendix 10.5.

The data contains no outliers   The presence of extreme, unusual values can frequently distort the analysis and therefore should be removed from the data set If a data point is classified as an outlier, the value is considered so unusual that it is not reasonable to assume it belongs to the same distribution as the remaining data values. Outliers can be identified from inspection of residuals or Dixon's Q-test may be used for small samples $(n < 25)$. For very small data sets $(n \leq 7)$ the test statistic is simply the difference between the suspected outlier and the nearest value to it, divided by the difference between the largest and smallest values:

$$Q = \frac{|\text{suspected outlier} - \text{nearest value}|}{\text{largest value} - \text{smallest value}}$$

where $|\ |$ indicates the absolute value. For larger samples sizes, the values need to be ranked $x_1, x_2, x_3, x_4, \ldots, x_n$, with the suspected outlier assigned x_1 regardless of whether it is the largest or smallest value. The appropriate formula in Appendix 10.6 is then applied. Critical values for assessing the significance of Q are also given in Appendix 10.6. Dixon's Q-test should only be applied to normally distributed data sets.

10.2.4 Transformations

Data transformations are frequently required to normalise data, to stabilise variance or to remove systematic variation in residuals. The variance may need to be stabilised if the sample variance depends on the mean; stabilisation removes this dependency. Some of the most useful transformations are outlined below.

Arcsine transformation

Proportions and percentage data should be arcsine transformed $(x \rightarrow \arcsin\sqrt{x})$. This extends the range of x, overcoming the problems caused by the truncated scale of proportion and percentage values (i.e. 0 to 1.0 and 0 to 100). The transformation can only be applied to proportions, i.e. values between 0 and 1.0; percentage values must be divided by 100. By hand the transformation is done in two stages: take the square root of x, then find arcsine of $\sqrt{x}$. On most calculators the arcsine key is marked $\sin^{-1}$. Back transformation is achieved by taking the sine of the value and then squaring it. It is not appropriate to arcsine transform ratios unless their range is constrained. In most cases a logarithmic transformation should be applied to ratios.

Log-ratio transformation

Percentage and proportional values may be affected by *closure*, where changes in the value of one variable cause changes in a second. Consider three variables A, B and C expressed as percentages of a common total:

$$\% A = A/(A + B + C) \times 100$$

$$\% B = B/(A + B + C) \times 100$$

$$\% C = C/(A + B + C) \times 100$$

The three variables are linked by the common total $(A + B + C)$. If A increases, the values of $\%B$ and $\%C$ will decrease even if the absolute values of B and C remain unchanged. Variables expressed as proportions or percentages are frequently not independent. Closure will be most marked where the number of variables contributing to the common total is small. This problem may be solved by using the log-ratio transformation:

$$x'_{ij} = \log\left(\frac{x_{ij}}{g_i}\right)$$

where x_{ij} = proportion of variable j in the ith sample
x'_{ij} = transformed value
$g_i = 1/n \sum_{k=1}^{n} \log x_{ik}$ = geometric mean
n = the number of variables in the data set

The number of variables in the data set is the number of variables which contribute to the total used to calculate the proportional values.

This transformation is often appropriate for community data sets where species abundance values are expressed on a percentage basis. In such cases n equals the number of species present in the data set, and i refers to a specific sample or site.

Logarithmic transformation

Logarithmic transformations $(x \rightarrow \log_{10} x$ or $x \rightarrow \ln x)$ are often appropriate when the sample variance is greater than the mean. They are frequently used for population data. The log transformation reduces the size of large values relative to small values, but it conserves their rates of change. For example, consider the sequence 2, 4, 8, 16, 32. As each number is doubled, the absolute difference between successive numbers increases. When expressed as logs to base 10, the sequence becomes 0.301 03, 0.602 06, 0.903 09, 1.204 12 and 1.505 15, and the difference between successive numbers becomes constant at 0.301 03. Log transformations may also be used to linearise relationships between variables.

Table 10.3 The ladder of powers

Power	Transformation	Formula
3	cube	$x \rightarrow x^3$
2	square	$x \rightarrow x^2$
1	raw data	$x \rightarrow x$
0.5	square root	$x \rightarrow \sqrt{x}$
0	logarithm	$x \rightarrow \log_{10} x$
−0.5	reciprocal root	$x \rightarrow 1/\sqrt{x}$
−1	reciprocal	$x \rightarrow 1/x$
−2	reciprocal square	$x \rightarrow 1/x^2$

The exponential function $y = a\,e^{cx}$ is linearised by taking logs of the y-variable to give a straight-line equation with intercept $\ln a$ and slope c, i.e. $\ln y = \ln a + cx$. If x and y are related by an allometric or power function, $y = ax^b$, then this non-linear relationship can be linearised by taking the logarithms of both x and y, giving the linear equations $\ln y = \ln a + b \ln x$. If the data contains zero values, the required transformation is $x \rightarrow \log_{10}(x + c)$ or $x \rightarrow \ln(x + c)$, where c is a small positive value, normally 1. Back transformations are achieved by taking the antilog and, if appropriate, subtracting c.

Square root transformation
The square root transformation $(x \rightarrow \sqrt{x})$ is appropriate when the sample variance and mean are approximately equal. Taking the square root of x decreases the size of large values relative to small values and will frequently linearise non-linear relationships. It is often used for count data, e.g. counts of individual animals or bacteria in a sample. It is particularly useful if the values follow a Poisson distribution, especially for small samples ($n < 20$), when the data is likely to be very skewed. If the data set contains zero values, the required transformation is $x \rightarrow \sqrt{x + 0.5}$. Back transformation is achieved by squaring values and, if appropriate, subtracting 0.5.

The ladder of powers
The logarithmic and square root transformations can both be viewed as taking a power of x. They are part of a series of possible transformations that have general form $x \rightarrow x^p$. This series is known as the ladder of powers (Table 10.3). The effect of the transformation becomes more extreme as the selected power moves further away from 1 in the negative direction or the positive direction.

Taylor's power law transformation
Taylor's power law and its application to the analysis of pattern are described in Chapter 4. It can also used be to select the power (p) for the transformation $x \rightarrow x^p$ that will stabilise variance. The relationship between the sample variance and the sample mean is given by the straight-line equation $\log_{10} S^2 = a + b \log_{10} \bar{x}$. Sample means and variances are calculated, then $\log_{10}$ (sample variance) is plotted on the y-axis and $\log_{10}$ (sample mean) is plotted on the x-axis. The slope of the plot (b) is estimated using linear regression (Section 10.3) and the required power is then calculated as $p = 1 - b/2$. The calculated power may be used directly, or the nearest power selected from the ladder of powers. The method works best

when there are at least six samples and requires that the log variances and sample means should be linearly related.

10.2.5 Extension of one-way ANOVA

The basic model of one-way ANOVA can be extended to include several factors, each of which may contribute to the overall variance of the data. Because of this, ANOVA is an extensively used and important general method of data analysis. Advanced applications of the procedure make it possible to investigate complex experimental designs and models of factor interaction. However, in each case the basic assumptions and the principles of the method remain the same. The total variance of the data set, as measured by SS_{total}, is partitioned between the various factors included in the model. The significance of each factor is then assessed by calculating appropriate MS ratios. Where more than one factor is included in the analysis, three new issues need to be considered: sample size, the nature of the treatment factors and the possibility of interactions between factors.

Equal size   Group or treatment samples should be of equal size, i.e. the analysis should be balanced. Although one-way ANOVA may be performed on data with unequal sample sizes, and although advanced methods exist which are capable of dealing with missing values, unbalanced data sets are best avoided. ANOVA, including one-way ANOVA, is best performed on balanced data sets. Balanced data makes the method more robust, the analysis easier to perform and the results much easier to interpret.

Random versus fixed   The investigator must distinguish between random and fixed effects. This is important as the choice determines how the F-ratios should be calculated. Typically in designed experiments, such as the growth experiment of Section 10.2.1, treatment levels can be considered as a random sample from a population of all possible treatment levels. The results of the experiment are viewed as providing information on the general response; in the plant growth experiment it is the general response of plant growth to salinity, not just to the specific treatment levels applied. The treatment factor can be considered as a random-effect factor, and the selection of treatment levels allows general inferences to be made about the effects of the factor.

Fixed-effect factors frequently occur in observational studies. Consider a study in which the density of a species was determined from samples taken at four distinct woodlands. The woods may have been selected because the species was known to occur at each one, or because they were convenient to visit, or because each differed in a particular way that interested the investigator. The selected woodland sites cannot be considered a random sample of all available woodland sites. In this case the sample sites, the woods, should be considered as a fixed-effect factor. Inferences drawn from the analysis will relate specifically to the sampled woods. Where fixed-effect factors are involved, care must be taken when interpreting the results. Any generalisation should be supported by additional reasoning and evidence, not simply based on an explicit or implicit extrapolation of results from a fixed-effect ANOVA.

Factor interactions   Consider an experiment involving two factors, A and B. The values for the treatment group means will depend on the effects of A and B. If there is no interaction, the combined effect of A and B will be equal to the effect of A on its own plus the effect of B on its own – the sum of their individual effects. If the factors interact, the combined effect of A and B will be greater or smaller than the sum of their individual effects (Figure 10.1). Analysis of variance makes it possible to determine the occurrence and significance of factor interactions.

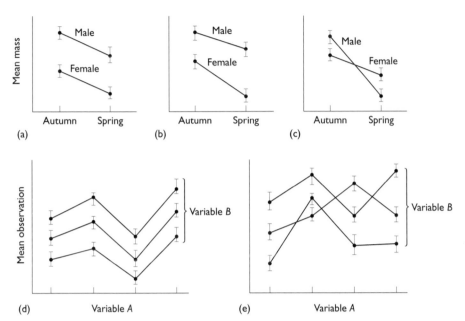

Figure 10.1 (a, b, c) Mean masses of samples of male and female animals weighed in autumn and spring: (a) no interaction, (b) positive interaction, (c) negative interaction. (d, e) Interaction effects between variables: (a) no interaction, (b) interaction. All confidence intervals are hypothetical. Reprinted, with permission, from Fowler and Cohen (1990).

Two-way ANOVA

In a two-way ANOVA the model used to partition SS is extended to included two factors, A and B, and their interaction:

$$\text{SS}_{total} = \underbrace{\text{SS}_A + \text{SS}_B + \text{SS}_{AB}}_{} + \text{SS}_{within}$$

the sum of these three terms corresponds to $\text{SS}_{between}$

Although it is possible to perform two-way ANOVA by hand, in practice it is best performed using a computer package. Some packages will automatically calculate the MS ratios assuming that all factors are random-effect factors, some allow you to specify the nature of each factor, and some produce a basic ANOVA but leave the calculation of F-ratios to the investigator, when the following rules should be applied:

- Both factors are fixed-effect factors

  MS_{within} (i.e. MS_{error}) should be used as the denominator when calculating F-ratio values to test the significance of all effects.

- Both factors are random-effect factors

  (i) MS_{within} (i.e. MS_{error}) should be used as the denominator when calculating the F-ratio value to test the significance of the interaction term.

  (ii) MS_{AB} should be used as the denominator to calculate the F-ratio values used to test the main effects, i.e. the two individual factors A and B, for significance.

- One factor fixed, the other a random-effect factor

  (i) The significance of the interaction and the random-effects factor should be tested using MS_{within} (i.e. MS_{error}) as the denominator when calculating F-ratio values.

  (ii) MS_{AB} should be used as the denominator when calculating the F-ratio value to test the significance of the fixed-effect factor.

As an example of two-way ANOVA, suppose that the seeds used in the simple plant growth experiment (Section 10.2.1) were collected from two different sites. The experimental design now incorporates two factors: the original factor of salinity treatment level and the new factor of seed source. The seed source could be considered as a random-effect factor or a fixed-effect factor. If the seeds were simply collected from two convenient salt marshes, the seed source should be considered as a fixed-effect factor. The results of the analysis would enable the investigator to say whether there were differences in the responses of plants derived from seeds obtained on the two salt marshes. However, if the sites of seed collection were selected at random from the upper and lower parts of the same marsh, it is possible to consider seed source as a random-effect factor.

Suppose a stratified random sampling scheme had been applied (Chapter 1) with the upper and lower parts of the marsh representing different strata, and each sampled randomly. The seed source could then be treated as a random-effect factor and the investigator might draw inferences on how the plants' response to salinity varies within the lower and upper salt-marsh populations. The strength with which such inferences are made would depend on whether the seed samples were replicated, how homogeneous were the upper and lower parts of the marsh, and whether the study site could legitimately be considered a representative salt marsh. In the present case, let's assume the seed sources come from two distinct but similar salt marshes. The data set thus consists of five replicated measures of growth response for two sources (sites) of seed at each of four salinity levels. Below is the output from MINITAB using the **Two-way** command selected from the **ANOVA** option in the **Stat** menu. As with most statistical computer packages, note how the ANOVA data has to be entered in 'stacked' form as a number of columns. One column contains the response variable, i.e. *all* the measured or recorded observations; a second column codes for the level of the first factor (normally 1, 2, 3, etc.), a code being entered for each data value; and a third column codes for the level of the second factor.

response variable　　　　coding values for factors 1 to *n* placed in columns C2 to C*n* + 1

C1	C2	C3	$\cdots$	C*n* + 1
⋮	⋮	⋮		
7.8	1	2		
⋮	⋮	⋮		

Assuming a two-way ANOVA, then 7.8 is an observation from the group subject to level 1 for the first factor and level 2 for the second. Replicates will have the same coding.

The options to generate means and graphs can be selected; additional options are available, e.g. storing and plotting residuals.

Two-way Analysis of Variance

Analysis of variance for Plant Growth

Source	DF	SS	MS
Salinity	3	3095.15	1031.72
Site	1	17.49	17.49
Interactions	3	231.95	77.32
Error	32	80.94	2.53
Total	39	3425.53	

Salinity was treated as a random-effect factor and site as a fixed-effect factor. Applying the rules for calculating *F*-ratios, given earlier, we arrive at Table 10.4.

Table 10.4 Calculating the *F*-ratios

Source	F-ratio calculation	F-ratio value	Significance
Salinity (random-effect factor)	$\mathrm{MS}_{salinity}/\mathrm{MS}_{error} = \dfrac{1031.72}{2.53}$	407.79 (d.f. = 3, 32)	$p < 0.001^{***}$
Interaction (salinity × site)	$\mathrm{MS}_{interaction}/\mathrm{MS}_{error} = \dfrac{77.32}{2.53}$	30.56 (d.f. = 3, 32)	$p < 0.001^{***}$
Site (fixed-effect factor)	$\mathrm{MS}_{site}/\mathrm{MS}_{interaction} = \dfrac{17.49}{77}$	0.227 (d.f. = 1, 3)	$p > 0.05$ NS

This analysis confirms the results obtained from the one-way ANOVA. For each population of seeds, plant growth is significantly affected by salinity; but although the interaction term is significant, overall differences between the two seed sources are not significant. If group means for each seed source are plotted against salinity level (Figure 10.2) an explanation for the results becomes clear. The graph shows that the general response to salinity is very similar for plants from both seed sources. But at low salinities, site 1 seedlings perform better than site 2 seedlings; and at high salinities, site 1 plants do not grow as well as site 2 plants.

If seed source had been treated as a random-effect factor, the *F*-ratio associated with the site would be significant as shown below. This illustrates the importance of distinguishing between random and fixed effect factors.

$$\frac{\mathrm{MS}_{site}}{\mathrm{MS}_{error}} \qquad \frac{17.49}{2.53} \qquad \begin{array}{c} F = 6.913 \\ (\mathrm{d.f.} = 1, 32) \end{array} \qquad \begin{array}{c} p < 0.05 \\ * \end{array}$$

Means are compared by applying the same procedures as described for one-way ANOVA.

Two-way ANOVA without replication
It is possible to perform a two-way ANOVA on unreplicated data values. Using the example above and assuming that sites 1 and 2 were randomly selected from the upper and lower portions of the same salt marsh, the table of plant growth responses might look like Table 10.5. Each treatment group and site combination is represented by a single, unreplicated value. The data can be analysed using ANOVA. This is possible because, under the null

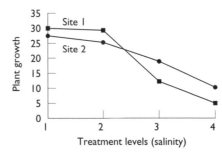

Figure 10.2 Variable interaction: the effects of salinity on plant growth measured as grams of dried biomass. The plants were derived from two seed sources, site 1 and site 2. Further details are given in the text.

Table 10.5 Plant growth responses in the salinity experiment

Site (source of seed)	Treatment group level (salt concentration)			
	1	2	3	4
1	27.25	25.486	19.03	10.21
2	30.458	29.295	12.109	4.943

hypothesis, the grand mean and the means and variances associated with each site and each salinity treatment should be equal. Thus, during the calculation, each value can be used to estimate the variance associated with both factors. That is, the sum of squares may be calculated by working across and down the table. SS_{total} may then be partitioned between SS_{site} and $SS_{treatment}$, all three of which can be calculated directly from the data. Since $SS_{total} = SS_{site} + SS_{treatment} + SS_{within}$, the error term SS_{within} can then be calculated as $SS_{within} = SS_{total} - (SS_{site} + SS_{treatment})$. However, because of the lack of replication, it is not possible to estimate a sum of squares for the interaction term. So without replication it is not possible to test for the occurrence of interactions. Using the data above, the MINITAB **Two-way** command gives the following output:

Two-way Analysis of Variance

```
Analysis of Variance for Plant Growth
Source          DF      SS          MS
Salinity        3       619.0       206.3
Site            1         3.5         3.5
Error           3        46.4        15.5
Total           7       669.9
```

Using the MINITAB results to calculate the F-ratios gives

Salinity 206.3/15.5 = 13.30   with d.f. = 3, 3 $p < 0.05$ significant at 5% level
Site   3.5/15.5   = 0.225   with d.f. = 1, 3 $p > 0.05$ not significant

Since $SS_{interaction}$ cannot be calculated, the implicit assumption is that the factors are random-effect factors.

Although it is always wise to incorporate replication in sampling schemes and experimental designs, the ability of two-way ANOVA to analyse unreplicated data sets illustrates the robust nature and efficiency of the procedure. As long as the basic assumptions are not violated, ANOVA can perform efficient analyses on data sets containing small sample sizes. The generalised ANOVA may be extended to analyse more complex designs with three or more factors (multi-way ANOVA). Multi-way ANOVA can be readily conducted using most statistical packages, but the design and analysis of the multifactorial experiments need to be planned carefully.

10.2.6 Procedures for ANOVA with replication

1. Test for normality of data set (Chapter 1 and Box 7.3).

   ● Transform the data if necessary (Section 10.2.4).

2. For each factor level, group or combination of factor levels, calculate the sample mean and variance. Test for homogeneity of variance using Hartley's F_{max} test (Section 10.2.3).

- If the variance is not homogeneous, transform the data. If it varies with the mean, consider using a transformation based on Taylor's power law (Section 10.2.4).

One-way ANOVA:

- Perform one-way ANOVA; store the residuals when using a computer package.

Two-way ANOVA:

- Classify factors as random-effect factors or fixed-effect factors.
- Perform two-way ANOVA; store the residuals when using a computer package.
- Calculate the appropriate F-ratios using the rules given in Section 10.2.5.

If residuals are stored:

- Test residuals for normality; if they are not normally distributed, re-examine the data carefully for non-normality and non-homogeneity of variance. Transform the data and repeat the analysis.
- Examine the residuals for unusual values, i.e. outliers. Test for outliers using Dixon's test (Section 10.2.3) and, if justified, remove them from the data set. If a two-way ANOVA is to be performed, the data set must be balanced, i.e. sample sizes must be equal. If outliers are removed, other data points may need to be removed to maintain equal sample sizes. These other data points should be selected at random.

3. Test for comparison of means (Section 10.2.2).

- Following the recommendations of Kleinbaum *et al.* (1998), select the tests using the flow diagram on p. 355.

Before conducting pairwise comparisons, consider why they are needed. Unless there are particular reasons for wishing to know whether individual group means differ, a plot of means with standard errors is often sufficient. What is important is whether the initial ANOVA results are significant. The fact that the means are not homogeneous, i.e. the effect factor in the ANOVA model is significant, is frequently more important than whether two particular means differ significantly. For example, in a study on the impact of simulated herbivory on plant seed production, it would be important to know whether herbivory affects seed output, and the relative impact of low and high herbivory on seed production. Whether the effects of two particular experimental levels of simulated herbivory differ significantly is likely to be less important.

In many studies the underlining processes are essentially continuous. For example, it is reasonable to assume that although there may be a threshold level of herbivory required before any effect on seed production is observed, once this threshold level has been reached, the effects of herbivory are progressive. As herbivory increases, we would expect seed production to respond in a continuous manner, not in a series of discrete jumps. Similarly, it is reasonable to assume that the growth rate of fledgling birds varies in a continuous manner with the amount of food supplied to the nest. The nature of ANOVA and the underlying experimental design tend to focus attention on a limited number of mean values which represent only a small (but we hope representative) sample of the whole process. Regression analysis (Section 10.3) may sometimes be more appropriate, particularly where the continuous nature of the process is clear, e.g. in ecological analogues of dose–response studies.

10.3 *Regression analysis*

10.3.1 *Introduction*

Linear regression

Linear regression is closely related to correlation analysis (Chapter 7). Correlation provides a measure of the strength of association between two variables (x, y), linear regression extends this analysis to find the best-fit line relating x to y. In least squares regression, the procedure described in this chapter, the fitted line pivots about the plotted point corresponding to the mean of x and y (i.e. $\bar{x}, \bar{y}$). The slope is chosen so that the sum-of-squares distance between each data point and the fitted line is minimised, hence the name least squares regression. As in ANOVA these distances correspond to residuals or error values (Figure 10.3).

Calculations

Manual calculation may be divided into two stages. The first stage is to calculate the Pearson product-moment correlation coefficient, and the second stage is to calculate the intercept and slope of the best-fit line. The data consists of paired values of x and y.

Calculating the correlation coefficient

1. Calculate the sample standard deviation for both x and y, i.e. S_x, S_y.
2. Calculate the covariance between x and y:

$$C_{xy} = \frac{1}{n-1} \sum_{i=1}^{n} (x_i - \bar{x})(y_i - \bar{y})$$

Remember to use the formula:

$$\sum_{i=1}^{n} x_i y_i - \frac{1}{n} \sum_{i=1}^{n} x_i \sum_{i=1}^{n} y_i$$

where n is the number of x, y pairs, can be used to calculate $\sum (x_i - \bar{x})(y_i - \bar{y})$.

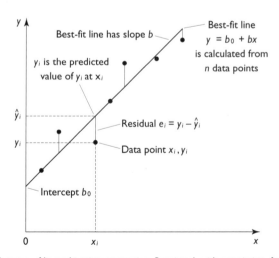

Figure 10.3 The key features of linear bivariate regression. Reprinted, with permission, from Fry (1993).

3. Calculate the correlation coefficient:

$$r = \frac{C_{xy}}{S_x S_y}$$

r has $n - 2$ degrees of freedom and its significance may be obtained from Appendix 10.7.

Calculating the fitted line

The equation of a straight line is y-value $=$ (intercept on x-axis) $+$ (slope of the line) $\times$ (x-value) or, more formally, $y = \beta_0 + \beta_1 x$.

- Slope can be calculated in two ways:

$$\beta_1 = C_{xy}/S_x^2 \quad \text{or} \quad \beta_1 = r(S_y/S_x)$$

- The intercept is obtained by substituting for $\bar{y}$, β_1, $\bar{x}$ in the equation for a straight line:

$$\beta_0 = \bar{y} - \beta_1 \bar{x}$$

Relationship between regression and ANOVA

The results of regression analysis may be presented in the form of a standard ANOVA table, allowing the F-statistic to be calculated (Table 10.6). The total sum of squares (SS_{total}) is partitioned between the amount explained by the fitted linear model ($SS_{regression}$ or SSR), equivalent to $SS_{between}$ and the residual or error sum of squares (SS_{error}), equivalent to SS_{within}. SS_{error} is obtained by summing and squaring the residuals, i.e. the difference between observed values of y and predicted values based on the fitted line.

If performing a regression ANOVA by hand, the following procedure can be used:

1. Calculate SSR

$$SSR = \frac{(\text{sum of products})^2}{\text{sum of squares of } x}$$

where

$$\text{Sum of products } (SS_{xy}) = \sum_{i=1}^{n} (x_i - \bar{x})(y_i - \bar{y}) = \sum_{i=1}^{n} x_i y_i - \frac{1}{n} \sum_{i=1}^{n} x_i \sum_{i=1}^{n} y_i$$

$$\text{Sum of squares of } x \ (SS_x) = \sum_{i=1}^{n} x_i^2 - \frac{1}{n} \left(\sum_{i=1}^{n} x_i \right)^2$$

SSR always has d.f. $= 1$.

Table 10.6 A standard ANOVA table for regression analysis

Source of variance	d.f.	SS	MS	F-ratio
Regression	1	$SSR = SS_{total} - SS_{error}$	$MSR = SSR/1 = SSR$	MSR/MSE
Error (i.e. residual)	$n - 2$	$SS_{error} = \sum_{i=1}^{n} (y_i - (\beta_0 + \beta_1 x_i))^2$	$MSE = SS_{error}/(n - 2)$	
Total	$n - 1$	$SS_{total} = \sum_{i=1}^{n} (y_i - \bar{y})^2$		

2. Calculate MSE:

$$MSE = \frac{1}{n-2}((\text{sum of squares of } y) - SSR)$$

where

$$\text{Sum of squares of } y \ (SS_y) = \sum_{i=1}^{n} y_i^2 - \frac{1}{n}\left(\sum_{i=1}^{n} y_i\right)^2$$

MSE always has d.f. $= n - 2$.

3. Calculate the *F*-value:

$$F = \frac{MSR}{MSE}$$

F always has d.f. $= 1, n - 2$.

If *F* exceeds the tabulated values for $p = 0.05$ with d.f. $= 1, n - 2$ then reject the null hypothesis that the variables are *not* linearly related and accept the alternative hypothesis that the relationship between *x* and *y* is modelled by the regression equation. The *F*-statistic thus provides a test for assessing the overall goodness of fit of the regression model.

10.3.2 Assumptions of linear regression

Linear regression makes several assumptions:

- The two variables *x* and *y* are linearly related and measured for each of the *n* observations.
- The independent variable *x* is measured without error.
- The errors associated with *y* are normally distributed and mutually independent.
- The variance of *y* is constant, i.e. it does not vary with *x*.

The requirement that measurements of *x* should be error-free is difficult if not impossible to achieve. The assumption will most closely be met by planned experiments where the different values of *x* are related to particular treatment levels or where *x* is an easily measured variable, e.g. age or sample distance from a fixed point. The importance of violating this assumption depends on the aim of the analysis. Where the primary aim is to predict unknown *y*-values from the fitted equation, every effort should be made to conform to the assumption. Often this is not case; the investigator simply wishes to show that the two variables are related and that the relationship is linear. In many studies the reason for fitting a regression is not obvious or warranted; the calculation of a correlation coefficient and a simple plot of *x* against *y* would be sufficient. In practice the investigator should try to ensure that measurement errors associated with variable *x* are minimised and smaller than those associated with *y*; they should also ensure that the values of *x* are evenly spread along the axis. If the distribution of values is noticeably skewed, the data should be transformed (Section 10.2.4).

Normality of error terms is only required if significance tests are to be made or fitted lines are to be compared. The errors do not need to be normally distributed to calculate the best-fit line or to predict values of *y* from this line (Fry, 1993). As with ANOVA, departures from these assumptions are most easily detected by inspecting the residuals, routinely generated by the vast majority of computer packages which support linear regression (Figure 10.4).

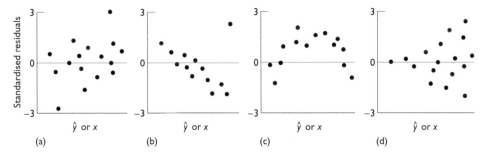

Figure 10.4 Residual patterns and the problems they indicate: (a) extreme outliers, (b) poorly fitted slope due to one extreme outlier, (c) non-linear data, (d) non-constant variance. Reprinted, with permission, from Fry (1993).

10.3.3 Confidence limits

Confidence limits about each coefficient, i.e. the slope and intercept, may be easily established (Section 10.3.4). Standard errors are needed to estimate the confidence zone about the fitted regression line, to establish confidence limits about an individual predicted y-value and to test for significant differences between regression slopes.

Establishing a zone of confidence about the fitted line   The confidence limits about the line are not constant, being wider at each end. A zone of confidence may be plotted about the line by calculating the 95% confidence limits for a range of x-values. The limits about the fitted line at point x' are given by

$$\pm t_{p(n-2)} \sqrt{S_r^2 \left(\frac{1}{n} + \frac{(x' - \bar{x})^2}{SS_x} \right)}$$

appropriate t-value (d.f. $= n - 2$)   term enclosed by the square root sign is the standard error of a point y' on the regression line corresponding to x'

where S_r^2 is the residual variance; it is the same as MSE.

Establishing confidence limits about predicted values of y for individual values of x   The limits about the individual predicted value y' are given by

$$\pm t_{p(n-2)} \sqrt{S_r^2 \left(1 + \frac{1}{n} + \frac{(x' - \bar{x})^2}{SS_x} \right)}$$

residual variance   inclusion of 1 increases the width of the interval, reflecting the additional source of error, i.e. the scatter of points about the regression line

where S_r^2 is the residual variance; it is the same as MSE.

Testing for significance between two regression slopes β_1 and β_2
Calculate the standard error (SE_β) for each slope:

$$SE_\beta = \sqrt{\frac{S_r^2}{SS_x}}$$

The standard error of the difference between the slopes:

$$SE_{\beta_1 - \beta_2} = \sqrt{SE_{\beta_1}^2 + SE_{\beta_2}^2}$$

Estimate the *t*-test statistic:

$$t = \frac{\beta_1 - \beta_2}{\mathrm{SE}_{\beta_1 - \beta_2}}$$

t has $(n_1 - 2) + (n_2 - 2)$ degrees of freedom.

10.3.4 Complications and extension of the method

Regression through the origin

In some circumstances, e.g. calibration curves, it is appropriate that the fitted line should be constrained to pass through the origin. Then the equation for the line is $y = \beta_0 x$ and the slope is given by $\beta_0 = \sum xy / \sum x^2$.

Reduced major axis regression

Linear regression assumes that *x* is not a random variable. Where this is clearly not the case, alternative (model 2) methods of regression should be used (Sokal and Rohlf, 1995). Reduced major axis regression is one of the simplest to apply (Fowler *et al.*, 1998). Using this procedure the slope of the fitted line is obtained from the ratio of the variables' standard deviations, i.e. $\beta = S_y / S_x$. The intercept is obtained by solving the equation $\bar{y} = a + \beta \bar{x}$ for *a*. The sign of the slope, whether positive or negative, is determined from the plot of *y* against *x*. The significance of the fitted line can be assessed by analysis of variance. The strength of the correlation between *x* and *y* is obtained by calculating the normal correlation coefficient.

Non-linear relationships

Where the relationship between the two variables is not linear, attempt to linearise the relationship by an appropriate transformation then perform a normal linear regression. If the plotted curve has a 'single bend', a linear relationship may often be obtained by using the transformations described in Section 10.2.4. The single logarithmic transformation ($\log x$) or the double logarithmic transformation ($\log x$, $\log y$) often prove successful. When the relationship has 'two bends', e.g. a sigmoid, the arcsine transformation may prove successful. Otherwise the *logit* or *probit* transformations may be used (see below).

Logit transformation

The logit transformation is derived from the logistic equation which is commonly used to describe the sigmoidal growth curves shown by many populations:

$$\mathrm{logit}(y) = \log_e \left(\frac{y}{1 - y} \right)$$

The logit transformation has been extensively used to analyse dose–response curves, when the proportional mortality of exposed test organisms is plotted against the concentration of the toxicant. Such curves are typically sigmoidal. The proportional mortality is low at the start and increases with dose concentration, often reaching a plateau at 1.0 where the mortality is 100%. Such data sets often suffer from two problems:

Inclusion of imprecise endpoints   The two extreme endpoints, 0 and 100% mortality, can exert an excessive influence on the regression of logit values against concentration. To deal with this problem, the two extreme values, 0 and 1.0, should be rescaled as follows:

Lowest point $0 \rightarrow 1/(2n_1)$

Highest point $1.0 \rightarrow 1 - 1/(2n_1)$

where n_1 is the number of individuals tested at the concentration for which the proportional mortality is being rescaled.

Unequal variance   Some authors advocate the use of weighted regression when applying the logit transformation. The variances at each concentration are not equal. A few moments thought should convince you of this. At the extremes of the concentration range, all the organisms in the test samples will either be alive or dead and the variance in each case will be 0; this does not happen at other concentrations. Since the variation associated with each point is different, the influence of each point on the regression will not be equal. A weighted regression uses a weighting factor (w_i) calculated for each individual value (i) where in this case y is the proportion killed and n_i is the number of organisms used in the test at concentration i:

$$w_i = n_i y_i (1 - y_i)$$

The estimates of the slope β and intercept α are obtained from the normal regression equation, modified to incorporate the weights:

$$\beta = \frac{\sum_{i=1}^{n} w_i y_i (x_i - \bar{x}_w)}{\sum_{i=1}^{n} w_i (x_i - \bar{x}_w)^2} \qquad \alpha = \bar{y}_w + \beta \bar{x}_w$$

where the weighted averages of y and x are given by

$$\bar{x}_w = \frac{\sum_{i=1}^{n} w_i x_i}{\sum_{i=1}^{n} w_i} \qquad \bar{y}_w = \frac{\sum_{i=1}^{n} w_i y_i}{\sum_{i=1}^{n} w_i}$$

To carry out a weighted regression using MINITAB, the weights are first calculated and stored. The subcommand **Weights** is used within the **Regression** command; the column containing the weights and the columns containing the x and y values are specified.

The formula given above for calculating weighting factors is specific to the logit transformation. The general form is $w_i = 1/\text{var}(Y_i)$ The effect of the weighting factors is to reduce the influence of the more variable, hence more unreliable, values on the position of the fitted regression line.

Probit transformation

Probit transformation or probit analysis is based on the cumulative probability curve of the normal distribution density function, which has a sigmoidal shape. Frequently the probits are taken as being normal equivalent deviates with mean 5.0 and standard deviation 1.0. Here are the relevant MINITAB commands:

```
                    ╱ untransformed values stored in column C3
INVCDF C3 C4;  ╲
NORMAL 5 1.        ╲ calculated probits stored in column C4
```

Finney (1971) provides a detailed discussion of probit analysis.

10.3.5 *Species–area relationship*

For a large number of taxonomic groups, empirical studies have shown that species number, i.e. species richness (Chapter 2), increases with the area sampled. In some ways this is not a very surprising result. From a sampling perspective it seems logical that this should be the case; increasing sample size will increase the likelihood of encountering rare species, and thus the number of species recorded will increase. However, what is intriguing is that the same simple equation can be used to describe the relationship for an incredibly diverse range of data sets, including the number of bird and plants species found on true islands of different sizes, breeding bird species in isolated woodlands (habitat islands), number of molluscs in lakes of different sizes, and the number of species recorded in arbitrary areas of mainland. In each case the relationship is described by the power function

$$S = cA^z$$

where S is the number of species, c and z are constants and A is the area of the island or sample. The equation may be linearised by taking logarithms of both sides:

$$\log S = \log c + z \log A$$

Linear regression may now be used to test for the presence of a linear relationship between $\log S$ and $\log A$ and to estimate values of z and $\log c$.

Using data based on the study by Lack (1976) into the number of resident land birds on islands in the Lesser Antilles (Table 10.7) the following results were obtained using MINTAB. Before the analysis, species number and island area were logged and stored as the named columns **Log.Spec** and **LogArea**. Regression is performed by either entering the commands shown below, or by selecting **Regression** from the **Stat** menu options.

```
MTB > Regress      'Log.Spec' 1      'LogArea';
SUBC> Constant.
```

Table 10.7 Number of resident land birds on islands in the Lesser Antilles

Island	Area (km²)	Altitude (m)	Distance from the mainland (km)	Distance to nearest island (km)	Number of species
St Bartholomew	25	300	800	20	12
St Bartholomew	12	860	750	25	18
St Bartholomew	21	600	750	15	18
St Kitts	180	1140	750	3	21
Nevis	130	1100	700	3	19
Barbuda	160	300	800	45	20
Antigua	280	400	700	60	20
Monserrat	100	910	650	35	22
Guadeloupe	1500	1500	600	40	34
Desirade	27	280	600	5	19
Marie Galante	24	300	600	35	14
Dominica	800	1450	550	40	39
Martinique	1100	1340	450	30	38
St Lucia	600	960	350	30	42
St Vincent	350	1240	300	40	35
Bequia	19	300	300	10	19
Carriacou	34	300	200	25	21
Grenada	310	840	150	100	35

Source: Lack (1976)

The 1 refers to the number of variables used in the model equation to explain the observed variation in the 'response' variable y. In this case a simple linear equation is being used, $y = \beta_0 + \beta_1 x$, with one predictor variable x.

```
Regression Analysis
The regression equation is
Log.Spec = 0.927 + 0.205 LogArea
```

fitted equation $\log C = 0.927$ and $z = 0.205$

```
Predictor    Coef      Stdev     t-ratio    p
Constant     0.92739   0.07905   11.73      0.000
LogArea      0.20527   0.03650    5.62      0.000
```

MINITAB only prints p to three decimal places; thus the p values can be taken as <0.001.

The standard deviation (**Stdev**) for the two constants or coefficients allows 95% confidence limits to be calculated about each constant. For $\log C$, $0.927\,39 \pm t_{0.05(n-2)}$ (**Stdev**) $= 0.927\,39 \pm t_{0.05(16)}(0.079\,05) = 0.927\,39 \pm 2.120 \times (0.079\,05)$ giving $0.927\,39 \pm 0.1675$. The t-ratio (**t-ratio**) tests that the coefficients differ from 0. The last column gives the significance of the calculated t-values; in this case both are highly significant as $p \ll 0.05$.

```
s = 0.1018    R-sq = 65.0%    R-sq(adj) = 63.0%
```

Here s is an estimate of the standard deviation of the errors in y, and represents a measure of the overall deviation of values from the regression line; its square corresponds to the residual variance S_r^2.

The coefficient of determination (**R-sq**) is equal to the square of r, the correlation coefficient for the relationship between x and y, thus in many texts it is given as R^2. **R-sq** has a very useful and straightforward interpretation: it is equal to the percentage variation in the data explained by the straight-line equation. In this case 65% of the observed variation in **Log.Spec** is explained by the variation in **LogArea**. Thus the fitted model fails to explain 35% of the variation in **Log.Spec**.

The correlation coefficient (r) may be obtained by taking the square root of **R-sq** expressed as a proportion *not as a percentage*; its significance is assessed in the normal way. In this case $r = \sqrt{0.65} = 0.806$, indicating a strong and significant correlation between species richness and island area.

Values of **R-sq** may be adjusted for the number of predictor variables included in the model equation, giving **R-sq(adj)**. It may be ignored in the case of linear regression, when only one predictor variable is used, but it should be used when undertaking a multiple regression (Section 10.3.6).

```
Analysis of Variance

SOURCE        DF   SS        MS        F        p
Regression    1    0.32775   0.32775   31.62    0.000
Error         17   0.17621   0.01037
Total         18   0.50396
```

This is a standard ANOVA table. The F-value and the associated p-value measure the overall fit of the model. In this case the fitted linear regression model provides a highly significant description of the data. The error mean square gives the variance about the regression line, i.e. the residual variance (S_r^2). Note $\sqrt{MSE} = s$, the standard deviation of the errors in y; $\sqrt{0.010\,37} = 0.101\,83$ which matches the values given above.

```
Unusual Observations
Obs.   LogArea   Log.Spec   Fit      Stdev.Fit   Residual    St.Resid
1      1.93      1.1139     1.3234   0.0239      -0.2095     -2.12R

R denotes an obs. with a large st. resid.
```

MINITAB identifies observations which may be outliers or which may unduly influence the position of the regression line. Observation 1 has been identified because of the size of its residual. Two types of residual are given. The ordinary residual (e_i) is equal to difference between the predicted and observed values of y_i. Standardised residuals (E_i) are obtained by dividing the residual (e_i) by s. That is, $E_i = e_i/\sqrt{\text{MSE}}$. As a result of this scaling, standardised residuals have mean 0, standard deviation 1.0 and they should be normally distributed. Thus, approximately 95% of E_i values should lie between $+2$ and -2. Observations with standardised residuals outside this range should be treated as outliers and consideration should be given to removing them from the data set before repeating the analysis.

If the identified outlier is removed and the analysis repeated, the following output is obtained:

```
The regression equation is

Log.Spec = 0.947 + 0.201 LogArea

Predictor   Coef      Stdev     t-ratio    p
Constant    0.94727   0.07041   13.45      0.000
LogArea     0.20130   0.03233    6.23      0.000

s = 0.09005   R-sq = 70.8%   R-sq(adj) = 69.0%
```

Note that the basic relationship remains the same. The value of the two constants, the intercept and the slope have changed only very slightly.

```
Analysis of Variance
SOURCE       DF   SS        MS        F        p
Regression    1   0.31436   0.31436   38.76    0.000
Error        16   0.12976   0.00811
Total        17   0.44412
```

R-sq has increased from 65% to 70.8%. Similarly the *F*-value in the ANOVA table has increased. These changes imply that the removal of the outlier has improved the description of the remaining data provided by the linear model.

This analysis suggests that the diversity of land birds on islands in the Lesser Antilles is related to the size of the island, and that the relationship conforms to $S = cA^z$, where $z = 0.201$, $\log c = 0.947$ and $c = 8.8$. Reported values of z vary. For arbitrary areas of mainland, typical z-values are low, around 0.15. For true oceanic islands, z ranges from about 0.2 to about 0.37. A value of 0.3 has been suggested as an average value (Wilson and Bossert, 1971). For habitat islands, z-values are considerably more variable; Begon *et al.* (1996) cite values ranging from 0.17 to 0.72. Various explanations for the relationship have been proposed.

MacArthur and Wilson (1967) suggested that the number of species on an island is determined by the balance between the rate of species immigration and the rate of species local extinction. Their theory proposed that small islands would have low species diversity due to low immigration rates combined with high local extinction rates. Large islands are able to sustain high species diversity because they have high immigration rates and low species extinction rates. Because of their size, large islands are more likely to be encountered by potential colonists and might be expected to provide a greater range of habitats for species to exploit, reducing the likelihood of species extinction. The effects of other factors, such as remoteness and the diversity of the potential species pool (i.e. species present on the source area, mainland), can be incorporated into the model through their effects on the rates of immigration and extinction.

Alternative explanations have been given, notably by May (1975), who suggests the relationship is a mathematical consequence of the lognormal distribution of species in a community and the size of the sample taken (Chapter 2). May (1975) suggested that a *z*-value of approximately 0.25 would be expected where species follow the lognormal distribution. More recently it has been shown that a range of *z*-values can be consistent with the lognormal distribution of species and the failure to completely sample the community (Wright, 1988). However, Ricklefs (1990) points out that the characteristics of the lognormal distribution cannot provide an explanation for all data sets which conform to the relationship. In many cases the species richness of a given taxon in an area is known with complete certainty; no additional species remain to be revealed with increasing samples or island size.

Whatever the explanation, the relationship does appears to be generally applicable and can be treated as a useful empirical relationship, allowing informed decisions to made on appropriate samples sizes (Chapter 1) and providing initial approximate estimates of the diversity supported by a given area.

10.3.6 *Multiple regression*

The simple linear regression model can be extended to include more than one independent variable:

$$y = \beta_0 + \beta_1 x_1 + \beta_2 x_2 + \cdots + \beta_n x_n$$

The ability to include more that one explanatory variable is extremely useful, allowing the relative importance of variables to be assessed. Where more that one independent variable is included, the model-fitting procedure is called multiple regression. Some texts treat multiple regression as a form of multivariate analysis (Chapters 8 and 9), but since there is only one dependent variable, it is best viewed as a univariate method (Manly, 1994). The assumptions behind multiple regression are the same as behind linear regression, but with the additional requirements that the explanatory variables should not be strongly correlated with each other, and each should be linearly related to the dependent variable. Adherence to these assumptions is most easily assessed by (i) plotting *y* against each of the explanatory variables to check for a linear relationship, and (ii) examining the correlation between all possible pairs of explanatory variables. Where two or more explanatory variables are strongly correlated, i.e. demonstrate the problem of *colinearity*, it becomes difficult to determine and interpret the partial regression coefficients (β_i). The simplest solution to this problem is to remove the surplus correlated variables so that only one is included in the regression model.

Using the data in Table 10.7, the following results were obtained using MINITAB to perform a multiple regression. The logarithm of species number (**Log.Spec**) was selected as the dependent variable and four explanatory variables were included in the model: **Altitude** is the height (m) of the highest land on the island; **Distance** is the distance (km) from the mainland; **LogArea** is the logarithm of the island's area (km^2); **Dist.Isl** is the distance (km) to the nearest island.

```
Regression Analysis

The regression equation is
Log.Spec = 1.21 +0.000147 Altitude -0.000333 Distance +0.000493 Dist.Isl
+0.101 LogArea

Predictor    Coef          Stdev          t-ratio    p
Constant     1.20631       0.07379        16.35      0.000
Altitude     0.00014672    0.00005227      2.81      0.014
Distance    -0.00033301    0.00007628     -4.37      0.001
Dist.Isl     0.0004930     0.0007895       0.62      0.542
LogArea      0.10058       0.03833         2.62      0.020
```

t-ratios test that each partial regression coefficient differs from zero. These results suggest that the coefficients associated with all explanatory variables, except Dist.Isl, differ significantly from zero.

```
s = 0.06263    R-sq = 89.1%    R-sq(adj) = 86.0%
```

R-sq(adj), the coefficient of determination adjusted for the number of explanatory variables included in the model, is equal to 86.0%. Thus, the fitted model explains 86.0% of the variation observed in the dependent variable. The multiple correlation coefficient $r = \sqrt{0.86} = 0.927$.

```
Analysis of Variance

SOURCE         DF    SS        MS        F        p
Regression      4    0.44904   0.11226   28.61    0.000
Error          14    0.05492   0.00392
Total          18    0.50396
```

The highly significant F-values indicates that the linear multiple regression model provides a significant description of the data.

```
SOURCE         DF    SEQ SS
Altitude        1    0.27912
Distance        1    0.12592
Dist.Isl        1    0.01699
LogArea         1    0.02701
```

This column sums to 0.449 04, the sum of squares accounted for by the regression model (SSR). Individual values indicate the contribution made by each explanatory variable.

```
MTB >
```

These results suggest that the diversity of island birds depends not only on island size but also on the topography and remoteness of the island. The *t*-ratios values are significant for the altitude and distance from the mainland, along with the logarithm of island area.

10.3.7 Recommendations

In basic x, y data sets, treat x as the independent variable and y as the dependent variable. If only paired data values (x, y) are being analysed then simple linear regression is appropriate; if more than one independent variable has been recorded (e.g. $x_1, x_2, \ldots, x_n$ and y) then multiple regression may be appropriate. When a regression analysis is undertaken the data should be checked to ensure it conforms to the assumption of the procedure. Except for data collected from planned experiments, where the values of the independent variable are fixed by the experimenter, it is rare for ecological or environmental data sets to conform perfectly to these requirements. It is important that the variables are normally distributed

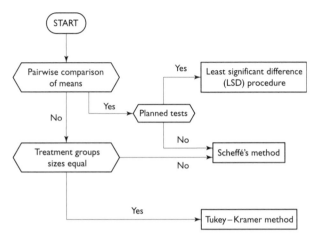

Figure 10.5 Comparisons of means following ANOVA

and linearly related. In most cases these properties may be achieved by appropriate transformation. It is also important that x and y values are evenly spread along the axes and that the errors associated with measurements of x are less than those associated with y. Where these conditions are clearly not met, then consider the extensions described in Section 10.3.4. The reasons for undertaking regression analysis should be considered carefully; often it cannot be justified and should not be applied to the data. The key question is whether you predict values of y from x using the fitted regression line. If not there is little to be gained from using regression to produce a best-fit line unless the exact form of the equation has some other particular importance to the study. Where it is not essential to fit a linear equation to the data, a more robust procedure is correlation analysis (Chapter 7) coupled with simple plots of variables against each other.

Appendix 10.1

Critical values for the *t*-test

	Level of significance for one-tailed test			
	0.05	0.025	0.01	0.005
	Level of significance for two-tailed test			
d.f.	0.10	0.05	0.02	0.01
1	6.314	12.706	31.821	63.657
2	2.920	4.303	6.965	9.925
3	2.353	3.182	4.541	5.841
4	2.132	2.776	3.747	4.604
5	2.015	2.571	3.365	4.032
6	1.943	2.447	3.143	3.707
7	1.895	2.365	2.998	3.499
8	1.860	2.306	2.896	3.355
9	1.833	2.262	2.821	3.250
10	1.812	2.228	2.764	3.169
11	1.796	2.201	2.718	3.106
12	1.782	2.179	2.681	3.055
13	1.771	2.160	2.650	3.012
14	1.761	2.145	2.624	2.977
15	1.753	2.131	2.602	2.947
16	1.746	2.120	2.583	2.921
17	1.740	2.110	2.567	2.898
18	1.734	2.101	2.552	2.878
19	1.729	2.093	2.539	2.861
20	1.725	2.086	2.528	2.845
21	1.721	2.080	2.518	2.831
22	1.717	2.074	2.508	2.819
23	1.714	2.069	2.500	2.807
24	1.711	2.064	2.492	2.797
25	1.708	2.060	2.485	2.787
26	1.706	2.056	2.479	2.779
27	1.703	2.052	2.473	2.771
28	1.701	2.048	2.467	2.763
29	1.699	2.045	2.462	2.756
30	1.697	2.042	2.457	2.750
40	1.684	2.021	2.423	2.704
60	1.671	2.000	2.390	2.660
120	1.658	1.980	2.358	2.617
∞	1.645	1.960	2.326	2.576

Source: Reprinted, with permission, from Fowler *et al.* (1998).

Appendix 10.2

Critical values for the *F*-distribution in two-tailed tests with *p* = 0.05

Use this table to check the equality of variance before a *z*-test or *t*-test.
ν_1 is the number of degrees of freedom for the sample with the larger variance.
ν_2 is the number of degrees of freedom for the sample with the smaller variance.

$\nu_0 \backslash \nu_0$	1	2	3	4	5	6	7	8	9	10	12	15	20	24	30	40	60	120	∞
1	647.8	799.5	864.2	899.6	921.8	937.1	948.2	956.7	963.3	968.6	976.7	984.9	993.1	997.2	1001	1006	1010	1014	1018
2	38.51	39.00	39.17	39.25	39.30	39.33	39.36	39.37	39.39	39.40	39.41	39.43	39.45	39.46	39.46	39.47	39.48	39.49	39.50
3	17.44	16.04	15.44	15.10	14.88	14.73	14.62	14.54	14.47	14.42	14.34	14.25	14.17	14.12	14.08	14.04	13.99	13.95	13.90
4	12.22	10.65	9.98	9.60	9.36	9.20	9.07	8.98	8.90	8.84	8.75	8.66	8.56	8.51	8.46	8.41	8.36	8.31	8.26
5	10.01	8.43	7.76	7.39	7.15	6.98	6.85	6.76	6.68	6.62	6.52	6.43	6.33	6.28	6.23	6.18	6.12	6.07	6.02
6	8.81	7.26	6.60	6.23	5.99	5.82	5.70	5.60	5.52	5.46	5.37	5.27	5.17	5.12	5.07	5.01	4.96	4.90	4.85
7	8.07	6.54	5.89	5.52	5.29	5.12	4.99	4.90	4.82	4.76	4.67	4.57	4.47	4.42	4.36	4.31	4.25	4.20	4.14
8	7.57	6.06	5.42	5.05	4.82	4.65	4.53	4.43	4.36	4.30	4.20	4.10	4.00	3.95	3.89	3.84	3.78	3.73	3.67
9	7.21	5.71	5.08	4.72	4.48	4.32	4.20	4.10	4.03	3.96	3.87	3.77	3.67	3.61	3.56	3.51	3.45	3.39	3.33
10	6.94	5.46	4.83	4.47	4.24	4.07	3.95	3.85	3.78	3.72	3.62	3.52	3.42	3.37	3.31	3.26	3.20	3.14	3.08
11	6.72	5.26	4.63	4.28	4.04	3.88	3.76	3.66	3.59	3.53	3.43	3.33	3.23	3.17	3.12	3.06	3.00	2.94	2.88
12	6.55	5.10	4.47	4.12	3.89	3.73	3.61	3.51	3.44	3.37	3.28	3.18	3.07	3.02	2.96	2.91	2.85	2.79	2.72
13	6.41	4.97	4.35	4.00	3.77	3.60	3.48	3.39	3.31	3.25	3.15	3.05	2.95	2.89	2.84	2.78	2.72	2.66	2.60
14	6.30	4.86	4.24	3.89	3.66	3.50	3.38	3.29	3.21	3.15	3.05	2.95	2.84	2.79	2.73	2.67	2.61	2.55	2.49
15	6.20	4.77	4.15	3.80	3.58	3.41	3.29	3.20	3.12	3.06	2.96	2.86	2.76	2.70	2.64	2.59	2.52	2.46	2.40
16	6.12	4.69	4.08	3.73	3.50	3.34	3.22	3.12	3.05	2.99	2.89	2.79	2.68	2.63	2.57	2.51	2.45	2.38	2.32
17	6.04	4.62	4.01	3.66	3.44	3.28	3.16	3.06	2.98	2.92	2.82	2.72	2.62	2.56	2.50	2.44	2.38	2.32	2.25
18	5.98	4.56	3.95	3.61	3.38	3.22	3.10	3.01	2.93	2.87	2.77	2.67	2.56	2.50	2.44	2.38	2.32	2.26	2.19
19	5.92	4.51	3.90	3.56	3.33	3.17	3.05	2.96	2.88	2.82	2.72	2.62	2.51	2.45	2.39	2.33	2.27	2.20	2.13
20	5.87	4.46	3.86	3.51	3.29	3.13	3.01	2.91	2.84	2.77	2.68	2.57	2.46	2.41	2.35	2.29	2.22	2.16	2.09
21	5.83	4.42	3.82	3.48	3.25	3.09	2.97	2.87	2.80	2.73	2.64	2.53	2.42	2.37	2.31	2.25	2.18	2.11	2.04
22	5.79	4.38	3.78	3.44	3.22	3.05	2.93	2.84	2.76	2.70	2.60	2.50	2.39	2.33	2.27	2.21	2.14	2.08	2.00
23	5.75	4.35	3.75	3.41	3.18	3.02	2.90	2.81	2.73	2.67	2.57	2.47	2.36	2.30	2.24	2.18	2.11	2.04	1.97
24	5.72	4.32	3.72	3.38	3.15	2.99	2.87	2.78	2.70	2.64	2.54	2.44	2.33	2.27	2.21	2.15	2.08	2.01	1.94
25	5.69	4.29	3.69	3.35	3.13	2.97	2.85	2.75	2.68	2.61	2.51	2.41	2.30	2.24	2.18	2.12	2.05	1.98	1.91
26	5.66	4.27	3.67	3.33	3.10	2.94	2.82	2.73	2.65	2.59	2.49	2.39	2.28	2.22	2.16	2.09	2.03	1.95	1.88
27	5.63	4.24	3.65	3.31	3.08	2.92	2.80	2.71	2.63	2.57	2.47	2.36	2.25	2.19	2.13	2.07	2.00	1.93	1.85
28	5.61	4.22	3.63	3.29	3.06	2.90	2.78	2.69	2.61	2.55	2.45	2.34	2.23	2.17	2.11	2.05	1.98	1.91	1.83
29	5.59	4.20	3.61	3.27	3.04	2.88	2.76	2.67	2.59	2.53	2.43	2.32	2.21	2.15	2.09	2.03	1.96	1.89	1.81
30	5.57	4.18	3.59	3.25	3.03	2.87	2.75	2.65	2.57	2.51	2.41	2.31	2.20	2.14	2.07	2.01	1.94	1.87	1.79
40	5.42	4.05	3.46	3.13	2.90	2.74	2.62	2.53	2.45	2.39	2.29	2.18	2.07	2.01	1.94	1.88	1.80	1.72	1.64
60	5.29	3.93	3.34	3.01	2.79	2.63	2.51	2.41	2.33	2.27	2.17	2.06	1.94	1.88	1.82	1.74	1.67	1.58	1.48
120	5.15	3.80	3.23	2.89	2.67	2.52	2.39	2.30	2.22	2.16	2.05	1.94	1.82	1.76	1.69	1.61	1.53	1.43	1.31
∞	5.02	3.69	3.12	2.79	2.57	2.41	2.29	2.19	2.11	2.05	1.94	1.83	1.71	1.64	1.57	1.48	1.39	1.27	1.00

Source: Reprinted, with permission, from Fowler *et al.* (1998).

Appendix 10.3

Critical values for the *F*-distribution in two-tailed tests with $p = 0.05$ for use with ANOVA

Use these tables for testing significance in analysis of variance.
0.05 level

ν_1 = df for the greater variance
ν_2 = df for the lesser variance

ν_2 \ ν_1	1	2	3	4	5	6	7	8	9
1	161.45	199.50	215.71	224.58	230.16	233.99	236.77	238.88	240.54
2	18.513	19.000	19.164	19.247	19.296	19.330	19.353	19.371	19.385
3	10.128	9.5521	9.2766	9.1172	9.0135	8.9406	8.8867	8.8452	8.8323
4	7.7086	6.9443	6.5914	6.3882	6.2561	6.1631	6.0942	6.0410	5.9938
5	6.6079	5.7861	5.4095	5.1922	5.0503	4.9503	4.8759	4.8183	4.7725
6	5.9874	5.1433	4.7571	4.5337	4.3874	4.2839	4.2067	4.1468	4.0990
7	5.5914	4.7374	4.3468	4.1203	3.9715	3.8660	3.7870	3.7257	3.6767
8	5.3177	4.4590	4.0662	3.8379	3.6875	3.5806	3.5005	3.4381	3.3881
9	5.1174	4.2565	3.8625	3.6331	3.4817	3.3738	3.2927	3.2296	3.1789
10	4.9646	4.1028	3.7083	3.4780	3.3258	3.2172	3.1355	3.0717	3.0204
11	4.8443	3.9823	3.5874	3.3567	3.2039	3.0946	3.0123	2.9480	2.8962
12	4.7472	3.8853	3.4903	3.2592	3.1059	2.9961	2.9134	2.8486	2.7964
13	4.6672	3.8056	3.4105	3.1791	3.0254	2.9153	2.8321	2.7669	2.7444
14	4.6001	3.7389	3.3439	3.1122	2.9582	2.8477	2.7642	2.6987	2.6458
15	4.5431	3.6823	3.2874	3.0556	2.9013	2.7905	2.7066	2.6408	2.5876
16	4.4940	3.6337	3.2389	3.0069	2.8524	2.7413	2.6572	2.5911	2.5377
17	4.4513	3.5915	3.1968	2.9647	2.8100	2.6987	2.6143	2.5480	2.4443
18	4.4139	3.5546	3.1599	2.9277	2.7729	2.6613	2.5767	2.5102	2.4563
19	4.3807	3.5219	3.1274	2.8951	2.7401	2.6283	2.5435	2.4768	2.4227
20	4.3512	3.4928	3.0984	2.8661	2.7109	2.5990	2.5140	2.4471	2.3928
21	4.3248	3.4668	3.0725	2.8401	2.6848	2.5727	2.4876	2.4205	2.3660
22	4.3009	3.4434	3.0491	2.8167	2.6613	2.5491	2.4638	2.3965	2.3219
23	4.2793	3.4221	3.0280	2.7955	2.6400	2.5277	2.4422	2.3748	2.3201
24	4.2597	3.4028	3.0088	2.7763	2.6207	2.5082	2.4226	2.3551	2.3002
25	4.2417	3.3852	2.9912	2.7587	2.6030	2.4904	2.4047	2.3371	2.2821
26	4.2252	3.3690	2.9752	2.7426	2.5868	2.4741	2.3883	2.3205	2.2655
27	4.2100	3.3541	2.9604	2.7278	2.5719	2.4591	2.3732	2.3053	2.2501
28	4.1960	3.3404	2.9467	2.7141	2.5581	2.4453	2.3593	2.2913	2.2360
29	4.1830	3.3277	2.9340	2.7014	2.5454	2.4324	2.3463	2.2783	2.2329
30	4.1709	3.3158	2.9223	2.6896	2.5336	2.4205	2.3343	2.2662	2.2507
40	4.0847	3.2317	2.8387	2.6060	2.4495	2.3359	2.2490	2.1802	2.1240
60	4.0012	3.1504	2.7581	2.5252	2.3683	2.2541	2.1665	2.0970	2.0401
120	3.9201	3.0718	2.6802	2.4472	2.2899	2.1750	2.0868	2.0164	1.9688
∞	3.8415	2.9957	2.6049	2.3719	2.2141	2.0986	2.0096	1.9384	1.8799

ν_1 ν_2	10	12	15	20	24	30	40	60	120	∞
1	241.88	243.91	245.95	248.01	249.05	250.10	251.14	252.20	253.25	254.31
2	19.396	19.413	19.429	19.446	19.454	19.462	19.471	19.479	19.437	19.496
3	8.7855	8.7446	8.7029	8.6602	8.6385	8.6166	8.5944	8.5720	8.5594	8.5264
4	5.9644	5.9117	5.8578	5.8025	5.7744	5.7459	5.7170	5.6877	5.6381	5.6281
5	4.7351	4.6777	4.6188	4.5581	4.5272	4.4957	4.4638	4.4314	4.3085	4.3650
6	4.0600	3.9999	3.9381	3.8742	3.8415	3.8082	3.7743	3.7398	3.7047	3.6689
7	3.6365	3.5747	3.5107	3.4445	3.4105	3.3758	3.3404	3.3043	3.2674	3.2298
8	3.3472	3.2839	3.2184	3.1503	3.1152	3.0794	3.0428	3.0053	2.9669	2.9276
9	3.1373	3.0729	3.0061	2.9365	2.9005	2.8637	2.8259	2.7872	2.7475	2.7067
10	2.9782	2.9130	2.8450	2.7740	2.7372	2.6996	2.6609	2.6211	2.5801	2.5379
11	2.8536	2.7876	2.7186	2.6464	2.6090	2.5705	2.5309	2.4901	2.4480	2.4045
12	2.7534	2.6866	2.6169	2.5436	2.5055	2.4663	2.4259	2.3842	2.3410	2.2962
13	2.6710	2.6037	2.5331	2.4589	2.4202	2.3803	2.3392	2.2966	2.2524	2.2064
14	2.6022	2.5342	2.4630	2.3879	2.3487	2.3082	2.2664	2.2229	2.1778	2.1307
15	2.5437	2.4753	2.4034	2.3275	2.2878	2.2468	2.2043	2.1601	2.1141	2.0658
16	2.4935	2.4247	2.3522	2.2756	2.2354	2.1938	2.1507	2.1058	2.0589	2.0096
17	2.4499	2.3807	2.3077	2.2304	2.1898	2.1477	2.1040	2.0584	2.0107	1.9604
18	2.4117	2.3421	2.2686	2.1906	2.1497	2.1071	2.0629	2.0166	1.9681	1.9168
19	2.3779	2.3080	2.2341	2.1555	2.1141	2.0712	2.0264	1.9795	1.9302	1.8780
20	2.3479	2.2776	2.2033	2.1242	2.0825	2.0391	1.9938	1.9464	1.8963	1.8432
21	2.3210	2.2504	2.1757	2.0960	2.0540	2.0102	1.9645	1.9165	1.8657	1.8117
22	2.2967	2.2258	2.1508	2.0707	2.0283	1.9842	1.9380	1.8894	1.8380	1.7831
23	2.2747	2.2036	2.1282	2.0476	2.0050	1.9605	1.9139	1.8648	1.8128	1.7570
24	2.2547	2.1834	2.1077	2.0267	1.9838	1.9390	1.8920	1.8424	1.7896	1.7330
25	2.2365	2.1649	2.0889	2.0075	1.9643	1.9192	1.8713	1.8217	1.7684	1.7110
26	2.2197	2.1479	2.0716	1.9898	1.9464	1.9010	1.8533	1.8027	1.7488	1.6906
27	2.2043	2.1323	2.0558	1.9736	1.9299	1.8842	1.8361	1.7851	1.7306	1.6717
28	2.1900	2.1179	2.0411	1.9586	1.9147	1.8687	1.8203	1.7689	1.7138	1.6541
29	2.1768	2.1045	2.0275	1.9446	1.9005	1.8543	1.8055	1.7537	1.6981	1.6376
30	2.1646	2.0921	2.0148	1.9317	1.8874	1.8409	1.7918	1.7396	1.6835	1.6223
40	2.0772	2.0035	1.9245	1.8389	1.7929	1.7444	1.6928	1.6373	1.5766	1.5089
60	1.9926	1.9174	1.8364	1.7480	1.7001	1.6491	1.5943	1.5343	1.4673	1.3893
120	1.9105	1.8337	1.7505	1.6587	1.6084	1.5543	1.4952	1.4290	1.3519	1.2539
∞	1.8307	1.7522	1.6664	1.5705	1.5173	1.4591	1.3940	1.3180	1.0214	1.0000

Source: Reprinted, with permission, from Fowler *et al.* (1998).

Appendix 10.4

Critical values for Q, the studentised range statistic, at $p = 0.05$

The values are tabulated for *a* groups at d.f. degrees of freedom; for the multiple range tests d.f. is normally $d.f._{error}$.

d.f.	*a* 2	*3*	*4*	*5*	*6*	*7*	*8*	*9*	*10*
1	17.97	26.98	32.82	37.08	40.41	43.12	45.40	47.36	49.07
2	6.085	8.331	9.798	10.88	11.75	12.44	13.03	13.54	13.99
3	4.501	5.910	6.825	7.502	8.037	8.478	8.853	9.177	9.462
4	3.927	5.040	5.757	6.287	6.707	7.053	7.347	7.602	7.826
5	3.635	4.602	5.218	5.673	6.033	6.330	6.582	6.802	6.995
6	3.461	4.339	4.896	5.305	5.628	5.895	6.122	6.319	6.493
7	3.344	4.165	4.681	5.060	5.359	5.606	5.815	5.998	6.158
8	3.261	4.041	4.529	4.886	5.167	5.399	5.597	5.767	5.918
9	3.199	3.949	4.415	4.756	5.024	5.244	5.432	5.595	5.739
10	3.151	3.877	4.327	4.654	4.912	5.124	5.305	5.461	5.599
11	3.113	3.820	4.256	4.574	4.823	5.028	5.202	5.353	5.487
12	3.082	3.773	4.199	4.508	4.751	4.950	5.119	5.265	5.395
13	3.055	3.735	4.151	4.453	4.690	4.885	5.049	5.192	5.318
14	3.033	3.702	4.111	4.407	4.639	4.829	4.990	5.131	5.254
15	3.014	3.674	4.076	4.367	4.595	4.782	4.940	5.077	5.198
16	2.998	3.649	4.046	4.333	4.557	4.741	4.897	5.031	5.150
17	2.984	3.628	4.020	4.303	4.524	4.705	4.858	4.991	5.108
18	2.971	3.609	3.997	4.277	4.495	4.673	4.824	4.956	5.071
19	2.960	3.593	3.977	4.253	4.469	4.645	4.794	4.924	5.038
20	2.950	3.578	3.958	4.232	4.445	4.620	4.768	4.896	5.008
24	2.919	3.532	3.901	4.166	4.373	4.541	4.684	4.807	4.915
30	2.888	3.486	3.845	4.102	4.302	4.464	4.602	4.720	4.824
40	2.858	3.442	3.791	4.039	4.232	4.389	4.521	4.635	4.735
60	2.829	3.399	3.737	3.977	4.163	4.314	4.441	4.550	4.646
120	2.800	3.356	3.685	3.917	4.096	4.241	4.363	4.468	4.560
∞	2.772	3.314	3.633	3.858	4.030	4.170	4.286	4.387	4.474

d.f.	a 11	12	13	14	15	16	17	18	19
1	50.59	51.96	53.20	54.33	55.36	56.32	57.22	58.04	58.83
2	14.39	14.75	15.08	15.38	15.65	15.91	16.14	16.37	16.57
3	9.717	9.946	10.15	10.35	10.53	10.69	10.84	10.98	11.11
4	8.027	8.208	8.373	8.525	8.664	8.794	8.914	9.028	9.134
5	7.168	7.324	7.466	7.596	7.717	7.828	7.932	8.030	8.122
6	6.649	6.789	6.917	7.034	7.143	7.244	7.338	7.426	7.508
7	6.302	6.431	6.550	6.658	6.759	6.852	6.939	7.020	7.097
8	6.054	6.175	6.287	6.389	6.483	6.571	6.653	6.729	6.802
9	5.867	5.983	6.089	6.186	6.276	6.359	6.437	6.510	6.579
10	5.722	5.833	5.935	6.028	6.114	6.194	6.269	6.339	6.405
11	5.605	5.713	5.811	5.901	5.984	6.062	6.134	6.202	6.265
12	5.511	5.615	5.710	5.798	5.878	5.953	6.023	6.089	6.151
13	5.431	5.533	5.625	5.711	5.789	5.862	5.931	5.995	6.055
14	5.364	5.463	5.554	5.637	5.714	5.786	5.852	5.915	5.974
15	5.306	5.404	5.493	5.574	5.649	5.720	5.785	5.846	5.904
16	5.256	5.352	5.439	5.520	5.593	5.662	5.727	5.786	5.843
17	5.212	5.307	5.392	5.471	5.544	5.612	5.675	5.734	5.790
18	5.174	5.267	5.352	5.429	5.501	5.568	5.630	5.688	5.743
19	5.140	5.231	5.315	5.391	5.462	5.528	5.589	5.647	5.701
20	5.108	5.199	5.282	5.357	5.427	5.493	5.553	5.610	5.663
24	5.012	5.099	5.179	5.251	5.319	5.381	5.439	5.494	5.545
30	4.917	5.001	5.077	5.147	5.211	5.271	5.327	5.379	5.429
40	4.824	4.904	4.977	5.044	5.106	5.163	5.216	5.266	5.313
60	4.732	4.808	4.878	4.942	5.001	5.056	5.107	5.154	5.199
120	4.641	4.714	4.781	4.842	4.898	4.950	4.998	5.044	5.086
∞	4.552	4.622	4.685	4.743	4.796	4.845	4.891	4.934	4.974

d.f. \ a	20	22	24	26	28	30	32	34	36
1	59.56	60.91	62.12	63.22	64.23	65.15	66.01	66.81	67.56
2	16.77	17.13	17.45	17.75	18.02	18.27	18.50	18.72	18.92
3	11.24	11.47	11.68	11.87	12.05	12.21	12.36	12.50	12.63
4	9.233	9.418	9.584	9.736	9.875	10.00	10.12	10.23	10.34
5	8.208	8.368	8.512	8.643	8.764	8.875	8.979	9.075	9.165
6	7.587	7.730	7.861	7.979	8.088	8.189	8.283	8.370	8.452
7	7.170	7.303	7.423	7.533	7.634	7.728	7.814	7.895	7.972
8	6.870	6.995	7.109	7.212	7.307	7.395	7.477	7.554	7.625
9	6.644	6.763	6.871	6.970	7.061	7.145	7.222	7.295	7.363
10	6.467	6.582	6.686	6.781	6.868	6.948	7.023	7.093	7.159
11	6.326	6.436	6.536	6.628	6.712	6.790	6.863	6.930	6.994
12	6.209	6.317	6.414	6.503	6.585	6.660	6.731	6.796	6.858
13	6.112	6.217	6.312	6.398	6.478	6.551	6.620	6.684	6.744
14	6.029	6.132	6.224	6.309	6.387	6.459	6.526	6.588	6.647
15	5.958	6.059	6.149	6.233	6.309	6.379	6.445	6.506	6.564
16	5.897	5.995	6.084	6.166	6.241	6.310	6.374	6.434	6.491
17	5.842	5.940	6.027	6.107	6.181	6.249	6.313	6.372	6.427
18	5.794	5.890	5.977	6.055	6.128	6.195	6.258	6.316	6.371
19	5.752	5.846	5.932	6.009	6.081	6.147	6.209	6.267	6.321
20	5.714	5.807	5.891	5.968	6.039	6.104	6.165	6.222	6.275
24	5.594	5.683	5.764	5.838	5.906	5.968	6.027	6.081	6.132
30	5.475	5.561	5.638	5.709	5.774	5.833	5.889	5.941	5.990
40	5.358	5.439	5.513	5.581	5.642	5.700	5.753	5.803	5.849
60	5.241	5.319	5.389	5.453	5.512	5.566	5.617	5.664	5.708
120	5.126	5.200	5.266	5.327	5.382	5.434	5.481	5.526	5.568
∞	5.012	5.081	5.144	5.201	5.253	5.301	5.346	5.388	5.427

d.f. \ a	38	40	50	60	70	80	90	100
1	68.26	68.92	71.73	73.97	75.82	77.40	78.77	79.98
2	19.11	19.28	20.05	20.66	21.16	21.59	21.96	22.29
3	12.75	12.87	13.36	13.76	14.08	14.36	14.61	14.82
4	10.44	10.53	10.93	11.24	11.51	11.73	11.92	12.09
5	9.250	9.330	9.674	9.949	10.18	10.38	10.54	10.69
6	8.529	8.601	8.913	9.163	9.370	9.548	9.702	9.839
7	8.043	8.110	8.400	8.632	8.824	8.989	9.133	9.261
8	7.693	7.756	8.029	8.248	8.430	8.586	8.722	8.843
9	7.428	7.488	7.749	7.958	8.132	8.281	8.410	8.526
10	7.220	7.279	7.529	7.730	7.897	8.041	8.166	8.276
11	7.053	7.110	7.352	7.546	7.708	7.847	7.968	8.075
12	6.916	6.970	7.205	7.394	7.552	7.687	7.804	7.909
13	6.800	6.854	7.083	7.267	7.421	7.552	7.667	7.769
14	6.702	6.754	6.979	7.159	7.309	7.438	7.650	7.650
15	6.618	6.669	6.888	7.065	7.212	7.339	7.449	7.546
16	6.544	6.594	6.810	6.984	7.128	7.252	7.360	7.457
17	6.479	6.529	6.741	6.912	7.054	7.176	7.283	7.377
18	6.422	6.471	6.680	6.848	6.989	7.109	7.213	7.307
19	6.371	6.419	6.626	6.792	6.930	7.048	7.152	7.244
20	6.325	6.373	6.576	6.740	6.877	6.994	7.097	7.187
24	6.181	6.226	6.421	6.579	6.710	6.822	6.920	7.008
30	6.037	6.080	6.267	6.417	6.543	6.650	6.744	6.827
40	5.893	5.934	6.112	6.255	6.375	6.477	6.566	6.645
60	5.750	5.789	5.958	6.093	6.206	6.303	6.387	6.462
120	5.607	5.644	5.802	5.929	6.035	6.126	6.205	6.275
∞	5.463	5.498	5.646	5.764	5.863	5.947	6.020	6.085

Source: Extracted, with permission, from F.J. Rohlf and R.R. Sokal, 1981, *Statistical Tables*, W.H. Freeman, San Francisco, CA.

Critical values of Hartley's F_{max} at $p = 0.05$

When the calculated F_{max} is less than the tabulated value for $F_{max(a, n-1)}$ the variances are homogeneous, where n is the group size and a is the number of groups.

$n-1$ \ a	2	3	4	5	6	7	8	9	10	11	12
2	39.0	87.5	142.	202.	266.	333.	403.	475.	550.	626.	704.
3	15.4	27.8	39.2	50.7	62.0	72.9	83.5	93.9	104.	114.	124.
4	9.60	15.5	20.6	25.2	29.5	33.6	37.5	41.1	44.6	48.0	51.4
5	7.15	10.8	13.7	16.3	18.7	20.8	22.9	24.7	26.5	28.2	29.9
6	5.82	8.38	10.4	12.1	13.7	15.0	16.3	17.5	18.6	19.7	20.7
7	4.99	6.94	8.44	9.70	10.8	11.8	12.7	13.5	14.3	15.1	15.8
8	4.43	6.0	7.18	8.12	9.03	9.78	10.5	11.1	11.7	12.2	12.7
9	4.03	5.34	6.31	7.11	7.80	8.41	8.95	9.45	9.91	10.3	10.7
10	3.72	4.85	5.67	6.34	6.92	7.42	7.87	8.28	8.66	9.01	9.34
12	3.28	4.16	4.79	5.30	5.72	6.09	6.42	6.72	7.00	7.25	7.48
15	2.86	3.54	4.01	4.37	4.68	4.95	5.19	5.40	5.59	5.77	5.93
20	2.46	2.95	3.29	3.54	3.76	3.94	4.10	4.24	4.37	4.49	4.59
30	2.07	2.40	2.61	2.78	2.91	3.02	3.12	3.21	3.29	3.36	3.39
60	1.67	1.85	1.96	2.04	2.11	2.17	2.22	2.26	2.30	2.33	2.36
∞	1.00	1.00	1.00	1.00	1.00	1.00	1.00	1.00	1.00	1.00	1.00

Source: Reprinted, with permission, from H.A. David, 1952, *Biometrika* **39**: 422–24..

Appendix 10.6

Critical values and formulae used in Dixon's Q-test for outliers

The formula is selected according to the group size (n) to which the tested outlier belongs. When r_n is greater than the critical value, the outlier is significantly different from the other values in the group. Adapted, with permission, from F.J. Rohlf and R.R. Sokal, 1981, *Statistical Tables*, W.H. Freeman, San Francisco, CA.

	Critical value at			
n	$p = 0.10$	$p = 0.05$	$p = 0.01$	*Formula*
3	0.886	0.941	0.988	
4	0.679	0.765	0.889	
5	0.557	0.642	0.780	$r_{10} = \dfrac{x_2 - x_1}{x_n - x_1}$
6	0.482	0.560	0.698	
7	0.434	0.507	0.637	
8	0.479	0.554	0.683	
9	0.441	0.512	0.635	$r_{11} = \dfrac{x_2 - x_1}{x_{n-1} - x_1}$
10	0.409	0.477	0.597	
11	0.517	0.576	0.679	
12	0.490	0.546	0.642	$r_{21} = \dfrac{x_3 - x_1}{x_{n-1} - x_1}$
13	0.467	0.521	0.615	
14	0.492	0.546	0.641	
15	0.472	0.525	0.616	
16	0.454	0.507	0.595	
17	0.438	0.490	0.577	
18	0.424	0.475	0.561	
19	0.412	0.462	0.547	$r_{22} = \dfrac{x_3 - x_1}{x_{n-2} - x_1}$
20	0.401	0.450	0.535	
21	0.391	0.440	0.524	
22	0.382	0.430	0.514	
23	0.374	0.421	0.505	
24	0.367	0.413	0.497	
25	0.360	0.406	0.489	

Source: Adapted, with permission, from F.J. Rohlf and R.R. Sokal, 1981, *Statistical Tables*, W.H. Freeman, San Francisco, CA.

Appendix 10.7

Critical values for *r*, product moment correlation coefficient with $p = 0.05$ and $p = 0.01$

d.f.	0.05	0.01	d.f.	0.05	0.01
1	0.997	0.9999	32	0.339	0.436
2	0.950	0.990	34	0.329	0.424
3	0.878	0.959	35	0.325	0.418
4	0.811	0.917	36	0.320	0.413
5	0.754	0.874	38	0.312	0.403
6	0.707	0.834	40	0.304	0.393
7	0.666	0.798	42	0.297	0.384
8	0.632	0.765	44	0.291	0.376
9	0.602	0.735	45	0.288	0.372
10	0.576	0.708	46	0.284	0.368
11	0.553	0.684	48	0.279	0.361
12	0.532	0.661	50	0.273	0.354
13	0.514	0.641	55	0.261	0.338
14	0.497	0.623	60	0.250	0.325
15	0.482	0.606	65	0.241	0.313
16	0.468	0.590	70	0.232	0.302
17	0.456	0.575	75	0.224	0.292
18	0.444	0.561	80	0.217	0.283
19	0.433	0.549	85	0.211	0.275
20	0.423	0.537	90	0.205	0.267
21	0.413	0.526	95	0.200	0.260
22	0.404	0.515	100	0.195	0.254
23	0.396	0.505	125	0.174	0.228
24	0.388	0.496	150	0.159	0.208
25	0.381	0.487	175	0.148	0.193
26	0.374	0.479	200	0.138	0.181
27	0.367	0.471	300	0.113	0.148
28	0.361	0.463	400	0.098	0.128
29	0.355	0.456	500	0.088	0.115
30	0.349	0.449	1,000	0.062	0.081

Source: Reprinted with permission, from Fowler *et al.* (1998).

Further reading

Fry, C.J. (ed.) (1993) *Biological Data Analysis: A Practical Approach*. Oirl Press at Oxford University Press, Oxford. An excellent book written for biologists; has chapters covering one-way ANOVA, two-way ANOVA, regression and multiple regression.

Kleinbaum, D.G., Kupper, L.L., Muller, K.E. and Nizam, A. (1998) *Applied Regression Analysis and Other Multivariable Methods*, 3rd edn. Duxbury Press, Pacific Grove, CA. Provides a very thorough treatment of regression and analysis of variance; although primarily written for students studying statistics, it should not prove too daunting or intimidating for the more mathematically confident biology student.

Manly, B.F.J. (1992) *The Design and Analysis of Research Studies*. Cambridge University Press, Cambridge. Written for the non-statistician, a very readable and accessible account of ANOVA, regression and design of experimental studies.

Underwood, A.J. (1997) *Experiments in Ecology: Their Logical Design and Interpretation Using Analysis of Variance*. Cambridge University Press, Cambridge. Provides a readable but advanced treatment of the subject.

Chapter Eleven

Relating community and environmental data sets: ordination and cluster analysis revisited

Summary

The methods of cluster analysis (Chapter 9) and ordination (Chapter 8) may be used to simplify large multivariate data sets. By combining similar sample units, cluster analysis reduces the number of groups (i.e. sample units) present in a data set. Ordination reduces the number of variables required to adequately describe each sample unit. Both methods may be applied to the same data set. This chapter presents methods for interpreting and relating the results of cluster analysis and ordination. It introduces multivariate versions of the *t*-test and ANOVA. And it considers the particular problems of analysing complex partitioned data tables, often encountered in environmental research.

11.1 *Introduction*

Cluster analysis (Chapter 9) and ordination (Chapter 8) may be used to simplify large multivariate data sets. By combining similar sample units, cluster analysis reduces the number of groups (i.e. sample units) present in a data set (Figure 11.1). Ordination reduces

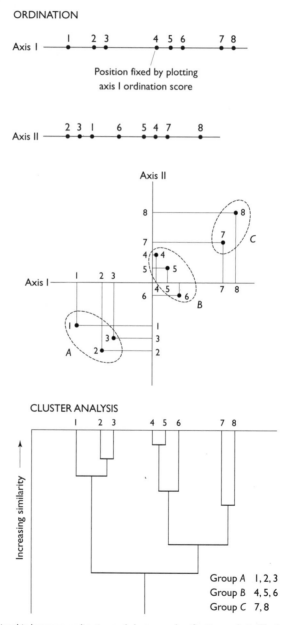

Figure 11.1 The relationship between ordination and cluster or classification analysis. The hypothetical data set consists of eight samples collected along an altitude gradient: sample 1 at the lowest altitude, sample 8 at the highest altitude. When ordinated the samples are clearly ordered along axis I according to sample altitude. But there exists further variation between the samples and this is described by their position along axis II. The ordering of species along axis II is not directly related to altitude. Cluster analysis identifies three distinct groups which do relate to altitude.

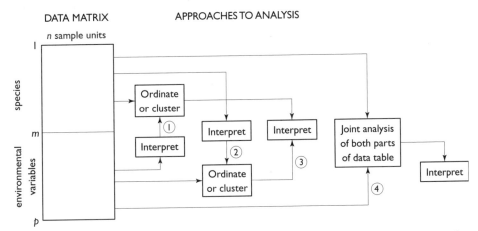

Figure 11.2 How to analyse a partitioned community data matrix: the matrix is formed by recording species abundances 1 to *m* and environmental factors *m* + 1 to *p*, for *n* sample units. Strategies 1, 2 and 3 are indirect strategies; strategy 4 is a direct strategy.

the number of variables required to adequately describe each sample unit. Following ordination each sample unit can be characterised by a limited number of ordination scores (numerical values). Ordination scores allow the data to be presented graphically, normally as a two-dimensional graph but sometimes as a three-dimensional graph (Figure 11.1); the similarity between sample units is mirrored by the relative positions of plotted points.

Classification or ordination diagrams may sometimes be interpretable without further analysis. Knowledge of the nature of the samples units, e.g. the location of sample units clustered in a group or occurring close together in the ordination diagram, can be sufficient to allow interpretation. But often this is not the case; interpretation can be problematic and further analysis is required. A particular problem arises when the data matrix is partitioned. For example, if the invertebrate species composition is determined along a stream and at each sampling site, a range of physical environmental factors (e.g. water velocity, pH, etc.) are measured the community data matrix may be partitioned into a species by sample submatrix and physical factors by sample submatrix (Figure 11.2). Such a data set may be analysed in several ways:

- One data submatrix is ordinated or clustered, and information in the second submatrix is used to help interpret the ordination or cluster diagram. For example, the species by samples data set might be ordinated and information on the physical environment at each of the sample sites used to help interpret the ordination diagram.

- One submatrix is ordinated or clustered and then the other; the non-clustered or ordinated submatrix is used to help interpretation. For example, data on the physical environment may be used to help interpret a species-based ordination or cluster diagram; the process may then be reversed, so the environmental data set is ordinated or clustered and information on the distribution of species is used to help interpret the environmental ordination or cluster diagram.

- Both submatrices are ordinated and clustered then visual or statistical comparison are used to help interpret the original data. Comparisons may be made between pairs of ordinations, between pairs of cluster diagrams, or between cluster and ordination diagrams produced from the same data. The latter comparison can often be very informative.

All of these approaches can be described as indirect. Each part of the partitioned data matrix is analysed separately, then the results are combined or compared to help interpret the original data set. The first three sections of this chapter outline these indirect approaches to the interpretation of cluster diagrams (Section 11.2) and ordination diagrams (Section 11.3). Section 11.4 considers the relationship between the results of ordination and cluster analysis. And Section 11.5 looks at the more demanding problem of attempting to analyse the relationships between both portions of a partitioned data matrix in one step – a direct strategy.

11.2 *Using classification and cluster diagrams*

11.2.1 *Descriptive interpretation of end groups*

As a result of clustering or classification, the original data set containing an initial n samples will be simplified and reduced to a data set composed of a smaller number of end groups ($<n$) each containing sample units which have characteristics in common. The investigator may be interested in attempting to answer three questions:

- How different are the end groups from each other?
- Which variables are important in accounting for the differences between end groups?
- Can the composition of the end groups be related to factors (variables) not used during their formation, i.e. not used to cluster or classify sample units?

In many cases these questions may be answered by looking carefully at the membership of each group. For example, if the original sample units were clustered on the basis of their species composition, listing the species present in each group can be informative. Where end groups contain a reasonable numbers of sample units, the frequency of species present in each end group can be calculated as n_i/N where n_i is the number of sample units containing species i and N is the total number of sample units in the group. The inspection of species distribution and frequency (constancy) among end groups may allow key characteristic species to be identified (Figure 11.3). Knowledge of the ecology or tolerances of these species can assist interpretation, allowing tentative inferences to be made about the relationship between the classification and other factors not necessarily recorded in the study. These relationships may be formalised and quantified by calculating weighted averages (Chapter 5) for each group.

When quantitative data is available, group means or medians can be calculated and used to compare end groups. Differences between end-group means can be tested using t-tests or ANOVA (Chapter 10). However, this approach should be used with care, and only considered if the original sample units are known to form a random and representative sample. Since end groups are likely to vary in size, one-way ANOVA will be the most appropriate form of ANOVA. As the number of variables and end groups compared increases, the likelihood of committing a type I error (i.e. falsely rejecting the null hypothesis) will increase. One solution to this problem is to use multivariate versions of univariate tests, some of which are outlined in Section 11.2.2.

The approach described above can be used whenever the data matrix is partitioned or where independent data is available for sample units. If we consider a community data

Species	1	2	3	4	5	6	7	8	9	10	11	12	13	14	15	16
Calluna vulgaris			●		●											
Molinia caerulea		●	●		●							●				·
Campylopus introflexus			·	·												
Polytrichum commune			·		●			●				●				
Sphagnum tenellum	●	●	●	●	●		●	●			●	●		●		
Drosera rotundifolia	·	●	●	●	●	·	●	●		●	·	●				
Erica tetralix	●	●	●	●	●	●	●	●			●	●				·
Eriophorum angustifolium	●	●	●	●	●	●	●	●	●	●	●	●	●	●	●	●
Juncus acutiflorus	·										·		·	·	●	
Narthecium ossifragum	●	·		●			●	●		●	●	●		●	●	·
Drosera intermedia						·		●		·						
Rhyncospora alba						●			●	●	●		●	●		
Sphagnum cuspidatum						·				·			●	·	●	●
Sphagnum papillosum				●		·	·			·			●	●		·
Sphagnum recurvum				·		●			·	●			●		●	·

Contained in the following fractions of the quadrats:

· 1–9%　　● 10–30%　　● 31–51%　　● >51%

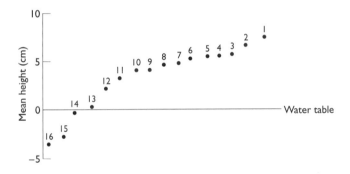

Figure 11.3 TWINSPAN clustering. The data was collected from a mire in southern England. The species abundance and height above the water table were recorded for two hundred 10 cm × 10 cm square quadrats. TWINSPAN analysis identified 16 end groups. Examination of the species composition suggests that grouping may partly relate to water availability. Species associated with waterlogged and wet sites, *Sphagnum cuspidatum, S. papillosum* and *S. recurvum*, occur in end groups 13 to 16 whereas *Calluna vulgaris*, a species sensitive to waterlogging and associated with dry sites, is restricted to end groups 3 and 5. The possible relation between end-group composition and water availability is further supported by plotting the mean height of the end groups above the local water table. Reprinted, with permission, from Greshon (1989).

matrix containing information on the species and physical environment present at each sample unit, end groups obtained by clustering the species by samples matrix (top half of the matrix) may be interpreted using the available physical data (bottom half of the matrix). The means of the physical variables can be calculated for each end group. The relationship between the two parts of the data matrix can then be explored by plotting end-group means and associated standard deviations (or standard errors) to produce an

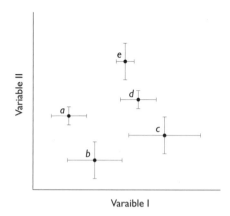

Figure 11.4 Hypothetical plot of cluster end-group means and standard errors for environmental variables I and II. The variation within end groups can be assessed using the size of the standard errors and the degree of overlap; they can also be used to assess the separation between groups for variables I and II.

ordination of end groups (Figure 11.4). The major limitation of such plots is that only two variables can be plotted at a time.

11.2.2 Statistical interpretations of end groups

Assessing the difference between groups

Hotelling's T^2-test is essentially a multivariate version of Student's t-test. The t-test (Chapter 10) is used to test for significant differences between the means of two samples. Hotelling's T^2-test considers the more demanding situation where a number of variables have been recorded for each individual (item or sample unit) in each sample. The question being asked is whether the samples differ significantly for any of the variables measured. One approach would be to test for significant differences between each pair of means using the univariate t-test. However, this approach entails a high risk of a *type I error*, where the test wrongly reports a significant difference between means that do not actually differ.

If the normal 5% significance level is applied (i.e. $\alpha = 0.05$), the probability is 0.95 of a *non-significant* result occurring by chance when the means are actually the same. If p pairs of means are compared, the probability of obtaining no significant results is 0.95^p. If $p = 6$, i.e. 6 comparisons are made, then the probability of at least one significant result occurring by chance alone is $1 - 0.95^6 = 0.2649$, so greater than 1 in 4 comparisons are likely to yield a significant result by chance alone. Multivariate tests avoid this problem. Using the Hotelling T^2-test at the 5% level of significance gives a probability of 0.05 of a type I error, irrespective of the number of variables involved. The calculation of T^2 is relatively straightforward but, because it involves matrix algebra, it is most easily performed with the help of a computer package that does matrix manipulations.

Step 1 Assume the data has been obtained by measuring the value of p variables for n individuals (items) present in two samples. It is desirable but not necessary for the samples to be of equal size. For *each* sample, calculate the mean for each of the p variables and the corresponding covariance matrix **C**. The covariance matrix is produced by calculating the covariance between each pair of variables. The elements of **C** give the covariance between each variable.

For sample 1

$$\mathbf{C}_1 = \begin{bmatrix} C_{11} & C_{12} & \cdots & C_{1p} \\ C_{21} & C_{22} & \cdots & C_{2p} \\ \vdots & \vdots & \cdots & \vdots \\ C_{p1} & C_{p2} & \cdots & C_{pp} \end{bmatrix}$$

The diagonals of the matrix correspond to the variances of each variable, hence in some texts C is called the variance-covariance matrix.

$$C_{jk} = \sum_{i=1}^{n} \frac{(x_{ij} - \bar{x}_j)(x_{ik} - \bar{x}_k)}{n-1}$$ **Formula for the covariance between variables *j* and *k*.**

where n is the number of individuals present in the sample; x_{ik}, x_{ij} are the values of variables j and k measured for the ith individual in the sample; $\bar{x}_j$, $\bar{x}_k$ are the means of variables j and k for sample 1.

The means of the p variables measured for sample 1 are represented as the column vector $\mathbf{X}_1$:

$$\mathbf{X}_1 = \begin{bmatrix} \bar{x}_1 \\ \bar{x}_2 \\ \vdots \\ \bar{x}_p \end{bmatrix}$$

The transposed column vector is $\mathbf{X}_1^T = [\bar{x}_1 \quad \bar{x}_2 \quad \cdots \quad \bar{x}_p]$. Now repeat the calculation for sample 2.

Step 2 Calculate a pooled covariance matrix for samples 1 and 2:

$$\mathbf{C} = \frac{(n_1 - 1)\mathbf{C}_1 + (n_2 - 1)\mathbf{C}_2}{n_1 + n_2 - 2}$$

This is analogous to calculating a pooled estimate of variance; n_1 and n_2 refer to the size of samples 1 and 2; $\mathbf{C}_1$ and $\mathbf{C}_2$ refer to the covariance matrices for samples 1 and 2.

Step 3 Calculate a column matrix of the differences between the means for samples 1 and 2, $\mathbf{d} = \mathbf{X}_1 - \mathbf{X}_2$. Now calculate the T^2-statistic:

$$T^2 = \frac{n_1 n_2}{n_1 + n_2}(\mathbf{X}_1 - \mathbf{X}_2)^T \mathbf{C}^{-1}(\mathbf{X}_1 - \mathbf{X}_2)$$
$$= \mathbf{d}^T \mathbf{C}^{-1} \mathbf{d}$$

column matrix of the differences between variable means for samples 1 and 2

inverse of pooled covariance matrix

single row matrix, transpose of column matrix for differences between variable means

Step 4 The significance of T^2 is assessed by calculating the associated F-statistic.

$$F = \frac{(n_1 + n_2 - p - 1)T^2}{(n_1 + n_2 - 2)p}$$

F has degrees of freedom p and $(n_1 + n_2 - p - 1)$.

A worked example is given in Box 11.1. A significant Hotelling T^2-statistic implies the mean vectors of two samples differ significantly and the null hypothesis that the mean vectors are

Box 11.1 How to calculate Hotelling's T^2

Based on figures for national emissions of sulphur published by the Swedish NGO Secretariat on Acid Rain, the relative reduction in sulphur and nitrogen emissions between 1980 and 1994 can be compared for groups of major and minor polluters. The ratios of 1994 levels to 1980 levels for sulphur (S), nitrogen oxides (NO_x) and ammonia (NH_4) were calculated for the five highest sulphur emitters in 1980 (France, Germany, Poland, United Kingdom and the Russian Federation) and the five lowest emitters (Iceland, Latvia, Luxembourg, Macedonia and Maldova). Use MINITAB to establish whether the two group of nations differ significantly in terms of their proportional decrease in S, NO_x and NH_4 emissions.

Begin by entering the data in columns C1 to C4; membership of the groups is given in column C1, where 1 indicates a major emitter and 2 indicates a minor emitter:

```
C1        C2      C3      C4
Groups    S       NOX     NH4
1         0.39    0.780   0.745
1         0.33    0.834   0.951
1         0.63    0.896   0.698
1         0.55    0.956   1.000
1         0.41    1.156   0.649
2         1.00    1.000   1.000
2         4.00    1.750   1.000
2         1.00    1.000   1.000
2         1.00    1.000   1.000
2         0.50    0.850   1.167
```

From the **Stat** option on the main menu bar, select the **Multivariate** option and then **Discriminant Analysis**; this should open a dialogue box. Within the dialogue box, specify **Groups** as **C1** and **Predictors** as **C2-C4**. From the **Option** submenu select the optional display output which gives the group means and covariance summary. The MINITAB output should look something like this:

```
MTB > Discriminant 'Groups' 'S'-'NH4';
SUBC> Brief 3.
```

Discriminant Analysis

```
Linear Method for Response: Groups
Predictors: S NOX NH4

Group     1     2
Count     5     5

Summary of Classification

Put into        ....True   Group....
Group             1         2
1                 4         0
2                 1         5
Total N           5         5
N Correct         4         5
Proport.          0.800     1.000

N = 10    N Correct = 9    Prop. Correct = 0.900
```

D^2 values for 'generalised distance'; note that MINITAB will calculate the measure between all groups identified.

```
Squared Distance Between Groups
          1         2
1     0.00000    5.24446
2     5.24446    0.00000
```

Coefficients for linear discriminant function for groups.

```
Linear Discriminant Function for Group
                 1         2
Constant      -79.65    -96.83
S             -25.30    -23.96
NOX           109.52    109.77
NH4            86.26    103.21
```

Pooled group mean, standard deviations and variance–covariance matrices are also displayed.

MTB >

Now use the relationship:

$$D^2 = \frac{n_1 + n_2}{n_1 n_2} T^2$$

so $\quad T^2 = \dfrac{n_1 n_2}{n_1 + n_2} D^2 = \dfrac{5 \times 5}{5 + 5}(5.244\,46) = 13.11$

The test statistic for Hotelling's T^2 is the F-statistic, obtained from

$$F = \frac{(n_1 + n_2 + p - 1)T^2}{(n_1 + n_2 - 2)p} = \frac{12 \times T^2}{(8 \times 3)} = \frac{12 \times 13.11}{24} = 6.555$$

d.f. $= p, (n_1 + n_2 + p - 1) = 3, 12$

The tabulated critical value of F with d.f. $= 3, 12$ is 5.096 at p $= 0.05$. Since the calculated value of 6.555 exceeds 5.096, the null hypothesis is rejected; it can be concluded that the group mean vectors differ significantly. This suggests that between 1980 and 1994 the reductions in S, NO_x and NH_4 achieved by the highest emitters did exceed the reductions achieved by the lowest emitters.

equal should be rejected. A significant Hotelling T^2 may be obtained even if the univariate comparison of variable means fails to find any significant differences. This is because the value of T^2 depends on the accumulative contributions of all the variables and is capable of detecting situations in which the combined differences become significant. The converse result is also possible where a t-test reports the presence of significant differences between a pair of means, but the multivariate test indicates that the mean vectors do not differ significantly. In this case the difference due to a single pair of means is swamped by the lack of differences among the other variables.

In the same way that the t-test can be viewed as a special case of ANOVA – an F-test resulting from the application of one-way analysis of variance to a data set containing only two samples – so Hotelling's T^2 test may be seen as a particular case of the more general multivariate analysis of variance (MANOVA). MANOVA is the multivariate generalisation of analysis of variance, allowing multiple sample mean vectors to be compared. This technique is extremely powerful and is increasingly being used for the analysis of environmental data, particularly data obtained from complex planned experiments. Manly (1994) provides a brief discussion of how the T^2-test procedure may be adapted and applied to multiple sample comparisons, and Harris (1985) provides a detailed but reasonably accessible treatment of the subject. MANOVA, along with discriminative function analysis (outlined below), is supported by several commonly available statistical computer packages, including SPSS and MINITAB; further details of the procedures may be found in their reference manuals. However, students are urged to guard against the blind application of these advanced techniques.

Assumptions made by Hotelling's T^2-test are analogous to those of the univariate t-test. It is assumed that the samples being compared follow a multivariate normal distribution and have equal covariance matrices. However, Manly (1994) suggests that the test is not seriously affected by minor deviations from these assumptions (particularly deviations from normality), especially if the sample sizes are equal or nearly equal. Where substantial deviations occur, an alternative form of the test is given by Yao (1965).

The F-test routinely used to test for equal sample variances (Chapter 10), is very sensitive to departures from normality. If the samples are not normally distributed, a significant result may be obtained even if the variances do not differ. Levene (1960) has suggested a more robust procedure. Levene's test of equal variance is performed by initially transforming the data for each sample into absolute deviations (i.e. $|x_{ij} - \bar{x}_j|$ where x_{ij} and $\bar{x}_j$ are the value of variable j for sample unit i and the mean of variable j). The difference between the mean absolute deviations for each sample is tested using the t-test procedure. A significant difference indicates that sample variability is not equal. The procedure is even more robust if the mean is replaced by the median when calculating absolute deviations (Schultz, 1983).

By extending this approach to the multivariate case, it is possible to test the equality of covariance matrices. To test for equal covariance, matrices of the original data values are transformed to absolute deviations (from either variable means or medians), then Hotelling's T^2-test is used to test for significant difference between the column vectors of variable deviation. A significant result implies that the covariance matrices of the untransformed data are not equal.

A multivariate measure of group distance
A measure of the overall difference between the two samples or groups is given by D^2, known as the generalised distance or Mahalanobis distance:

$$D^2 = \frac{n_1 + n_2}{n_1 n_2} T^2 \quad \text{or more directly} \quad D^2 = (\mathbf{X}_1 - \mathbf{X}_2)^T \mathbf{C}^{-1} (\mathbf{X}_1 - \mathbf{X}_2)$$

This relationship is sometimes written as $D^2 = \mathbf{d}^T \mathbf{C}^{-1} \mathbf{d}$, where $\mathbf{d}$ is the column matrix of the differences between sample variable means. In addition to providing a measure of the overall distance or difference between two groups (Figure 11.5), D^2 can also be used to assess whether a particular observation or sample unit belongs to a group or whether it should be treated as an outlier or a member of another group. The same formulae are used, except the mean difference column matrix ($\mathbf{d}$) contains the difference between the group means and the values measured for the suspected outlier:

$$D^2 = \sum_{r=1}^{p} \sum_{s=1}^{p} (x_r - \bar{x}_r) \nu^{rs} (x_s - \bar{x}_s) \quad \text{or} \quad D^2 = \mathbf{d}^T \mathbf{C}^{-1} \mathbf{d}$$

This formula can be used during the calculation of T^2; r and s refer to the possible pairs of the p variables, ν^{rs} is the element in the rth row and sth column of the *inverse* of covariance matrix $\mathbf{C}^{-1}$.

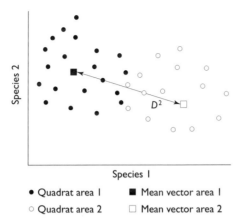

Species 2

Species 1

- • Quadrat area 1   ■ Mean vector area 1
- ○ Quadrat area 2   □ Mean vector area 2

Figure 11.5 Two groups of quadrats from two areas plotted on two species to illustrate the concept of an average quadrat and the distance between two average quadrats. Reprinted, with permission, from Poole (1974).

When used in this way, D^2 may be thought of as a multivariate residual giving a measure of the distance between the suspected outlier and the centre of the group. If the population of values is assumed to be multivariate normal, D^2 will follow a chi-squared distribution[1] with p degrees of freedom. Large significant values of D^2 can arise because the observation is either an outlier or because the p variable values contain one or several errors and should be checked (Manly, 1994). Where the problem is one of allocating new observations to previously formed groups, D^2-values can provide a useful criterion; the observation is allocated to the group to which it has the lowest D^2-value.

Simple linear discriminant functions

In its normal form, D^2 measures the overall difference between two groups of sample units, but it can be useful to know how much each variable contributes to this difference. For each observation it is possible to calculate a score z, and these scores allow an observation to be assigned to one of the two groups so it gives the minimum error:

value of pth variable

$$z = a_1 x_1 + a_2 x_2 + \cdots + a_p x_p$$

discriminant coefficient for pth variable

The set discriminant coefficients $(a_1, \ldots, a_p)$ account for the difference between the two groups and allow z-scores for each observation to be calculated; they are the elements of the column matrix $\mathbf{a}$ obtained from $\mathbf{a} = \mathbf{C}^{-1}\mathbf{d}$ where $\mathbf{C}^{-1}$ is the inverse of the pooled sample covariance matrix and $\mathbf{d}$ is the difference between the mean vectors of the two groups. Thus, if the distance (D^2) between two groups of observations is calculated, a corresponding discriminative function must exist which can be used to assign observations to one or other of the groups. Its usefulness comes from the fact that these observations may be new, i.e. not part of the data set used to generate the discriminative function.

A discriminative function score z is calculated for each observation; the values of z can then be used to place an observation in the appropriate group. Observation with high z-values are placed in one group and observations with low z-values are placed in the other group. The importance of particular variables in accounting for differences between the groups is given by the relative size of the discriminative coefficients (a_i). The larger the discriminative coefficient associated with a variable, the greater the contribution of that variable to the overall distance between the samples. This is only a very brief introduction to the simplest form of discriminative functions, applicable to situations where two groups are being considered. More detailed accounts of discriminative analysis may be found in Harris (1985) and Manly (1994).

11.3 *Using ordination diagrams*

11.3.1 *How to interpret ordination diagrams*

Where ordinations diagrams are derived from simple data matrices, e.g. species by sample units, a similar approach to Section 11.2 can be adopted; the species composition of the sample units is examined and an attempt is made to identify patterns or trends in the distribution of species along each ordination axis. One useful approach is to plot species abundance (or variable values) against the axis score. These diagrams allow the relationships between species and ordination scores to be easily identified. Three patterns are commonly found. Some species will show no obvious trend, being equally abundant along the entire axis. Some will be most abundant towards the centre of the ordination axis, abundance declining in both directions towards the ends of the axis. Others may demonstrate a clear trend, increasing in abundance in one direction along the axis; they can be considered as indicator species and may help to characterise the nature of the complex gradient represented by the ordination axis.

The differential distribution of species along an ordination axis forms the basis of TWIN-SPAN classifications described in Section 9.2.3. Although this type of analysis can be very informative, it is only strictly necessary when using polar ordination. For all other commonly used ordination procedures, inspection of the loading factors (component coefficients) generated during the analysis provide a direct measure of the strength of correlation between each variable and a given ordination axis. Ordination is a procedure which extracts a series of equations (components) from the data matrix, equations that account for the maximum amount of variation present in the data, and it allows each sample unit to be characterised by a single ordination score (z). Here is the generalised form of this equation for a data set where p variables have been recorded for each sample unit:

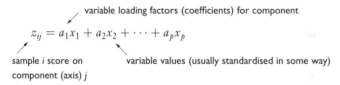

$$z_{ij} = a_1 x_1 + a_2 x_2 + \cdots + a_p x_p$$

variable loading factors (coefficients) for component

sample i score on component (axis) j

variable values (usually standardised in some way)

The size of the loading coefficient associated with a variable is a direct measure of the correlation between the variable and the axis. Biplots, described in Chapter 8, provide a way of plotting loading factors and sample scores in a single ordination diagram, allowing the key variables to be identified and the direction in which they change most rapidly. Another aid to interpretation is to make simple plots of variable loading factors for the principal axes (Figure 11.6).

11.3.2 *Looking for other relationships*

Where additional data exists that has not been used to produce the ordination, e.g. for an ordination based on sample species composition, additional information might exist on environmental factors or current and past management practice at each location; this data

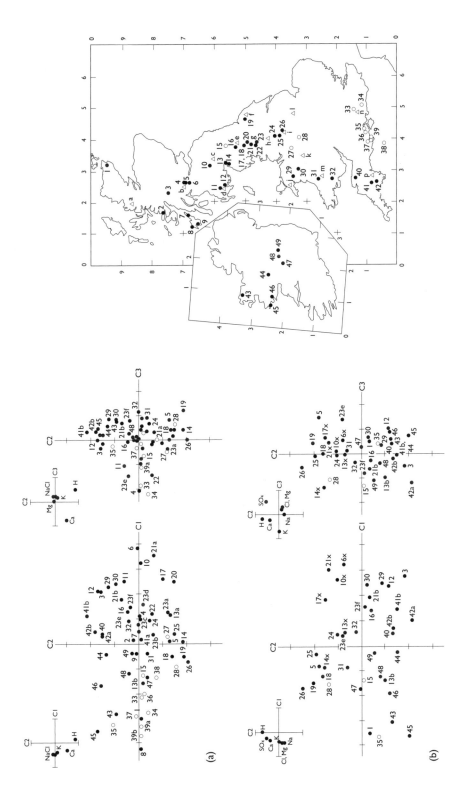

Figure 11.6 Principal component analysis of logarithmically transformed data for surface water samples taken from 49 mires in Britain and Ireland (numbers refer to site locations on the map): (a) cations and Cl⁻ values, (b) anions. Key to symbols: (●) ombrogenous sites, (○) mires in basins and valleys. Insets plot the component loading factors on axis I and axis II. Reprinted, with permission, from Proctor (1992).

may be used to help interpret the ordination. Variable values can be plotted against sample ordinations scores or as overlays or zones on the ordination diagram (Figure 11.7). If the original data was obtained from a random and representative sample, the relationship between ordination axis scores and measured variables may be explored more rigorously by using correlation and linear regression. The ordinations scores derived from procedures based on, or related to, principal component analysis (PCA) will be normally distributed (this will not necessarily be true for axis scores obtained from a polar ordination). Depending on the nature and the amount of the additional data, there are several possibilities:

- Ordination scores and variable values normally distributed, preliminary plots suggest linear relationships (data may need to be transformed before analysis)
    - Limited number of variables, linear relationship between variable and axis scores.
        - Either a Pearson moment correlation analysis (Chapter 7)
        - Or a multiple linear regression (Chapter 10)
    - Large number of variables, i.e. multiple comparisons
        - Either a Pearson moment correlation analysis, but adjust probability to account for multiple comparisons and to reduce the likelihood of committing a type I error (Chapter 7)
        - Or a multiple linear regression (Chapter 10)
- Ordination scores and variable values not normally distributed and/or preliminary plots suggest relationships are not linear; transformation unsuccessful
    - Use non-parametric correlations based on ranked data, e.g. Spearman's rank correlation (Chapter 7, Appendix 1.1); if necessary, correct probability levels for multiple comparisons

Sometimes it may only be possible to code a variable as 0 or 1; for example, the presence or absence of a species, or whether the samples units were located on or off a particular geological stratum. In this situation the point biserial correlation coefficient (r_p) may be calculated. This procedure allows a correlation coefficient to be calculated between a coded discontinuous variable and a continuous variable:

$$r_p = \frac{|M_p - M_q|}{S_x} \times \sqrt{pq}$$

with the annotation: absolute difference between M_p and M_q (pointing to $|M_p - M_q|$)

where p = proportion of samples in the first group
M_p = mean of the continuous variable recorded for samples in the first group
q = proportion of samples in the second group
M_q = mean of the continuous variable recorded for samples in the second group
S_x = standard deviation of continuous variable x.

The significance of r_p can be assessed by calculating the associated t-statistic which has $n - 2$ degrees of freedom, where n is the total number of paired observations. The same formula may be used to assess the significance of the product-moment correlation coefficient if appropriate tables of r are not available.

$$t = r\sqrt{\frac{n - 2}{1 - r^2}}$$

As an alternative to point biserial correlation, sample units may be divided into groups on the basis of the coded variable and the mean ordination scores calculated for each group

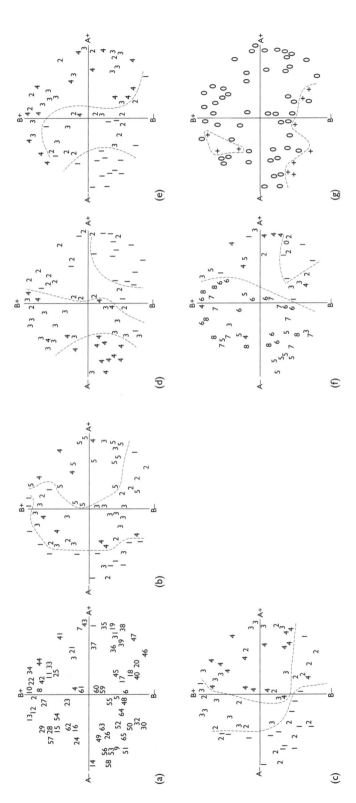

Figure 11.7 (a to c) Quadrat ordination for principal component analysis of sea cliff data on Anglesey, Wales: (a) quadrat plot; (b) species richness in quadrats plotted as quintiles (1 = low, 5 = high); (c) total plant cover plotted as quartiles (1 = low, 4 = high). (d to g) Plots of environmental data superimposed on the quadrat ordination: (d) soil conductivity/salinity as quartiles (1 = low, 4 = high); (e) aspect (SSW = 9; SW, S = 8; WSW, SSE = 7; W, SE = 6; WNW, ESE = 5; NW, E = 4; NNW, ENE = 3; N, NE = 2; NNE = 1; flat = 0; (f) soil moisture as quartiles (1 = low, 4 = high); (g) bird influence. Reprinted, with permission, from Goldsmith (1973).

and compared using the *t*-test. In theory this approach could be extended as follows. On the basis of a categorical variable, suppose that sample units can be allocated to a number of groups, then differences between group mean ordination scores could be tested using one-way analysis of variance or a non-parametric equivalent (Appendix 1.1).

11.4 *Ordination diagrams versus cluster diagrams*

When applied to the same data, the results of ordination and cluster analysis must be related. Each procedure accentuates different but complementary data properties. Ordination accentuates the continuous nature of the data, allowing gradients of change to be identified; classification and cluster analysis emphasise the discontinuous nature of data, allowing distinct groups of sample units to be identified. Although ordination is normally the preferred procedure, particularly for analysing community data sets, there is often no convincing a priori reason for assuming the data set does not contain marked discontinuities at differing scales that will be best identified by clustering or classifying the data. Because of this, and since both procedures are complementary, the most sensible strategy is to do both, ordination and cluster analysis. The results of both sets of analysis may then be compared.

Early in the analysis it should become clear whether it is possible to do a robust clustering or classification of sample units (Chapter 9). Where clustering fails to identify distinct groups capable of biological interpretation, our confidence in the appropriateness of the ordination will be increased. Where clustering proves successful, interpretation and understanding of the structure present in the data set can be improved by careful comparison between the results of two procedures. Here are the easiest procedures for comparing ordination and cluster diagrams:

- Overlay the sample unit end-group identities onto the ordination diagram and inspect the result. Are the end-group members associated with particular parts of the ordination axes? Are the similarity relationships between the end groups reflected in the distribution of group members in the ordination?
- Calculate and compare the end-group mean ordination scores (Figure 11.8). Do they differ between end groups?

11.5 *Direct analysis of partitioned data matrices*

The simplest direct approach to the analysis of a partitioned data table is to treat the data as a single table, i.e. effectively mixing together the environmental and species variables. The data can then be ordinated, with no distinction being made between variable types. There are several problems with this approach:

- If the numbers of environmental and species variables differ greatly, the ordination will either become an environmental ordination with passive species variables or a species ordination with passive environmental variables (Hill, 1988).
- The ordination may account for the majority of variation present in the data but fail to yield principal components with high loading coefficients for any particular groups of variables (Austin, 1968), making interpretation difficult if not impossible.

For these reasons, and because of the availability of alternative methods, this approach has not been extensively used, and it cannot be recommended as a general procedure for investigating the relationship between species abundance and environmental factors (Dolédec and Chessel, 1994).

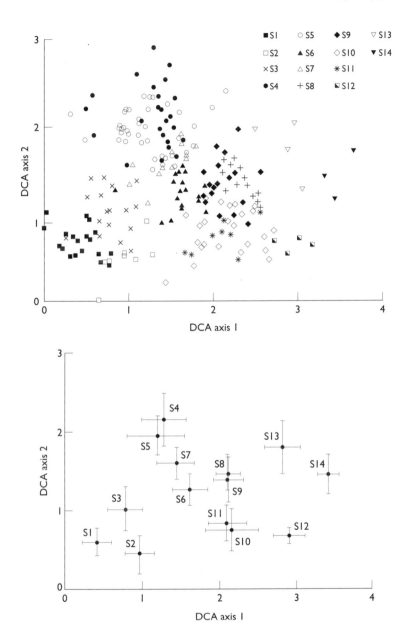

Figure 11.8 Combining a detrended correspondence analysis (DCA) with a TWINSPAN analysis on the vegetation of a valley mire at Thursley Common in southern England: (a) ordination of quartile data, (b) plot of mean DCA scores for end groups identified using TWINSPAN. Adapted from Greshon (1989).

However, exceptions may exist where ordination of the complete table could be appropriate. The underlying theoretical model normally adopted during community ordination (ter Braak and Prentice, 1988) assumes that the abundance and distribution of species may be explained in terms of environmental differences between sample units (Chapter 10 and see below). A primary aim of ordination is to identify which environmental variables (gradients) or combination of variables (complex or compound gradients) account for the observed variation in species abundance among sample units. However, this model will not be appropriate in all situations. In some habitats, or among sample units from similar environments (e.g. samples drawn from short environmental gradients), the abundance of species may not be influenced by the physical environment alone; biotic factors and species interaction[2] may be equally important.

Biotic factors may sometimes be more important than abiotic factors; species abundance and distribution may reflect the underlying pattern of community species interactions. It is possible to conceive of situations where it may be appropriate to ordinate the complete data table, i.e. where the primary aim of the analysis is not the interpretation of species distributions in terms of environmental factors. This will be true if there is no reason to distinguish between species factors and environmental factors, both being viewed as equally important characteristics of the samples. This situation might arise in a study of the environmental impact of human activity on a landscape. For each sample unit (e.g. blocks of land) information could be recorded on the selective presence of certain plant and animal species (e.g. abundance of a limited number of indicator or rare species) and on a range of environmental variables (e.g. susceptibility to soil erosion, length of hedgerow); each variable could legitimately be considered equally informative and valid for the characterisation of the sampled landscape plots.

Even where the aim of the analysis is to elucidate relationships between species factors and environmental factors, it may be appropriate to consider some species as pseudo-environmental variables. If a direct analysis of a partitioned data table is undertaken, care must be taken to ensure that appropriate weightings are given to the different variable types. It would be unwise to attach too much importance to the results of a single cycle of analysis. The influences of individual variables should be considered carefully by their selective exclusion and inclusion. The investigator should be guided by the nature of the data available and the aims of the study.

11.5.1 Correlation between ordination scores

Perhaps the simplest approach to relating two sets of variables from a partitioned data matrix is to correlate the ordination scores obtained from the separate analyses of each part of the table (Jeffers, 1978). Application of this procedure to a matrix of species and environmental factors by sample community would involve the following steps:

1. Ordinate the species by sample part of the data matrix. Attempt to interpret principal components by examining the variable loading coefficients.
2. Ordinate the environmental factors by sample part of the data matrix. Attempt to interpret principal components by examining the variable loading coefficients.
3. Correlate ordination scores from both the species and environmental ordinations. Attempt to interpret any significant correlation. All combinations of axis scores should be correlated; the first axis scores of one ordination may be correlated with the second or third axis scores of the other ordination.

This procedure has been used in a number of early studies (Barkham and Norris, 1970; Fourt *et al.*, 1971) and in the absence of access to specialised computer programs it may be the only practicable procedure.

Canonical correlation analysis provides a true direct method capable of relating two sets of variables. The method has similarities with principal component analysis, but maximises the correlation between linear combinations of each set of variables. Each set of variables may be summarised by a limited number of canonical variables which have the form

$$U_i = a_{i1}x_1 + a_{i2}x_2 + \cdots + a_{ip}x_p$$

$$V_i = b_{i1}y_1 + b_{i2}y_2 + \cdots + b_{iq}y_q$$

where U_i and V_i correspond to the canonical scores for the ith canonical variable extracted from a data matrix containing n samples for each of which p x-variables and q y-variables have been recorded. As a procedure, canonical correlation extracts the canonical variables U_i and V_i such that the correlation between each pair is maximised. The significance of the canonical correlations between each pair of extracted canonical variables may be tested and the importance of each individual variable assessed from inspection of the relative size of canonical coefficients (b_{ij} and a_{ij}). In essence the canonical correlations may be viewed as a multivariate generalisation of the normal univariate correlation analysis. Both Jeffers (1978) and Manly (1994) provide concise and very readable introductions to the methods; Harris (1985) provides a more rigorous description and Gittins (1985) reviews the application of the method in biology.

Dolédec and Chessel (1994) point out that the methods may be limited by the requirements that the numbers of x and y variables should be similar; the sample size n should exceed the number of variables; the canonical variables relating the two sets of variables should be orthogonal; and the variables should be linearly related. But despite these constraints, some of which are not unique to canonical correlation (Chapter 10), the method does provide a more elegant solution than the indirect methods outlined above. Unfortunately, although many textbooks provide outline calculations, in practice they are difficult to apply without access to appropriate statistical software. With the exception of SPSS,[3] the procedure does not appear to be widely supported by the more common statistical packages.

11.5.2 *Canonical correspondence analysis*

Canonical correspondence analysis (CCA), an extension of correspondence analysis (CA) developed by ter Braak (1985, 1986), provides an efficient procedure for the direct analysis of combined species and environmental data sets. The method has been extensively applied and has become the method of choice for many ecologists (Birks and Austin, 1992; Kent and Coker, 1992). CCA was originally described as an eigenanalysis-based ordination method that incorporated correlation and multiple regression to produce an integrated ordination relating species and environmental factors. Like CA it is an iterative process, using multiple regression to select a linear combination of environmental variables that explains the maximum amount of variation in the species scores on each axis of the site (sample unit) ordination. However, ter Braak (1987) and ter Braak and Verdonschot (1995) provide an alternative derivation in which the method can be seen as an extension of weighted averaging. Following ter Braak (1987), Figure 11.9 shows the hypothetical response curves (abundance against environmental factors) for four species A, B, C and D. Species A is associated with dry sites, whereas species D is confined to the wetter end of the gradient. A measure of the 'location' of each species along the gradient may be obtained by calculating a weighted average for moisture:

$$u_k = \sum_{i=1}^{n} \frac{s_{ik} x_i}{S} \quad \text{with} \quad S = \sum_{i=1}^{n} s_{ik}$$

where u_k = weighted average of the kth species (out of m)
s_{ik} = abundance of species k at site i (out of n)
S = total abundance of species k
x_i = value of environmental variable x (moisture) at site i

For presence–absence data the weighted average will simply be the average moisture value of the sites at which species k occurs. The arrows in Figure 11.9a indicate the weighted moisture

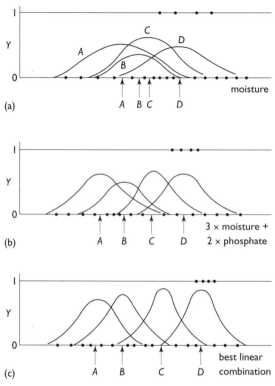

Figure 11.9 Artificial example of single-peaked response curves for four species (A to D) with respect to standard-ised environmental variables showing different degrees of separation: (a) moisture, (b) a linear combination of moisture and phosphate, chosen a priori; (c) the best linear combination of environmental variables, chosen by CCA. Sites are shown by dots at $y = 1$ if species D is present and as dots at $y = 0$ if species D is absent. Reprinted, with permission, from ter Braak (1987).

average values for the four species; the occurrences of species D along the gradient are indicated by the dots on the top line of Figure 11.9. The explanatory power of a weighted average depends on whether the species are clearly separated along the gradient by their weighted average values. The greater the separation (distance between the arrows), the greater the explanatory power of the environmental factor used to calculate the weighted average. Similar weighted averages imply that the species response curves for that variable are similar and that the variable has little predictive value, being unable to account for the distribution of species among the sampled sites. The explanatory power of different environmental variables can be measured by the dispersion of the weighted average (δ); the higher the dispersion, the greater the ability of the variable to explain the variation observed in the species data:

$$\delta = \sum_{k=1}^{m} \frac{S_k u_k^2}{T}$$

where $T = \sum_{k=1}^{m} S_k$ is the overall species total for the data table.

Notice that δ is obtained by summing over all the m species present in the data. To calculate the weighted variable dispersion, each environmental variable must first be standardised to mean 0 and variance 1.0. And weighted average variances must be standardised so that

$$\sum_{i=1}^{n} t_i x_i = 0 \quad \text{and} \quad \sum_{i=1}^{n} \frac{t_i x_i^2}{T} = 1$$

where t_i is the total abundance of species present in sample i.

The best single explanatory variable can be selected by comparing dispersion values. However, it is possible that a combination of variables may provide a better description of the relationship between species abundance and the environment. For example, a combination of moisture and phosphate (e.g. 3 times moisture plus 2 times phosphate) might have a higher average weight dispersion than moisture alone, and thus provide a better explanation of species data (Figure 11.9b). The improved explanation provided by the combined variable is shown by the reduced width and increased separation of the species response curves and the concentration of D within a shorter length of the gradient (Figure 11.9b). It follows that other linear combinations of variables might provide an even better basis for separating the response of species to the environmental variables. All linear combination of variables will have the general form

$$x_i = b_1 z_{i1} + b_2 z_{i2} + \cdots + b_p z_{ip}$$

where $x_i =$ the value of the compound environmental variable at site i
   $z_{ij} =$ the value of the jth environmental variable at site i
   $b_j =$ the weight belonging to the jth variable

The weight b_j may be negative or positive. CCA chooses the optimal weights for the linear combination of environmental variables that maximises the dispersion of the species scores. The result represents the 'best' linear combination that accounts for the maximum amount of variation present in the species data set. When calculated using the best linear combination of variables, the weighted averages for the four species reduce the width of the species response curves and maximise the separation between species (Figure 11.9c).

CCA can produce four types of output: standard ordination diagrams for species and site (sample), a biplot of the species ordination together with the environmental variables, and a triplot combining ordinations of species, samples and environmental variables. Environmental factors are depicted as axes indicated by arrows pointing in the direction of maximum change of the variable across the diagram. The length of the arrow marking a variable is proportional to the rate of change of the variable along the direction indicated by the arrow. Environmental variables with long arrows are most strongly correlated with the ordination axis and thus with the pattern of community variation described by the ordination (Figure 11.10). Plotted species points can be projected onto a variable axis indicated by an arrow. The order of the projected points along the axis corresponds approximately to the ranking of the species' weighted averages and the approximate position of their distribution along that environmental gradient (ter Braak, 1987). Unfortunately, CCA can only be realistically performed if the investigator has access to the CANCO or similar computer packages, which are not widely available outside of specialised academic departments.

11.6 *Conclusion*

Remember that ordination and cluster analysis are essentially methods for exploring complex data sets. It is all too easy to overinterpret results. And it is all too easy to see an ordination or cluster diagram as a valid end to a study; it is not. Although the identification of pattern and regularities in complex data sets is vital to the scientific study of ecology and the environment,

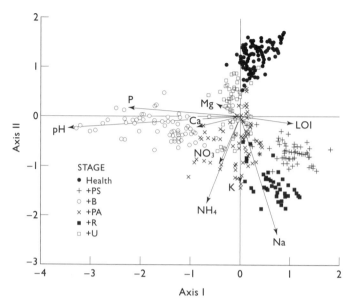

Figure 11.10 Ordination diagram from CANOCO for the first two axes, showing the relationship between the different successional stages and the soil nutrients. The soil nutrient vectors are shown by arrows and their length is multiplied by a factor of 10. Heath = open heathland, +PS = *Pinus sylvestris* is the major invader; +B = *Betula* spp. are the major invaders; +PA = *Pteridium aquilinum* is the major invader; +R = *Rhododendron ponticum is* the major invader; +U = *Ulex europaeus* is the major invader; Ca = exchangeable calcium, K = exchangeable potassium; LOI = loss on ignition; Mg = exchangeable magnesium; Na = exchangeable sodium; NH_4 = extractable ammonium nitrogen; NO_3 = extractable nitrite/nitrate nitrogen; P = extractable phosphorus; pH = pH. Reprinted, with permission, from Mitchell *et al.* (1997).

little is achieved if the patterns identified cannot be logically interpreted or cannot be used to generate testable hypotheses. This chapter has looked at how to interpret ordination and cluster diagrams (or classifications). Most of the approaches were essentially descriptive, in keeping with the exploratory nature of ordination and cluster analysis when applied to environmental data sets. There are more rigorous statistical procedures (Digby and Kempton, 1987) but they are rarely appropriate for ecological data sets, which are often poorly defined and fail to meet the required characteristics.

It is a mistake to assume that any one approach will always yield the best results, i.e. the most interpretable. Although some methods are clearly more elegant than others, no single approach is guaranteed to perform better than others in all circumstances. The choice of available method will be governed by three factors: the aims of the study, the amount and type of data collected, and the availability of appropriate computer software. Only two general recommendations can be made:

- Unless strong a priori reasons exist for only ordinating or clustering a data set, both techniques should be applied to the data.
- Use canonical correspondence analysis (Section 11.5.2) for community data sets containing information on species abundance and environmental factors and where ordination is considered most appropriate. If this is not possible then consider the simpler alternative of correlating environmental factors with ordination scores (Section 11.3) in preference to the other direct procedures outlined in Section 11.5.

Further reading

Digby, P.G.N and Kempton, R.A. (1987) *Multivariate Analysis of Ecological Communities*. Chapman & Hall, London.

Gittins, R. (1985) *Canonical Analysis: A Review with Applications in Ecology*. Springer-Verlag, Berlin.

Harris, R.J. (1985) *A Primer of Multivariate Statistics*. Academic Press, New York.

Kent, M. and Coker, P. (1992) *Vegetation Description and Analysis: A Practical Approach*. CRC and Belhaven Press, London.

Manly, B.F.J. (1994) *Multivariate Statistical Methods: A Primer*, 2nd edn. Chapman & Hall, London.

Notes

Chapter 1

1. Often with pairs of variables the value of one, the dependent variable, is clearly dependent on the value of the other, the independent variable. In experiments, values of the independent variable are normally fixed or set by the experimenter and their effects on the dependent variable are measured.
2. In this context neither of these properties is necessarily desirable.
3. Note that part of the reduction in confidence interval is due to the influence of n on the value of t, and the presence of $\sqrt{n}$ in the denominator of the equation.
4. The central limit theorem states that as the sample size increases, the mean of samples drawn from a population with any shaped distribution will approach a normal distribution.
5. The occurrence of runs can often be identified from visually inspecting control charts; alternatively, runs or excessive numbers of unusually high or low values can be identified statistically using several non-parametric tests, including the runs test, described in Chapter 4.
6. PCR, the polymerase chain reaction, allows amplification of DNA sequences.

Chapter 3

1. Rounding estimates down to the nearest 'whole animal'.
2. Unfortunately the label l_x has not been used consistently. Some authors use it to denote the number of individuals out of a standardised cohort size of 1000 surviving to age x. Similarly, d_x may be defined, as it is here, to be the number of individuals dying in a particular age class. But it may also be defined as the probability of survival between successive age classes, then $d_x = l_x - l_{x+1}$. I

have tried to adopt labelling which is logical and in common use among undergraduate textbooks.

Chapter 4

1. This may vary between versions, but the default conditions can be specified by the user.
2. The absolute magnitudes are not important: Perhaps 1 might code for the smallest, 2 for middle values and 3 for the largest.
3. Since the null hypothesis is that the subjects of study, e.g. plants, are randomly distributed in space, a random sampling scheme is not required. If the object of the analysis is simply to test for the presence of a non-random distribution a regular sampling scheme can be used.
4. This is the mean distance from the point to all neighbouring points. Neighbours are defined as those points which would contribute a side to the polygon that surrounds the point from which the distances are measured.
5. This measures the distance of the centre of gravity of the polygon from the point about which the polygon is drawn.

Chapter 5

1. This is using the functional definition of a community as the sum of interacting species.
2. Percentage similarity (PS) was introduced in Chapter 1 and is covered in more detail in Chapter 6, along with other measures of similarity.
3. If the binomial variable is the number field voles with a particular species of ectoparasite, the probability of success will be equal to the proportion of voles found to have the ectoparasite and the number of trials will be equal to the number of voles.

4. The required computer procedures in MINITAB can be found by selecting the **Calc** option from the menu bar and then the **Random Data** option.
5. A BIDS citation search in 1998 showed that the original paper from 1974 has been cited 150 times, the 1977 paper over 600 times and the 1979 book, which details the model, over 1800 times.

Chapter 6

1. If more than two samples are being compared r_i is equal to the difference between the smallest value and the largest value of x_i in the complete data set, so that the distance measure is scaled across the complete range of x_i.
2. Used here as a descriptive statistic only.

Chapter 7

1. This corrects for the effects of using discrete values to calculate a test statistic which has a continuous distribution.
2. Normally when tests are carried out, they are said to be two tailed; that is, they test for deviation from the null hypothesis in both direction, e.g. whether the mean is larger or smaller than expected. In a one-tailed test, deviation is tested in one direction only, e.g. whether the mean is larger than expected. By discounting one possible direction of deviation, the one-tailed test is more powerful than the two-tailed test. The one-tailed procedure must only be used where there is good evidence for excluding the possibility of deviation in one direction.
3. In statistics the expected value of a variable is equivalent to its mean.
4. In this context an individual may represent a clump or patch of a single species.
5. Alternatively the binomial function may be used.

6. Spearman's correlation test should not be used for $n < 7$; the critical values of r_s at $p = 0.05$ for $n = 7$ to $n = 10$ are as follows: $r_s = 0.750$ for $n = 7$, $r_s = 0.714$ for $n = 8$, $r_s = 0.683$ for $n = 9$, $r_s = 0.648$ for $n = 10$.

Chapter 8

1. Principal coordinate analysis is also known as classical scaling; it is one of several multidimensional scaling methods.
2. This Euclidean space, may be viewed as a multidimensional volume, a hypervolume, in which samples are plotted on the basis of n species or variable dimensions. Ordination methods are able to produce a two- or three-dimensional representation of this space.
3. The DECORANA program, developed by Hill (1979) to perform DCA, multiples the SD units by 100, so an axis score of 400 means an axis of length 4 SD units.
4. This differs slightly from the convention of using a bold lower case letter to indicate a column matrix. But I have found that it can cause confusion to have lower case letters for column vectors and for matrix elements. I have used a bold upper case letter for all matrices, be they row matrices, column matrices or rectangular matrices. I have used an italic lower case letter for all matrix elements.

Chapter 11

1. As an alternative measure of significance $D/2$ is distributed as a standard normal deviate.
2. Important interaction may occur at more than one trophic level and between organisms at two different trophic levels.
3. Release 5 and above of SPSS for Windows provides a macro CANCORR to do canonical correlation analysis.

Glossary

accuracy A measure of the closeness of the sample statistic to the true population value (e.g. the accuracy of the sample estimate of density $(\hat{N})$ is equal to the difference between $\hat{N}$ and the true population density (N)). Also used to describe the nearness of an individual measurement or measure to its true value.

a posteriori Describes the situation where the test or hypothesis is developed after the data has been collected.

a priori Describes the situation where the tests are planned or the hypothesis is developed before the data has been collected.

ANOVA Acronym for analysis of variance, a procedure used to test for differences among sample means.

arcsine transformation Arcsine is the inverse of the sine function, $\sin^{-1}$. Arcsine transformation, where the arcsine is taken of the square root of the value is often used to normalise proportional data.

association Measures the strength of relationship between two variables.

attribute Synonymous with trait; a particular type of observation that can be recorded for a sample unit. For a trait or attribute, several categories of record may be possible, e.g. flower colour might be classed as red, pink or white.

autocorrelation Occurs where members of a set of observations are correlated amongst themselves. This may occur where observations are taken close to one another in time or where sample units are spatially close together. Where autocorrelation occurs the observations in the sample are not independent or random.

average, arithmetic mean, mean Synonymous terms for a measure of the central tendency (or most typical value). The mean is equal to the sum of values, divided by the number of observations.

between-sample sum of squares ($SS_{between}$) A term used in analysis of variance (ANOVA) to describe the variation in data due to differences between treatment means. It is a measure for the variation between groups of observations resulting from different group treatment levels.

bias A consistent over- or underestimate of the true population value. Bias most frequently results from inadequate or unrepresentative sampling, although some statistical procedures or data manipulations may introduce bias.

bimodal distribution A frequency distribution that has two separate peaks.

binomial distribution A theoretical probability distribution used to describe situations that can be represented as a series of independent trials, where the outcome of each can be classed as one of only two possible categories. Each individual trial is called a Bernoulli trial.

bootstrapping A method for estimating the variance and mean of a calculated statistic by repeated subsampling of a data set.

canonical analysis, canonical variant analysis (CVA), canonical correspondence analysis (CCA) Advanced forms of multivariate analysis used to analyse complex data sets that may be partitioned into groups of observations. CCA is frequently used in ecology to examine the relationships between sets of environmental variables and species abundance values.

chi-squared (χ^2) distribution A theoretical probability distribution based on the difference between the sample variance and the true variance of a population. Many statistical tests generate test statistics that follow the χ^2-distribution; the significance of these test statistics is assessed by comparing their value with tabulated values of χ^2.

cluster analysis A procedure for grouping sample units based on their similarity.

confidence interval A measure of the spread of data. It may be derived for different probability levels and is enclosed by a lower limit and an upper limit. For a 90% confidence interval about a mean, the probability of the true mean occurring within the interval is 90%.

contingency tables A way of displaying categories for two or more variables. The term is often used as synonymous with a 2×2 contingency table, where the data for two variables, each of which may occur in two states only, is presented as a table. Presence and absence data for two variables (*A* and *B*) is frequently summarised in a 2×2 contingency table. The chi-squared test (*q.v.*) is often used to analyse data summarised as a contingency table.

control General term used to refer to an unmodified or untreated part of an experimental design. The impacts of treatments are assessed by comparing treatment parts of the experimental design (e.g. plots, organisms, populations) with the untreated control.

correlation Measure of the strength of association between two variables. A positive association means that both variables increase together; a negative association means that one variable increases in size as the other decreases.

correspondence analysis (CA) Also known as reciprocal averaging, a multivariate procedure for ordination.

cumulative frequency The number of times an observation or a sample unit takes a particular value.

degrees of freedom A number often needed to assess the significance of a statistical test. Its value depends on the sample size, the number of treatments or categories and the way in which the data has been manipulated.

dependent variable An observed variable, sometimes called the response variable, its value is not set by the experimenter but depends on the effects of the experimental treatment or manipulation. The treatment or treatment levels are the independent variable and are set or determined by the experimenter.

dispersion Spread of data values, often measured by the standard deviation.

diversity An ecological term normally used to refer to the richness or variety of species present in a community sample and their relative abundance. In a wider context it refers to the heterogeneity of a data set.

error Difference between a statistic and the true population value. Errors may arise from many sources. For example, sampling errors and measurement or determination errors may contribute to the overall total error associated with a statistic. Individual errors are assumed to be independent and equally likely to be positive or negative, i.e. normally distributed about the true population value.

estimate Any statistic calculated from a sample and used to approximate the value of the statistic for the whole population.

factorial (experiment) An experimental design in which all possible combinations of treatment factors levels (set by the experimenter) occur in the data. A balanced design is where there are the same numbers of 'observations' for each combination of treatment factors.

frequency The number of times a value or range of values occur in a sample. But often used as the percentage or proportional frequency, which is the frequency of the value in the sample divided by the total number of observations in the sample. The frequency distribution is the number of times each possible value occurs in the sample. The percentage or proportional frequency distribution is the percentage or proportional frequency of every possible value in the sample.

F-test A statistical test used to test for equal-group sample variance. Based on the *F*-distribution, an asymmetric continuous distribution with a mode of 1.0 used in ANOVA.

geometric mean A measure of position or central tendency of data equal to the antilogarithm of the sum of the logarithms of individual data values.

goodness of fit Normally used for the difference between observed data values and data values generated from a theoretical distribution chosen by the investigator. Goodness-of-fit tests, such as the *G*-test and chi-squared procedure, can be used to assess whether the differences between the observed and expected (i.e. generated values) are significant.

G-test Name given to the log-likelihood ratio test, which can be used as an alternative to the chi-squared procedure.

harmonic mean A measure of position or central tendency of data equal to the reciprocal of the sum of the reciprocals of individual data values.

homogeneity of variances An assumption of some test, e.g. *t*-tests, ANOVA, that treatment group or sample variances are equal.

independence Most statistical tests assume that individual data values or observations are independent of each other. That is, for a particular variable x the value of one observation does not determine or affect the value of another; each value of x is unaffected by other values of x in the sample.

index and indices General term for derived measures that provides a single value which emphasises one particular feature or property of a data set. Indices are often scaled to range from 0 to 1.0.

individual A single statistical observation. In many computer packages an observation corresponds to a single row element; the total number of observations (rows in a column) is the number of cases.

integer A whole number.

interquartile range A measure of spread; where the data is ranked, the interquartile range equals the range from the value 25% down the list to the value 75% down the list.

interval scale Observations are ordered and grouped into non-overlapping but continuous intervals (units). The interval scale incorporates the classification and ordering of observations but allows the difference between units of the scale to be determined.

jackknifing A method to estimate the variance and bias of a statistic by recalculating the statistic using a subset of the data.

kurtosis A measure of the shape of a distribution.

linear regression A statistical procedure for assessing the strength of relationship between two variables (x, y) and fitting a linear equation to the data ($y = c + mx$ where c is the intercept of the plotted line on the y-axis at $x = 0$ and m is the slope of the line). The method can be extended to describe the relation between the dependent variable y and more than one independent variable; this is multiple regression ($q.v.$).

logistic regression A form of linear regression where the dependent variable is transformed using logits. Logistic regression is a useful procedure for predicting values that have a restricted range of possible values, e.g. proportions or percentages.

logit transformation Used to convert values on a scale with limits (e.g. proportions) to a scale without limits. Transformation for a proportion, x: $\text{logit}(x) = \ln(x/(1 - x))$.

matched samples or data Synonym for paired samples or repeated measures. Where two different variables (x_1 and x_2) are measured from one sample unit, the values of x_1 and x_2 are paired or matched. Paired or matched data may be obtained where one variable only is measured. If the weights of the same 10 fish are measured at the start and at the end of the study, the data will be paired or matched. If a different sample of 10 fish are measured at the start and end of the study the data set will be unmatched.

mean A measure of the central tendency (or most typical value). The mean is equal to the sum of values, divided by the number of observations.

mean square (MS) An estimate of variance, used in ANOVA, equal to the sum of squares (SS) divided by the degrees of freedom.

median A measure of position or central tendency of data equal to the middle value of a ranked data set.

mode A crude measure of position or central tendency of data equal to the value of the most common (frequent) value in a data set.

multivariate statistics A range of statistical procedures used to analyse and summarise data sets where more than one dependent variable is measured for each sample unit.

negative binomial distribution A theoretical discrete probability distribution which is frequently used to describe non-random, aggregated (clumped) distributions.

nominal scales Where individuals, sample units, or samples are classified as belonging to mutually exclusive categories, e.g., species, sex, colour, habitat type. Binary variables coded as 1 or 0 are an example. In ecological studies, species presence or absence is an example of a commonly encountered binary variable.

non-parametric test A test that makes few (if any) assumptions about the nature of the data distribution.

normal distribution A unimodal continuous probability distribution characterised by two parameters, the mean and the standard deviation. Many data sets are assumed to follow the normal distribution. Non-normally distributed values may often be transformed so they become normally distributed. Parametric tests, e.g. t-tests, ANOVA and linear regression, assume the data is normally distributed.

one-tailed test A test in which the null hypothesis is rejected only when the deviation from expected values under the null hypothesis is in one direction only. Suppose the weights of two samples of seeds A and B have been measured. One-tailed procedures can be used to test two possible null hypotheses that $A > B$ or that $A < B$. If the null hypothesis is that A and B are equal, a two-tailed test procedure would be used to reject the null hypothesis. For a given probability value (p), one-tailed tests are less conservative than two-tailed tests, i.e. they are more likely to reject the null hypothesis.

ordinal scales Ordinal scales involve classifying and ordering observations. Observations are classified into mutually exclusive categories that are ranked. For example, species abundance may be assessed subjectively as dominant, abundant, frequent, occasional and rare (the DAFOR scale). Ranking the classes from 1 (rare) to 5 (dominant) allows species abundance to be recorded as an ordinal scale: dominant species are recorded as 5, abundant as 4, frequent as 3, etc.

ordination General term for a group of multivariate procedures which allow samples or sample units to be ordered according to their relative similarities.

outlier An extreme or aberrant observation lying well away from the rest of the data.

paired samples or data Synonym for matched or repeated measures; *see* matched samples or data.

parameter A known characteristic of a statistical population of items (e.g. density).

parametric tests Tests that assume data are normally distributed.

platykurtic A measure or description of the shape of the distribution. In comparison to a normal distribution, a platykurtic distribution has more observations associated with the shoulders than one would expect, and fewer values associated with the region about the mean and the tails of the distribution.

Poisson distribution A theoretical discrete frequency distribution that occurs when events occur randomly.

polar ordination (PO) A multivariate method of sample ordination based on measures of sample unit similarity.

population The entire collection of individuals or potential sample units. The population of trees in a wood consists of every tree present. In statistics, population refers to the potential pool of all possible sample units. The population mean of tree height would be obtained by calculating the average tree height using measurements taken from every tree in the wood. Since it is rarely possible to record the entire population, a sample must be taken and used to draw inferences about the population.

post-hoc Means after this.

precision Measures the repeatability of a statistic; that is, the variation in the statistic obtained from replicated samples collected and treated in the same way. The smaller the range or variation between replicate sample estimates, the greater the precision.

principal component analysis (PCA) A multivariate statistical method of sample ordination and variable reduction.

pseudoreplication A situation that occurs where replicate sample units or values are not independent. Pseudoreplication is a frequent problem encountered in ecological and environmental studies.

p-**value** The probability that the calculated statistic *does* differ from the expected value of the statistic under the null hypothesis. Traditionally in science the null hypothesis is rejected only when $p < 0.05$. That is, the likelihood of obtaining the calculated value and of the null hypothesis being true is less than 0.05. If the process of sampling and calculation were repeated 100 times, the value used to reject the null hypothesis would be obtained less then 5 times due to chance alone.

quadrat A fixed sample area, normally square but rectangular and circular quadrats can be used.

qualitative An observation that can be assigned to a descriptive category. The category or categories may subsequently be coded numerically, but the coded value does not relate directly to the nature of the data categories recorded.

quantitative An observation that can be meaningfully recorded as a numerical value.

random sample A sample where each individual or sample unit in the population has an equal chance of being measured or collected.

range A crude measure of data spread or dispersion, equal to the difference between the largest and smallest values.

ratio scale Observations that can be ordered along the real number line. The highest level of measurement, it incorporates the properties of the interval scale but includes zero.

relative frequency Equal to the proportional frequency of a value. The relative frequency of *A* is equal to the frequency of *A* divided by the sum of all frequency values. Where data is tabulated – sample or sample unit values represented as columns, variables as rows – relative frequency values are obtained by dividing column elements by column totals.

residuals The difference or variation in the data not explained by a fitted statistical model. The term is sometimes used more generally to describe the difference between the observed data value and the expected value.

sample A collection of individuals or sample units drawn from the statistical population. The sample mean is the average of all the values recorded for each item (individual or sample unit) in the sample. For example, the sample mean of tree height might be obtained by calculating the mean of height measurements made on 50 randomly selected trees.

sample size Number of sample units used to form the sample.

sample unit A basic item that is recorded or collected to form a sample, i.e. the sampling unit corresponds to the level at which individual observations are made. Suppose 20 quadrats are randomly placed in the study site, then the sample unit corresponds to the quadrat and the sample to 20 sample units.

scales of measurement Variables may be measured using four types of scale: nominal, ordinal, interval and ratio.

significance level The probability of obtaining a significant result if the null hypothesis is true. That is, the probability of making a type II error, where the null hypothesis is falsely accepted. In science this is traditionally set at $p = 0.05$.

skewed distribution A distribution which is non-symmetrical, i.e. has unequal numbers of values above and below the mean. Skewed distributions may be described as having a long tail to the right or left of the mean.

spread of values Synonymous with dispersion, often measured by the standard deviation.

standard deviation A measure of the spread or dispersion of data values.

standard error (SE) A measure of the spread or dispersion of sample mean values, sometimes called the standard deviation of the mean.

statistic An estimator of a population parameter, e.g. the estimate of mean population density obtained from a sample can be described as a statistic.

stratified random sample Where random samples are selected from a number of strata. Examples of strata include sections of a study area (e.g. sections of a field), particular populations of the species of interest, or categories of organisms. Stratified random sampling helps to ensure that a representative sample is obtained.

symmetric distribution The shape of the distribution is the same either side of the mean. The bell-shaped normal distribution is an example of a symmetric distribution.

t-**distribution** A family of theoretical distributions derived from the distribution of the sample means with respect to the true population mean.

t-**test (Student's *t*-test)** A parametric test frequently used to test whether two sample means are equal. The test statistic follows a *t*-distribution.

two-tailed test Adopted by most statistical tests; tests for the presence of a significant deviation of a test statistic in both directions, above and below its expected value under the null hypothesis. A two-tailed test procedure is used if the null hypothesis is that A and B are equal. At a significance level of $p = 0.05$, the two-tailed test will reject the null hypothesis if either $A > B$ or $B > A$ occurs with a probability greater than or equal to 0.025. Notice the combined probability value for exceeding either tail is 0.05.

type I error Made when the null hypothesis is wrongly rejected when it is actually true.

type II error Made when the null hypothesis is wrongly accepted when it is actually false.

uniform distribution A flat distribution where the probability of any value occurring is approximately equal.

unimodal distribution A distribution that has a single peak.

value A single piece of data (datum)

variable (variate) Anything that may be measured or recorded and varies between individual sample units. Variables may be measured using four types of scale: nominal, ordinal, interval and ratio.

variance A measure of the spread or dispersion of a data set. An important measure of dispersion, it is used or underlies the basis of several important statistical procedures, e.g. ANOVA.

within-sample variance (SS_{within}) Used in ANOVA, it measures the variation within a sample or group of values.

References

Chapter 1

Eckblad, J.W. (1991) How many samples should be taken? *Bioscience* **41**(5):346–48.

Ferris-Kaan, R. and Patterson, G.S. (1992) *Monitoring Vegetation Changes in Conservation Management of Forests*. Forestry Commission Bulletin 108. HMSO, London.

Fowler, J., Cohen, L. and Jarvis, P. (1998) *Practical Statistics for Field Biology*, 2nd edn. John Wiley, Chichester.

Glass, G., Peckham, P.D. and Sanders, J.R. (1972) Consequences of failure to meet assumptions underlying the fixed effects analyses of variance and covariance. *Reviews in Educational Research* **42**:237–88.

Goldsmith, F.B. (1991) Vegetation monitoring. In *Monitoring for Conservation and Ecology*, F.B. Goldsmith (ed.). Chapman & Hall, London, pp. 77–86.

Green, R.H. (1979) *Sampling Design and Statistical Methods for Environmental Biologists*. John Wiley, New York.

Greene, O. (1991) Tackling global warming. In *Environmental Global Issues*, P.M. Smith and K. Warr (eds). Hodder & Stoughton, London, pp. 203–42.

Greenwood, J.J.D. (1996) Basic techniques. In *Ecological Census Techniques*, W.J. Sutherland (ed.). Cambridge University Press, Cambridge, pp. 11–109.

Greig-Smith P. (1983) *Quantitative Plant Ecology*, 3rd edn. Blackwell Scientific, Oxford.

Greshon, S. (1989) A study of the plant community structure of a valley mire complex at Thursley Common National Nature Reserve, Surrey. PhD thesis, Polytechnic of Central London.

Hardman, D.J., McEldowney, S. and Waite, S. (1993) *Pollution: Ecology and Biotreatment*. Longman, Harlow.

Hellawell, J.M. (1991) Development of a rationale for monitoring. In *Monitoring for Conservation and Ecology*, F.B. Goldsmith (ed.). Chapman & Hall, London, pp. 1–32.

Hopkin, S.P. (1993) In situ biological monitoring of pollution in terrestrial and acquatic ecosystems. In *Handbook of Ecotoxicology*, Vol. 1, P. Calow (ed.). Blackwell Scientific, Oxford, pp. 397–427.

Hurlbert, S.H. (1984) Pseudoreplication and the design of ecological field experiments. *Ecological Monographs* **54**:187–211.

Kent, K.J. and Coker, P.D. (1992) *Vegetation Description and Analysis: A Practical Approach*. Belhaven Press, London.

Lehner, P.N. (1996) *Handbook of ethological methods*, 2nd edn. Cambridge University Press, Cambridge.

Ludwig, J.A. and Reynolds, J.F. (1988) *Statistical Ecology: A Primer on Methods and Computing*. John Wiley, New York.

Maher, W.A., Cullen, P.W. and Norris, R.H. (1994) Framework for designing sampling programs. *Environmental Monitoring and Assessment* **30**:139–62.

Moore, P.D. and Chapman, S.B. (eds) (1986) *Methods in Plant Ecology*, 2nd edn. Blackwell, Oxford.

Neave, H.R. (1979) *Elementary Statistics Tables*. George Allen and Unwin, London.

Rafaelli, D. and Hawkins, S. (1996) *Intertidal Ecology*. Chapman & Hall, London.

Siegel, A.F. (1988) *Statistics and Data Analysis: An Introduction*. John Wiley, New York.

Sokal, R.R. and Rohlf, F.J. (1995) *Biometry: the principles and practice of statistics in biological research*, 3rd edn. W.H. Freeman, New York.

Solomon, A.M. and Shugart, H.H. (eds) (1993) *Vegetation Dynamics and Global Change*. Chapman & Hall, New York.

Streever, W.J. and Bloom, S.A. (1993) The self-similarity curve: a new method of determining the sampling effort required to characterize communities. *Journal of Freshwater Ecology* **8**(4):401–3.

Wiener, J. and Solbrig, O.T. (1984) The meaning and measurement of size hierarchies in plant populations. *Oecologia* **61**:334–36.

Wolda, H. (1981) Similarity indices, sample size and diversity. *Oecologia* **50**:296–302.

Zane, L., Nelson, W.S., Jones, A.G. and Avise, J.C. (1999) Microsatellite assessment of multiple paternity in natural populations of a live-bearing fish. *Gambusia holbrooki*. *Journal of Evolutionary Biology* **12**:61–69.

Chapter 2

Anscombe, F.J. (1950) Sampling theory of the negative binomial and logarithmic series distributions. *Biometrika* **37**:358–82.

Bazzaz, F.A. (1975) Plant species diversity in old-field successional ecosystems in southern Illinois. *Ecology* **56**:485–88.

Begon, M., Harper, L.J. and Townsend, C.R. (1996) *Ecology*, 3rd edn. Blackwell Science, Oxford.

Camargo, J.A. (1993) Must dominance increase with the number of subordinate species in competitive interactions? *Journal of Theoretical Biology* **161**:537–42.

Farina, A. (1998) *Principles and Methods in Landscape Ecology*. Cambridge University Press, Cambridge.

Fisher, R.A., Corbet, A.S. and Williams, C.B. (1943) The relation between the number of species and the number of individuals in a random sample of an animal population. *Journal of Animal Ecology* **12**:42–58.

Fowler, J., Cohen, L. and Jarvis, P. (1998) *Practical Statistics for Field Biology*, 2nd edn. John Wiley, Chichester.

French, D.D. (1994) Hierarchical richness index (HRD): a simple procedure for scoring 'richness', for use with grouped data. *Biological Conservation* **69**:207–12.

Gaston, K.J. (1998) Biodiversity. In *Conservation Science and Action*, W.J. Sutherland (ed.). Blackwell Science, Oxford, pp. 1–19.

Gregoire, T.G. (1984) The jackknife: an introduction with applications in forestry data analysis. *Canadian Journal of Forestry Research* **14**:493–97.

Harvey, P.H. and Godfray, H.C.J. (1987) How species divide resources. *American Naturalist* **129**:318–20.

Heck, K.L.J., van Belle, G. and Simberloff, D. (1975) Explicit calculation of the rarefaction diversity measurement and the determination of sufficient sample size. *Ecology* **56**:1459–61.

Heip, C. (1974) A new index measuring evenness. *Journal of the UK Marine Biological Association* **54**:555–57.

Heltshe, J.F. and Forrester, N.E. (1983a) Estimating diversity using quadrat sampling. *Biometrics* **39**:1073–76.

Heltshe, J.F. and Forrester, N.E. (1983b) Estimating species richness using the jackknife procedure. *Biometrics* **39**:1–11.

Heltshe, J.F. and Forrester, N.E. (1985) Statistical evaluation of the jackknife estimate of diversity when using quadrat samples. *Ecology* **66**:107–11.

Heywood, V.H. (ed.) (1995) *Global Biodiversity Assessment*. Cambridge University Press, Cambridge.

Hill, M.O. (1973) Diversity and evenness: a unifying notation and its consequences. *Ecology* **54**:225–36.

Hughes, R.G. (1986) Theories and models of species abundance. *American Naturalist* **128**:879–99.

Hurlbert, S.H. (1971) The non-concept of species diversity: a critique and alternative parameters. *Ecology* **52**:577–86.

Hutcheson, K. (1970) A test for comparing diversities based on the Shannon formula. *Journal of Theoretical Biology* **29**:151–54.

James, F.C. and Rathbun, S. (1981) Rarefaction, relative abundance, and diversity of avian communities. *Auk* **98**:785–800.

Kempton, R.A. and Taylor, L.R. (1974a) The *Q*-statistic and the diversity of floras. *Nature* **275**:252–53.

Kempton, R.A. and Taylor, L.R. (1974b) Log-series and log-normal parameters as diversity determinants for the Lepidoptera. *Journal of Animal Ecology* **43**:381–99.

Krebs, C.J. (1989) *Ecological Methodology*. HarperCollins, New York.

Krebs, C.J. (1999) *Ecological Methodology*, 2nd edn. Addison Wesley Longman, Menlo Park CA.

Ludwig, J.A. and Reynolds, J.F. (1988) *Statistical Ecology: A Primer on Methods and Computing*. John Wiley, Chichester.

Magurran, A.E. (1988) *Ecological Diversity and Its Measurement*. Croom Helm, London.

Margalef, R. (1958) Information theory in ecology. *General Systematics* **3**:36–71.

May, R.M. (1975) Patterns of species abundance and diversity. In *Ecology and Evolution of Communities*, M.L. Cody and J.M. Diamond (eds). Harvard University Press, Cambridge MA, pp. 81–120.

Menhinick, E.F. (1964) A comparison of some species–individual diversity indices applied to samples of field insects. *Ecology* **45**:859–61.

Minshall, G., Petersen, R.C. Jr and Nimz, C.F. (1985) Species richness in streams of different size from the same drainage basin. *American Naturalist* **125**:16–38.

Peet, R.K. (1974) The measurement of species diversity. *Annual Review of Ecology and Systematics* **5**:285–307.

Pielou, E.C. (1975) *Ecological Diversity*. John Wiley, New York.

Pielou, E.C. (1977) *Mathematical Ecology*. John Wiley, New York.

Poole, R.W. (1974) *An Introduction to Quantitative Ecology*. McGraw-Hill, Tokyo.

Preston, F.W. (1948) The commonness and rarity of species. *Ecology* **29**:254–83.

Routledge, R.D. (1980) Bias in estimating the diversity of large, uncensused communities. *Ecology* **61**:276–81.

Sanders, H.L. (1968) Marine benthic diversity: a comparative study. *American Naturalist* **102**:243–82.

Schlesinger, C.R., Funk, D.T., Roth, P.L. and Myers, C.C. (1994) Assessing changes in biological diversity over time. *Natural Areas Journal* **14**:235–40.

Sheldon, A.L. (1969) Equitability indices: dependence on the species count. *Ecology* **50**:466–67.

Sokal, R.R. and Rohlf, F.J. (1987) *Introduction to Biostatistics*, 2nd edn. W.H. Freeman, New York.

Southwood, T.R.E. (1978) *Ecological Methods: with particular reference to the study of insect populations*, 2nd edn. Chapman & Hall, London.

Stiling, P. (1999) *Ecology: Theories and Applications*, 3rd edn. Prentice-Hall, Englewood Cliffs NJ.

Sugihara, G. (1980) Minimal community structure: an explanation of species abundance patterns. *American Naturalist* **116**:459–94.

Taylor, L.R. (1978) Bates, Williams, Hutchinson – a variety of diversities. In *Diversity of Insect Fauna*, Proceedings of the 9th Symposium of the Royal Entomological Society, L.A. Mound and N. Warloff (eds). Blackwell, Oxford, pp. 1–18.

Tokeshi, M. (1993) Species abundance patterns and community structure. *Advances in Ecological Research* **24**:112–85.

Whittaker, R.H. (1965) Dominance and diversity in land plant communities. *Science* **147**:250–60.

Whittaker, R.H. (1977) Evolution of species diversity in land communities. In *Evolutionary Biology*, Vol. 10, M.K. Hecht, W.C. Streere and B. Wallace (eds). Plenum, New York, pp. 1–67.

Williams, C.B. (1947) The logarithmic series and the comparison of island floras. *Proceedings of the Linnaean Society of London* **158**:104–8.

Williams, C.B. (1964) *Patterns in the Balance of Nature*. Academic Press, London.

Wilson, M.V. and Shmida, A. (1984) Measuring beta diversity with presence–absence data. *Journal of Ecology* **72**:1055–64.

Zahl, J.H. (1977) Jackknifing an index of diversity. *Ecology* **58**:907–13.

Chapter 3

Atlas, R.M. and Bartha, R. (1998) *Microbial Ecology: Fundamentals and Applications*, 4th edn. Addison Wesley Longman, Menlo Park CA.

Bailey, N.T.J. (1952) Improvements in the interpretation of recapture data. *Journal of Animal Ecology* **21**:120–27.

Begon, M., Harper, C.R. and Townsend, C.R. (1996) *Ecology*, 3rd edn. Blackwell, Oxford.

Biddy, C.J., Phillips, B.N. and Seddon, A.J.E. (1985) Birds of restocked conifer plantations in Wales. *Journal of Applied Ecology* **22**:619–33.

Blower, J.G., Cook, L.M. and Bishop, J.A. (1981) *Estimating the Size of Animal Populations*. Allen & Unwin, London.

Byrd, J.J. and Colwell, R.R. (1992) Microscopy applications for analysis of environmental samples. In *Microbial Ecology: Principles, Methods and Applications*, M.A. Levin, R.J. Seider and M. Rogul (eds). McGraw-Hill, New York, pp. 93–112.

Caughley, G. (1977) *Analysis of Vertebrate Populations*. John Wiley, London.

Chalmers, N. and Parker, P. (1986) *The OU Project Guide: Fieldwork and Statistics for Ecological Projects*. Field Studies Council, Taunton.

Clark, F.E. (1965) Agar-plate method for total microbial count. In *Methods of Soil Analysis, Part 2: Chemical and Microbial Properties*, C.A. Black, D.D. Evans, L.E. Ensminger, J.L. White and F.E. Clark (eds). American Society for Agronomy, Madison WI, pp. 1460–66.

Cochran, W.G. (1950) Estimation of bacterial densities by means of the 'most probable number'. *Biometrics* **6**:105–16.

Eberhardt, L.L. (1978) Transect methods for population studies. *Journal of Wildlife Management* **46**:1–31.

Eberhardt, L.L. (1982) Calibrating an index by using removal data. *Journal of Wildlife Management* **46**:734–40.

Fowler, J., Cohen, L. and Jarvis, P. (1998) *Practical Statistics for Field Biology*, 2nd edn. John Wiley, Chichester.

Fox, G.A. (1993) Failure-time analysis: emergence, flowering, survivorship, and other waiting times. In *Design and Analysis of Ecological Experiments*, S.M. Scheiner and J. Gurevitch (eds). Chapman & Hall, New York, pp. 254–89.

Gotelli, N.J. (1998) *A Primer of Ecology*, 2nd edn. Sinauer, Sunderland MA.

Greenwood, J.J.D. (1996) Basic techniques. In *Ecological Census Techniques: A Handbook*, W.J. Sutherland (ed.). Cambridge University Press, Cambridge.

Greig-Smith, P. (1983) *Quantitative Plant Ecology*, 3rd edn. Blackwell Scientific, Oxford.

Halvorson, H.O. and Ziegler, N.R. (1933) Application of statistics to problems in bacteriology I. A means of determining bacterial populations by the dilution method. *Journal of Bacteriology* **25**:101–21.

Hirst, D. (1994) An improved method for estimating animal abundance. *Biometrics* **50**:501–5.

Hutchings, M.J. (1997) The structure of plant populations. In *Plant Ecology*, 2nd edn, M.J. Crawley (ed.). Blackwell Science, Oxford.

Hutchings, M.J., Booth, K.D. and Waite, S. (1991) Comparison of survivorship by the logrank test: criticisms and alternatives. *Ecology* **72**(6):2290–93.

Kendall, M.G. and Stuart, A. (1973) *The Advanced Theory of Statistics*, Vol. 2. Macmillan, New York.

Krebs, C.J. (1999) *Ecological Methodology*, 2nd edn. Addison Wesley Longman, Menlo Park CA.

Laska, E.M. and Meisner, M. (1993) A plant–capture method for estimating the size of a population from a single sample. *Biometrics* 49:209–20.

Moore, P.D. and Chapman, S.B. (1986) *Methods in Plant Ecology*. Blackwell, Oxford.

Muttlak, H.A. and Sabooghi-Alvandi, S.M. (1993) A note on the line intercept sampling method. *Biometrics* 49:1209–15.

Pollock, K.H., Nicholas, J.D., Brownie, C. and Hines, J.E. (1990) Statistical inference for capture–recapture experiments. *Wildlife Monographs* 107:1–97.

Pyke, D.A. and Thompson, J.N. (1986) Statistical analysis of survival and removal rate experiments. *Ecology* 67:240–45.

Pyke, D.A. and Thompson, J.N. (1987) Erratum. *Ecology* 68:232.

Rees, M. and Long, M.J. (1993) The analysis and interpretation of seedling recruitment curves. *American Naturalist* 141:233–62.

Seber, G.A.F. (1982) *The Estimation of Animal Abundance and Related Parameters*, 2nd edn. Macmillan, New York.

Southwood, T.R.E. (1978) *Ecological Methods*. Chapman & Hall, London.

Stewart, S.C. (1994) Statistical analysis of cohort demographic data. *American Midland Naturalist* 131:238–47.

Sutherland, W.J. (ed.) (1996) *Ecological Census Techniques: A Handbook*. Cambridge University Press, Cambridge.

Varley, G.C., Gradwell, G.R. and Hassell, M.P. (1973) *Insect Population Ecology: An Analytical Approach*. Blackwell Scientific, Oxford.

Waite, S. (1984) Changes in the demography of *Plantago coronopus* at two coastal sites. *Journal of Ecology* 72:809–26.

Chapter 4

Begon, M., Harper, J.L. and Townsend, C.R. (1996) *Ecology: Individuals, Populations and Communities*, 3rd edn. Blackwell Science, Oxford.

Boag, B., Legg, R.K., Neilson, R., Palmer, L.F. and Hackett, C.A. (1994) The use of Taylor's power law to describe the aggregated distribution of earthworms in permanent pasture and arable soil in Scotland. *Pedobiologia* 38:303–6.

Bouxin, G. (1991) The measurement of horizontal patterns in vegetation: a review and proposal for models. In *Computer Assisted Vegetation Analysis*, E. Feoli and L. Orloci (eds). Kluwer Academic, Dordrecht, pp. 337–53.

Brown, D. and Rothery, P. (1993) *Models in Biology: Mathematics, Statistics and Computing*. John Wiley, Chichester.

Buckland, S.T. and Elston, D.A. (1993) Empirical models for spatial distribution of wildlife. *Journal of Applied Ecology* 30:478–95.

Burt, J.E. and Barber, G.M. (1996) *Elementary Statistics for Geographers*, 2nd edn. Guilford Press, New York.

Clark, P.F. and Evans, F.C. (1954) Distance to nearest neighbour as a measure of spatial relationships in populations. *Ecology* 35:445–53.

Czaran, T. and Bartha, S. (1992) Spatiotemporal dynamic models of plant populations and communities. *Trends in Ecology Evolution* 7(2):38–42.

Dale, M.R.T. and Powell, R.D. (1994) Scales of segregation and aggregation of plants of different kinds. *Canadian Journal of Botany* 72:448–53.

David, F.N. and Moore, P.G. (1954) Notes on contagious distributions in plant populations. *Annals of Botany* 18:47–53.

Diggle, P.J. (1983) *Statistical Analysis of Spatial Point Patterns*. Academic Press, London.

Ebdon, D. (1985) *Statistics in Geography*, 2nd edn. Basil Blackwell, Oxford.

Fowler, J., Cohen, L. and Jarvis, P. (1998) *Practical Statistics for Field Biology*. John Wiley, Chichester.

Goldsmith, F.B., Harrison, C.M. and Morton, A.J. (1986) Description and analysis of vegetation. In *Methods in Plant Ecology*, 2nd edn, P.D. Moore and S.B. Chapman (eds). Blackwell Scientific, Oxford, pp. 437–524.

Goodall, D.W. (1954) Minimal area: a new approach. In *Proceedings of the VIIth International Botanical Congress*, pp. 19–21.

Goodall, D.W. (1974) A new method for the analysis of spatial pattern by random pairing of quadrats. *Vegetatio* 29:135–46.

Green, P.J. and Sibson, R. (1978) Computing Dirichlet tessellations in the plane. *Computer Journal* 21:168–73.

Green, R.H. (1966) Measurement of non-randomness in spatial distributions. *Researches in Population Ecology* 8:1–7.

Greig-Smith, P. (1952) The use of random and contiguous quadrats in the study of the structure of plant communities. *Annals of Botany* 16:293–316.

Greig-Smith, P. (1983) *Quantitative Plant Ecology*, 3rd edn. University of California Press, Berkeley CA.

Haining, R. (1990) *Spatial Data Analysis in the Social and Environmental Sciences*. Cambridge University Press, Cambridge.

Hammond, R.H. and McCullagh, P. (1978) *Quantitative Techniques in Geography: An Introduction*. Clarendon Press, Oxford.

Harsch, G. (1991) Finding patterns in data: is it really random? *School Science Review* 73(253):55–63.

Hill, M.O. (1973) The intensity of spatial pattern in plant communities. *Journal of Ecology* **61**:225–36.

Hutchings, M.J. and Discombe, R.J. (1986) The detection of spatial pattern in plant populations. *Journal of Biogeography* **13**:225–36.

Hutchings, M.J. and Waite, S. (1985) Cohort behaviour and life-history determination in a natural population of *Plantago coronopus* L. In *Structure and functioning of plant populations II. Phenotypic and genotypic variation in plant populations*, J. Haek and J.W. Woldendorp (eds). North-Holland, Amsterdam, pp. 171–84.

Johnson, R.B. and Zimmer, W.J. (1985) A more powerful test for dispersion using distance measurements. *Ecology* **66**:1084–85.

Kendall, M.G. and Stuart, A. (1966) *The Advanced Theory of Statistics*, Vol. 3. Griffin, London.

Kershaw, K.A. (1961) Association and co-variance analysis of plant communities. *Journal of Ecology* **49**:643–54.

Kershaw, K.A. (1973) *Quantitative and Dynamic Plant Ecology*, 2nd edn. Edward Arnold, London.

Kershaw, K.A. and Looney, J.H.H. (1985) *Quantitative and dynamic plant ecology*, 3rd edn. Edward Arnold, London.

Kingsland, S.E. (1985) *Modeling Nature: Episodes in the History of Population Ecology*. University of Chicago Press, Chicago IL.

Lloyd, M. (1967) Mean crowding. *Journal of Animal Ecology* **36**:1–30.

Ludwig, J.A. and Goodall, D.W. (1978) A comparison of paired- with blocked-quadrat variance methods for the analysis of spatial pattern. *Vegetatio* **38**:49–59.

Ludwig, J.A. and Reynolds, J.F. (1988) *Statistical Ecology: A Primer on Methods and Computing*. John Wiley, New York.

MacArthur, R.H. (1972) *Geographical Ecology: Patterns in the Distribution of Species*. Harper & Row, New York.

Pielou, E.C. (1974) *Population and Community Ecology: Principles and Methods*. Gordon & Breach, New York.

Pielou, E.C. (1977) *Mathematical Ecology*. John Wiley, New York.

Pinder, D.A. and Witherick, M.E. (1975) A modification of nearest-neighbour analysis for use in linear situations. *Geography* **60**(266):16–23.

Pringle, K.L. and Giliomee, J.H. (1992) Dispersion statistics and sample size estimates for monitoring mite populations in commercial apple orchards. *Journal of Applied Ecology* **29**:143–49.

Silvertown, J.W. and Lovett Doust, J. (1993) *Introduction to Plant Population Biology*. Blackwell Scientific, Oxford.

Sinclair, D.F. (1985) On a test of spatial randomness using mean nearest-neighbor distance. *Ecology* **66**:1084–85.

Smallwood, K.S. (1993) Understanding ecological patterns and processes by association and order. *Acta Ecologia* **14**(3):443–62.

Sokal, R.R. and Rohlf, F.J. (1987) *Introduction to Biostatistics*, 2nd edn. W.H. Freeman, New York.

Southwood, T.R.E. (1978) *Ecological Methods: with particular reference to the study of insect populations*. Chapman & Hall, London.

Taylor, A.D. (1992) Deterministic stability analysis can predict the dynamics of some stochastic population models. *Journal of Animal Ecology* **61**:241–48.

Taylor, L.R. (1961) Aggregation, variance and the mean. *Nature* **189**:732–35.

Taylor, L.R., Woiwod, I.P. and Perry, J.N. (1978) The density-dependence of spatial behaviour and the rarity of randomness. *Journal of Animal Ecology* **47**:383–406.

Taylor, L.R., Woiwod, I.P. and Perry, J.N. (1979a) The negative binomial as a dynamic model for aggregation, and the density dependence of k. *Journal of Animal Ecology* **48**:289–304.

Taylor, L.R., Woiwod, I.P. and Taylor, R.A.J. (1979b) The migratory ambit of the hop aphid and its significance in aphid population dynamics. *Journal of Animal Ecology* **48**:955–72.

Taylor, L.R., Woiwod, I.P. and Perry, J.N. (1980) The variance and large-scale spatial stability of aphids, moths and birds. *Journal of Animal Ecology* **49**:831–54.

Thompson, H.R. (1956) Distribution of distance to the nth neighbour in a population of randomly distributed individuals. *Ecology* **37**:391–94.

Vincent, P.J., Haworth, J.M., Griffiths, J.G. and Collins, R. (1976) The detection of randomness in plant patterns. *Journal of Biogeography* **3**:373–80.

Waters, W.E. (1959) A quantitative measure of aggregation in insects. *Journal of Economic Entomology* **52**:1180–84.

Chapter 5

Abrams, P. (1983) The theory of limiting similarity. *Annual Review of Ecology and Systematics* **14**:359–76.

Atkinson, R.B., Perry, J.E., Smith, E. and Cairns, J. Jr (1993) Use of created wetlands delineation and weighted averages as a component of assessment. *Wetlands* **13**(3):185–93.

Beckman Instruments (1982) *Microtox System Operating Manual*. Beckman Instruments, Inc., Carlsbad CA.

Begon, M., Harper, J.L. and Townsend, C.R. (1996) *Ecology: Individuals, Populations and Communities*, 3rd edn. Blackwell Science, Oxford.

Burt, J.E. and Barber, G.M. (1996) *Elementary Statistics for Geographers*, 2nd edn. Guilford Press, London.

Colwell, R.K. and Futuyama, D.J. (1971) Experimental studies of niche breadth and overlap. *Ecology* **52**:567–76.

Crawford, T.J. (1991) The calculation of index numbers from wildlife monitoring data. In *Monitoring for Conservation and Ecology*, F.B. Goldsmith (ed.). Chapman & Hall, London, pp. 225–46.

Crothers, J.H. (1981) On the graphical presentation of quantitative data. *Field Studies* **5**:487–511.

Dixon, P.M. (1993) The bootstrap and jackknife: describing the precision of ecological indices. In *Design and Analysis of Ecological Experiments*, S.M. Scheiner and J. Gurevitch (eds). Chapman & Hall, London, pp. 290–318.

Efron, B. (1982) *The jackknife, the bootstrap, and other resampling plans*. Society of Industrial and Applied Mathematics, CBMS-NSF Monograph 38.

Efron, B. (1987) Better bootstrap confidence intervals (with discussion). *Journal of the American Statistical Association* 82:171–200.

Ellison, A.M. (1993) Exploratory data analysis and graphic display. In *Design and Analysis of Ecological Experiments*, S.M. Scheiner and J. Gurevitch (eds). Chapman & Hall, London, pp. 14–45.

Feininger, P., Spears, E.E. and Poole, R.W. (1981) A simple measure of niche breadth. *Ecology* 62:27–31.

Glime, J.M. and Vitt, D.H. (1987) A comparison of bryophyte species diversity and niche structure of montane streams. *Canadian Journal of Botany* 65:1824–37.

Greig-Smith, P. (1983) *Quantitative Plant Ecology*, 3rd edn. University of California Press, Berkeley CA.

Greshon, S. (1989) A study of the plants community structure of a valley mire complex at Thursley Common National Nature Reserve, Surrey. PhD thesis, Polytechnic of Central London.

Grime, J.P. (1974) Vegetation classification by reference to strategies. *Nature* 250:26–31.

Grime, J.P. (1977) Evidence for the existence of three primary strategies in plants and its relevance to ecological and evolutionary theory. *American Naturalist* 11:1169–94.

Grime, J.P. (1979) *Plant Strategies and Vegetation Processes*. John Wiley, Chichester.

Grubb, R.J. (1998) A reassessment of strategies of plants which cope with shortages of resources. *Perspectives in Plant Ecology, Evolution and Systematics* 1:1–29.

Hardman, D.J., McEldowney, S. and Waite, S. (1993) *Pollution: Ecology and Biotreatment*. Longman, Harlow.

Haslam, S.M. (1990) *River Pollution and Ecological Perspective*. John Wiley, Chichester.

Hutchinson, G.E. (1957) Concluding remarks. *Cold Spring Harbor Symposium on Quantitative Biology* 22:415–27.

Jongman, R.H., ter Braak, C.J.F. and van Torgeren, O.F.R. (1987). In: *Data Analysis in Community and Landscape*. Pudoc, Wageningen, pp. 83–86.

Krebs, C.J. (1989) *Ecological Methodology*. Harper & Row, New York.

Krebs, C.J. (1999) *Ecological Methodology*, 2nd edn. Addison Wesley Longman, Menlo Park CA.

Leblanc, F. and De Sloover, J. (1970) Relationship between industrialization and the distribution and growth of epiphytic lichens and mosses in Montreal. *Canadian Journal of Botany* 48:1485–96.

Levins, R. (1968) *Evolution in Changing Environments*. Princeton University Press, Princeton NJ.

Loehle, C. (1988) Problems with the triangular model for representing plant strategies. *Ecology* 69:284–86.

Ludwig, J.A. and Reynolds, J.F. (1988) *Statistical Ecology. A Primer on Methods and Computing*. John Wiley, Chichester.

Mason, C.F. (1996) *Biology of Freshwater Pollution*, 3rd edn. Longman, Harlow.

Meyer, J.S., Ingersoll, C.G., McDonald, L.L. and Boyce, M.S. (1986) Estimating uncertainty in population growth rates: jackknife vs. bootstrap techniques. *Ecology* 67:1156–66.

Perring, F.H. and Farrel, L. (1977) *British Red Data Books 1: Vascular Plants*. Royal Society for the Promotion of Nature Conservation, Nettleham.

Pianka, E.R. (1973) The structure of lizard communities. *Annual Review of Ecology and Systematics* 4:53–74.

Proctor, M.C.F. (1960) Mosses and liverworts of Malham district. *Field Studies* 1:61–85.

Prys-Jones, R.P., Underhill, L.G. and Waters, R.J. (1994) Index numbers for waterbird populations II. Coastal wintering waders in the United Kingdom, 1970/71–1990/91. *Journal of Applied Ecology* 31:481–92.

Reed, P.B. Jr (1988) *National List of Plants Species That Occur in Wetlands: National Summary*. Biological Report 88(24). US Fish and Wildlife Service, Washington DC.

Showman, R.E. (1988) Mapping air quality with lichens, the North American experience. In *Lichens, Bryophytes and Air Quality*, T. Nash and J. Cramer (eds), Borntraeger, Berlin, pp. 67–89.

Smith, E.P. (1982) Niche breadth, resource availability, and inference. *Ecology* 63:1675–81.

Spellerberg, I.F. (1991) *Monitoring Ecological Change*. Cambridge University Press, Cambridge.

Spellerberg, I.F. (1992) *Evaluation and Assessment for Conservation*. Chapman & Hall, London.

Stilings, P. (1999) *Ecology: Theories and Applications*, 3rd edn. Prentice Hall, Upper Saddle River NJ.

ter Braak, C.J.F. and Verdonschot, P.F.M. (1995) Canonical correspondence analysis and related multivariate methods in aquatic ecology. *Aquatic Sciences* 57(3):254–89.

Tukey, P.A. and Tukey, J.W. (1981) Graphical display of data in 3 or more dimensions. In *Interpreting Multivariate Data*, V. Barnett (ed.). John Wiley, Chichester, pp. 189–275.

Underhill, L.G. and Prys-Jones, R.P. (1994) Index numbers for waterbird population and methodology. *Journal of Applied Ecology* 31:463–80.

Williams, J.M., Tasker, M.L., Carter I.C. and Webb, A. (1995) A method of assessing seabird vulnerability to surface pollutants. *Ibis* 137(S):147–52.

Williamson, M. (1972) *The analysis of biological populations*. Edward Arnold, London.

Chapter 6

Atlas, R.M. and Bartha, R. (1998) *Microbial Ecology: Fundamentals and Applications*, 4th edn. Addison Wesley Longman, Menlo Park CA.

Beals, E.W. (1984) Bray–Curtis ordination: an effective strategy for analysis of multivariate ecological data. *Advances in Ecological Research* 14:1–55.

Bray, J.R. and Curtis, J.T. (1957) An ordination of the upland forest communities of southern Wisconsin. *Ecological Monographs* 27:325–49.

Causton, D.R. (1988) *An Introduction to Vegetation Analysis*. Unwin Hyman, London.

Digby, P.G.N. and Kempton, R.A. (1987) *Multivariate Analysis of Ecological Communities*. Chapman & Hall, London.

Dunn, G. and Everitt, B.S. (1982) *An Introduction to Mathematical Taxonomy*. Cambridge University Press, Cambridge.

Eilers, H.P., Taylor, A. and Sanville, W. (1983) Vegetative delineation of coastal salt-marsh boundaries. *Environmental Management* 7(5):443–52.

Fry, R. (ed.) (1993) *Biological Data Analysis: A Practical Approach*. Oirl Press at Oxford University Press, Oxford.

Greig-Smith, P. (1983) *Quantitative Plant Ecology*, 3rd edn. University of California Press, Berkeley CA.

Gullberg, A., Olsson, M. and Telgelström, H. (1999) Evolution in populations of Swedish sand lizards: genetic differentiation and loss of variability revealed by multilocus DNA fingerprinting. *Journal of Evolutionary Biology* 12:17–26.

Krebs, C.J. (1989) *Ecological Methodology*. Harper Collins, New York.

Krebs, C.J. (1999) *Ecological Methodology*, 2nd edn. Addison Wesley Longman, Menlo Park CA.

Lance, G.N. and Williams, W.T. (1967) A general theory for classificatory sorting strategies 1. Hierarchical systems. *Computer Journal* 9:373–80.

Legendre, J.T. and Legendre, P. (1983) *Numerical Ecology*. Elsevier, New York.

Ludwig, J.A. and Reynolds, J.F. (1988) *Statistical Ecology: A Primer on Methods and Computing*. John Wiley, New York.

Lynch, M. (1990) The similarity index and DNA fingerprinting. *Molecular Biology and Evolution* 7:478–84.

Ochiai, A. (1957) Zoogeographic studies on the soleoid fishes found in Japan and its neighbouring regions. *Bulletin of the Japanese Society for Fisheries Science* 22:526–30.

Sorensen, T. (1948) A method for establishing groups of equal amplitude in plant sociology based on similarity of species content and its application to analyses of vegetation on Danish commons. *Kong. Dabish Vidensk. Selsk. Biol. Skr. (Copenhagen)* 5:1–34.

Wetton, J.H., Carter, R.E., Parkin, D.T. and Walters, D.T. (1987) Demographic study of a wild house-sparrow population by DNA-fingerprinting. *Nature* 327:147–49.

Wolda, H. (1981) Similarity indices, sample size, and diversity. *Oecologia* 50:296–302.

Chapter 7

Aarssen, L.W. and Turkington, R. (1985) Vegetation dynamics and neighbour associations in pasture-community evolution. *Journal of Ecology* 73:585–603.

Beyer, W.H. (ed.) (1968) *Handbook of Tables for Probability and Statistics*, 2nd edn. Chemical Rubber Company, Cleveland OH.

Causton, D.R. (1988) *An Introduction to Vegetation Analysis*. Unwin Hyman, London.

De Jong, P., Aarrssen, L.W. and Turkington, R. (1980) The analysis of contact sampling data. *Oecologia* 45:322–24.

De Jong, P., Aarrssen, L.W. and Turkington, R. (1983) The use of contact sampling in studies of association in vegetation. *Journal of Ecology* 71:545–59.

Finney, D.J., Latasha, R., Bennett, B.M. and Hsu, D. (1963) *Tables for Testing Significance in a 2 × 2 Contingency Table*. Cambridge University Press, Cambridge.

Fowler, J., Cohen, L. and Jarvis, P. (1998) *Practical Statistics for Field Biology*, 2nd edn, John Wiley, Chichester.

Goodall, D.W. (1973) Sample similarity and species correlation. In *Handbook of Vegetation Sciences*, R.H. Whittaker (ed.). W. Junk, The Hague.

Greig-Smith, P. (1983) *Quantitative Plant Ecology*, 3rd edn. University of California Press, Berkeley CA.

Kent, M. and Coker, P. (1992) *Vegetation Description Analysis: A Practical Approach*. Belhaven Press, London.

Kershaw, K.A. and Looney, J.H.H. (1985) *Quantitative and Dynamic Plant Ecology*, 3rd edn. Edward Arnold, London.

Knight, W. (1974) A run-like statistic for ecological transects. *Biometrics* 30:553–55.

Ludwig, J.A. and Reynolds, J.F. (1988) *Statistical Ecology: A Primer on Methods and Computing*. John Wiley, New York.

Meagher, T.R. and Burdick, D.S. (1980) The use of nearest-neighbor frequency analyses in studies of association. *Ecology* 61:1253–55.

Meddis, R. (1975) *Statistical Handbook for Non-Statisticians*. McGraw-Hill, Maidenhead.

Pielou, E.C. (1961) Segregation and symmetry in two-species populations as studied by nearest-neighbour relationships. *Journal of Ecology* 49:255–69.

Pielou, E.C. (1962) Runs of one species with respect to another in transects through plant populations. *Biometrics* 18:579–93.

Pielou, E.C. (1977) *Mathematical Ecology*. John Wiley, New York.

Poole, R. (1974) *An Introduction to Quantitative Ecology*. McGraw-Hill, Tokyo.

Schluter, D. (1984) A variance test for detecting species associations, with some example applications. *Ecology* 65:998–1005.

Sokal, R.R. and Rohlf, F.J. (1987) *Introduction to Biostatistics*, 2nd edn. W.H. Freeman, New York.

Stowe, L.G. and Wade, M.J. (1979) The detection of small-scale patterns in vegetation. *Journal of Ecology* 67:1047–64.

Turkington, R. and Harper, J.L. (1979a) The growth, distribution and neighbour relationships of *Trifolium repens* in a permanent pasture I. Ordination, pattern and contact. *Journal of Ecology* 67:201–18.

Turkington, R. and Harper, J.L. (1979b) The growth, distribution and neighbour relationships of *Trifolium repens* in a permanent pasture II. Inter- and intra-specific contact. *Journal of Ecology* 67: 219–30.

Yarranton, G.A. (1966) A plotless method of sampling vegetation. *Journal of Ecology* 54:229–37.

Chapter 8

Allen, T.F.H. and Starr, T.B. (1982) *Hierarchy: Perspectives for Ecological Complexity*. University of Chicago Press, Chicago IL.

Barbour, M.G., Burk, J.H. and Pitts, W.D. (1987) *Terrestrial Plant Ecology*, 2nd edn. Benjamin/Cummings, Menlo Park, CA.

Beals, E.W. (1984) Bray–Curtis ordination: an effective strategy for analysis of multivariate ecological data. *Advances in Ecological Research* 14:1–55.

Berrow, S.D. (1991) Heavy metals in sediments and shellfish from Cork Harbour, Ireland. *Marine Pollution Bulletin* 22:467–69.

Branko, K. and Ranka, P. (1994) A generalized standardization procedure in ecological ordination. Tests with principal components analysis. *Journal of Vegetation Science* 5:259–62.

Bray, J.R. and Curtis, J.T. (1957) An ordination of the upland forest communities of southern Wisconsin. *Ecological Monographs* 27:325–49.

Causton, D.R. (1988) *An Introduction to Vegetation Analysis*. Unwin Hyman, Boston MA.

Cullen, M.R. (1983) *Mathematics for the Biosciences*, PWS Publishers, Boston MA.

Digby, P.G.N. and Kempton, R.A. (1987) *Multivariate Analysis of Ecological Communities*. Chapman & Hall, London.

Dunn, G. and Everitt, B.S. (1982) *An Introduction to Mathematical Taxonomy*. Cambridge University Press, Cambridge.

Fromentin, J.M., Ibanez, F., Dauvin, J.C., Dewarumez, J.M. and Elkaim, B. (1997) Long-term changes of four macrobenthic assemblages from 1978 to 1992. *Journal of the UK Marine Biological Association* 77:287–310.

Gauch, H.G. (1982) *Multivariate Analysis in Community Ecology*. Cambridge University Press, Cambridge.

Gauch, H.G., Whittaker, R.H. and Wentworth, T.R. (1977) A comparative study of reciprocal averaging and other ordination techniques. *Journal of Ecology* 65:157–74.

Gauch, H.G., Whittaker, R.H. and Singer, S.B. (1981) A comparative study of nonmetric ordinations. *Journal of Ecology* 69:135–52.

Gillman, M. and Hails, R. (1997) *An Introduction to Ecological Modelling*. Blackwell, Oxford.

Gower, J.C. (1966) Some distance properties of latent root and vector methods used in multivariate analysis. *Biometrika* 53:325–38.

Hill, M.O. (1973) Reciprocal averaging, an eigenvector method of ordination. *Journal of Ecology* 61:237–50.

Hill, M.O. (1979) DECORANA: a FORTRAN program for detrended correspondence analysis and reciprocal averaging. Cornell University, Department of Ecology and Systematics, Ithaca NY.

Hill, M.O. and Gauch, H.G. (1980) Detrended correspondence analysis, an improved ordination technique. *Vegetatio* 42:47–58.

Jackson, D.A. (1993) Multivariate analysis of benthic invertebrate communities: the implications of choosing particular data standardizations, measures of association, and ordination. *Hydrobiologia* 268:9–29.

James, C.F. and McCulloch, C.E. (1990) Multivariate analysis in ecology and systematics: panacea or Pandora's box? *Annual Review of Ecology and Systematics* 21:129–66.

Jollife, I.T. (1986) *Principal Component Analysis*. Springer-Verlag, Berlin.

Jongman, R.G.H., ter Braack, C.J.F. and van Tongeren, O.F.R. (eds) (1987) *Data Analysis in Community and Landscape Ecology*. Pudoc, Wageningen.

Kenkel, N.C. and Orloci, L. (1986) Applying metric and nonmetric multidimensional scaling to ecological studies: some new results. *Ecology* 67:919–28.

Kent, M. and Coker, P. (1992) *Vegetation Description and Analysis: A Practical Approach*. Belhaven Press, London.

Kline, P. (1994) *An Easy Guide to Factor Analysis*. Routledge, London.

Legendre, L. and Legendre, P. (1983) *Numerical Ecology*. Elsevier, New York.

Ludwig, J.A. and Reynolds, J.F. (1988) *Statistical Ecology: A Primer on Methods and Computing*. John Wiley, New York.

Manly, B.F.J. (1994) *Multivariate Statistical Methods: A Primer*. Chapman & Hall, London.

Minchin, P.R. (1987) An evaluation of the relative robustness of techniques for ecological ordination. *Vegetatio* 69:89–107.

Mohler, C.I. (1981) Effects of sample distribution along a gradient on eigenvector ordination. *Vegetatio* **45**:141–45.

Namboodiri, K. (1984) *Matrix Algebra: An Introduction.* Sage, Beverly Hills CA.

Noy-Meir, I. (1973) Data transformations in ecological ordination I. Some advantages of non-centering. *Journal of Ecology* **61**:329–41.

Orloci, L. (1978) *Multivariate Analysis in Vegetation Research*, 2nd edn. W. Junk, The Hague.

Phillips, D.L. (1978) Polynomial ordination: field and computer simulations testing of a new method. *Vegetatio* **37**:129–40.

Pielou, E.C. (1984) *The interpretation of ecological data: a primer on classification and ordination.* John Wiley, New York.

Randerson, P.F. (1993) Ordination. In *Biological Data Analysis: A Practical Approach*, R. Fry (ed.). Oirl Press at Oxford University Press, Oxford, pp. 173–218.

ter Braak, C.J.F. (1983) Principal component biplots and alpha and beta diversity. *Ecology* **64**:454–62.

ter Braak, C.J.F. (1985) Correspondence analysis of incidence and abundance data: properties in terms of a unimodal response model. *Biometrics* **41**:859–73.

ter Braak, C.J.F. (1987) Ordination. In *Data Analysis in Community and Landscape Ecology*, R.H.G. Jongman, C.J.F. ter Braak and O.F.R. van Tongeren (eds). PUDOC, Wageningen, pp. 91–173.

ter Braak, C.J.F. and Prentice, I.C. (1988) A theory of gradient analysis. *Advances in Ecological Research* **18**:271–317.

Wartenberg, D., Ferson, S. and Rohlf, F.J. (1987) Putting things in order: a critique of detrended correspondence analysis. *American Naturalist* **129**:434–48.

Yarranton, G.A. (1966) A plotless method of sampling vegetation. *Journal of Ecology* **54**:229–37.

Zitko, V. (1994) Principal component analysis in the evaluation of environmental data. *Marine Pollution Bulletin* **28**:718–22.

Chapter 9

Boesch, D.F. (1977) *Applications of Numerical Classification in Ecological Investigations of Water Pollution.* EPA-600/3-77-033. US Environmental Protection Agency, Corvallis OR.

Causton, D.R. (1988) *An Introduction to Vegetation Analysis.* Unwin Hyman, Boston MA.

Digby, P.G.N. and Kempton, R.A. (1987) *Multivariate Analysis of Ecological Communities.* Chapman & Hall, London.

Dunn, G. and Everitt, B.S. (1982) *An Introduction to Mathematical Taxonomy.* Cambridge University Press, Cambridge.

Everitt, B.S. (1980) *Cluster Analysis*, 2nd edn. Heinemann, London.

Gauch, H.G. (1982) *Multivariate Analysis in Community Ecology.* Cambridge University Press, Cambridge.

Goodall, D.W. (1954) Objective methods for the comparison of vegetation III. An essay in the use of factor analysis. *Australian Journal of Botany* **2**:304–24.

Hill, M.O. (1979a) DECORAN: a FORTRAN program for detrended correspondence analysis and reciprocal averaging. Cornell University, Department of Ecology and Systematics, Ithaca NY.

Hill, M.O. (1979b) TWINSPAN: a FORTRAN program for arranging multivariate data in an ordered two-way table by classification. Cornell University, Department of Ecology and Systematics, Ithaca NY.

Hill, M.O., Bunce, R.G.H. and Shaw, M.W. (1975) Indicator species analysis, a divisive polythetic method of classification and its application to a survey of native pinewood in Scotland. *Journal of Ecology* **63**:597–613.

Ivimey-Cook, R.B. and Proctor, M.C.F. (1966) The application of association analysis to phytosociology. *Journal of Ecology* **54**:547–79.

James, C.F. and McCulloch, C.E. (1990) Multivariate analysis in ecology and systematics: panacea or Pandora's box? *Annual Review of Ecology and Systematics* **21**:129–66.

Kent, M. and Ballard, J. (1988) Trends and problems in the application of classification and ordination methods in plant ecology. *Vegetatio* **78**:109–24.

Kent, M. and Coker, P. (1992) *Vegetation Description and Analysis: A Practical Approach.* CRC and Belhaven Press, London.

Kershaw, K.A. (1961) Association and co-variance analysis of plant communities. *Journal of Ecology* **49**:643–54.

Kershaw, K.A. and Looney, J.H.H. (1985) *Quantitative and Dynamic Plant Ecology*, 3rd edn. Edward Arnold, London.

Lambert, J.M. and Williams, W.T. (1962) Multivariate methods in plant ecology VI. Nodal analysis. *Journal of Ecology* **50**:775–802.

Ludwig, J.A. and Reynolds, J.F. (1988) *Statistical Ecology: A Primer on Methods and Computing.* John Wiley, New York.

Madgwick, H.A.I. and Desrochers, P.A. (1972) Association-analysis and the classification of forest vegetation of the Jefferson National Forest. *Journal of Ecology* **60**:285–92.

Poole, R.W. (1974) *An Introduction to Quantitative Ecology.* McGraw-Hill, London.

Rohlf, F.J. (1970) Adaptive hierarchical clustering schemes. *Systematic Zoology* **17**:246–55.

Sokal, R.R., Fiala, K.L. and Hart, G. (1984) On stability and factors determining taxonomic stability: examples from the Caminalcules and the Leptododomorpha. *Systematic Zoology* **33**:387–407.

Strauss, R.E. (1982) Statistical significance of species clusters in association analysis. *Ecology* **62**:634–49.

Wildi, O. and Orloci, L. (1990) *Numerical Exploration of Community Patterns*. SPB Academic Publishing, The Hague.

Williams, W.T. and Lambert, J.M. (1959a) Multivariate methods in plant ecology I. Association analysis in plant communities. *Journal of Ecology* **47**:83–101.

Williams, W.T. and Lambert, J.M. (1959b) Multivariate methods in plant ecology II. The use of an electronic digital computer for association analysis. *Journal of Ecology* **48**:689–710.

Wratten, S.D. and Fry, G.L.A. (1980) *Field Laboratory Exercises in Ecology*. Edward Arnold, London.

Chapter 10

Begon, M., Harper, J.L. and Townsend, C.R. (1996) *Ecology*, 3rd edn. Blackwell Science, Oxford.

Finney, D.J. (1971) *Probit Analysis*, 3rd edn. Cambridge University Press, Cambridge.

Fowler, J., Cohen, L. and Jarvis, P. (1998) *Practical Statistics for Field Biology*, 2nd edn. John Wiley, Chichester.

Fry, C.J. (ed.) (1993) One-way analysis of variance. In *Biological Data Analysis: A Practical Approach*. Oirl Press at Oxford University Press, Oxford, pp. 1–33.

Green, R.H. (1979) *Sampling Design and Statistical Methods for Environmental Biologists*. John Wiley, New York.

Kleinbaum, D.G., Kupper, L.L., Muller, K.E. and Nizam, A. (1998) *Applied Regression Analysis and Other Multivariable Methods*, 3rd edn. Duxbury Press, Pacific Grove CA.

Lack, D. (1976) *Island Birds*. Blackwell Scientific, Oxford.

MacArthur, R.H. and Wilson, E.O. (1967) *The Theory of Island Biogeography*. Princeton University Press, Princeton NJ.

Manly, B.F.J. (1994) *Multivariate Statistical Methods: A primer*, 2nd edn. Chapman & Hall, London.

May, R.M. (1975) Patterns of species abundance and diversity. In *Ecology and Evolution of Communities*, M.L. Cody and J.M. Diamond (eds). Harvard University Press, Cambridge MA.

Ricklefs, R.E. (1990) *Ecology*, 3rd edn. W.H. Freeman, New York.

Sokal, R.R. and Rohlf, F.L. (1995) *Biometry*, 3rd edn. W.H. Freeman, New York.

Wilson, E.O. and Bossert, W.H. (1971) *A Primer of Population Biology*. Sinauer, Stamford CT.

Wright, S.J. (1988) Patterns of abundance and the form of the species–area relation. *American Naturalist* **131**:401–11.

Chapter 11

Austin, M.P. (1968) The structure of some upland plant communities in Caernarvonshire III. The continuum analysis. *Journal of Ecology* **51**:403–14.

Barkham, J.P. and Norris, J.M. (1970) Multivariate procedures in an investigation of vegetation and soil relations of two beach woodlands, Cotswold Hills, England. *Ecology* **51**:630–39.

Birks, H.J.B. and Austin, H.A. (1992) *An Annotated Bibliography of Canonical Correspondence Analysis and Related Constrained Ordination Methods 1986–1991*. University of Bergen, Bergen.

Digby, P.G.N. and Kempton, R.A. (1987) *Multivariate Analysis of Ecological Communities*. Chapman & Hall, London.

Dolédec, S. and Chessel, D. (1994) Co-inertia analysis: an alternative method for studying species–environmental relationships. *Freshwater Biology* **31**:227–94.

Fourt, D.E., Donald, D.G., Jeffers, J.N.R. and Binns, W.O. (1971) Corsican pine (*Pinus nigra* var *maritima* (AIT) Melville) in southern Britain – a study of growth and site factors. *Forestry* **44**:189-207.

Gittins, R. (1985) *Canonical Analysis: A Review with Applications in Ecology*. Springer-Verlag, Berlin.

Goldsmith, F.B. (1973) The vegetation of exposed sea cliffs at South Stack, Anglesey I. The multivariate approach. *Journal of Ecology* **61**:787–818.

Greshon, S. (1989) A study of the plant community structure of a valley mire complex at Thursley Common National Nature Reserve, Surrey. PhD thesis, Polytechnic of Central London.

Harris, R.J. (1985) *A Primer of Multivariate Statistics*. Academic Press, New York.

Hill, M.O. (1988) How effective is ordination as a means of relating vegetation to ecological factors? *Bulletin de la Société Royale de Botanique* **121**:134–41.

Jeffers, J.N.R. (1978) *An Introduction to Systems: with ecological applications*. Edward Arnold, London.

Kent, M. and Coker, P. (1992) *Vegetation Description and Analysis: A Practical Approach*. CRC and Belhaven Press, London.

Levene, H. (1960) Robust tests for equality of variance. In *Contributions to Probability and Statistics*, I. Olkin, S.G. Ghurye, W. Hoeffding, W.G. Madow and H.B. Mann (eds). Stanford Univesity Press, Stanford CA, pp. 278–92.

Manly, B.F.J. (1994) *Multivariate Statistical Methods: A Primer*, 2nd edn. Chapman & Hall, London.

Mitchell, R.J., Marrs, R.H., Le Duc, M.G. and Auld, M.H.D. (1997) A study of succession on lowland heaths in Dorset, southern England: changes in vegetation and soil chemical properties. *Journal of Applied Ecology* **34**:1426–44.

Poole, R.W. (1974) *An Introduction to Quantitative Ecology.* McGraw-Hill, London.

Proctor, M.C.F. (1992) Regional and local variation in the chemical composition of ombrogenous mire waters in Britain and Ireland. *Journal of Ecology* **80**:719–36.

Schultz, B. (1983) On Levene's test and other statistics of variation. *Evolutionary Theory* **6**:197–203.

ter Braak, C.J.F. (1985) Correspondence analysis of incidence and abundance data: properties in terms of a unimodal response model. *Biometrics* **41**:859–73.

ter Braak, C.J.F. (1986) Canonical correspondence analysis: a new eigenvector technique for multivariate direct gradient analysis. *Ecology* **67**:1167–79.

ter Braak, C.J.F. (1987) The analysis of vegetation–environment relationship by canonical correspondence analysis. *Vegetatio* **69**:69–77.

ter Braak, C.J.F. and Prentice, I.C. (1988) A theory of gradient analysis. *Advances in Ecological Research* **18**:271–317.

ter Braak, C.J.F. and Verdonschot, P.F.M. (1995) Canonical correspondence analysis and related multivariate methods in aquatic ecology. *Aquatic Sciences* **57**(3):254–89.

Yao, Y. (1965) An approximate degrees of freedom solution to the multivariate Behrens–Fisher problem. *Biometrika* **52**:139–47.

Procedures index

Index of topics